MAGNETOCHEMISTRY

MAGNETOCHEMISTRY

PIERCE W. SELWOOD

Department of Chemistry
Northwestern University, Evanston, Illinois

SECOND EDITION
Completely Revised and Rewritten

INTERSCIENCE PUBLISHERS, INC., NEW YORK
a division of John Wiley & Sons, New York · London · Sydney

First Edition, 1943
Second Revised Edition, 1956
SECOND PRINTING, NOVEMBER, 1964

PRINTED IN THE UNITED STATES OF AMERICA BY

PREFACE

Magnetochemistry began with Michael Faraday more than one hundred years ago. It enjoyed a vigorous growth at the hands of Langevin, Curie, Weiss, and Pascal; but it did not come of age, so to speak, until Gilbert N. Lewis pointed out, in the early 1920's, the fruitful relationship between atomic magnetic moment and chemical valence.

Magnetochemistry is concerned with magnetic moments and related quantities applied to chemical problems. Many of these problems lie in the area of molecular structure. There are excellent works available on magnetism in general, on atomic magnetism, and on the technologically important ferromagnetic metals and alloys, but this book is not intended to compete with them. Rather I have tried to show what information of a chemical nature may be obtained from magnetic measurements and to indicate in some detail how these measurements may be made. It is hoped that the theoretical background given will be adequate for the purposes of those readers for whom the book was written. It is also hoped that no important application of magnetism to structural chemistry has been overlooked.

An attempt has been made to cover the literature fully up through the last issue of *Chemical Abstracts* in 1955. A few papers of later date in the more accessible journals have been included. If the reader is appalled at the number of references, let him reflect that as many more have been omitted. I have included those references which seemed to offer some important theoretical or practical advance, or some data pertinent to the topic under discussion. But many excellent papers have been omitted, and this is especially so of the coordination compound field. As is true of every branch of science, magnetochemistry has proliferated since World War II. As is true of every author, I have had to be a little arbitrary in deciding what to include and what to omit. What seemed a fairly easy task in 1943 has now become both difficult and sometimes vexing.

I gratefully acknowledge the granting of permission by the American Chemical Society, the American Physical Society, the American Society for Metals, the American Institute of Mining and Metallurgical Engineers, and the Williams and Wilkins Company to reproduce diagrams from their respective publications. My thanks are due also to the editors of these publications and of the *Journal of Chemical Education* and of the *Record of Chemical Progress.*   Many other sources of diagrams and information are acknowledged in the text.   I want also to thank both collectively and individually that large group of colleagues in almost every part of the world for their kindness in sending me reprints and in promptly answering the flood of inquiring letters with which I deluged them.   I trust that their names have all been mentioned at appropriate places in the text.

It is a special pleasure to acknowledge, once again, the never failing aid received from my wife, Alice Taylor Selwood.

PIERCE W. SELWOOD

Evanston, Illinois
June 1956

CONTENTS

SYMBOLS

A	cross-sectional area		atoms of same kind (number of nearest neighbors)
B	magnetic induction		
C	Curie constant	α	a temperature independent term in susceptibility; an angle
c	velocity of light; a torsional constant; concentration		
d	density	β	Bohr magneton; an angle
e	electron charge	γ	gyromagnetic ratio
f	force	Δh	change in height
g	gravitational constant; Landé splitting factor; spectroscopic splitting factor	Δw	apparent change in weight
		$\Delta\chi$	magnetic anisotropy, e.g., $\chi_1 - \chi_2$
H	magnetic field	η	viscosity
H_0	field (static)	θ	angular displacement; an angle
h	Planck's constant		
I	nuclear spin quantum number	K_1, K_2, K_3	principal molecular suscepti- bilities
ϑ	intensity of magnetization		
J	vector sum of S and L	K_{av}	average molecular suscepti- bility $(K_1 + K_2 + K_3)/3$
K	a constant		
k	a constant; Boltzmann con- stant	K_p	molecular susceptibility cal- culated by Pascal's method
L	resultant orbital moment	κ	susceptibility per unit volume
l	a quantum number	λ	a constitutive (Pascal) correc- tion; an angle
M	molecular (formula) weight		
m	mass; electron mass	μ	magnetic moment
m_p	proton rest mass	μ_B	electron magnetic moment expressed in Bohr magnetons
N	Avogadro's number		
N_{ion}	number of paramagnetic ions per cc.	μ_{eff}	effective Bohr magneton num- ber
n	a number; a quantum num- ber; number of atoms; num- ber of unpaired electrons	μ_n	nuclear magnetic moment
		ν	frequency; precession fre- quency; an angle
n'	effective quantum number		
n_A	atoms of susceptibility χ_A	ρ	distance of electron from axis passing through nucleus
P	permeability		
p	weight fraction	σ	specific magnetization
r	electron orbital radius	χ	susceptibility per gram
S	resultant spin moment	χ_A	susceptibility per gram-atom
s	screening constant; area bonded by electron path	χ_M	susceptibility per mole
		χ_{av} or χ	average (powder or solution) susceptibility
T	temperature (generally abso- lute)		
		χ_1, χ_2, χ_3	principal susceptibilities per gram or per mole
T_1	spin-lattice relaxation time		
T_c	Curie temperature	$\chi_{\parallel}$	susceptibility parallel to a given axis
t	time; oscillation time		
v	volume; angular velocity of precession	$\chi_{\perp}$	susceptibility perpendicular to a given axis
Z	atomic number (charge)	ψ	an angle
z	coordination number for	ω	electron angular velocity

CHAPTER ONE

CLASSICAL DETERMINATION OF AVERAGE SUSCEPTIBILITY

1. Introduction

The strength of a magnetic field is expressed in "oersteds," although the word "gauss" is often used in the same sense. A field of one oersted is of such strength that a unit magnetic pole placed in it experiences a force of one dyne.

If a substance is placed in a field of strength H, then the magnetic induction is given by B, where

$$B = H + 4\pi\vartheta$$

The quantity ϑ is the intensity of magnetization, and $\vartheta/H = \kappa$ is the magnetic susceptibility per unit volume. The magnetic susceptibility per unit mass is obtained by dividing κ by the density. The symbol χ will be used in this book for magnetic susceptibility per gram. The molar susceptibility is designated by χ_M.

There is some confusion concerning the dimensions of κ and χ. This confusion arises from uncertainty as to whether or not B and H are quantities of the same kind; that is, whether they are dimensionally equivalent. For the purposes of this book, it is assumed that the magnetic susceptibility per unit volume, κ, is dimensionless, and that the susceptibility per unit mass has the dimensions of reciprocal density.

Gases and liquids, in which the molecules are arranged essentially at random, are magnetically isotropic. This is to say that the magnetic susceptibility is the same in every direction. Effective isotropy may be shown by a solid, the microcrystals of which have completely random orientation. The magnetic susceptibility of isotropic, or effectively isotropic substances, is often referred to as the *average* susceptibility. In crystals of low symmetry there are three mutually perpendicular directions known as the axes of principal magnetism. Along these axes the direction of magnetization corresponds with the direction of the applied field. The magnetic susceptibilities along these axes are called *principal*

1

susceptibilities. Their values are often unequal. In this chapter we shall be concerned with the measurement of average susceptibility only.

If a substance is placed in a magnetic field, the intensity of magnetization in the substance may be either slightly smaller, or somewhat larger, than that produced in a vacuum by the same field (Fig. 1). In the first case the substance is called *diamagnetic*, in the second *paramagnetic*. There is also the case of *ferromagnetism* in which the intensity of magnetization may be very much larger. But ferromagnetism, although of great technological importance, is comparatively rare in nature. It occurs in only a few metals, alloys, and compounds. Paramagnetism is common, especially among the transition group elements. Diamagnetism is a uni-

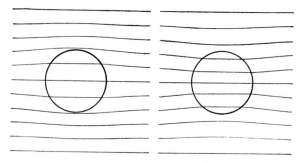

Fig. 1. Diamagnetic bodies (left) are less permeable than a vacuum to magnetic lines of force. Paramagnetic bodies are more permeable than a vacuum.

versal property of matter. All substances, even though paramagnetic, have at least an underlying diamagnetism for which correction must be made in precise determination of the permanent magnetic moment. A substance may be both diamagnetic and paramagnetic, but generally whenever paramagnetism is present it is so much larger that it hides the diamagnetism.

In general the susceptibility of diamagnetic substances is independent of temperature (although exceptions occur) and of field strength. The susceptibility of paramagnetic substances is often inversely proportional to the absolute temperature, but independent of field strength. The susceptibility of ferromagnetic substances is dependent both on temperature and on field strength in a rather complicated way.

There are many methods available for the measurement of magnetic susceptibility. Choice of method depends on the problem to be solved. There is no single method of universal applicability. The more important methods are described in the following pages, and literature references are given to a number of other methods. A few highly specialized methods are described in later chapters. Some general references are given below.[1-5]

Any substance placed in a magnetic field develops an induced moment not unlike the induced electric moment developed by a nonpolar molecule in an electric field. A paramagnetic substance possesses a permanent moment something like the permanent electric dipole moment possessed by a polar molecule. If, therefore, a body is placed in a uniform magnetic field it will suffer an orienting effect unless the body is magnetically isotropic. (There is also a small orienting effect due to the shape of the body, but this may generally be ignored.) The magnetic moment acquired by the body under these circumstances will be proportional to the susceptibility per unit volume times the volume of the body multiplied by the field, that is, to $\kappa v H$, but the body will experience no displacing force if the field is uniform. Now, if the field is made nonuniform with a gradient $\partial H/\partial s$ in the s direction, the body will experience a linear displacing force in the s direction and this will be proportional to the product of the moment and the gradient, or:

$$f = \kappa v H \partial H/\partial s$$

Magnetic susceptibility is not infrequently defined in terms of this equation, and the equation serves also as the basis for all commonly used classical methods for the measurement of susceptibility. Derivation of the above expression, and of its application to the Gouy, Quincke, Faraday, and other methods given below, will be found in Bates.[4]

2. The Gouy Method[6]

If a cylindrical sample of matter is suspended between the poles of a magnet as in Fig. 2 so that one end of the sample is in a region of large field strength and the other in a region of negligible field, then the force acting on the sample is that described by the equation previously given, $f = \kappa v H \partial H/\partial s$, integrated over all layers from the region of maximum field out to the region of negligible field. This integration gives a resultant force

$$f = {}^1\!/_2 \kappa H^2 A$$

where A is the cross-section area of the sample. If the atmosphere sur-

[1] E. C. Stoner, *Magnetism and Matter.* Methuen and Company, Ltd., London, 1934.

[2] S. S. Bhatnagar and K. N. Mathur, *Physical Principles and Applications of Magnetochemistry.* Macmillan and Company, Ltd., London, 1935.

[3] W. Klemm, *Magnetochemie.* Akademische Verlagsgesellschaft, Leipzig, 1936.

[4] L. F. Bates, *Modern Magnetism.* Cambridge University Press, Cambridge, 1951.

[5] R. M. Bozorth, *Ferromagnetism.* D. Van Nostrand Co. Inc., New York, 1951.

[6] L. G. Gouy, *Compt. rend.*, **109**, 935 (1889).

rounding the sample does not have a negligible susceptibility, the equation becomes

$$f = \tfrac{1}{2}(\kappa - \kappa_0)\, H^2 A$$

where κ_0 is the volume susceptibility of the atmosphere. If the field does not become negligible at the outer end of the sample, then the equation becomes

$$f = \tfrac{1}{2}(\kappa - \kappa_0)\,(H^2 - H_0^2)A$$

where H_0 is the field at the outer end of the sample. In practice H_0 may be made negligible and, by using hydrogen or nitrogen for the surrounding

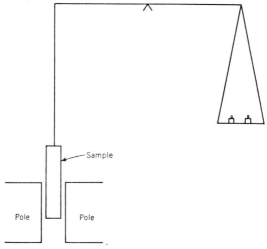

Fig. 2. Principle of the Gouy magnetic susceptibility balance.

atmosphere, κ_0 may also be made negligible. It is convenient to measure f by suspending the sample from a balance, in which case one may have

$$f = \tfrac{1}{2}\kappa H^2 A = g\Delta w$$

where g is the gravitational constant, and Δw the apparent change in weight of the sample on application of the magnetic field.

For many types of investigations it is convenient to use a magnetic field of from 5000 to 15,000 oersteds. For strongly paramagnetic samples Δw may then be of the order of several tenths of a gram, if the cylindrical sample has a diameter of 5 to 10 mm. An ordinary analytical balance therefore gives a sufficient degree of accuracy for some purposes. But for more refined measurements, especially on solutions, it is necessary to use a microbalance. A refinement in which the weighing is done by electrodynamic balancing is described by Hilal and Fredericks.[7] This and similar methods could readily be adapted to automatic recording if, for any reason, this seemed desirable.

Other methods are available for obtaining f. For instance, the sample may be suspended from a spring, the extension of which on application of the field may be observed with a microscope, or interferometrically.[8] Sucksmith[9] has described an optical method based on the distortion of a phosphor bronze ring (Fig. 11). While this method was developed for use with the Faraday magnetic balance, it could readily be adapted to the Gouy balance. Or, the sample may be suspended horizontally, from a torsion,[10] or bifilar, suspension.[11,12] The latter method lends itself to magnetic measurements on microsamples,[13] and to studies on magneto-chemical changes taking place as a function of time.[14-16] The horizontal suspension methods lack nothing in sensitivity, but they tend to become cumbersome when low temperature ranges are necessary.

Measurements on metals or alloys are very simple by the Gouy method. The sample has only to be cast or machined into the desired cylindrical shape. The accuracy of the magnetic measurement will generally be limited by the reproducibility of the sample. The Gouy method gives, of course, the volume susceptibility so that an independent determination of the density is necessary for calculation of the mass susceptibility.

Powdered samples may be measured by packing them into cylindrical glass sample tubes. Correction must be made for the susceptibility of the glass, which is generally diamagnetic with a slight temperature coefficient. The accuracy of measurements on powdered samples is severely limited by the uniformity and reproducibility of packing. It is difficult to exceed an accuracy of $\pm 1\%$.

However, some methods for improving the precision are described by French and Harrison.[17] One of the most serious possible errors in measurements on powdered sample is the preferential orientation of magneti-

[7] O. M. Hilal and G. E. Fredericks, *J. Chem. Soc.*, **1954**, 785.

[8] S. S. Bhatnagar, K. N. Mathur, and P. L. Kapur, *Indian J. Phys.*, **3**, 53 (1928).

[9] W. Sucksmith, *Phil. Mag.*, **8**, 158 (1929).

[10] G. Foëx, *Ann. phys.*, **16**, 174 (1921).

[11] G. Foëx and R. Forrer, *J. phys. radium*, **7**, 180 (1926).

[12] A. Pacault, A. Vankerckhoven, J. Hoarau, and J. Joussot-Dubien, *J. chim. phys.*, **49**, 470 (1952).

[13] H. Theorell and A. Ehrenberg, *Arkiv Fysik*, **3**, 299 (1951).

[14] G. N. Lewis and M. Calvin, *J. Am. Chem. Soc.*, **67**, 1232 (1945).

[15] P. W. Selwood, R. P. Eischens, M. Ellis, and K. Wethington, *ibid.*, **71**, 3039 (1949).

[16] H. Boardman and P. W. Selwood, *ibid.*, **72**, 1372 (1950).

[17] C. M. French and D. Harrison, *J. Chem. Soc.*, **1953**, 2538.

cally anisotropic crystals. This may be strikingly illustrated by graphite. If the flakes are arranged at random the susceptibility may be about -2×10^{-6}; but if the flakes should happen to lie more or less parallel to each other and perpendicular to the cylinder axis, the apparent diamagnetic susceptibility might be over three times greater.

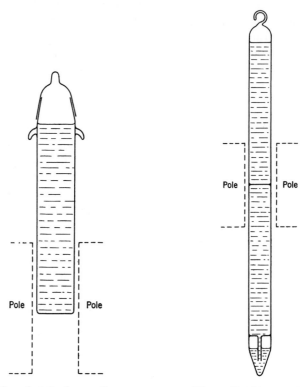

Fig. 3. Sample tube for routine measurements by the Gouy method.

Fig. 4. Double sample tube for precision measurements by the Gouy method.

The susceptibility of pure liquids is also conveniently measured in glass sample tubes. As the difficulty of packing does not arise with liquids, the accuracy may be considerably greater.

For moderate precision on liquids it is sufficient to use a simple glass cylindrical sample tube about 15 cm. long, but the exact length depends, of course, on the shape and size of the magnetic field. For work at room temperature the sample tube may be 2 to 3 cm. in diameter, nearly filling the space between the poles, but if susceptibilities at high and low temperatures are to be measured, the diameter of the sample tube must be a compromise between the largest possible diameter in the smallest space to accommodate the Dewar flask, or other equipment used to maintain the desired temperature. It is rarely advantageous to increase the space between the poles of the magnet because this sharply lowers the field. The sample tube is conveniently capped to prevent evaporation or reaction of the contents with the atmosphere. A useful design is shown in Fig. 3.

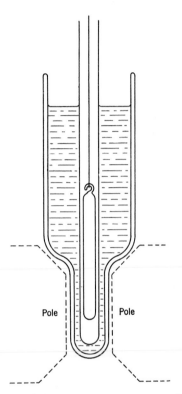

Fig. 5. Typical Dewar flask for low-temperature susceptibility measurements.

For very volatile liquids, or highly reactive substances like many free radicals, it is necessary to seal the sample tube.

Much magnetochemical research is done on solutions. Very accurate semi-differential methods are available for solutions. The glass sample tube may be double-ended, extending below the magnetic field just as far as above. The two ends are separated by a glass partition, in the region of which the magnetic field is applied. The solution under investigation is placed in one end of the sample tube, while the pure solvent is placed in the other. The arrangement is shown in Fig. 4. This sample tube must be supplied with a reservoir for change in volume of the solvent in the lower compartment with temperature.   Otherwise the tube would break whenever the temperature was raised or, when the temperature was lowered, a bubble of vapor would form at the partition.   In the tube shown, solvent completely fills the lower half of the main tube, and half fills the reservoir.

TO BALANCE

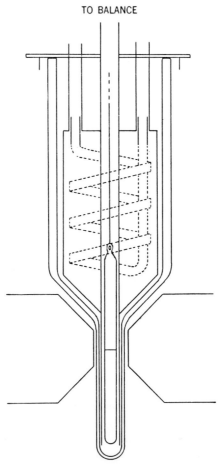

Fig. 6. A convenient arrangement for temperature control from −190°C. to 100°C. Thermocouples, heating coil, and other subsidiary equipment are not shown.

Then, as the solvent warms up, it expands through a capillary tube into the reservoir or, if the solvent contracts, it sucks up more solvent from the reservoir without forming a bubble at the partition.   For the most accurate measurements, it is necessary to use sample tubes of constant internal diameter. With all refinements, measurements to four significant figures are possible without too much difficulty.

The Gouy method is not well adapted to the investigation of gases, although rough measurements on oxygen and on other paramagnetic gases and vapors have been made.

Most magnetic measurements require a range of temperature and often a very accurate control of the temperature. During measurements on

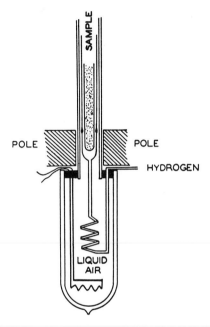

Fig. 7. Apparatus for automatically controlled low-temperature measurements.

solutions using a microbalance, it is often necessary to control the temperature to within 0.1°C. This is not because of any very large temperature dependence of magnetic susceptibility, but because the buoyancy effect of the surrounding atmosphere is markedly dependent on the temperature. This is a difficulty to which the horizontal suspension methods are not subject.

High temperatures are easily obtained by surrounding the sample tube with a tubular electric furnace. The only precautions necessary are to protect the sample and balance from currents of air, and the magnet pole-pieces from extremes of temperature. Some consideration should be given to the influence of the magnetic field on the furnace windings. Actual measurement of the temperature may be made with a thermocouple or, in some cases, the buoyancy effect of the surrounding atmosphere may be calibrated in terms of temperature.

Moderately low temperatures may be achieved by surrounding the sample tube with a Dewar flask of appropriate design to go between the pole-pieces. Various low-boiling liquids may be used as refrigerants. An alternative method is to use a large lead block suspended by plastic tubes inside the Dewar flask. This block has a central cylindrical opening in which the sample hangs. It is also supplied with a spiral opening into which liquid air may be injected. More sensitive control may be achieved by passing oxygen through a liquid nitrogen condenser and allowing the liquefied oxygen to drip into the lead block. The rate of oxygen gas flowing into the condenser controls the rate of cooling. A small heating coil is available as required. The apparatus is shown diagrammatically in Fig. 6. Temperatures are measured by a multi-junction thermocouple. This apparatus has proved very satisfactory for the temperature range of $-190°$ to $+100°C$.

A third convenient method for obtaining low temperatures is to boil liquid air, or nitrogen, in a flask under the sample so that the cold vapors rise over the sample. This method, shown in Fig. 7, lends itself readily to automatic control. Another cryostat is described by Smith and Johnston.[18]

3. The Quincke Method[19]

This method is similar in principle to the Gouy method except that the force on the liquid sample is measured in terms of the hydrostatic

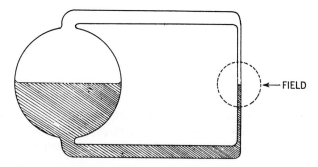

←—FIELD

Fig. 8. Diagrammatic representation of the Quincke magnetic balance.

pressure developed when the liquid is placed in a capillary tube so that the meniscus stands in a strong magnetic field. The apparatus is shown

[18] A. L. Smith and H. L. Johnston, *Rev. Sci. Instr.*, **24**, 420 (1953).
[19] G. Quincke, *Ann. Physik*, **24**, 347 (1885); **34**, 401 (1888).

diagrammatically in Fig. 8.   On application of the field, the meniscus will rise if the liquid is paramagnetic or will fall if the liquid is diamagnetic.   It is often possible and convenient to use fields of the order of 25,000 oersteds. For a diamagnetic liquid such as water, the change in height of the meniscus may be several millimeters.   When the reservoir is of large diameter compared with the capillary, and when the susceptibility of the vapor above the meniscus is negligible, the mass susceptibility of the sample is given by

$$\chi = \frac{2\Delta h g}{H^2}$$

where Δh is the change in vertical height of the meniscus, and the other terms have their usual significance.   This method has the advantage that independent measurement of the density is not necessary.

Sometimes rise or fall of the meniscus is observed directly.   More frequently the meniscus is returned to its original position by changing the height of the reservoir, or by changing the gas pressure over the meniscus. Accuracy of the readings may be increased slightly by inclining the capillary.

The Quincke method is well adapted to the measurement of liquids, and the accuracy possible is at least as great as with the Gouy method. Unfortunately, arrangements for changing the temperature over a wide range are not convenient.   For measurements near room temperature, it is possible to control the temperature with a high degree of accuracy.

The Quincke method may also be used for gases.   If the susceptibility of the vapor over the meniscus is not negligible, the hydrostatic pressure developed on application of the field is

$$p = \frac{1}{2}(\kappa - \kappa_0)H^2$$

where κ, κ_0 are the volume susceptibilities of the liquid and vapor, respectively.

Some very sensitive adaptations of the Quincke balance as applied to liquids and to gases are described by Wills and Hector,[20] Bauer and Piccard,[21] Bitter,[22] and Woodbridge.[23]

4. The Faraday Method[24]

If the poles of a magnet are inclined toward each other (Fig. 9), there is produced a nonhomogeneous field with an axis of symmetry.   A non-

[20] A. P. Wills and L. G. Hector, *Phys. Rev.*, **23**, 209 (1924).

[21] E. Bauer and A. Piccard, *J. phys. radium*, **1**, 97 (1920).

[22] F. Bitter, *Phys. Rev.*, **33**, 389 (1929).

[23] D. B. Woodbridge, *Phys. Rev.*, **48**, 672 (1935).

[24] M. Faraday, *Experimental Researches*, Vol. III.   Taylor and Francis, London, 1855, pp. 27 and 497.

homogeneous field may also be found, and often with more convenience, between appropriately shaped pole-pieces (Fig. 10) or near the edges of plane or truncated poles (Fig. 11). If, now, a substance of susceptibility

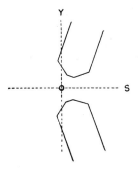

Fig. 9. Principle of the Faraday magnetic balance. The sample, shown here at the origin, is placed where the product $H\partial H/\partial s$ is a maximum. The sample is free to move along the s-axis, and may be suspended from a torsion arm.

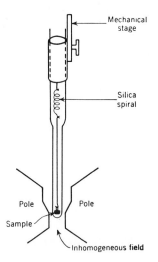

Fig. 10. Faraday balance using vertical suspension from a silica spiral spring.

other than zero is placed in a region where the strength of the field (H) changes with displacement along the axis of symmetry (s), then the substance will be subjected to a force along the axis

$$f = m\chi H \ \partial H/\partial s$$

where m is the mass of the sample, χ the mass susceptibility, H the field strength, and $\partial H/\partial s$ the field gradient along the s-axis.

This method is convenient and sensitive.   Small amounts of material are needed, and no separate determination of density is required.   The method was used extensively by Pierre Curie[25] in his classical studies, and has been used and developed by many investigators since then.   The sample may conveniently be mounted on a torsion arm.   Displacements may

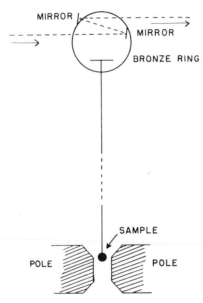

Fig. 11. Sucksmith modification of the Faraday balance.

be observed directly, or by a mirror, lamp, and scale arrangement.   The sample is generally restored to its original position with the aid of a torsion head.   The electrical torsion head is satisfactory for this purpose.[26]

Although the torsion method is sensitive, it becomes somewhat cumbersome for measurements at low temperature.   Alternatively, the force may be measured as a horizontal or as a vertical force.   The horizontal force method, involving a bifilar suspension, has been developed by Weiss. A null method is used, the force being compensated by the attraction between two current-bearing coils.   The method is described at length by Foëx.[10,11]

The vertical force method has been developed in a very useful piece

[25] P. Curie, *Ann. chim. phys.*, **5**, 289 (1895).
[26] A. N. Guthrie and L. T. Bourland, *Phys. Rev.*, **37**, 303 (1931).

of apparatus by Sucksmith.[27]   Instead of using a balance, he suspends the sample, as previously mentioned, from a ring of phosphor bronze which is fixed at its upper side.   Two small mirrors are fixed to the ring at the optimum positions so that on a scale at one meter distance the image of a lamp filament may be observed.   Movement of the filament image is at least 150 times the movement of the sample under investigation.   A diagram of the apparatus is shown in Fig. 11.   The method appears to combine some of the most valuable features of the Faraday and Gouy methods. The balance may conveniently be adapted[28] for susceptibility determinations in vacuum or in a controlled atmosphere up to 1500°C.   The theory of the Sucksmith ring is given by Bates.[4]

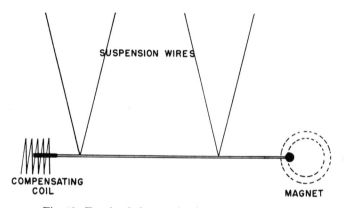

Fig. 12. Faraday balance using horizontal suspension.

A useful alternative which has given satisfaction in the writer's laboratory consists of suspending the sample from a silica spiral spring, elongation of which is observed with a micrometer microscope.   The whole assembly of sample, spring, and surrounding glass tube is mounted on a mechanical slide from a microscope so that vertical motion is possible (Fig. 10).   The method is quite similar to that described by Milligan and Whitehurst[29] in an apparatus designed for simultaneous measurement of magnetic susceptibility and adsorption isotherms.

Many observations, using the Faraday method, have been made at both high and low temperatures.   The method is a strong competitor of the Gouy method for many types of investigations.   Refinements, some of them of quite extraordinary sensitivity, have been described by many

[27] W. Sucksmith, *Phil. Mag.*, **8**, 158 (1929).

[28] W. Sucksmith and R. R. Pearce, *Proc. Roy. Soc. (London)*, **A167**, 189 (1938).

[29] W. O. Milligan and H. B. Whitehurst, *Rev. Sci. Instr.*, **23**, 618 (1952).

workers, a few of whom are mentioned below.[30-33] Adaptation of a quartz fiber microbalance to susceptibility measurements, with the use of exceptionally small samples, is described by Blaha.[34]

A modification which has often been used is known as the Curie-Chéneveau balance.[35] This balance is similar in principle to the Faraday method except that setting of the sample in the most favorable position is simplified. The balance is shown diagrammatically in Fig. 13. It consists of a torsion arm suspended by a fine wire. One end of the torsion arm supports the sample which is free to move between the poles of a small

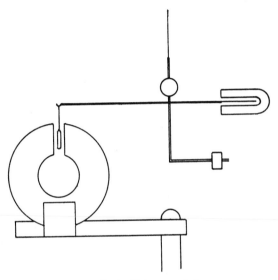

Fig. 13. Curie-Chéneveau balance.

permanent magnet. The magnet may be moved forward or backward with respect to the sample and, because of its magnetic susceptibility, the sample is either repelled or attracted. Movement of the torsion arm may be followed by a pointer, or by a mirror, lamp, and scale. The sample automatically places itself in the region of maximum attraction or repulsion. The force acting on the sample is zero when the sample is between the poles. It is also zero when the sample is well removed from the

[30] S. S. Bhatnagar and K. N. Mathur, *Phil. Mag.*, **8**, 1041 (1929).

[31] B. Cabrera, *J. phys. radium*, **9**, 209 (1938).

[32] A. Pacault, *Ann. chim.*, **1**, 527 (1946).

[33] S. Broersma, *Magnetic Measurements on Organic Compounds* (Dissertation). Martinus Nijhoff, The Hague, 1947.

[34] F. Blaha, *Mikrochemie ver. Mikrochim. Acta*, **39**, 339 (1952).

[35] C. Chéneveau, *Phil. Mag.*, **20**, 357 (1910).

poles. There are then two regions in which the force is a maximum as the magnet is moved from far on one side of the sample to far on the other side. The mass susceptibility of the sample is given by

$$\chi = \chi_0 \, \frac{m_0}{m} \left(\frac{\theta - \theta_t}{\theta_0 - \theta_t} \right)$$

where χ_0, m_0 are the mass susceptibility and mass, respectively, of a known substance, m is the mass of the unknown sample, θ is the difference in corresponding maximum deflections on either side of zero for the unknown sample, θ_0 the difference for the known substance, and θ_t the difference for the empty tube.

Various refinements have been suggested by Gray and Farquharson[36] and by others. Relatively small quantities of sample are required and the measurements may be made rapidly. On the other hand, it is difficult to introduce temperature control, and the sensitivity is not very high. The Curie-Chéneveau balance is of most use in magnetochemical analyses such as may be required in rare earth work. Useful elaborations of the Curie-Chéneveau balance are described by Wilson,[37] Oxley,[38] and Vaidyanathan.[39] Some workers have adapted the method for use with an electromagnet. The availability of powerful permanent magnets would appear to enlarge the possible scope of this balance.

The Faraday method has still further applicability in a variety of devices which, superficially, bear little resemblance to those already described. If an elongated specimen is suspended in a field which is not homogeneous, it will tend to take up an equilibrium position. A diamagnetic specimen will tend to set itself at right angles to the field, a paramagnetic specimen parallel to the field. The force acting on the specimen depends on the difference in mass susceptibilities of specimen and surrounding atmosphere. This affords a convenient method for the investigation of liquids. The specimen may be made of glass or quartz, and the liquid takes the place of the surrounding atmosphere. The method was developed by Decker,[40] and has been used by the author.[41]

A very sensitive balance for gases and vapors has been developed by Bitter[42] from a method apparently originally suggested by Glaser.[43] This

[36] F. W. Gray and J. Farquharson, *J. Sci. Instr.*, **9**, 1 (1932).

[37] E. Wilson, *Proc. Roy. Soc. (London)*, **A96**, 429 (1920).

[38] A. E. Oxley, *Phil. Trans. Roy. Soc. (London)*, **A214**, 109 (1914); **A215**, 79 (1915).

[39] V. I. Vaidyanathan, *Indian J. Phys.*, **1**, 183 (1926).

[40] H. Decker, *Ann. Physik*, **79**, 324 (1926).

[41] P. W. Selwood, *J. Am. Chem. Soc.*, **55**, 3161 (1933).

[42] F. Bitter, *Phys. Rev.*, **35**, 1572 (1930).

[43] A. Glaser, *Ann. Physik*, **75**, 459 (1924).

method is somewhat similar to that of Decker, but much more elaborate. A test body, made of Pyrex glass, consists of a cylindrical vessel divided radially into four equal chambers. The chamber is suspended from a torsion fiber between the poles of an electromagnet. Two of the chambers, diametrically opposite one another, are open to the surrounding gas, the other two are evacuated and sealed off. On application of the field the test body turns through an angle which is a function of the magnetic susceptibility of the gas in the open chambers. A similar device for the the study of vapors has been developed to an unusual degree of sensitivity by Reber and Boeker.[44]

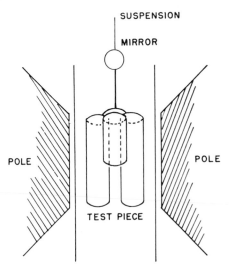

SUSPENSION

MIRROR

POLE

POLE

TEST PIECE

Fig. 14. Reber and Boeker test-piece for use on vapors.

Methods for control of temperature with the Faraday balance are, in general, similar to those described for the Gouy method. The small size of sample required tends to make the problem of design simpler.

Down to the temperature of boiling hydrogen, magnetic measurements by the Gouy or Faraday methods offer no difficulties. But below about 14°K., the measurements present increasingly difficult experimental and theoretical problems. Most of the work in this field has come from the Leiden laboratory and from the University of California. A description of magnetic and other phenomena at very low temperatures is given by Burton, Smith, and Wilhelm.[45] The rapidly increasing availability of

[44] R. K. Reber and G. F. Boeker, *J. Chem. Phys.*, **15**, 508 (1947).
[45] E. F. Burton, H. G. Smith, and J. O. Wilhelm, *Phenomena at the Temperature of Liquid Helium.* Reinhold Publ. Corp., New York, 1940.

liquid helium makes it certain that many routine studies will be pushed down to this region. A convenient balance for measurements in the liquid helium range is described by McGuire and Lane.[46]

5. Related Methods

If a bar magnet stands parallel to a plane surface, the induced polarity on the surface exerts a force on the magnet. This force is an attraction if the surface consists of a paramagnetic substance, a repulsion if the substance is diamagnetic. The magnitude of the force depends on the magnetic susceptibility of the substance. Use of this principle for magnetic

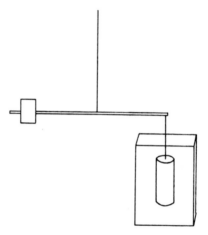

Fig. 15. Rankine magnetic balance.

measurements was suggested by Rankine[47] and developed by Iskenderian.[48] The arrangement is shown diagrammatically in Fig. 15. The magnet is suspended by a quartz fiber from a horizontal beam supported by another quartz fiber. This arrangement minimizes the effect of the earth's magnetic field and of stray accidental fields. The relative magnetic susceptibilities of different materials can be deduced from the magnitudes of the torques produced in the torsion fiber.

Owing to the effects of stray fields, the method is rather difficult and it is necessary that all parts of the balance, other than the magnet, be constructed of nonferromagnetic materials. The apparatus is capable of giving accurate results, with the interesting difference from other methods

[46] T. R. McGuire and C. T. Lane, *Rev. Sci. Instr.*, **20**, 489 (1949).

[47] A. O. Rankine, *Proc. Phys. Soc. (London)*, **46**, 1, 391 (1934).

[48] H. P. Iskenderian, *Phys. Rev.*, **51**, 1092 (1937); **52**, 1244 (1937).

that very weak fields are used. The fields may be of the order of 15 to 100 oersteds. A detailed description of a Rankine balance is given by Bockris and Parsons.[49] By the use of elaborate precautions, including tungsten fibers and a photoelectric method for measuring deflections, it has been possible to observe volume susceptibility changes of 0.0004×10^{-6} unit. This makes the method of considerable interest in the detection of transient phenomena such as the formation and decay of free radicals. Use of the balance for measuring the susceptibilities of oxygen and of nitric oxide at low fields is described by Burris and Hause.[50]

Among the many other methods which have been suggested for the measurement of magnetic susceptibility, only two will be mentioned. These are chosen because of their possible application to chemical problems.

Salceanu has developed a method of "magnetically neutral" solutions.[51] If a paramagnetic substance is dissolved in a diamagnetic solvent, such as water, there must be a certain concentration, at a definite temperature, at which the susceptibility is zero. Salceanu determines this condition by the rotation of a glass float placed in the liquid under investigation, between the poles of a magnet. The susceptibility of the solute may be calculated from a knowledge of the concentration at which the susceptibility of the solution is zero. The method would appear to be of rather limited applicability.

The problem of measurements on nonhomogeneous systems has been studied by Bates, Baker, and Meakin,[52] particularly with reference to amalgams which separate on standing. One pole tip has a cylindrical surface and the other has a plane surface. When an amalgam is placed in a vertical tube, suspended in the field from a torsion balance, each portion of the amalgam is exposed to the same value of the gradient of H^2 in the direction along which motion of the tube is possible.

Similarly, although magnetometer methods for the measurement of susceptibilities have been described,[53] they are subject to the same difficulty, namely failure to saturate ferromagnetic impurities. It is difficult to evaluate such instruments on the basis of published data.

6. Production and Control of Magnetic Fields

Most magnetochemical investigations are carried out in fields ranging from 5000 to 25,000 oersteds. Fields of this magnitude over several cubic centimeters of space are readily produced by electromagnets drawing up-

[49] J. O'M. Bockris and D. F. Parsons, *J. Sci. Instr.*, **30**, 362 (1953).

[50] A. Burris and C. D. Hause, *J. Chem. Phys.*, **11**, 442 (1943).

[51] C. Salceanu, *Z. Physik*, **108**, 439 (1938).

[52] L. F. Bates, C. J. W. Baker, and R. Meakin, *Proc. Phys. Soc. (London)*, **52**, 425 (1940).

[53] E. A. Johnson and W. F. Steiner, *Rev. Sci. Instr.*, **8**, 236 (1937).

wards of 1 kw. of electrical energy.   Most such magnets are after the design
of Weiss,[54] and at one time or another several models have been offered by
manufacturers of scientific instruments.   Many workers in the field have

Fig. 16. Gouy magnetic balance.

had magnets of their own design made in local shops.   Figure 16 shows such
a magnet used in connection with a Gouy balance in the author's laboratory.
Actual design of the magnet depends so much on individual needs that no
detailed plans need be given here.   There are, however, a few general
principles to be borne in mind.   For most purposes a considerable degree
of flexibility is to be preferred.   The distance between the coils should be

[54] P. Weiss, *J. phys.*, *6*, 353 (1907).

adequate for all temperature-control mechanisms that may be necessary. The pole-pieces should be removable and interchangeable. The magnet should preferably have little remanence; that is, the field should return as nearly as possible to zero after removal of the current through the coils. The field should also have a good degree of reproducibility for a given current. Soft iron and certain types of commercial steels are suitable for both these purposes.

The shape and material of the pole-pieces are important. For the Gouy method, flat cylinder faces or truncated conical poles are most satis-

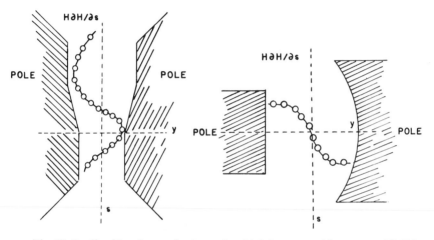

Fig. 17. Profile of two forms of pole gap for obtaining reasonably constant $H\partial H/\partial s$ over a small region. The Fereday gap (*right*) is described in *Proc. Phys. Soc.*, **43**, 383 (1931); it is used for ferromagnetic measurements.

factory. The plane face of the pole should not be less than 2 in. in diameter if a region of reasonably uniform field is to be produced. For maximum intensity, conical pole-pieces may be used. The Faraday method for susceptibility determination requires that the sample be placed in a region of fairly high field where the product $H\partial H/\partial s$ is constant over the sample, at least. Field profiles for two shapes of pole face are shown in Fig. 17. Ferrocobalt is useful for the pole-tips because of its high saturation intensity. In the writer's experience, high intensity is less important than the ability to reach, at reasonable currents, a fairly flat region of the B/H curve for the pole interspace. The flatter this region is, the less effect fluctuations of current will have on the accuracy of the results.

Many large magnets have cooling arrangements to dissipate the fairly large energies used. The coil windings may be made of tubing through which water circulates, or water jackets may be spaced between the coil layers. Alternatively, oil, cooled in an exchanger, may be pumped over the coil layers. There is no question that for very high fields and time-consuming experiments, some form of cooling is essential. This is true not only to protect the magnet from injury but also because the strength of the field depends on the temperature of the iron core. But for many types of magnetochemical measurements, the current is turned on intermittently and there is little danger of the core becoming warm. For such measurements the introduction of cooling is an unnecessary expense.

A very large magnet of more or less conventional design has been described by Cotton.[55] With this magnet, fields in excess of 70,000 oersteds have been produced over a much larger volume than is normally possible. Large fields of very great volume are familiar in the cyclotron. For still more intense fields, there is nothing more to be gained by using iron cores, and the practice is to use coreless coils. Kapitza[56] has produced fields in excess of 300,000 oersteds by momentarily passing very large currents through specially constructed coils. Bitter[57] has described coreless magnets producing fields in excess of 40,000 oersteds over long periods. In such magnets, the construction of the cooling system and the cost of electricity and of cooling become primary considerations.

In almost all magnetic measurements, it is necessary to control the strength of the field, and in many the actual field strength must be known and be variable at will. For many cases, the control of the current through the coils is sufficient, provided the temperature of the magnet is reasonably constant. In the author's laboratory, control has been achieved by passing all the magnet current through a standard 0.01 ohm resistance. Leads from this resistance are connected to a potentiometer which in turn is connected to a galvanometer. Deviation of the galvanometer from a predetermined setting operates one of two photoelectric relays which are arranged to change the resistance in the field coils of the D.C. generator supplying the magnet. This apparatus has proved satisfactory over a period of years. The sensitivity may be altered as desired. Other circuits for achieving the same purpose will readily suggest themselves. A very simple circuit for stabilizing the magnet current through the use of a small compensating current from a storage battery is described by Potter.[58] In the writer's experience, most magnetochemical studies are readily carried out with no more stabilizing equipment than a rectifier, a variable transformer, and a good ammeter—the current through the magnet being adjusted by hand.

[55] A. Cotton, *Report of the 6th Solvay Conference.* Gautier-Villars, Paris, 1932.
[56] P. Kapitza, *Proc. Roy. Soc. (London)*, **A115**, 658 (1927).
[57] F. Bitter, *Rev. Sci. Instr.*, **10**, 373 (1939).
[58] H. H. Potter, *J. Sci. Instr.*, **11**, 95 (1934)

Direct control of the field strength, rather than of the current, is more difficult. Use has been made of the fact that the electrical resistance of

(a)

(b)

Fig. 18 (a) Permanent magnet made by Indiana Steel Products Co. (b) Electromagnet made by Varian Associates.

bismuth changes in a magnetic field.[59]   A spiral of bismuth wire mounted
in the field may serve as part of a controlling device.   It is difficult to make
the control sensitive enough, and temperature fluctuations must be prevented.   Stansfield[60] has suggested using the anisotropy of calcite or sodium nitrate crystals as a means of controlling field intensities.   Nuclear
resonance has been adapted for the same purpose.[61]

There are available certain alloys which combine very high remanence
with high coercive power.   Such alloys may be cast into permanent magnets which rival electromagnets in intensity of field.   The fields produced
may be constant over long periods.   It is even possible to vary the fields,
by passing a suitable current through a magnetizing coil surrounding the
magnet or by use of a magnetic shunt.   Permanent magnets have the
obvious difficulty that the field may not readily be reduced to zero, so that
the specimen being investigated must be removed mechanically from the
neighborhood when the zero field readings are being taken.   A permanent
magnet has been used by Rawlinson[62] for studies on hemoglobin and its
derivatives.   Figure 18 shows an Alnico magnet in the author's laboratory.
This magnet produces a field of about 8500 oersteds. The pole gap is 1 in.
and the flat part of the truncated poles is 2 in. in diameter.   The cost was
somewhat less than that of a comparable electromagnet.   Permanent
magnets have advantages for certain types of magnetic measurements.
They are particularly useful for studying changes which occur as a function
of time, such as the disappearance of molecular oxygen from a styrene
solution, the transient formation of a free radical, or, for instance, the
magnetic changes which occur in a dry cell during discharge.   On the other
hand, permanent magnets are not convenient for use on substances which
may contain traces of ferromagnetic impurities or components.

Measurement of field intensity in both permanent and electromagnets is
commonly achieved by finding the force exerted on a current-bearing wire
in the field, or by use of an induction method such as the fluxmeter.   These
are both described in all texts on electricity and magnetism.   More frequently in magnetochemical investigations, the field is estimated by use of a
substance of known magnetic susceptibility and one of the standard methods, such as the Gouy balance.   In certain instances where the whole field
must be mapped, as in precise absolute determinations by the Faraday
method, this may be done with the aid of a bismuth spiral, or more readily,
with a proton-resonance probe.

[59] H. Decker, *Ann. Physik*, **79,** 324 (1926).
[60] R. G. Stansfield, *Proc. Cambridge Phil. Soc.*, **34,** 625 (1938).
[61] M. E. Packard, *Rev. Sci. Instr.*, **19,** 435 (1948).
[62] W. A. Rawlinson, *Australian J. Biol. Med. Sci.*, **18,** 185 (1940).

7. Calibration

Magnetic balances are frequently calibrated with the aid of substances of known susceptibility. No single substance is completely satisfactory as a calibrating agent for all types of measurements. The Gouy, Quincke, Faraday, and related balances are often calibrated with water, provided the substance under investigation is one of low susceptibility. The magnetic susceptibility of water at 20°C. may be assumed to be -0.720×10^{-6} unit per gram. The various measurements leading to this value and the temperature coefficient of susceptibility of water (which is slight) are discussed in a later chapter. A necessary precaution in the use of water for this purpose is that the water should be free from dissolved air. Oxygen dissolved in water has an appreciable susceptibility, but what is even more important is that no bubbles of air should come out of solution on the walls of the container during measurement.

The calibration of the Gouy balance has been investigated by Angus[63,64] who points out that water, as a calibrating agent, has some deficiencies, and who recommends benzene, the susceptibility of which at 25°C is often given as -0.702×10^{-6}. It has, however, been pointed out[65] that oxygen is fairly soluble in benzene and that if the dissolved oxygen exhibits its normal paramagnetism, the susceptibility of benzene saturated with air may be quite measureably different from air-free benzene. This appears to be the case, because if benzene saturated with air is taken as having a susceptibility of -0.7020 ($\times 10^{-6}$), then that of benzene saturated with nitrogen is -0.7081, and saturated with oxygen is -0.6756.

A carefully prepared solution of nickel chloride is useful as a calibrating agent of somewhat higher susceptibility than water. This solution has been investigated by Brant,[66] by Cabrera, Moles, and Guzman,[67] by Weiss and Bruins,[68] and by Nettleton and Sugden.[69] They agree that the molar susceptibility of nickel chloride at 20°C. is $4433 \pm 12 \times 10^{-6}$, and that this value is independent of concentration in the neighborhood of 30% $NiCl_2$ by weight. There are cases in which the susceptibility of a mixture is not a linear function of the concentration, but for nickel chloride in water at 20°C. the susceptibility per gram is given to a very fair degree of accuracy by the relationship

$$\chi = [34.21p - 0.720(1 - p)] \times 10^{-6}$$

[63] W. R. Angus and W. K. Hill, *Trans. Faraday Soc.*, **40**, 185 (1943).

[64] W. R. Angus and D. V. Tilston, *ibid.*, **43**, 235 (1946).

[65] B. C. Eggleston, D. F. Evans, and R. E. Richards, *J. Chem. Soc.*, **1954**, 941.

[66] L. Brant, *Phys. Rev.*, **17**, 678 (1921).

[67] B. Cabrera, E. Moles, and J. Guzman, *Arch. sci. phys. nat.*, **37**, 324 (1914).

[68] P. Weiss and E. D. Bruins, *Proc. Acad. Sci. Amsterdam*, **18**, 346 (1915).

[69] H. R. Nettleton and S. Sugden, *Proc. Roy. Soc. (London)*, **A173**, 313 (1939).

where p is the proportion of $NiCl_2$ present by weight. The temperature coefficient of nickel chloride solution has been investigated by Nettleton and Sugden[69] who find that the gram susceptibility of the solution may be represented by

$$\chi = \left[\frac{10{,}030p}{T} - 0.720(1 - p) \right] \times 10^{-6}$$

where T is the absolute temperature. This simply means that the susceptibility of the solute varies inversely as the absolute temperature over the range in which the solution is liquid.

Many substances have been suggested as calibration agents of high susceptibility. Probably as useful a compound as any is hydrated ferrous ammonium sulfate (Mohr's salt) for which the susceptibility per gram is given by $\chi = 9500 \times 10^{-6}/(T + 1)$ where T is the absolute temperature.[70] In common with other solids, this substance has the difficulty that homogeneity of packing in the sample tube is seldom obtained. Nevertheless, Mohr's salt has been used in the author's laboratory for many years, with considerable satisfaction.

A readily available diamagnetic solid which has given some satisfaction in the writer's laboratory as a calibrating agent for the Faraday method is ordinary cane sugar, the susceptibility of which over the room temperature range is -0.566×10^{-6}.

In every choice of a solid calibration agent some consideration should be given to the chemical characterization of the substance. If a compound is acceptable as an analytical standard, as is Mohr's salt, it is probably, but not always, acceptable as a magnetic standard. The choice, for instance, of manganese dioxide would be quite indefensible.

A suitable gas for calibration purpose is oxygen,[71] the *volume* susceptibility of which at $20°C$. and 760 mm. pressure is $\kappa = (0.1434 \pm 0.0004) \times 10^{-6}$.

It not infrequently happens that substances subjected to magnetochemical investigation contain traces of ferromagnetic impurities. In a substance chosen as a calibrating agent, the occurrence of ferromagnetic impurities could be disastrous so far as significant results are concerned. Freedom from ferromagnetic impurity can generallly be taken for granted in organic and inorganic compounds which have been purified by distillation or recrystallization. But ferromagnetism is often very difficult to eliminate from inorganic solids.

Such impurities may completely mask the true susceptibility of the

[70] L. C. Jackson, *Phil. Trans. Roy. Soc. (London)*, **A224**, 1 (1923).

[71] E. Bauer and A. Piccard, *J. phys. radium*, **1**, 97 (1920). See also Stoner (*op. cit.*[1]) for a discussion of this matter.

substance. For instance, Fig. 19 shows the difference in Δw, the apparent change in weight by the Gouy method, before and after recrystallization to remove a few microscopic traces of ferromagnetic impurity from some triphenylgermanium, under investigation by the writer. Such impurities are readily detected by the apparent field-strength dependence of the susceptibility, whether dia- or paramagnetic. Measurements at two or more field strengths should always be made on solid samples. If ferro-

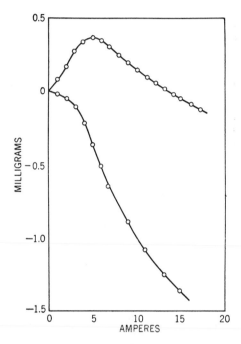

Fig. 19. Apparent change in weight, Aw, plotted against current through the magnet. The upper curve shows the presence of a trace of ferromagnetic impurity. The lower curve shows the same substance after recrystallization.

magnetic impurities cannot be removed by purification of the sample, there are two methods available for eliminating their effect. The first is to heat the substance and to take the measurements above the Curie point of the impurity. The second is to take the measurements over a range of field strength and to extrapolate the susceptibility to infinite field strength. This is conveniently done by plotting apparent susceptibility against reciprocal field.

The writer's experience in this matter is that while the Gouy method is remarkably sensitive for the *detection* of ferromagnetic impurities, it is not possible to obtain the correct susceptibility of a sample in which ferro-magnetism is present.   The reason for this difficulty is that the Gouy method requires that part of the sample must be in a negligible, and hence nonsaturating, field.   This difficulty is not encountered with the Faraday method in which all the sample may be held in a saturating field.   For this reason the Faraday method is strongly recommended for all studies on inorganic solids of a type which may possibly contain traces of ferromagnetic impurities.   On the other hand, Bates indicates that under certain conditions correction for ferromagnetism is possible with the Gouy method. Perhaps the lack of agreement here is actually a matter of how much ferro-

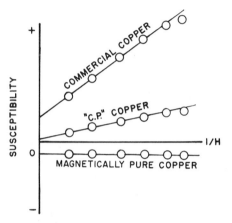

Fig. 20. Plot of apparent susceptibility *versus* reciprocal field for several samples of copper.   Traces of ferromagnetic impurity are shown by some field strength dependence of apparent susceptibility.

magnetism may be corrected for.   It should be emphasized that chemical purity or spectroscopic purity is no guarantee of "magnetic purity."   No magnetic measurement on a diamagnetic or paramagnetic inorganic solid should be accepted unless it has been made at two or more field strengths. The matter is further discussed by Knappwost.[71a]

The presence of paramagnetic impurities in a diamagnetic substance is also easy to detect, and to correct for, because the susceptibility of the former is nearly always inversely proportional to the temperature while that of the latter is independent of temperature.

In general, corrections for all types of impurities may be made provided the amounts present and susceptibilities are known, because the suscep-tibilities of mechanical mixtures are, at least to a first approximation,

[71a] A. Knappwost, *Z. Elektrochem.*, **59**, 561 (1955).

linear functions of the concentrations. But indiscriminate application of such methods to solid solutions, particularly to those containing paramagnetic ions, can often lead to gross errors.

8. Induction Methods for Dia- and Paramagnetic Substances

It might be thought that induction methods, similar to those used in the study of ferromagnetics, would be useful in the determination of magnetic susceptibilities of dia- and paramagnetic substances. There is no doubt that induction methods may be made sufficiently sensitive to measure the magnetic susceptibility of an organic compound with a precision of about 0.1%. The experimental difficulties are fairly great, and such methods appear to be useless if traces of ferromagnetic impurities are present. Furthermore, the methods so far developed cannot be adapted for measurements over a range of temperature without considerable difficulty and loss of precision. Nevertheless, the induction method has considerable attractiveness because it eliminates the need for a large magnet and the inevitably awkward suspension of the sample that is required in the Faraday or Gouy methods.

The method described by Broersma[72] consists of two opposing secondary coils placed inside a long solenoid energized with about 50 amperes A.C. at 175 cycles per second. The observation is made in the change of inductance when a sample is placed in one of the secondary coils.

A related method consists in measuring the change of resonance frequency of an oscillating circuit by introducing the sample to be measured into a solenoid which forms part of the circuit. Such a high frequency apparatus has been developed by Pacault.[73] The results obtainable with this apparatus with liquids such as benzene are in good agreement with those obtained by classical methods. Liquids of high dielectric constant such as water give, as expected, somewhat less accurate results. The method would appear to lend itself to the study of transitory phenomena, and makes the measurement of magnetic susceptibility in favorable cases little more difficult than the determination of pH or of refractive index. An apparatus similar to Pacault's but somewhat more elaborate, is described by Effemey et al.[73a]

The reader will not confuse these methods with the various, newer resonance techniques to be described in Chapter 4.

---

[72] S. Broersma, *Rev. Sci. Instr.*, **20**, 660 (1949). An apparatus of apparently similar design is mentioned by E. Müller, *Fortschr. chem. Forsch.*, **1**, 325 (1949).

[73] A. Pacault, B. Lemanceau, and J. Joussot-Dubien, *Compt. rend.*, **237**, 1156 (1953); *J. chim. phys. France*, **1956**, 198. This apparatus is available commercially in France.

[73a] H. G. Effemey, D. F. Parsons, and J. O'M. Bockris, *J. Sci. Instr.* **32**, 99 (1955).

9. The *Ortho-Para* Hydrogen Method

The spin isomerization of hydrogen is catalyzed by inhomogeneous magnetic fields such as exist near paramagnetic ions or molecules. The effect is observed both for heterogeneous and homogeneous catalysis.[74] The rate of conversion is a function of the magnetic moment of the paramagnetic ion or molecule, and hence may be used as a rough measure of the susceptibility. The theory of this process is given by Wigner[75] and by Kalckar and Teller.[76]

The method consists, in brief, of passing approximately 1,1-*ortho-para* hydrogen over the catalyst and then of analyzing the resultant mixture. The 1,1-*ortho-para* hydrogen may be prepared by passing tank hydrogen over charcoal or chromium oxide gel at liquid air temperature. Analysis of the mixture is made by the thermal conductivity method.[77] Modifications of this method, especially with reference to micro quantities of hydrogen, are discussed by Farkas.[78,79]

This interesting method cannot compete in terms of accuracy with the more conventional methods for determining susceptibility. Furthermore, it is complicated by the fact that the low-temperature conversion is strongly catalyzed by substances such as charcoal which are diamagnetic.[80] This has been explained as due to the existence of magnetic dipoles on the surface of the charcoal. Furthermore, the rate of conversion on paramagnetic surfaces is greatly modified by adsorption. Nevertheless, in favorable cases[81,82] the change in catalytic activity between a diamagnetic surface such as that of lanthanum oxide, and a paramagnetic one such as gadolinium oxide, is very striking.[83] Application of the *ortho-para* hydrogen method to organic free radicals is reviewed by Müller.[84] Some recent work involving

[74] G. M. Schwab, H. S. Taylor, and R. Spence, *Catalysis*. D. Van Nostrand Co., New York 1937, p. 213.

[75] E. Wigner, *Z. physik. Chem.*, **B23**, 28 (1938).

[76] F. Kalckar and E. Teller, *Proc. Roy. Soc. (London)*, **A150**, 520 (1935).

[77] K. F. Bonhoeffer and P. Harteck, *Z. physik. Chem.*, **4B**, 113 (1929).

[78] A. Farkas, *Light and Heavy Hydrogen*. Cambridge University Press, Cambridge, 1935.

[79] A. Farkas and H. W. Melville, *Experimental Methods in Gas Reactions*. MacMillan and Company, London, 1939.

[80] K. F. Bonhoeffer, A. Farkas, and K. W. Rummel, *Z. physik. Chem.*, **B21**, 225 (1933).

[81] H. S. Taylor and A. Sherman, *J. Am. Chem. Soc.*, **53**, 1614 (1931); *Trans. Faraday Soc.*, **28**, 247 (1932).

[82] L. Farkas and L. Sandler, *J. Chem. Phys.*, **8**, 248 (1940).

[83] H. S. Taylor and H. Diamond, *J. Am. Chem. Soc.*, **55**, 2613 (1933); **57**, 1251 (1935).

[84] E. Müller, *Fortschr. chem. Forsch.*, **1**, 325 (1949).

application of the method to paramagnetic solids is described by Sandler.[85] The method has been successfully applied to a number of structural problems, to some of which reference will be made later. It seems unlikely, however, that the method will increase in importance. This is because of the unique character of the reaction involved. In the study of catalysis the *ortho-para* hydrogen conversion as a working tool has been succeeded for most purposes by such reactions as the hydrogen-deuterium exchange. For measuring the magnetic, and hence structural, properties of substances, the *ortho-para* hydrogen method seems likely to be superseded by recent developments in nuclear magnetism.

[85] Y. L. Sandler, *Can. J. Chem.*, **32**, 249 (1954).

CHAPTER TWO

THE MEASUREMENT OF PRINCIPAL SUSCEPTIBILITIES

10. Introduction

It will be recalled that crystals of low symmetry have three mutually perpendicular directions in which the direction of magnetization corresponds with the direction of an applied field. The magnetic susceptibilities along these axes, which do not necessarily coincide with the crystallographic axes, are often unequal. They are known as *principal* susceptibilities. In recent years, measurement of principal susceptibilities has become useful in structural chemistry. Crystals showing unequal principal susceptibilities are said to exhibit magnetic anisotropy.

If an anisotropic crystal is powdered, the average susceptibility of the powder, which is that susceptibility to which reference was made in the last chapter, is the mean of the three principal susceptibilities,

$$\chi = (\chi_1 + \chi_2 + \chi_3)/3$$

The most obvious method for measuring magnetic anisotropy is to determine the susceptibility by one of the standard methods, but to have the crystal oriented in such a way that the force of attraction, or repulsion, is exerted along one magnetic axis only. This method is not particularly accurate except for strongly paramagnetic substances, and some difficulty may be experienced in having the sample properly oriented.

11. Oscillation Methods

An elegant method of high sensitivity has been described in two modifications, by Krishnan.[1] This method, which originated with Stenger,[2,3] gives the difference between any two principal susceptibilities.

[1] K. S. Krishnan, B. C. Guha, and S. Banerjee, *Phil. Trans. Roy. Soc. (London)*, **A231**, 235 (1933).

[2] F. Stenger, *Wied. Ann.*, **20**, 304 (1883).

[3] W. König, *ibid.*, **31**, 273 (1887).

If an isotropic sample is cut to spherical shape, it will suffer no orientation in a nonuniform field.   Alternatively, an isotropic sample of any shape will suffer no orientation in a uniform field, but an anisotropic sample of any shape will suffer an orienting force in a uniform field.   This is the basis of the Krishnan method.

The sample is suspended by a fine torsion fiber in a homogeneous field. A field of sufficient homogeneity may be found in a small region between relatively large plane pole-pieces.   The field may be 5000 to 10,000 oersteds. In general, one magnetic axis of the sample is in the axis of the torsion fiber.

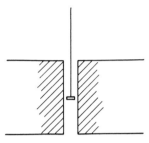

Fig. 21. Principle of the Krishnan anisotropy balance.

If the crystal is isotropic, it will suffer no orientation on application of the field, but if it is anisotropic, it will turn until the algebraically largest susceptibility approaches the direction of the lines of force.   The torsion head may now be turned until the crystal suffers no orientation on application of the field.   The largest algebraic susceptibility perpendicular to the fiber is now parallel to the field.

If the crystal is made to oscillate, the period of oscillation is related to the molar magnetic anisotropy as follows:

$$\chi_1 - \chi_2 = \Delta\chi = \frac{t_0^2 - t^2}{t^2} \cdot \frac{c}{H^2} \cdot \frac{M}{m}$$

where t_0 and t are oscillation periods with the field off and on, respectively, c is the torsional constant of the fiber, m is the mass of the crystal, M is the molecular (or formula) weight, H is the field, and $\Delta\chi$ is the difference between the two principal molar susceptibilities in the plane of rotation. Derivation of this formula is given by Wooster.[4]

Krishnan[5] has also developed a modification of the above method.

[4] W. A. Wooster, *Textbook of Crystal Physics*.   Macmillan and Company, Inc., New York, 1938.

[5] K. S. Krishnan and S. Banerjee, *Phil. Trans. Roy. Soc. (London)*, **A234**, 265 (1935).

The crystal orientation in the field is adjusted as above so that the largest algebraic susceptibility in the plane of rotation lies in the direction of the field. Now, if the torsion head is turned through an angle α, the crystal will turn through a smaller angle ϕ. When α is much larger than ϕ the relation between these angles is

$$c(\alpha - \phi) = \frac{1}{2} \frac{m}{M} H^2 \Delta\chi \sin 2\phi$$

where the terms have the same significance as above. If, now, the torsion head rotation is continued until $\phi = \pi/4$ radians, the crystal will suddenly flip around to a new equilibrium position; hence the usual name "Krishnan's flip-angle method." For this to occur, the torsion head must be turned through an angle α_c, and we have

$$c(\alpha_c - \pi/4) = \frac{1}{2} \frac{m}{M} H^2 \Delta\chi$$

or

$$\Delta\chi = (2\alpha_c - \pi/2) \frac{c}{H^2} \cdot \frac{M}{m}$$

It will be clear that the anisotropy obtained by Krishnan's methods is that which exists in the plane of oscillation. The third principal susceptibility may be investigated by reorienting the crystal. Absolute principal susceptibilities may be obtained by measuring one susceptibility by a direct method; or by using the average (powder) susceptibility. The latter is somewhat less accurate but is much more convenient.

Use of the Krishnan method has recently been described by Rogers.[6] A convenient device for low-temperature work is given by Bose.[7] In the author's laboratory, a permanent Alnico magnet has given satisfaction for anisotropy measurements. Very fine quartz or glass fibers are generally used, and the value of α_c may be as many as 20 complete revolutions.

Calibration of a Krishnan anisotropy balance is commonly achieved by measuring the field strength by a standard method, and by obtaining the torsion constant through observation of the oscillation period when an object of known moment of inertia is suspended from the fiber. It is more convenient to calibrate the balance directly with the aid of a crystal of known anisotropy. The author hesitates to recommend any particular substance for this purpose. Copper sulfate pentahydrate has been used with satisfaction in the author's laboratory, but the chief reason for its

[6] M. T. Rogers, *J. Am. Chem. Soc.*, **69**, 1506 (1947).
[7] A. Bose, *Indian J. Phys.*, **21**, 275 (1947).

choice was the ease of obtaining well-formed crystals. An isometric crystal would be more satisfactory. A large number of substances has been reported in the literature. These may be used for comparison purposes. The investigator starting this type of work will probably be guided by the availability of good crystals.

12. Absolute Methods

Principal susceptibilities may be obtained by Jackson's method or by a procedure due to Rabi. Jackson[8] and others have had considerable success with crystals of rare earth compounds and other paramagnetic substances. The procedure is that suggested above, namely to mount the crystal with one magnetic axis along the direction of the gradient in the

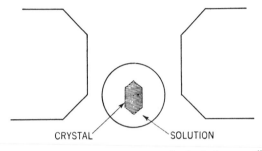

CRYSTAL   SOLUTION

Fig. 22. Rabi method for measurement of principal susceptibilities.

Faraday balance. The apparatus used is an adaptation of the Sucksmith modification of the Faraday magnetic balance. Measurements are possible over a wide range of temperature.

In Rabi's[9] method, the crystal to be investigated is suspended vertically in a nonhomogeneous field. The crystal is then surrounded with a solution, the susceptibility of which is varied, and the orientation of the crystal adjusted, until there is no movement of the crystal due to the magnetic field. A diagram of the apparatus is shown in Fig. 22. The susceptibility of the solution is then measured by the Gouy (or other) method. Each axis of the crystal may be investigated in turn, if this is required. The method does not require preparation of crystal sections or measurement of the magnetic field. As many crystalline substances are soluble in water, the solutions used are first saturated with the substance under investigation. The method may, of course, be extended to include nonaqueous solutions.

[8] L. C. Jackson, *Proc. Roy. Soc.* (*London*), **A140,** 695 (1933).

[9] I. I. Rabi, *Phys. Rev.,* **29,** 174 (1927).

CHAPTER THREE

SPECIFIC MAGNETIZATION AND THERMOMAGNETIC ANALYSIS

13. Definitions

The relationship between several magnetic quantities is shown in Fig. 23. With increasing field strength, H, the intensity of magnetization, ϑ, decreases slightly for diamagnetic substances, and increases for paramagnetic substances. For ferromagnetic substances, the situation is quite different. The intensity of magnetization changes in a complicated, irreversible manner as H is changed, giving rise to the familiar hysteresis curves.

It will be recalled that the magnetic induction, B, is related to H by $B = H + 4\pi\vartheta$. The intensity of magnetization, ϑ, divided by the density, or ϑ/d, is called the specific magnetization, for which the symbol σ will be used. The relation between specific magnetization and mass susceptibility is, of course, that $\sigma = \chi H$. The specific magnetization is also the magnetic moment per gram of specimen. (This should not be confused with the atomic magnetic moment to which it is related only under certain conditions to be described in a later chapter.)

The quantity B/H is called the permeability, for which the symbol P will be used. The permeability is related to the volume susceptibility by $P = 1 + 4\pi\kappa$. For dia- and paramagnetic substances both P and κ are independent of field strength, except that at extremely low temperatures and high fields, paramagnetic substances approach saturation. For ferromagnetic substances, σ is dependent on H at low fields, but at higher fields the specific magnetization becomes independent of field strength. The specimen is then said to be saturated. Saturation occurs at a few hundred, or at most a few thousand, oersteds.

When a ferromagnetic body is placed in a magnetic field and then removed, B may not return to zero as H becomes zero. The body is then said to be permanently magnetized. The magnitude of B under conditions of permanent magnetization is called the remanence. The field of opposite sign necessary to reduce B to zero is called the coercive force. Permeability, intensity of magnetization at saturation, remanence, and coercive force are all commonly measured magnetic quantities.   But the quantities and methods used in determining the magnetic characteristics of a steel are often different from those used in magnetochemistry.

The quantities which have so far proved to be of value in magnetochemical studies are the specific magnetization and the Curie point.   The Curie point is the temperature above which a ferromagnetic substance loses its ferromagnetism and becomes paramagnetic.   Different ferromagnetic substances have different Curie points, and the principal utility for

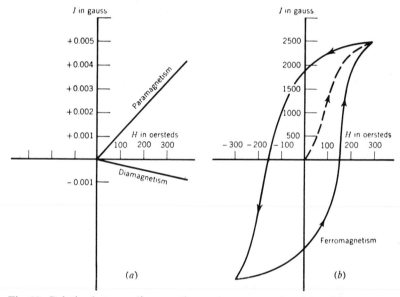

Fig. 23. Relation between diamagnetism and paramagnetism (a) and ferromagnetism (b).   Note the change in ordinate scale.

this determination in the solution of chemical problems is one of identification.   Curie temperatures are, like melting points, characteristic of certain chemical species.   Reviews of this field are given by Bittel and Gerlach[1] and by Neumann.[2]

In similar fashion, the specific magnetization of a ferromagnetic substance may be used for quantitative analysis.   The several other characteristic properties of ferromagnetics, such as remanence, coercive force, and so forth, have not had very many applications to chemical problems.

This general field of applying Curie points and specific magnetizations

[1] H. Bittel and W. Gerlach, *Physik regelmass.*, **7**, No. 3, 119 (1939).

[2] H. Neumann, *Arch. Eisenhüttenw.*, **11**, 483 (1938).

to the solution of chemical problems is called thermomagnetic analysis.   It
is a very powerful method which is, unfortunately, limited in its scope to the
relatively few known ferromagnetic substances.   It might be thought that
similar methods could be developed for paramagnetic substances.   This
has been done, as will be described in a later chapter.

In Table I there are given Curie points and specific magnetizations for
several pure substances likely to be encountered by workers in this field.

TABLE I

Curie Points and Specific Magnetizations

Substance	T_c, °C.	$\sigma \sim 25°$
Iron (Fe)	770 ± 10	218 ± 2
Cobalt (Co)	1180 ± 20	163 ± 2
Nickel (Ni)	355 ± 5	55.5 ± 1
Magnetite (Fe_3O_4)	572 ± 7	95 ± 2
Maghemite (γ-Fe_2O_3)	675?	95?
Cementite (Fe_3C)	212	139
Hägg carbide (χ) (Fe_2C?)	247	128
Hexagonal c.p. carbide (ϵ) (Fe_2C?)	380 ± 10	139

14. Induction Methods

All treatises on experimental electricity and magnetism describe two
fundamental methods used in "ferromagnetic" investigations, namely, induction methods and magnetometer methods.[3]   The first implies the
magnetization of a specimen by inserting it in a field produced by a solenoid.   On removal or reversal of the primary current, an induced charge is
set up in a secondary coil which may be connected to a ballistic galvanometer.   Innumerable modifications of experimental arrangement, frequency, and detection of the induced charge, have been described.   The
magnetometer method, on the other hand, involves the use of a small, permanent magnet system suspended so as to turn, like a compass needle,
under the influence of an external field.   This method also has been subjected to many modifications.   Both methods have some applications in
magnetochemistry, but consideration must be given to the fact that neither
method, in general, involves saturation of the sample.   For many types of
magnetochemical investigation, this is an insurmountable objection.   The

[3] *Cf.*, Müller-Pouillets, *Lehrbuch der Physik*, 11th ed., edited by A. Eucken, O.
Lummer, and E. Waetzmann, **Vol. IV,** Part 4: *Elektrische Eigenschaften der Metalle
und Elektrolyte; magnetische Eigenschaften der Materie.*   F. Vieweg und Sohn, Brunswick,
1934.

induction methods described in this section should not be confused with the new nuclear induction developments to be discussed in the following chapter.

A simple, effective induction method is described by Barnett.[4] The circuit diagram is shown in Fig. 24. A long uniform solenoid produces a field, H, of 75 to 200 oersteds. A secondary coil, (1), is connected in opposition to another secondary coil, (2). The sample, first placed in (1) is rapidly moved to coil (2), whereupon the change of induction produces a deflection on a shunted galvanometer. The deflection is directly proportional to the volume susceptibility of the sample. Alternatively, the current in the magnetizing coil may simply be reversed. It is claimed that for a specimen of about 2.5 cu. in., it is possible to detect volume susceptibilities as low as 10^{-5}.

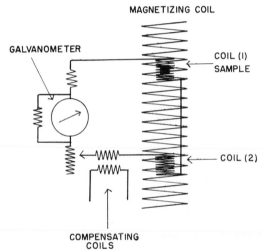

Fig. 24. A simple, effective induction method (as described by S. J. Barnett).

Elmore[5] has described an induction bridge designed by F. Bitter. This bridge consists of two nearly identical mutual inductances connected in opposition and through a calibrated, variable mutual inductance for restoration of balance. Balance is detected by a sensitive ballistic galvanometer connected to secondaries wound around each primary. The sample is placed inside one of the primaries. The method is suitable for susceptibilities of the order of 10^{-3}, and for fields from 0 to 400 oersteds.

Application of magnetometer methods to magnetochemical problems has been due chiefly to Tobusch.[6] More recently refined forms of the

[4] S. J. Barnett, *J. Appl. Phys.*, **23**, 975 (1952).

[5] W. C. Elmore, *Phys. Rev.*, **54**, 1092 (1938).

[6] H. Tobusch, *Ann. Physik*, **26**, 439 (1908).

Tobusch magnetometer have been described by Bozorth[7] and by others.[8] A slightly different form is described by Grube and Winkler.[9] The instrument has considerable flexibility over a range of field strength and temperature.

15. Saturation Methods

Many, if not most, magnetochemical studies on ferromagnetic substances require that the sample be saturated.   This is to say that the permeability must reach a value which is little increased by increasing field

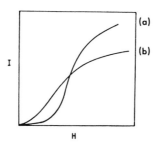

Fig. 25. Intensity of magnetization as a function of field
strength for two different substances (a) and (b).

strength.   The reasons for this are two fold.   First, many specimens vary greatly in the ease with which they may be magnetized.   If it is desired to compare the specific magnetizations of two samples, it is necessary to make sure that the field is adequate to saturate both samples, as shown in Fig. 25. Second, it is easy to calculate atomic magnetic moments for ferromagnetic substances by methods to be described in a later chapter.   But here again, meaningful results may be obtained only if the sample is saturated.   The specific magnetizations given in Table I are those obtained in saturating fields.

Various adaptations of the Curie and Weiss modifications of the Faraday method have been used for determination of the magnetization curve and related properties.   The Sucksmith modification,[10,11] described on p. 13, has been adapted to ferromagnetic investigations with considerable success.   The force, exerted vertically on a few milligrams of specimen, is

[7] R. M. Bozorth, *J. Optical Soc. Am.*, **10**, 591 (1925).

[8] D. P. Raychaudhuri, *Indian J. Phys.*, **9**, 417 (1935).

[9] G. Grube and O. Winkler, *Z. Elektrochem.*, **41**, 52 (1935).

[10] W. Sucksmith, *Proc. Roy. Soc.* (*London*), **A170**, 551 (1939).

[11] W. Sucksmith, *Le Magnetisme*, **Vol. II.**   Proceedings of the Strasbourg Congress on Magnetism, 1939.

measured by Sucksmith's ring which, however, may be much less sensitive than for paramagnetic substances. In order to produce a field of high intensity and constant gradient the pole-pieces are planed, as shown in

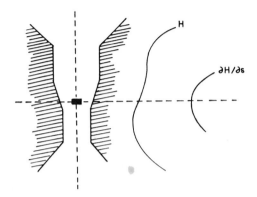

Fig. 26. Field and field gradient in Sucksmith gap.

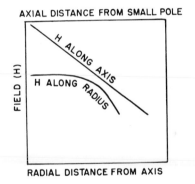

AXIAL DISTANCE FROM SMALL POLE

RADIAL DISTANCE FROM AXIS

Fig. 27. Variation of field radially and axially in the Fereday gap, as found by Buehl and Wulff. The field varies uniformly along the axis and is essentially constant for several centimeters out from the axis. See Fig. 17, p. 21, for design of pole-pieces.

Fig. 26. The force acting on the sample in the direction S is given by $f = m\sigma\partial H/\partial s$ where m is the mass. The method lacks nothing in sensitivity. For a readily attainable field of 18,000 oersteds, $\partial H/\partial s$ may be approximately 900 gauss per centimeter. A 30-mg. sample of iron will then experience a force of about 6 g. It should be pointed out that fields of a few thousand oersteds generally suffice to saturate the sample. Sucksmith[12] gives experimental details for temperatures up to 1500°C.

[12] W. Sucksmith and R. R. Pearce, *Proc. Roy. Soc.* (*London*), **A167**, 189 (1938)

A slightly more complicated balance of the same type is described by
Lange and Mathieu,[13] who give many examples of measurements on differ-

Fig. 28. Faraday type of apparatus used for *in situ* study of catalyst components.

ent steels, carbides, and other ferromagnetic substances. A method in
which the force is exerted horizontally is given by Rogers and Stamm.[14]

    [13] H. Lange and K. Mathieu, *Mitt. Kaiser-Wilhelm Inst. Eisenforsch. Dusseldorf,*
20, 239 (1938).
    [14] B. A. Rogers and K. O. Stamm, *Am. Inst. Mining Met. Engrs., Tech. Pub.,* **No.**
1133 (1939).

The method is of moderate sensitivity.   Apparatus which permits a very wide range of field strength (up to 40,000 oersteds) and a wide range of temperature is described by Bitter and Kaufmann.[15]   Other modifications are given by Broniewski, Franczak and Witkowski,[16] by Dorfman and Sidorov,[17] by Becker,[18] and by Becker and Döring.[19]

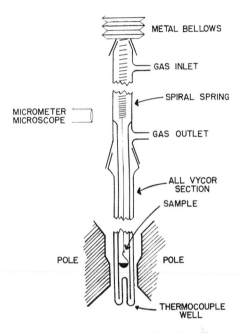

METAL BELLOWS

GAS INLET

SPIRAL SPRING

MICROMETER
MICROSCOPE

GAS OUTLET

ALL VYCOR
SECTION

SAMPLE

POLE   POLE

THERMOCOUPLE
WELL

Fig. 29. Diagram of apparatus shown in Fig. 28.   Temperature control equipment may be slipped over the lower end of the apparatus, between the poles.

A similar method has been described by Buehl and Wulff.[20]   In this method, the uniform $\partial H/\partial s$ in a high field is obtained by the use of a cylindrical pole opposite to a slightly larger pole in which the face has been cut concave, as shown in Fig. 17 (p. 21).   Variation of the field in this pole gap is shown in Fig. 27 (p. 41).   The sample is mounted on a torsion beam. A small furnace is provided for work at elevated temperatures.   This apparatus appears to be one of the more satisfactory for work on ferromagnetic

[15] F. Bitter and A. R. Kaufmann, *Phys. Rev.*, **56**, 1044 (1939).

[16] W. Broniewski, S. Franczak, and R. Witkowski, *Ann. phys.*, **10**, 5 (1938).

[17] Y. G. Dorfman and S. Sidorov, *Compt. rend. acad. sci. U.R.S.S.*, **19**, 381 (1938).

[18] R. Becker, *Probleme der technischen Magnetisierungskurve.* Julius Springer, Berlin, 1938, p. 162.

[19] R. Becker and W. Döring, *Ferromagnetismus.* Julius Springer, Berlin, 1939.

[20] R. Buehl and J. Wulff, *Rev. Sci. Instr.*, **9**, 224 (1938).

substances.[21]   The sensitivity is such that as little as 0.01% of iron carbide may be determined in stainless steel by the Curie point discontinuity
at about 210°C.

In some types of work, such as the study of a reduced supported nickel
catalyst, it is necessary to carry out chemical changes and to make the
measurements themselves in the absence of air.   This requirement has led
to the development of modifications which possess very great versatility.

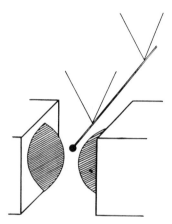

Fig. 30. Pendulum balance of Rathenau and Snoek.

One such apparatus in use in the writer's laboratory is shown in Fig. 28
and, in part, diagrammatically in Fig. 29.   This is essentially the Sucksmith adaptation, but with the use of a bronze spring to measure the force.
With this apparatus, it is possible to reduce a catalyst sample *in situ*,
and to make thermomagnetic observations in the presence or absence of adsorbed gases at any temperature from 20°K. to about 1200°K.   It is even
possible to measure the magnetic moment of a catalyst sample while it is
exhibiting catalytic activity as, for instance, in the hydrogenation of benzene.   A similar apparatus of equal versatility, but using the Sucksmith
ring to measure the force, has been described by van Oort.[22]

A somewhat different method, fairly frequently used, is described by
Rathenau and Snoek.[23]   The pole faces are cylindrical, as shown in Fig. 30.
The sample is attached to a horizontal pendulum suspended from four
wires, and moving perpendicularly to the inhomogeneous field.   In this
device the specific magnetization is given by

[21] L. J. E. Hofer, W. C. Peebles, and W. E. Dieter, *J. Am. Chem. Soc.*, **68**, 1953
(1946).
[22] W. P. van Oort, *J. Sci. Instr.*, **28**, 279 (1951).
[23] G. W. Rathenau and J. L. Snoek, *Philips Research Rept.*, **1**, 239 (1946).

$$\sigma = \frac{K}{m} \left(\frac{t_0^2}{t^2} - 1 \right)$$

where K is a constant, t and t_0 are the periods of oscillation of the pendulum with and without the sample being present, and m is the weight of the sample. The constant K may be found by calibration with pure iron or nickel.

Magnetic measurements over a range of temperature can become quite tedious. There is a definite advantage in introducing automatic recording. In the author's laboratory, specific magnetization and temperature are both automatically recorded as a function of time. The apparatus is similar to that of Buehl and Wulff except that the Sucksmith gap is used. The torsion beam is arranged with electric contacts which operate a reversible motor attached to the torsion head. Angular deflection of the torsion head is translated into a small variable voltage through a potentiometer slide wire attached to the motor shaft. Output from this wire, and from the thermocouple, are led into a two-point recording and controlling potentiometer. The apparatus operates without attention and will automatically raise the temperature at a predetermined rate to a predetermined height. If so desired, the temperature cycle will then reverse, to search for possible thermal hysteresis effects.[24] A similar instrument of somewhat more flexible design has also been described.[25] Somewhat similar instruments of semi-automatic design have been in use in France for a number of years, after a design originally due to Chaudron and Forestier.[26]

It not infrequently occurs that the ferromagnetism under investigation in magnetochemical studies is no larger than the paramagnetism or diamagnetism which may also be present. This is a situation which rarely concerns workers in the field of technological ferromagnetism. In such circumstances, the ordinary methods as used for measuring dia- or paramagnetism are entirely adequate. The detection of ferromagnetic impurities by this method has already been described.

In a system containing, say, a paramagnetic component plus a trace of a ferromagnetic component, it is expedient simply to measure the susceptibility at several different field strengths. The susceptibility may then be plotted against reciprocal field. Types of data thus obtained are shown in Fig. 31. If the curves are extrapolated to $1/H = 0$, the intercept on the χ-axis gives the susceptibility of the paramagnetic component free from ferromagnetism. This is true because, in general, the ferromagnetic component is present in trace amounts and so makes a negligible contribu-

[24] R. F. S. Robertson and P. W. Selwood, *Rev. Sci. Instr.*, **22**, 146 (1951).

[25] J. D. Eisler, G. R. Newton, and W. A. Adcock, *ibid.*, **23**, 17 (1952).

[26] P. Chévenard, *J. phys. radium*, **3**, 264 (1932).

tion to the paramagnetism. The specific magnetization of the ferromagnetic component is given by $(\chi_H - \chi_0)H$ where χ_H is the apparent susceptibility at field H, and χ_0 is the susceptibility for $1/H = 0$. As will be shown in a later chapter, this method is of some use in dealing with catalytically active inorganic solids.

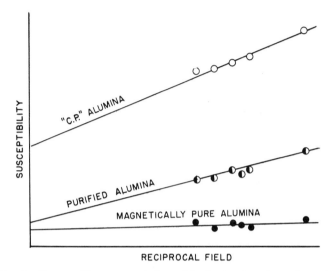

Fig. 31. Traces of ferromagnetic impurities in alumina, shown by a plot of apparent susceptibility *versus* reciprocal field.

16. Thermomagnetic Analysis

Later in this book there will be many references to the interpretation of magnetic measurements on ferromagnetic substances, and especially to the use of thermomagnetic methods in solving chemical problems. The principal applications to chemistry may be divided into identification procedures and into solution and reaction studies. This section will be concerned with some general principles and a few examples.

A familiar application of thermomagnetic analysis is the microdetermination of cementite in steel. Various devices have been used for this and related analytical problems. Fig. 32 shows a simple apparatus made from a precision electric meter. The sample holder is mounted in the variable field of an electromagnet and is surrounded by a small non-inductive electric oven. The temperature is measured by a thermocouple of very fine wire mounted so that it is in contact with the bottom of the sample holder. The sample itself is distributed in an inert diluent such as very pure silica, thoroughly mixed and sealed off in a small glass bulb.

By measuring the force of attraction on the sample above and below the Curie point, it is possible to detect cementite and to estimate the amount present.   Application of this and similar devices to related analytical problems is obvious.   For research studies it is, however, convenient and time-saving to use a recording thermomagnetic balance such as that previously described.

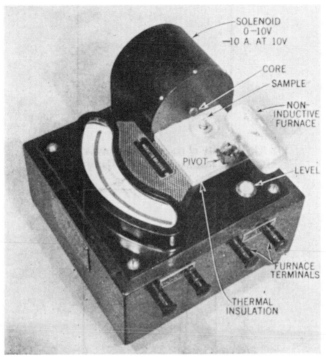

Fig. 32. General Electric magnetic balance for Curie point determinations.

It has previously been pointed out that there is some uncertainty in the precise location of the Curie point, and that there is some dependence of the shape of the thermomagnetic curve on field strength.   At low fields, the Curie point is more sharply defined, while high fields may be necessary to saturate all ferromagnetic components, particularly those of small particle size.   Most workers compromise on a field of 3000 to 5000 oersteds, and take the Curie point as the point of inflection in the thermomagnetic curve. This can generally be located within two or three degrees.   Occasionally some improvement in definition may be obtained by making a differential plot, namely the change of magnetic moment per temperature interval against temperature.   In this way Curie points, and hence ferromagnetic phases, appear as peaks rather than as points of inflection.[27]   Somewhat more precise methods for locating the Curie point are described by Stoner.[28]

Thermomagnetic identification of components is of considerable use in the study of certain catalytically active solids.   The following examples are chosen from this field, although applications to other fields are by no

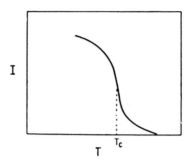

Fig. 33. Intensity of magnetization *versus* temperature in the neighborhood of the Curie point.

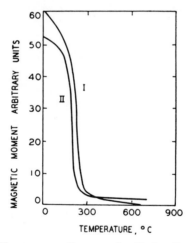

Fig. 34. Thermomagnetic curve for Fischer-Tropsch iron catalyst: I, original; II, after heating to 800°C.

means unknown.   The presence of cementite and of metallic iron was identified by Hilpert and Dieckmann[29] in an iron oxide used for the catalytic

[27] E. M. Cohn and L. J. E. Hofer, *J. Am. Chem. Soc.*, **72**, 4662 (1950).

[28] E. C. Stoner, *Magnetism and Matter*.   Methuen and Company, Ltd., London, 1934, p. 382.

[29] S. Hilpert and T. Dieckmann, *Ber.*, **48**, 1281 (1915).

disproportionation of carbon monoxide.   Similarly, identifications on a synthetic ammonia catalyst have been made by Mittasch and Kuss.[30] In Fig. 34 there are shown thermomagnetic curves obtained by Pichler and Merkel[31] for a Fischer-Tropsch catalyst which had been carbonized by carbon monoxide.   Curve I indicates a Curie point at about 260°C. When these data were first obtained, the 260°C. Curie point could not be identified with that of any known substance.   Later work by Hofer, Cohn, and Peebles[32] identified this substance with the Hägg iron carbide, Fe_2C, although the Pichler-Merkel Curie point proved to be a little high.   If

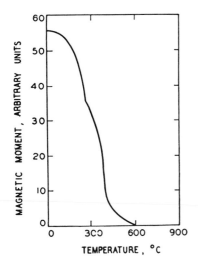

Fig. 35. Thermomagnetic curves for Fischer-Tropsch catalyst showing the presence of two iron carbides.

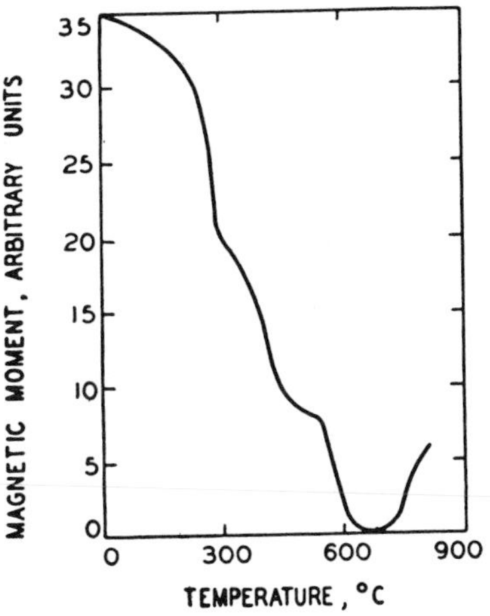

Fig. 36. Thermomagnetic curve showing reactions proceeding as the temperature is raised.

the catalyst sample is heated to 800°C. in a stream of nitrogen, the specific magnetization falls to about 205°C., which is near the Curie point for cementite, indicating the instability of the Hägg carbide at high temperature.   Further reference to this reaction is made below.

If two or more ferromagnetic phases are present in mechanical mixture, the specific magnetizations are additive.   The degree to which the several Curie points are separately resolved depends on the relative amounts of each substance, their specific magnetizations, and the distance between

[30] A. Mittasch and E. Kuss, *Z. Elektrochem.*, **34**, 159 (1928).

[31] H. Pichler and H. Merkel, translated by R. Brinkley, *Chemical and Thermomagnetic Studies on Iron Catalysts for the Synthesis of Hydrocarbons.*   U. S. Bureau of Mines Tech. Paper 718 (1949).

[32] L. J. E. Hofer, E. M. Cohn, and W. C. Peebles, *J. Am. Chem. Soc.*, **71**, 189 (1949).

their Curie points. In Fig. 35 there is shown one of the curves obtained by Pichler and Merkel for a catalyst sample containing two iron carbides.

Results such as that shown in Fig. 35 cannot be obtained if the components in a mixture mutually dissolve or react. It should be remembered that such processes may take place during thermomagnetic analysis. In Fig. 36 there is evidence for three iron carbides, but these decompose, at least in part, to form metallic iron. Thus, as the temperature is raised, the sample may become more magnetic rather than less, until the Curie point for iron itself is reached. Thermomagnetic analysis in such a case would yield quite a different curve with falling temperature than with rising temperature. This kind of thermal "hysteresis" is often an excellent indication that solution or reaction processes have taken place during measurement.

Other related applications include identification of the products formed on superficial oxidation of iron.[33] Together with x-ray diffraction studies, the method shows the varying amounts of the several oxides produced under changing conditions of oxidation.

Specific magnetization is a measure of the amount of ferromagnetic phase present. Thus, for nickel supported on magnesia, it is found that the specific magnetization may be much lower than would be expected for an equivalent weight of pure metallic nickel. This discrepancy might mean that some of the supported nickel remains as oxide. More probably it means that most of the nickel is present in particles too small to exhibit ferromagnetism at the temperature of measurement. This illustrates one complication in the application of magnetic methods to problems in catalysis. Care must be taken in the interpretation of thermomagnetic data. Curie points are influenced by the purity of the sample and by the particle size. Further reference to this point, which is of considerable importance in connection with catalytically active solids, will be made in a later chapter. A good example of thermomagnetic identification of catalyst components is given by Hofer et al.[34]

There will be mentioned a few examples of the application of magnetic methods to problems concerned with alloy structure. Reference will be restricted here to systems in which at least one phase of those present is ferromagnetic. Many changes in the magnetic properties of alloys produced by heat treatment may be closely related to atomic rearrangements. Sometimes these changes are on such a small scale that magnetic measurements are more useful in their interpretation than microscopic or x-ray investigations.

[33] A. Michel, J. Bénard, and G. Chaudron, *Bull. soc. chim. France,* 11, 175 (1944).
[34] M. Manes, A. O. Damick, M. Mentser, E. M. Cohn, and L. J. E. Hofer, *J. Am. Chem. Soc.,* 74, 6207 (1952).

One of the first studies in this field was that of Tammann and Oelsen[35] who determined the solubilities of the transition group metals in a large number of nonferromagnetic metals. The apparatus used was a Faraday balance in which the force was exerted horizontally. Sometimes the phase diagrams are complicated as, for example, in the cobalt-copper system shown in Fig. 37 in which the magnetization depends greatly on the temperature from which the alloy is quenched. In such cases, interpretations

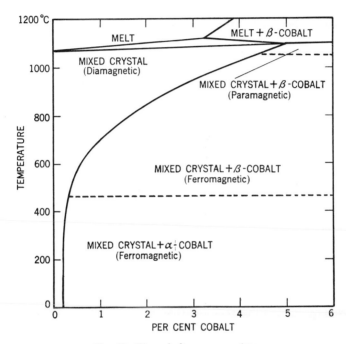

Fig. 37. The cobalt-copper system.

of the magnetic data may be difficult. The subject is reviewed by Vogt[36] and von Auwers.[37]

The form and arrangement of ferromagnetic precipitates have also

[35] G. Tammann and W. Oelsen, *Z. anorg. u. allgem. Chem.*, **186,** 257 (1930). See also K. Honda and T. Murakami, *Science Repts. Tôhoku Imp. Univ., First Ser.*, **10,** 79 (1921); and K. Honda and H. Endo, *Science Repts. Tôhoku Imp. Univ., First Ser.*, **16,** 627 (1927), for thermomagnetic studies of the iron-silicon and iron-carbon systems respectively.

[36] E. Vogt, *Ann. Physik*, **29,** 358 (1937); *Z. Elektrochem.*, **45,** 597 (1939). This excellent review gives many experimental results and their interpretation.

[37] O. von Auwers, *Wiss. Veröffentl. Siemens-Werken*, **16,** 92 (1937); **17,** 74 (1938).

been studied by use of the magnetic balance.[38-40] Bitter and his co-
workers have used this method to study the precipitation of iron from copper. The reactions are complex. Alloys in which all the iron is in solid
solution in electrolytic copper may be prepared by quenching from above
the solubility limits. Not only is it possible to examine the nature of
ferromagnetic precipitates in alloys, but the kinetics of the precipitation
process may be followed.[41] The magnetic method is obviously a powerful
one for such studies, but it is clear that much work remains to be done on it.

Study of solution rates by thermomagnetic analysis seems to have
been limited. Selwood and Nash[42] studied the rate of mutual diffusion

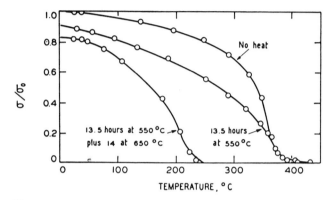

Fig. 38. Thermomagnetic curves for copper-nickel powder mixture as a function of sintering.

of powdered copper-nickel compacts. Metal powders of about 300 mesh
were mixed by stirring together and then compacted into pellets and heated
in vacuum for various times and temperatures. Thermomagnetic curves
were obtained at various stages of sintering. Some of the results found for
a powder mixture containing 90% nickel are shown in Fig. 38. After
13 1/2 hours of heating at 550°C., diffusion between copper and nickel had
definitely taken place, but some pure nickel remained as such, as shown by
the Curie point at about 360°C. After 14 hours at 650°C., all the nickel
had been diluted with copper and there is indicated some approach to
homogeneity with a Curie point near 200°C. In a mixture of powdered
metals, before sintering, one may regard the particles as being simply

[38] E. Gerold, Z. Metallkunde, 24, 255 (1932).
[39] F. Bitter and A. R. Kaufmann, Phys. Rev., 56, 1044 (1939).
[40] F. Bitter, A. R. Kaufmann, C. Starr, and S. T. Pan, ibid., 60, 134 (1941).
[41] H. Auer, Z. Elektrochem., 45, 608 (1939).
[42] P. W. Selwood and J. Nash, Trans. Am. Soc. Metals, 35, 609 (1945).

mechanically juxtaposed.   During sintering, there must be formed a continuous series of solid solutions which ultimately approach homogeneity.
It has been shown by Marian[43] and others[44] that for solid solutions of copper
and nickel, both Curie point and specific magnetization are linear with
concentration (Fig. 39).   A homogeneous solid solution of copper and
nickel has a thermomagnetic curve of the same shape as has pure nickel,
but both specific magnetization and Curie point are lower.   But in a nonhomogeneous solid solution, that is to say, a one-phase continuous series of
solid solutions, the thermomagnetic curves are the summation of an infinite
number of curves, each showing its own Curie point.   Such mixtures will

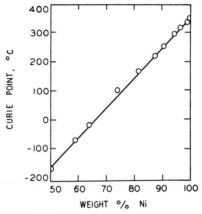

Fig. 39. Curie point *versus* concentration for
nickel-copper alloys (after Marian).

show, instead of a single Curie point, a gradual diminution of magnetization
over a wide range of temperature.   These curves will be reversible unless
the temperature remains high long enough to promote further diffusion.
   An inspection of Fig. 38 will show that a rough calculation may be
made of the distribution of nickel at any degree of sintering and that this
may be used to estimate the rate of approach to homogeneity.   The distribution curve shown in Fig. 40 is found in the following way.   Consider a
partially sintered alloy which yields a thermomagnetic curve such as
shown in Fig. 41.   Take two temperatures close together, T_1 and T_2.
The fall of specific magnetization, σ', between T_1 and T_2 is caused by the
presence of a *homogeneous* alloy for which the Curie point lies between T_2
and T_2 and for which the concentration of nickel is then readily obtained
from Fig. 39.   Hence we may write $\sigma' = kmc$ where k is a constant and m

[43] V. Marian, *Ann. Phys.*, **7**, 459 (1937).
[44] W. H. Ross, *Phys. Rev.*, **46**, 46 (1934).

is the weight per cent of nickel at concentration c. The constant k may be found from the data for pure nickel; hence m may be computed at a series of points running through the whole concentration range.

This method has obvious applications in powder metallurgy, but its scope is somewhat limited by the small number of systems which form continuous solid solutions, as do copper and nickel.

The application of thermomagnetic methods to reaction processes will be illustrated by reference to studies on iron carbides, on cobalt carbide,

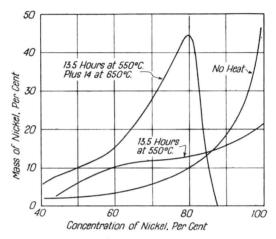

Fig. 40. Distribution of nickel concentrations in a 90 per cent nickel, 10 per cent copper, powder mixture at several stages of sintering.

and certain oxides of iron. It will be clear that the method is most useful when related to parallel studies by x-ray methods and chemical analysis. When thus supported, the thermomagnetic method is a tool of exceptional power in the study of reactions in the solid state.

The first work to be described is that of Hofer, Cohn, and Peebles[32] on the carbides of iron. Hägg carbide, Fe_2C, was prepared by reduction and carburization of a synthetic ammonia catalyst containing mostly magnetite, with small amounts of magnesia, silica, and chromia. The identity of this carbide was established by x-ray methods. A thermomagnetic curve for the Hägg carbide is shown in Fig. 42-I, care having been taken not to raise the temperature above 300°C. This curve is reversible, with a clearly defined Curie point of 247° ± 3°C. Above the Curie point, the specific magnetization does not drop quite to zero. This trace of residual ferromagnetism may be due to a little metallic iron or possibly to some magnetite. If, now, the Hägg carbide is heated to 580°C. for 2 hours, the thermomagnetic curve obtained is shown in Fig. 42-II.

The new Curie point at 208°C., together with x-ray analysis, establish that this product is cementite. One may, therefore, write $3Fe_2C \rightarrow 2Fe_3C + C$.

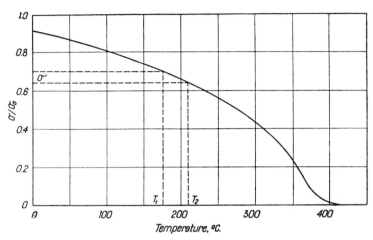

Fig. 41. Method for interpreting magnetization-temperature curves for partially sintered nickel-copper mixtures.

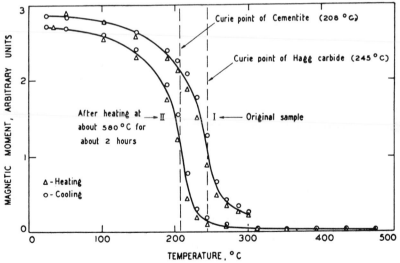

Fig. 42. Thermomagnetic curves: I, for Hägg carbide; II, same after heating to 580°C.

The hexagonal close-packed carbide, Fe_2C, may be prepared by reduction and carburization of an iron-copper Fischer-Tropsch catalyst containing a little potassium oxide. A thermomagnetic curve, taken with rising temperature, for this substance is shown in Fig. 43. This curve shows two Curie points, one of which at 247°C. is due to some Hägg carbide, the other at 380°C. presumably due to the hexagonal carbide. If, now, the thermomagnetic analysis is repeated with falling temperature, Curve II is obtained, corresponding to more or less pure Hägg carbide. The transition of hexagonal close-packed to Hägg carbides has a measurable velocity at 300°C., but by rapid heating it is possible to obtain a sharp Curie point at 380°. It is clear that studies such as these can bring some order out of a rather complex situation.

Other thermomagnetic studies on the reactions of cementite include those of Michel and Bernier,[45] and Cohn and Hofer.[27]

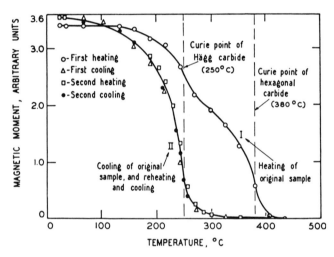

Fig. 43. Thermomagnetic curves for hexagonal iron carbide: I, with rising temperature; II, with falling and subsequent temperature cycles.

A somewhat more complicated problem is the isothermal decomposition of cobalt carbide, according to the equation $Co_2C \rightarrow 2\alpha\text{-}Co + C$. This reaction has also been studied by Hofer, Cohn, and Peebles.[46] The specific magnetization of the α-cobalt product is large compared with that of the cobalt carbide. The principle of the method is based upon the measurement of the change of specific magnetization which occurs with time. The quantity of interest in this study is, therefore, not the Curie point but rather the specific magnetization.

Cobalt carbide was produced by reduction and carburization of a

[45] A. Michel and R. Bernier, *Rev. mét.*, **46**, 821 (1949).

[46] L. J. E. Hofer, E. M. Cohn, and W. C. Peebles, *J. Phys. & Colloid Chem.*, **53**, 661 (1949).

raw cobalt-thoria-kieselguhr Fischer-Tropsch catalyst. The carbide showed a moderate ferromagnetism, some of which may have been due to a trace of metallic α-cobalt. The sample was placed in a magnetic balance, quickly raised to the desired reaction temperature, and held there until

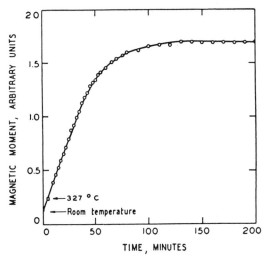

Fig. 44. Specific magnetization *versus* time for decomposing cobalt carbide.

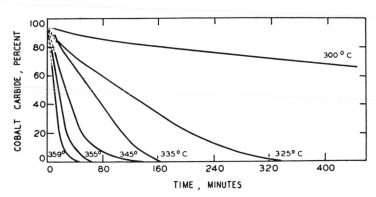

Fig. 45. Per cent cobalt carbide *versus* time, at several temperatures.

reaction was complete, as shown by no further change of specific magnetization. Measurements were made at various time intervals, and studies were carried out over a range of reaction temperatures. The data obtained at 345°C. are shown in Fig. 44. These data were converted to per cent cobalt metal on the assumption that the force shown in the magnetic balance was directly proportional to the amount of cobalt metal formed.

Results are shown in Fig. 45 and have been confirmed by much more tedious chemical methods. Other systems which have been similarly studied include nickel carbide and a variety of boroferrites.[47,48]

The disproportionation of ferrous oxide is a process which lends itself well to thermomagnetic analysis.[49] It is well known that the phase diagram of the iron-oxygen system in the FeO region shows a phase known as wüstite, stable above 570°C. This phase extends from about 76% iron up almost exactly to 77.7% iron, which is an iron-oxygen atom ratio of 1 to 1; but the eutectic lies at 76.9% iron. By quenching an appropriate composition, it is possible to obtain a homogeneous substance quite close in stoichiometric ratio to FeO. This substance disproportionates rapidly

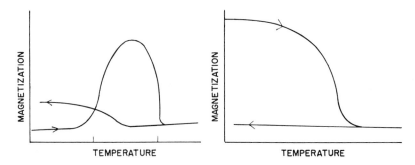

Fig. 46. Heating and cooling thermomagnetic curves showing disproportionation of FeO eutectoid.

Fig. 47. Heating and cooling thermomagnetic curves showing phase transition of gamma-Fe$_2$O$_3$ to alpha-Fe$_2$O$_3$.

at 480°C. in accordance with the equation $4FeO \rightarrow Fe_3O_4 + Fe$. The ferrous oxide is not ferromagnetic; hence, thermomagnetic analysis with rising temperature will show a rapid rise of magnetization as disproportionation starts in the neighborhood of 300°C. As the temperature is raised further, the equilibrium will begin to shift toward the wüstite phase and the magnetization will drop, becoming negligible at about 570°C. Now, on slowly lowering the temperature, excess iron will be precipitated and disproportionation may be complete so that the magnetization will remain high down to room temperature and below. These changes are indicated in Fig. 46. It will be clear that similarly complex thermomagnetic curves will be obtained with samples less rich in oxygen.

Reference to the irreversible transformation of γ-Fe$_2$O$_3$ to α-Fe$_2$O$_3$ will be made in a later chapter. This also lends itself well to thermo-

[47] L. J. E. Hofer, E. M. Cohn, and W. C. Peebles, *ibid.*, **54**, 1161 (1950).

[48] R. Benoit, *Compt. rend.*, **231**, 1216 (1950).

[49] G. Chaudron and J. Bénard, *Bull. soc. chim. France*, **1949**, D117.

magnetic analysis.[50]   As shown in Fig. 47, the magnetization starts high, but as the temperature is raised the increasing speed of transformation rapidly cuts the magnetization down.   Cooling now simply gives the non-ferromagnetic curve for α-Fe_2O_3.   A quantitative study of this reaction, with the object of obtaining activation energies and the influence thereon of impurity ions, has been described by De Boer and the writer.[51]   Many other examples of rate studies involving thermomagnetic analysis will be found in the literature.

Some remarks are perhaps called for in connection with rate studies such as that just described.   The simplest case is when a nonferromagnetic substance is converted into a feromagnetic, or vice versa.   If both reactants and products are ferromagnetic, the method loses sensitivity as the respective specific magnetizations approach each other.   But if the Curie points differ considerably, then it may be possible to work at some temperature above the Curie point of one substance and below that of the other.   A further point to be mentioned is that the specific magnetization falls somewhat as the temperature approaches the Curie point.   Thus, if a rate study is being made not far below the Curie point of a component, it is necessary to have increasing accuracy of temperature control.   Also, it must be repeated that Curie points depend on purity and on particle size.   Further discussion of thermomagnetic analysis will be found in Chapters 12 and 15.

[50] A. Michel, G. Chaudron, and J. Bénard, *Colloques Internationaux, Ferromagnetism and Antiferromagnetism.*   Grenoble 1950, p. 46.
[51] F E. DeBoer and P. W. Selwood, *J. Am. Chem. Soc.,* **76**, 3365 (1954).

CHAPTER FOUR

RESONANCE METHODS

17. Introduction

The last few years have seen an exponential increase of interest in a group of techniques which, for want of a better name, may be called "resonance methods." These methods promise precision and applicability far beyond classical magnetic methods in many areas of chemistry. This is by no means to say that classical methods have been made obsolete; but resonance has become fashionable in physics and chemistry to such an extent that almost everyone has something to say about NMR (nuclear magnetic resonance) or PMR (paramagnetic resonance).

In these circumstances, no book on magnetochemistry would be complete without some reference to resonance methods. On the other hand, the problem of what to include and what to omit is always present. If magnetic resonance is to be included, then why not magneto-optical effects, neutron diffraction, and a host of techniques of which not one may be said to be of no interest in both chemistry and magnetism? As is usual in such cases, the writer will be forced to make an arbitrary decision, which will be to present in outline only the theory and techniques of the resonance methods and to indicate where these methods can be of service in the solution of chemical problems. Reference to specific applications will appear in later chapters. The field is so new and advancing so rapidly that the few reviews so far published tend to be out of date before they are printed. That, the writer fears, will be true of this review. In what follows emphasis has, of course, been placed on applications of the methods to chemistry rather than to the areas of nuclear and atomic structure of greatest interest to physicists.

There are three resonance effects to be considered. If a substance is placed within a coil which forms part of an oscillating circuit, there will, of course, be a frequency change, as mentioned in a previous chapter. If the coil and sample are themselves placed in a steady field of several thousand oersteds, a whole new set of phenomena appears. These resonance phenomena are shown at radiofrequencies of a few megacycles per second by atomic nuclei possessing a resultant nuclear magnetic moment; at frequencies of several thousand megacycles by unpaired electron spins as in paramagnetic substances; and at frequencies of tens of thousands of megacycles by ferromagnetic substances. The first group of phenomena is called nuclear magnetic resonance, the second paramagnetic (or electron) resonance, and the third ferromagnetic resonance. The first, NMR, seems well on its way to becoming a major tool in chemical research and control; the second, PMR, is increasingly important; but ferromagnetic resonance has not at the time of writing achieved much importance to chemistry.

18. Nuclear Resonance[1,2]

In the previous edition of this book, it was possible to dismiss nuclear magnetism as having little or no application to chemical problems. This situation has now changed. The reasons for this are two fold. First, since 1946 there have been developed two elegant, related methods for the study of nuclear magnetic moments and the nuclear relaxation effect; and second, these methods have had an immediate application to a considerable variety of problems of interest to chemists.

The two methods to which reference is made are the nuclear induction experiment described by Bloch, Hansen, and Packard[3] and the method of nuclear magnetic resonance absorption described by Bloembergen, Purcell, and Pound.[4] The two experiments are closely related; they take advantage of somewhat different manifestations of the same fundamental process.

Nuclear induction will be described, but this is not to venture any statement concerning the relative merits of the two methods.

Some atomic nuclei possess a permanent magnetic moment, just as some atoms and molecules possess a permanent magnetic moment due to unpaired electrons. Nuclear moments are about one thousand times smaller than electronic moments. Protons possess a nuclear moment and these as present, say, in a drop of water are, in the absence of an external magnetic field, oriented at random. If the drop of water is placed in a magnetic field, a slight excess of protons will orientate in the direction of the field, although the actual fraction of protons doing so in any realizable field is quite small. Conservation of angular momentum requires that some energy transfer should occur before thermal equilibrium can be complete, and this can only occur if the energy given up during orientation of the nuclear spins is converted to heat in the molecular environment, or lattice.

[1] F. Bloch, *Science*, **118**, 425 (1953).
[2] E. M. Purcell, *ibid.*, **118**, 431 (1953).
[3] F. Bloch, W. W. Hansen, and M. Packard, *Phys. Rev.*, **70**, 474 (1946).
[4] N. Bloembergen, E. M. Purcell, and R. V. Pound, *ibid.*, **73**, 679 (1948).

It follows that there will be a lag in the establishment of thermal equilibrium and that the duration of this lag will depend on the efficiency of interaction between nuclei and lattice.   The time lag, which is of basic importance, is measured as a "relaxation time" which will be more precisely defined below.

A spinning proton in a magnetic field is analogous to a gyroscope in the earth's gravitational field.   If subject to a displacement, the proton will precess about the direction of the applied magnetic field.   The angular frequency of precession, ν, is given by

$$\nu = \mu_n H_0 / I h$$

where μ_n is the nuclear magnetic moment, H_0 is the applied steady field, I is the nuclear spin quantum number, and h is Planck's constant.   The precessing protons in the drop of water in a magnetic field are like little rotating compass needles.   They will induce an emf in a coil of wire wound around the sample.   The induced emf is readily detectable by standard techniques of rectification and amplification.   This is the phenomenon of nuclear induction.

The actual measurement of nuclear induction takes advantage of nuclear resonance.   Let us place a coil carrying an alternating current so that the axis of the coil is at right angles to the steady external field.   Now the nuclear induction will be detected as a maximum when the frequency of the alternating current in the coil is equal to the angular frequency of precession; that is to say, when the weak alternating field in the coil is in resonance with the precessing protons.   As an example, it is found that in pure water, with $H_0 = 10{,}000$ oersteds, the frequency of precession is 42.5 megacycles per second.   The resonance frequency is readily found by modulating H_0 slightly, as described below.

Turning back to the relaxation time, if interaction between nuclear spin and lattice (molecular environment) is strong, the effect will be like a friction between a nucleus and its surroundings.   This will yield a short relaxation time and a diminished intensity of nuclear induction for a given amplitude of the alternating field.   This makes it possible to measure the relaxation time, which is defined as follows: on application of the steady field the nuclear magnetic moments will approach thermal equilibrium with the lattice according to an exponential rate law

$$dn/dt = (1/T_1)(n_0 - n)$$

where n is the surplus population of the lower level (that is the excess of oriented spins in the applied field), n_0 is the value of n corresponding to thermal equilibrium at the lattice temperature, and T_1 is the quantity of most concern, namely the spin-lattice relaxation time.   There is another relaxation time, "spin-spin," which is less important for present purposes.

A diagram of Bloch's apparatus is given in Fig. 48. The sample, which may be a cubic centimeter of water in a small test tube, is placed in a uniform field, H_0, of a few thousand oersteds. This field is modulated at 20 to 60 cycles by coils, the axes of which are parallel to each other and to H_0. The effect of this modulation is to cause a recurrent scanning of the resonance condition. A high-frequency radio transmitter supplies energy to the system through a coil placed with its axis at 90° to H_0. The effect

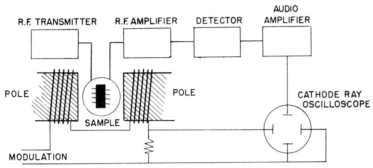

Fig. 48. Block diagram of Bloch, Hansen, and Packard nuclear induction apparatus.

of this small alternating field is to change the tilt of the nuclei already oriented and precessing in H_0. The choice of frequency is governed by the relation already given which, for protons that have $I = {}^1/_2$, becomes $\nu = 2\mu_n H_0/h$.

The precessing nuclear magnetic moments induce voltages in a receiving coil which is placed at 90° both to H_0 and to the axis of the coil providing the driving field. These induced voltages are amplified and detected on an oscilloscope in a resonant circuit. Detailed description of an advanced design of apparatus is given by Gutowsky.[5] Commercial apparatus for nuclear magnetic resonance is available.

In later chapters there will be mentioned from time to time some of the contributions being made by resonance methods to the solution of chemical problems. A few examples will be given here. If the applied field, H_0, is held constant while the frequency of the alternating field is slowly varied, it is found that the nuclear resonance may possess a fine structure. Liquid water possesses a very sharply defined resonance line extending over a very few cycles per second, but ice at low temperatures has a line width extending over some 50 cycles. In such cases the center of the resonance line is at or near the same frequency. The reason for this

[5] H. S. Gutowsky, L. H. Meyer, and R. E. McClure, *Rev. Sci. Instr.*, **24**, 644 (1953).

behavior is that each proton in ice is subject not only to the applied field of several thousand oersteds, but also to the random fields (of a few oersteds) produced by each of the nearest proton neighbors. In liquid water, molecular motion is so rapid that the mutual influence of one proton on another is very slight. This phenomenon makes it possible to study with great precision known and hitherto unknown examples of molecular motion in solids.[6]

Another application of resonance methods is in connection with so-called "chemical shifts." Identical atoms in chemically-different molecules do not precess at exactly the same frequency even though placed in the same applied field. The reason for this effect, which may be observed at high resolution, is that the valence forces (the electronic environment) of each atom vary somewhat in different chemical situations as in, for instance, the hydrogen atoms in water as compared with the hydrogen atoms in methane. This results in a slightly different degree of magnetic shielding around each proton. A striking example of chemical shift is to be found in ethyl alcohol[7] in which there are, of course, three chemically different kinds of hydrogen namely, the three methyl hydrogens, the two methylene, and the one hydroxyl. These give rise to three well-resolved resonance lines. The application of this to chemical structure problems is so great and obvious as to require no amplification here.

The nuclear relaxation times shown by various substances under various conditions may also yield valuable chemical information. In ammonium bromide at 88°K., the value of T_1 is about 32 seconds, a surprisingly long time for a nuclear process. As the temperature is raised, the relaxation time falls to about 0.01 second. This change is caused by the onset of internal molecular motions and is related to the cause of line-width narrowing, as mentioned above. The relaxation time, as of protons in water, is markedly reduced by the presence of paramagnetic atoms or molecules. For pure water, T_1 is about 2 seconds, but a little ferric nitrate dissolved in the water will reduce the relaxation time to a few thousandths of a second. The effect is analogous to the catalysis of the ortho-para hydrogen conversion by paramagnetic substances, as described in Chapter 1.

Purcell[4] et al. have shown that the effect of dissolved paramagnetic substances may be predicted from the relation

$$1/T_1 = 12\pi^2\gamma^2\eta N_{ion}\mu_{eff.}^2/5kT$$

where γ is the gyromagnetic ratio, η is the viscosity, N_{ion} is the number of

[6] H. S. Gutowsky, G. B. Kistiakowsky, G. E. Pake, and E. M. Purcell, *J. Chem. Phys.*, **17**, 972 (1949).

[7] J. T. Arnold, S. S. Dharmatti, and M. E. Packard, *ibid.*, **19**, 507 (1951).

paramagnetic ions per cubic centimeter, μ_{eff} is the effective magnetic moment of the paramagnetic ions in solution, k is the Boltzmann constant, and T the temperature.

It is clear from the above relation that one has, in principle, a convenient method for the detection and estimation of paramagnetic substances in solution. The method has an advantage over those of Faraday and Gouy in that the sample may be fixed in position and does not need to be suspended at the end of a delicate thread. There is, however, a circumstance which makes the method less attractive than it seems at first. Conger and the writer[8] have found that while in general the above expression correctly predicts the change of relaxation time to be expected for some kinds of paramagnetic ions, for other paramagnetic ions the predicted effect is too large by a factor of 10 or more. Those ions such as Fe^{3+} and Gd^{3+} which are in S spectroscopic states give predictable effects, as do those such as Cr^{3+} and Cu^{2+} which are effectively in S states through quenching of the orbital component. But ions in which spin-orbital coupling may be appreciable, as in Ni^{2+} and Co^{2+}, or strong as in Nd^{3+}, and all other paramagnetic rare earths except Gd^{3+}, give subnormal effects on the proton relaxation time. Even the effect of dissolved ferric salts may be anomalous because hydrolysis depresses the magnetic moment of the iron almost 50% as will be described in a later chapter.

The above discussion has barely scratched the surface of possible resonance applications. Good reviews are given by Pake[9] and by Smith.[10] It will be clear that the methods are applicable to nuclei other than hydrogen, provided these possess a resultant magnetic moment.

19. Paramagnetic Resonance

If a paramagnetic substance is placed in an alternating field and is also subject to a steady field of several thousand oersteds, there appears a group of phenomena known as paramagnetic absorption and paramagnetic dispersion. The starting point for this type of study was made by Gorter.[11] If the alternating field is one of several thousand megacycles per second, and if the steady field is applied perpendicular to the alternating field, then one observes the phenomenon of paramagnetic resonance.[12] The theory of paramagnetic resonance is analogous to that of nuclear resonance. Certain radiofrequencies will induce transitions between the different energy

[8] R. L. Conger and P. W. Selwood, *ibid.*, **20**, 383 (1952).

[9] G. E. Pake, *Am. J. Phys.*, **18**, 438, 473 (1950).

[10] J. A. S. Smith, *Quart. Revs. (London)*, **7**, 279 (1953).

[11] C. J. Gorter, *Phys. Rev.*, **42**, 437 (1936).

[12] E. Zavoisky, *J. Phys. (U.S.S.R.)*, **9** , 211 (1945) *et seq.*

levels corresponding to the various orientations of electron spins in a steady
field.   The radiofrequencies at which this will occur are given by

$$\nu = \frac{g\mu_B H_0}{h}$$

where ν is the frequency, g is the Landé splitting factor, μ_B is the electron-
spin magnetic moment expressed in Bohr magnetons, H_0 is the applied
steady field, and h is Planck's constant.   Further reference to the Landé
g-factor will be made in Chapter 8.   For a free electron spin, $g = 2$, but
various interactions cause some deviations.   The g-values obtained from

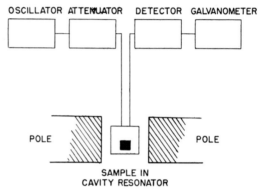

Fig. 49. Block diagram of paramagnetic resonance apparatus.

paramagnetic resonance measurements are sometimes called "spectroscopic splitting factors."   The g-factor is related to the gyromagnetic
ratio, γ, by $\gamma = g\mu/h$.

This basic equation for the resonance condition is the same as that
already given for nuclear magnetic resonance because the g-factor is
equal to μ/I provided that this quantity is expressed in units of the nuclear
magneton, namely $eh/4\pi m_p c$, where m_p is the rest mass of the proton and
the other units have their usual significance.

Apparatus[13] for observation of paramagnetic resonance consists of
a magnet similar to that used for nuclear resonance, as described in the
previous section, and a frequency-stabilized microwave generator, together with appropriate amplification and detection circuits.   It is usual
to maintain the radiofrequency at a fixed value while sweeping the steady
field through the resonance condition.   The steady field is generally
modulated.   For a g-factor of 2 and a steady field of 3330 oersteds, the

[13] W. Gordy, W. V. Smith, and R. F. Trambularo, *Microwave Spectroscopy.*   J. Wiley and Sons, Inc., New York 1953.

resonance frequency occurs at 9000 megacycles per second. A block diagram is shown in Fig. 49. More elaborate equipment is described by Hirshon and Fraenkel.[14] Paramagnetic resonance apparatus is available commercially.

The observation of paramagnetic resonance makes possible a careful study of energy levels in a paramagnetic ion without the necessity of making diamagnetic corrections. From the point of view of chemistry, this means a major advance in the detection and estimation of paramagnetic species such as free radicals under conditions much more favorable to the observation of transient phenomena than heretofore possible. In crystalline material it is also possible to find the number of paramagnetic ions in the unit cell, and to draw conclusions concerning their mutual interactions. From the point of view of physics, paramagnetic resonance is proving of great value in obtaining the relevant g-values, in measuring quite small energy-level splittings, and in the observation of very short spin-lattice relaxation times.

Other areas in which paramagnetic resonance is solving chemical problems, together with a few representative references, will be mentioned. Most of these will be referred to again in later chapters. The application to free radicals is probably of as much or more interest to chemists as any other. Holden et al.[15] and Hutchison et al.[16] have, for instance, studied diphenylpicrylhydrazyl, sodium ketyl, porphyrindine, and other radicals. Luminescent solids,[17] irradiated solids,[18] and semiconductors[19] have also been studied. Hutchison[20] has also studied paramagnetic resonance of potassium dissolved in liquid ammonia. Possible applications of the method to structure and bond type in coordination complexes have recently been explored.[21,22] Excellent recent reviews of the whole field of paramagnetic resonance are available.[23,24]

20. Ferromagnetic Resonance

Ferromagnetic specimens show resonance effects similar to those de-

[14] J. M. Hirshon and G. K. Fraenkel, Rev. Sci. Instr., 26, 34 (1955).

[15] A. N. Holden, W. A. Yager, and F. R. Merritt, J. Chem. Phys., 19, 1319 (1951).

[16] C. A. Hutchison, Jr., R. C. Pastor, and A. Kowalsky, ibid., 20, 534 (1952).

[17] W. D. Hershberger and H. N. Leifer, Phys. Rev., 88, 714 (1952).

[18] C. A. Hutchison, Jr., ibid., 75, 1769 (1949).

[19] R. C. Fletcher, W. A. Yager, G. L. Pearson, and F. R. Merritt, ibid., 95, 844 (1954).

[20] C. A. Hutchison, Jr. and R. C. Pastor, ibid., 81, 282 (1951).

[21] M. Cohn and J. Townsend, Nature, 173, 1090 (1954).

[22] D. J. E. Ingram and J. E. Bennett, J. Chem. Phys., 22, 1136 (1954).

[23] K. K. Darrow, Bell System Tech. J., 32, 384 (1953).

[24] B. Bleaney and K. W. H. Stevens, Repts. on Progress in Physics, 16, 108 (1953).

scribed in the previous section. The resonance condition, in a field of a few thousand oersteds, occurs, as first shown by Griffiths,[25] at the microwave frequencies corresponding to wave lengths of one or two centimeters. In the previous section it was indicated that paramagnetic resonance occurs when the frequency is related to the static field by $\nu = \gamma H_0$ where γ is the gyromagnetic ratio. Ferromagnetic resonance is found, that is the radiofrequency permeability is a maximum, when $\nu = \gamma(BH_0)^{1/2}$ where B is the induction corresponding to H_0.

The experimental arrangement necessarily involves a microwave circuit. The specimen, in the form of a thin layer, is placed on the end of a waveguide and between the poles of a magnet supplying the static field, H_0. The waveguide mode of excitation is such that the radiofrequency field is in the plane of the specimen, and at right angles to H_0. Reviews are given by Rado,[26] Bozorth,[27] and Kittel.[28]

Thus far, ferromagnetic resonance does not appear to have had any applications to chemical problems, but it would seem that the chemical study of thin metal films might be approached in this way.

Antiferromagnetic substances also exhibit comparable resonance phenomena.[29] Reference to some studies will be made later.

[25] J. H. E. Griffiths, *Nature*, **158**, 670 (1946).
[26] G. T. Rado, *Advances in Electronics*, **Vol. II.** L. Marton, Editor. Academic Press, Inc., New York, 1950, p. 287.
[27] R. M. Bozorth, *Ferromagnetism.* D. Van Nostrand Co., Inc., New York, 1951, p. 803.
[28] C. Kittel, *J. phys. radium*, **12**, 291 (1951).
[29] L. R. Maxwell, *Am. J. Physics*, **20**, 80 (1952).

CHAPTER FIVE

ATOMIC DIAMAGNETISM

21. Theory of Diamagnetism

It will be recalled that in diamagnetic substances the flux density is less than in the surrounding magnetic field, and that in general the susceptibility is independent of temperature. The classical theory of this phenomenon is due to Langevin.[1,2] A brief outline of Langevin's theory will be given here because it contributes greatly to an understanding of the effect.

An electron of mass, m, moving in a closed orbit is equivalent to a current in a wire. The magnitude of this equivalent current is $e/c \cdot \omega/2\pi$ electromagnetic units, where e is the electronic charge, c the velocity of light, and ω the angular velocity of the electron. Such a current will produce a magnetic field of the same intensity at a given distance as a magnet of moment μ, such that

$$\mu = \frac{e\omega S}{2\pi c} = \frac{e\omega\pi r_1^2}{2\pi c} = \frac{e\omega r_1^2}{2c}$$

where S is the area of the bounded surface around which the electron moves, and r_1 is the radius of the orbit. If the orbit is not circular, ωr_1^2 may be replaced by an average so that

$$\mu = \frac{e\omega \overline{r^2}}{2c}$$

It has been shown by Larmor[3] that the imposition of a perpendicular external field, H, on such a system superposes on the electronic motion an angular velocity of precession given by

[1] P. Langevin, *J. phys.*, **4**, 678 (1905).

[2] A good presentation of the theory will be found in E. C. Stoner's *Magnetism and Matter*. Methuen and Company, Ltd., London, 1934.

[3] J. Larmor, *Aether and Matter*. Cambridge University Press, London, 1900, p. 341.

$$\nu = -\frac{eH}{2mc}$$

The magnetic moment associated with the orbit will therefore be changed by

$$\Delta\mu = \frac{e\,\overline{r_1^2(\omega + \nu)}}{2c} - \frac{e\,\overline{r_1^2\omega}}{2c}$$

$$= \frac{e\,\overline{r_1^2}\,\nu}{2c}$$

$$= \frac{e^2\,\overline{r_1^2}H}{4mc^2}$$

For a system of n orbits oriented at random to the field, $\overline{r_1^2}$, the mean square radius of the projected orbit perpendicular to H becomes $\overline{r_1^2} = {}^2/_3\,\overline{r^2}$ where $\overline{r^2}$ is the mean square radius of the orbit. The change of magnetic moment per gram-atom will therefore be

$$\Delta\mu = -N\frac{e^2H}{6mc^2}\sum_n \overline{r^2}$$

where N is Avogadro's number. The susceptibility per gram-atom is then

$$\chi_A = \frac{\Delta\mu_A}{H} = -N\frac{e^2}{6mc^2}\sum \overline{r^2}$$

$$= -2.832\sum \overline{r^2} \times 10^{10}$$

It is clear that the negative sign of diamagnetism is a consequence of the Larmor precession, and that diamagnetism will be found in all atoms regardless of whether or not they also possess permanent moments. Diamagnetism depends only on the effective radius of the electronic orbits and is therefore independent of temperature, to a first approximation.

The quantum-mechanical theory of magnetic susceptibilities has been treated by Van Vleck,[4] and it will suffice here to state a few of the results. The most interesting result is that the expression for diamagnetic susceptibilities is exactly the same as that already given in the classical theory. It is possible, however, to go much farther. For instance, the atomic diamagnetic susceptibility of hydrogen may be calculated directly from the expression

[4] J. H. Van Vleck, *The Theory of Electric and Magnetic Susceptibilities*. Oxford University Press, Oxford, 1932.

$$\chi_A = -2.832 \times 10^{10} \left\{ \frac{h^2}{4\pi^2 Z^2 e^2 \, m} \right\} \left[\frac{5}{2} n^4 - \frac{3}{2} n^2 l(l+1) + \frac{1}{2} n^2 \right]$$

$$= -0.790 \times 10^{-6} \left\{ \frac{5n^4 - 3n^2 l(l+1) + n^2}{2Z^2} \right\}$$

where n and l are the principal and subordinate quantum numbers respectively, and Z is the atomic number. The quantity h is Planck's constant, and m the electron mass. For atomic hydrogen $n = 1$, $l = 0$, and $Z = 1$, hence the gram-atomic susceptibility is -2.37×10^{-6}. Unfortunately, there is no direct method of measuring the magnetic susceptibility of atomic hydrogen. Furthermore, atomic hydrogen is highly paramagnetic and the diamagnetism would be concealed. An indirect method using Pascal's constants for combined hydrogen gives a value of -2.93×10^{-6}, which is about as good agreement as could be expected. Somewhat similar types of calculations have been made for helium and for heavier atoms.[5-8] For all but the lightest atoms it is necessary to allow for shielding of the nuclear charge by the various electrons in the atom. This may be done by subtracting an appropriate screening constant, s, from the nuclear charge number Z, in the expression given above, to give the effective nuclear charge $(Z - s)$. Slater,[5] in particular, has shown that reasonably satisfactory agreement between calculated and experimental values is obtained if one uses an effective quantum number, n', such that n' and s give agreement between calculated and experimental energy values. The values of n' thus replacing n are $n'/n = 1/1$, $2/2$, $3/3$, $3.7/4$, $4.0/5$, and $4.2/6$, and the expression is

$$\chi_A = -0.79 \times 10^{-6} \sum_Z \frac{(n')^2 \, (n' + 1/2) \, (n' + 1)}{(Z - s)^2}$$

There are relatively few stable monatomic molecules known to chemists. Of these, the inert gases are diamagnetic and of sufficiently long life to be investigated by the methods described in Chapter I. Measurements on the inert gases are of considerable interest because these substances have relatively simple atomic systems, and the atoms are not greatly perturbed by the fields of adjacent atoms.

The most satisfactory determinations on the inert gases are probably those of Wills and Hector[9] and of Havens.[10] Their data and some others

[5] J. C. Slater, *Phys. Rev.*, **32**, 349 (1928); **36**, 57 (1930).

[6] E. C. Stoner, *Proc. Leeds Phil. Lit. Soc., Sci. Sect.*, **1**, 484 (1929).

[7] L. Pauling, *Proc. Roy. Soc. (London)*, **A114**, 181 (1927).

[8] D. R. Hartree, *Proc. Cambridge Phil. Soc.*, **24**, 89 (1928).

[9] A. P. Wills and L. G. Hector, *Phys. Rev.*, **23**, 209 (1924); **24**, 418 (1924).

[10] G. G. Havens, *ibid.*, **43**, 992 (1933). This paper gives references to previous work on gases.

are summarized in Table II, which includes a comparison with theoretical results obtained by the Slater, and other methods.   These values and some others are discussed by Stoner (*op. cit.*[2]) and Angus.[14]

TABLE II

Gram-Atomic Susceptibilities of the Inert Gases

$$-\chi_A \times 10^6$$

	Helium	Neon	Argon	Krypton	Xenon
Wills and Hector (obs.)[9]	1.88	6.66	18.13	—	—
Havens (obs.)[10]	1.91	7.65	19.23	—	—
Mann (obs.)[11]	—	6.75	19.54	28.02	42.40
Abonnenc (obs.)[12]	—	—	19.2	29.2	44.1
Slater (calc.)[5]	1.853	5.7	18.9	31.7	48.0
Pauling (calc.)[7]	1.54	5.7	21.5	42	66
Hartree (calc.)[8]	1.90	8.6	24.8	—	—
Umeda (calc.)[13]	3.51	13.73	21.04	33.38	42.90

Another diamagnetic substance for which data are available and which is believed to be monatomic is mercury vapor,[15,16] for which the susceptibility per gram is -0.389×10^{-6}, compared with -0.42×10^{-6} calculated by Slater's method.

22. Diamagnetism of Ions

Theoretical calculation of the diamagnetic susceptibilities of ions is similar to that of atoms.   Unfortunately, experimentation gives $\chi_M = \chi_{cation} + \chi_{anion}$, assuming that the ionic susceptibilities are additive and that no constitutive correction need be applied.   The problem, therefore, of obtaining ionic susceptibilities from experimental data is similar to that involved in finding ionic refractivities and certain other ionic properties. There are two reasons for establishing a set of standard ionic susceptibility values; first, to compare with the various theoretical values for ions, and second, to obtain an accurate set of diamagnetic correction constants for paramagnetic substances.   This problem has been discussed by a substantial number of authors.   The reader is referred to the exhaustive re-

[11] K. E. Mann, *Z. Physik*, **98**, 548 (1936).   This paper contains a review of earlier experimental and theoretical work.

[12] L. Abonnenc, *Compt. rend.*, **208**, 986 (1939).

[13] K. Umeda, *J. Fac. Sci. Hokkaido Univ.*, Ser. II, **3**, 246 (1949).

[14] W. R. Angus, *Ann. Reports on Progr. Chem.*, **38**, 44 (1941).

[15] S. S. Bhatnagar and M. B. Nevgi, *Current Sci.*, **6**, 53 (1937).

[16] J. S. Shur, *Nature*, **139**, 804 (1937).

views by Pacault[17] and by Myers.[18] The subject will be presented in outline here.

In the following chapter there will be presented the system developed by Pascal for computing (empirically) the magnetic susceptibilities of organic and other compounds of considerable complexity. Pascal has also applied that method to ionic substances but, in general, the results are not so satisfactory as they are for molecular substances. A somewhat more satisfying method is to consider the hydrogen ion, H^+, as having zero magnetic susceptibility because it has no electron.[19] Then the measured susceptibility of an acid, such as hydrochloric, is essentially that of the chloride ion. From that point, it is easy to develop a complete system of ionic susceptibilities with the only obvious difficulty being the rather poor experimental precision in most published susceptibility work. But this method is based on the assumption that susceptibilities are additive—a disputed point to which we shall return later.

Another method[20] is to consider the susceptibilities of the ions in an isoelectronic pair, such as potassium chloride, to vary inversely as the square of their respective nuclear charges. A more accurate estimate is given by the ratio $1/(Z - s)^2 : 1/(Z' - s')^2$ where Z, Z' are the respective nuclear charges, and s, s' are the respective screening constants given by Slater's method. The ionic susceptibility of, for instance, the cation is given by

$$\chi_{cation} = \chi_M \frac{\sum \bar{r}^2_{cation}}{\sum \bar{r}^2_{cation} + \sum \bar{r}^2_{anion}}$$

where

$$\sum \bar{r}^2 = \frac{(n')^2 (n' + 1/2)(n' + 1)}{(Z - s)^2}$$

$\sum \bar{r}^2$ represents the electron density distribution summed for each shell, n' is the effective quantum number of the shell.[21,22]

Another method relies on an assumed relationship between the ionic susceptibility and the apparent atomic susceptibility of the element in a covalent compound. For instance, to calculate the ionic susceptibility of Cl^-, find the molar susceptibility of chlorine gas, then divide by two to obtain the susceptibility for the covalent chlorine atom. This is the Pascal

[17] A. Pacault, *Rev. sci.*, **84**, 169 (1946).
[18] W. R. Myers, *Revs. Modern Physics*, **24**, 15 (1952).
[19] K. Reicheneder, *Ann. Physik*, **3**, 58 (1929).
[20] G. Joos, *Z. Physik*, **19**, 347 (1923); **32**, 835 (1925).
[21] G. W. Brindley, *Phil. Mag.*, **11**, 786 (1931).
[22] W. R. Angus, *Proc. Roy. Soc. (London)*, **A136**, 569 (1932)

constant for chlorine.   This value is related to the ionic susceptibility by the expression $A/B = C/D$ where A is the theoretical susceptibility for the covalent atom, B is the experimental value for the covalent atom, C is the theoretical susceptibility for the ion, and D the experimental ionic susceptibility.   This procedure seems to the writer to be rather extraordinary, but it gives results in fair agreement with those obtained by other methods.[23]   The method is not applicable to elements which do not form diatomic covalent molecules.

Another method for adapting Pascal's constants for atoms to ionic susceptibilities is by addition or subtraction of a constant factor to correct for the covalent bond.   It should be pointed out that the magnitude of this bond effect is not constant, but varies with atomic number.   But here, too, the results are in fair agreement with those obtained by other methods.

A final method is as follows: from a large number of measurements of molar susceptibilities on various salts there are plotted curves in which salts of metals in the same group of the Periodic Table, with a common anion, are compared.   When the molar susceptibility is plotted against number of electrons in the cation for the series, a group of straight lines results.   For example, the alkali halides give a set of parallel straight lines. Susceptibility values for the anion are deduced by extrapolating to atomic number zero.   The method is open to theoretical objection but, like several other dubious methods, gives fairly satisfactory results.[24]

Both Pacault[17] and Myers[18] summarize the results obtainable for the halide ions and for the alkali metal and alkaline earth ions.   The substantial deviations in the results found by different methods for the same ion is sufficient evidence that one is still far from understanding how to calculate ionic susceptibilities.   This observation is made even more pointed by the discovery of wide discrepancies between the results given by these two authors for the same ion calculated in presumably the same way.

In all attempts to calculate ionic susceptibilities from experimental data and to compare these with theoretical ionic susceptibilities, there are some inherent questions, to most of which no very definite answer can yet be given.   For instance, a primary question is whether ionic susceptibilities are fixed values, or are dependent on the chemical environment.   Another question is whether susceptibilities in solution are the same as those found for the solids.   A third question is the possible effect of concentration on susceptibilities in solution.

Some of these problems have at least a partial answer.   Within the

[23] V. C. G. Trew, *Trans. Faraday Soc.*, **37**, 476 (1941).
[24] M. Prasad, S. S. Dharmatti, and H. V. Amin, *Proc. Indian Acad. Sci.*, **A26**, 312 (1947).

rather poor limits of accuracy of published data, it seems safe to say that diamagnetic ionic susceptibilities are additive except for Li^+ and H^+, unless some rather obvious chemical change takes place.

The most obvious test of additivity is to compare differences in molar susceptibilities in sequences of compounds, such as the alkali halides and the alkaline earth halides. If, for instance, χ_M for LiF is 10.1 ($\times 10^{-6}$) and for NaF is 15.6, then the difference 5.5 should be repeated for LiCl and

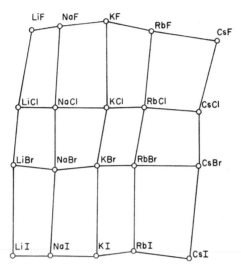

Fig. 50. Method of Veiel for estimating validity
of ionic diamagnetic susceptibilities.

NaCl provided that the ionic susceptibilities are truly additive. Actually in this case, for the data of Brindley and Hoare[25,26] on solids, the difference is 7.1, but on the whole agreement is more satisfactory. Another method for testing additivity is given by Veiel.[27] This method is illustrated in Fig. 50. Let us start with KBr as the origin and plot alkali metal bromide susceptibilities along a horizontal line and potassium halide susceptibilities along a vertical line. Deviations from strict additivity will then appear as deviations from rectangular form in all parts of the figure. The cases of Li^+ and H^+ are exceptional because the low ratio of radius to charge would suggest, in accordance with Fajan's well-known rules, that these two ions would have a maximum influence on the electron clouds of neighboring ions or of oriented polar-solvent molecules, such as water. This

[25] F. E. Hoare, *Proc. Roy. Soc. (London)*, **A147**, 88 (1934).

[26] G. W. Brindley and F. E. Hoare, *ibid.*, **A152**, 342 (1935); **159**, 395 (1938).

[27] U. Veiel, *Ann. Physik*, **24**, 697 (1935).

seems actually to be the case. Several of the methods for calculating ionic susceptibilities from experimental data actually yield positive apparent susceptibilities when applied to H^+. This is sometimes referred to as the "paramagnetism" of H^+, but the term is unfortunate. What apparently occurs is that the presence of H^+ ions lowers the diamagnetism of the water perceptibly[28]—a phenomenon which ought to lend itself to study by nuclear resonance.

A comparison of susceptibilities in solution with those in the solid state shows that, in general, diamagnetic susceptibilities are larger in aqueous solution. A careful comparison of diamagnetic susceptibilities in the solid and dissolved states has been made by Flordal and Frivold[29] and by Brindley and Hoare.[30] They find that the aqueous solution values are generally higher. The susceptibilities of large univalent ions in solution are comparable with their values in the crystalline state, whereas the susceptibilities of small and bivalent ions in solution are much smaller than in the crystalline state. This, of course, suggests that magnetic changes may be occurring in the solvent rather than in the solute. The problem has been studied by Lee,[31] who finds that diamagnetic susceptibility in the dissolved state, χ_s, and in the crystalline state, χ_c, are related as follows: $\chi_s = a\chi_c + b$ where a and b are constants characteristic of each ion.

Frivold and Sogn[32] have studied the susceptibilities of LiCl, LiBr, $CaCl_2$, $CaBr_2$, $SrBr_2$, $NaClO_4$, $Ca(NO_3)_2$ and $Ba(ClO_4)_2$ in water, ethyl alcohol, and for a few salts, in acetone. In most cases the susceptibilities are greater in aqueous solution than in the other solvents. In some cases, the differences were within the experimental error. On the whole, susceptibilities in nonaqueous solvents have not been very thoroughly investigated.

Efforts have been made by several workers, for instance by Frivold and Olsen,[33] to correct the ionic susceptibility in aqueous solution to that for the free gaseous ion. The correction is not large.

The effect of concentration on the diamagnetism of solutions has been studied by many investigators. Veiel[27] measured alkali and alkaline earth halides and in all cases found the susceptibility to be a linear function of the concentration as required by the Wiedemann additivity law. Similarly, Ranganadham and Qureshi[34] found the susceptibilities of sodium

[28] P. Weiss, *J. phys. radium*, **1**, 185 (1930).

[29] M. Flordal and O. E. Frivold, *Ann. Physik*, **23**, 425 (1935).

[30] G. W. Brindley and F. E. Hoare, *Trans. Faraday Soc.*, **33**, 268 (1937).

[31] F.-H. Lee, *J. Chinese Chem. Soc.*, **12**, 80 (1945).

[32] O. E. Frivold and H. Sogn, *Ann. Physik*, **23**, 413 (1935).

[33] O. E. Frivold and N. G. Olsen, *Avhandl. Norske Videnskaps-Akad. Oslo, I. Mat.-Naturw. Klasse*, 1940, No. 2.

[34] S. P. Ranganadham and M. Qureshi, *Indian J. Phys.*, **14**, 129 (1940).

and of potassium nitrates to be linear with concentration from 1 to 20%. On the other hand, Scott and Blair[35] found that while aqueous solutions of hydrogen chloride show linearity between susceptibility and concentration, this is not true of lithium chloride solutions.

The influence of hydrate formation on ionic diamagnetism has been studied by Rao[36] and by Varadachari.[37] At high concentrations, the susceptibility of sulfuric acid is partly dependent on the particular hydrate formed, but for salts such as the alkali halides the effect is slight.

The effect of temperature on diamagnetic susceptibilities is generally negligible. But even water, which is often used as a standard, has a slight temperature coefficient of susceptibility. This question has been investigated by Bhatnagar, Nevgi, and Sharma,[38] particularly with reference to the Sn^{4+} ion. They find that the diamagnetism of salts of this ion increases slightly with increasing temperature.

The only important practical use of diamagnetic ionic susceptibilities is their application as correction factors to measured susceptibilities. All substances, even though paramagnetic, have an underlying diamagnetism. A precise estimate of the paramagnetic susceptibility of, say, cupric ion in cupric sulfate should include subtraction, from the measured molar susceptibility, of the diamagnetic ionic susceptibility not only of the sulfate ion but of the cupric ion as well. This latter is likely to be small. At room temperature it may amount to 1%, of the total susceptibility. For this reason, Table III gives diamagnetic ionic susceptibilities for many paramagnetic ions, as well as for diamagnetic ions. Table III is based on a compilation by Klemm.[39] This is not to say that Klemm's method for calculating diamagnetic ionic susceptibilities is to be preferred. The method has, in fact, been severely criticized (cf. Myers).[18] But there is considerable virtue in having a set of self-consistent corrections, even though these may not be very accurate in an absolute sense. In the example given above, of cupric sulfate, an error in the diamagnetic correction for the sulfate ion is likely to be cancelled by a corresponding error of opposite sign in the correction for the cupric ion. At least this is true if self-consistent corrections have been used and, as the total correction rarely exceeds 1%, one may use the data in Table III with confidence. But the use of these data as absolute diamagnetic suceptibilities is another matter. For instance, in Table III the susceptibility per gram-ion of Ca^{2+} is given

[35] A. F. Scott and C. M. Blair, *J. Phys. Chem.*, **37**, 475 (1933).

[36] S. R. Rao and P. S. Varadachari, *Current Sci.*, **3**, 249 (1934).

[37] P. S. Varadachari, *Proc. Indian Acad. Sci.*, **2**, 161 (1935).

[38] S. S. Bhatnagar, M. B. Nevgi, and R. L. Sharma, *J. Indian Chem. Soc.*, **13**, 273 (1936).

[39] W. Klemm, *Z. anorg. u. allgem. Chem.*, **244**, 377 (1940); **246**, 347 (1941).

TABLE III
Diamagnetic Susceptibilities per Gram-Ion

Ion	$-\chi \times 10^6$	Ion	$-\chi \times 10^6$	Ion	$-\chi \times 10^6$	Ion	$-\chi \times 10^6$
Ag^+	24	*Dy^{3+}	19	NO_3^-	20	Se^{4+}	8
*Ag^{2+}	24?	*Er^{3+}	18	Na^+	5	Se^{6+}	5
Al^{3+}	2	*Eu^{2+}	22	*Nd^{3+}	20	SeO_3^{2-}	44
As^{3+}	9?	*Eu^{3+}	20	*Ni^{2+}	12	SeO_4^{2-}	51
As^{5+}	6	F^-	11	O^{2-}	12	Si^{4+}	1
AsO_3^{3-}	51	*Fe^{2+}	13	OH^-	12	SiO_3^{2-}	36
AsO_4^{3-}	60	*Fe^{3+}	10	*Os^{2+}	44	*Sm^{2+}	23
Au^+	40?	Ga^{3+}	8	*Os^{3+}	36	*Sm^{3+}	20
Au^{3+}	32	Ge^{4+}	7	*Os^{4+}	29	Sn^{2+}	20
B^{3+}	0.2	*Gd^{3+}	20	*Os^{6+}	18	Sn^{4+}	16
BF_4^-	39	H^+	0	Os^{8+}	11	Sr^{2+}	15
BO_3^{3-}	35	Hf^{4+}	16	P^{3+}	4	Ta^{5+}	14
Ba^{2+}	32	Hg^{2+}	37	P^{5+}	1	*Tb^{3+}	19
Be^{2+}	0.4	*Ho^{2+}	19	PO_3^-	30	*Tb^{4+}	17
Bi^{3+}	25?	I^-	52	PO_3^{3-}	42	Te^{2-}	70
Bi^{5+}	23	I^{5+}	12	Pb^{2+}	28	Te^{4+}	14
Br^-	36	I^{7+}	10	Pb^{4+}	26	Te^{6+}	12
Br^{5+}	6	IO_3^-	50	*Pd^{2+}	25	TeO_3^{2-}	63
BrO_3^-	40	IO_4^-	54	*Pd^{4+}	18	TeO_4^{2-}	55
C^{4+}	0.1	In^{3+}	19	*Pr^{3+}	20	Th^{4+}	23
CN^-	18	*Ir^+	50	*Pr^{4+}	17	*Ti^{3+}	9
CNO^-	21	*Ir^{2+}	42	*Pt^{2+}	40	Ti^{4+}	5
CNS^-	35	*Ir^{3+}	35	*Pt^{3+}	33	Tl^+	34
CO_3^{2-}	34	*Ir^{4+}	29	*Pt^{4+}	28	Tl^{3+}	31
Ca^{2+}	8	*Ir^{5+}	20	Rb^+	20	*Tm^{3+}	18
Cb^{5+}	9	K^+	13	*Re^{3+}	36	*U^{3+}	46
Cd^{+2}	22	La^{3+}	20	*Re^{4+}	28	*U^{4+}	35
*Ce^{3+}	20	Li^+	0.6	*Re^{6+}	16	*U^{5+}	26
Ce^{4+}	17	Lu^{3+}	17	Re^{7+}	12	U^{6+}	19
Cl^-	26	Mg^{2+}	3	*Rh^{3+}	22	*V^{2+}	15
Cl^{5+}	2	Mn^{2+}	14	*Rh^{4+}	18	*V^{3+}	10
ClO_3^-	32	Mn^{3+}	10	*Ru^{3+}	23	*V^{4+}	7
ClO_4^-	34	*Mn^{4+}	8	*Ru^{4+}	18	V^{5+}	4
*Co^{2+}	12	*Mn^{6+}	4	S^{2-}	38?	*W^{2+}	41
*Co^{3+}	10	*Mn^{7+}	3	S^{4+}	3	*W^{3+}	36
*Cr^{2+}	15	*Mo^{2+}	31	S^{6+}	1	*W^{4+}	23
*Cr^{3+}	11	*Mo^{3+}	23	SO_3^{2-}	38	*W^{5+}	19
*Cr^{4+}	8	*Mo^{4+}	17	SO_4^{2-}	40	W^{6+}	13
*Cr^{5+}	5	*Mo^{5+}	12	$S_2O_8^{2-}$	78	Y^{3+}	12
Cr^{6+}	3	Mo^{6+}	7	Sb^{3+}	17?	Yb^{2+}	20
Cs^+	31	N^{5+}	0.1	Sb^{5+}	14	*Yb^{3+}	18
Cu^+	12	NH_4^+	11.5	Sc^{3+}	6	Zn^{2+}	10
*Cu^{2+}	11	NO_2^-	10	Se^{2-}	48?	Zr^{4+}	10

* Paramagnetic ion.   The table gives the underlying diamagnetism only.

as -8×10^{-6}. Myers gives the following nine values as computed by an assortment of theoretical and experimental methods: $(11.6, 10.8, 18.5, 4.5, 10.7, 13.3, 13.1, 11.1,$ and $10.2) \times 10^{-6}$. It must also be emphasized, again, that Table III gives the underlying diamagnetic susceptibilities. For ions which are paramagnetic, this may be very different from the observed susceptibility. In order that there should be no misunderstanding on this point, those ions which may be paramagnetic are marked with an asterisk. The underlying diamagnetism of paramagnetic ions must be estimated from the ionic radii.

A few examples of many recent publications in this area are given below.[40-51] The case of the yttrium ion, Y^{3+}, is interesting. Klemm does not list it as paramagnetic but various workers, including the writer, have found yttrium compounds to have a small paramagnetism. This is confirmed by Sugden[52] who reports a susceptibility of $+0.20 \times 10^{-6}$ for Y^{3+} in solution. The obvious explanation was that the yttrium contained a trace of the highly paramagnetic erbium or dysprosium, but spectroscopic investigation failed to reveal any significant amount of these elements. This is, then, perhaps an exaggerated example of the effect mentioned above of distortion produced by the highly-charged small Y^{3+} ion. But the problem has apparently been resolved by Loriers and Quesney,[52a] who find a sample purified by ion exchange to be diamagnetic with a susceptibility close to that of lanthanum.

[40] M. Prasad, S. S. Dharmatti, and S. V. Gokhale, *Proc. Indian Acad. Sci.*, **20A**, 224 (1944). (Ca^{2+}, Sr^{2+}.)

[41] M. Prasad, S. S. Dharmatti, and H. V. Amin, *ibid.*, **26A**, 312 (1947). (Mg^{2+}, Zn^{2+}.)

[42] M. Prasad, S. S. Dharmatti, and D. D. Khanolkar, *Proc. Indian Acad. Sci.*, **26A**, 328 (1947). (Pb^{2+}.)

[43] E. Grillot, *J. chim. phys.*, **43**, 169 (1946). (Pb^{2+}.)

[44] M. E. Bedwell, J. F. Spencer, and V. C. G. Trew, *Trans. Faraday Soc.*, **45**, 217 (1949). (Ammonium salts.)

[45] A. Pacault and M. Stoltz, *Compt. rend.*, **228**, 74 (1949). (Alkali and alkaline earth perchlorates.)

[46] M. Prasad, C. R. Kanekar, S. P. Walvekar, and D. D. Khanolkar, *J. Chem. Phys.*, **18**, 936 (1950). (Alkaline earth salts of organic acids.)

[47] M. Prasad, S. S. Dharmatti, C. R. Kanekar, and D. D. Khanolkar, *ibid.*, **18**, 941 (1950). (Alkali salts of organic acids.)

[48] M. Prasad, C. R. Kanekar, D. D. Khanolkar, and M. G. Datar, *ibid.*, **20**, 129 (1952). (NH_4^+.)

[49] U. Croatto, V. Genta, and P. Maltese, *Gazz. chim. ital.*, **81**, 827 (1951). (Nitrides.)

[50] M. Prasad, S. S. Dharmatti, C. R. Kanekar, and M. G. Datar, *Proc. Indian Acad. Sci.*, **31A**, 389 (1950). (Ag^+.)

[51] O. M. Hilal and F. A. Saleh, *J. Chem. Soc.*, **1954**, 2635. (La^{3+}.)

[52] F. G. Baddar, O. M. Hilal, and S. Sugden, *ibid.*, **1949**, 132.

[52a] J. Loriers and J. Quesney, *Compt. rend.*, **239**, 1643 (1954).

Another paper which should be mentioned is the calculation by Jagannadham[53] of diamagnetic susceptibilities for a substantial number of paramagnetic ions.

23. Diamagnetic Ionic Crystals

Many, if not most, magnetic measurements have been performed on powdered ionic crystals, yet there is still much to be learned of the forces acting on the individual ions in such crystals. The relation between solid and dissolved ionic compounds has already been mentioned.

All the theoretical methods for calculating ionic susceptibilities deal with electronic systems subject to central forces, such as isolated ions in field-free space. Since the only experimental data available refer to ions in crystals or solutions, there is always present the question of validity of such comparisons. Lithium hydride is cubic, and it is one of the simplest of all ionic lattices. This substance has been investigated by Freed and Thode.[54] They find the molar susceptibility of LiH to be $-(4.60 \pm 0.09) \times 10^{-6}$ at 300°K. and at 78°K. Various theoretical computations indicate a diamagnetism of from 90 to 130% higher. The discrepancy between experiment and theory is here unusually large. Freed and Thode suggest that the difference is due to a temperature-independent paramagnetism, which is present in all crystals, but which is not included in the theoretical calculations. It is not clear how such a possibility could be confirmed experimentally. Temperature-independent paramagnetism is, however, actually found experimentally in such compounds as $KMnO_4$, $K_2Cr_2O_7$, K_2MoO_4, and UO_2SO_4. The question has been considered by Van Vleck (op. cit.[4]), and Pascal[55] has assembled considerable data and offered some useful suggestions related to the problem. For salts of the alkali metals, the susceptibilities are approximately additive functions of the respective susceptibilities of cation and anion. The same is true for salts of other metal ions and oxygenated anions, but the halides of silver, mercury, lead, and the alkaline earth metals show large deviations from additivity. In general, a rough prediction of additivity in such cases may be made from a consideration of Fajan's rules respecting "deformability" of ions, the ions having the greatest "deformability" being, of course, those which show the maximum deviation from additivity of susceptibilities.

Diamagnetic susceptibilities of solids might be expected to depend on crystalline form, and this is generally true. The problem may be investigated by measurements on closely related substances, such as anhy-

[53] A. V. Jagannadham, Proc. Rajasthan Acad. Sci., 1, 6 (1950). The original of this paper was not available to the writer.
[54] S. Freed and H. G. Thode, J. Chem. Phys., 3, 212 (1935).
[55] P. Pascal, Compt. rend., 218, 175 (1944).

drous and hydrated salts, or better on polymorphic compounds. Zimens and Hedvall[56] found little relation between crystal structure and magnetic susceptibility of titanium dioxide, selenium, zinc sulfide, sodium carbonate decahydrate, alum, and kaolin. On the other hand, Duchemin[57] found definite susceptibility dependence on structure for hydrated and double magnesium sulfates, as did Mathur and Nevgi[58] for sulfur and for oxides of lead.

Tanaevsky[59] reports an increase of diamagnetism with decreasing particle size for several colloidal dispersions of diamagnetic inorganic solids, such as SnO_2, HgO, but not for others, such as Ag, Hg, ZnS, CdS, and AgS sols. The effect is apparently related to structural anisotropy.[60]

The magnetic properties of solid solutions of diamagnetic ionic compounds are illustrated by the work of Bhatnagar and Kapur.[61] The susceptibility of a mechanical mixture follows Wiedemann's additivity law, so far as is known. But the susceptibility-concentration curve of a true solid solution may follow a linear course, or it may pass through a maximum. In $KClO_4$-$KMnO_4$, which is a truly isomorphous system, the relationship is almost strictly linear. But in solid solutions of KCl-KBr, of NaCl-KCl, and of NaBr-KBr, the susceptibility-concentration curve passes through a maximum. The maximum in the system KCl-KBr is at 70 mole % KBr, and in the systems NaCl-KCl and NaBr-KBr it is at 50%. Solid solutions such as KCl-KBr show a minimum in the freezing point diagram, and the susceptibility shows a maximum deviation from linearity at the same concentration. Somewhat similar susceptibility-concentration deviations are said to occur in mixed aqueous solutions of potassium nitrate and lead nitrate,[62] and in other double salts.[63] The related problem of diamagnetic ionic susceptibilities in glass systems has received attention from Majumdar.[64-66] The deviations from additivity in such systems are reported to be large, and in a direction opposite to that which might have been predicted from Fajan's rules.

The magnetic properties of atomic crystals such as diamond have

[56] K. E. Zimens and J. A. Hedvall, *Svensk. Kem. Tid.*, **53**, 12 (1941).

[57] E. Duchemin, *Compt. rend.*, 199, 571 (1934).

[58] R. N. Mathur and M. B. Nevgi, *Z. Physik*, **100**, 615 (1936).

[59] O. Tanaevsky, *Compt. rend.*, **234**, 2067 (1952).

[60] A. Pacault, *ibid.*, **234**, 2169 (1952).

[61] S. S. Bhatnagar and P. L. Kapur, *J. Indian Chem. Soc.*, **9**, 347 (1932).

[62] S. S. Srivastava, C. S. Pande, and M. R. Nayar, *Current Sci.*, **16**, 225 (1947).

[63] M. Prasad, D. D. Khanolkar, and M. G. Datar, *Proc. Indian Acad. Sci.*, **36A**, 544 (1952).

[64] S. K. Majumdar and H. Saha, *J. Indian Chem. Soc.*, **22**, 147 (1945).

[65] S. K. Majumdar and R. P. Banerjee, *Indian J. Phys.*, **20**, 218 (1946).

[66] S. K. Majumdar, *Nature*, **161**, 684 (1948).

generally been measured, but few intensive studies of such substances have been made. The mass susceptibility of diamond,[67] about -0.45×10^{-6} is of interest chiefly in comparison with that of graphite[68] which is about -6×10^{-6}. This great diamagnetism in graphite is due to the so-called conduction electrons which are believed also to contribute to the abnormal diamagnetism of silver subfluoride.[69] Silicon carbide may probably be considered as an atomic crystal.[70] The mean molar susceptibility is -12.8×10^{-6}, and the crystal is slightly anisotropic.

[67] A. Sigamony, *Proc. Indian Acad. Sci.*, **19A**, 310 (1944).

[68] M. Owen, *Ann. Physik*, **37**, 657 (1912).

[69] S. Freed, N. Sugarman, and R. P. Metcalf, *J. Chem. Phys.*, **8**, 225 (1940).

[70] A. Sigamony, *Proc. Indian Acad. Sci.*, **19A**, 377 (1944).

CHAPTER SIX

MOLECULAR DIAMAGNETISM

24. Theories of Diamagnetism in Polynuclear Molecules

The classical theory of diamagnetism has no solution for molecules containing more than one nucleus, because the Larmor precession applies strictly to mononuclear systems. The quantum theory has, at least in principle, a complete solution to the problem, and one which for simple molecules like hydrogen yields a reasonably satisfactory result.

According to Van Vleck[1] the molar susceptibility of a polyatomic molecule with no resultant electron spin moment is given by

$$\chi_M = -\frac{Ne^2}{6mc} \sum \overline{r^2} + \frac{2}{3} N \sum_{n' \neq n} \frac{|m^\circ(n'; n)|^2}{h\nu(n'; n)}$$

where $m^\circ(n'; n)$ is a nondiagonal element of the matrix for the angular momentum of the system, $\nu(n'; n)$ is the frequency corresponding to n'; n transition, and the other terms have their usual significance. The susceptibility is small and independent of temperature. The substance is either diamagnetic or feebly paramagnetic, depending on which term is the larger.

Quantitative calculation of susceptibility by the above expression is difficult even for hydrogen because the wave functions are not accurately known. For hydrogen the first term is -4.71×10^{-6} and the second about $+0.51 \times 10^{-6}$, which gives a computed molar susceptibility of -4.20×10^{-6}. Experimental values range from about -3.9 to -4.0×10^{-6}, the most accurate being probably that of Havens,[2] -4.0051×10^{-6}. In view of the various uncertainties, the agreement is fairly satisfactory.

Making use of the James and Coolidge wave-functions for hydrogen, Witmer[3] has found that the average of the best calculated values lies between -3.78 and -3.90×10^{-6}. This is in slightly better agreement with

---

[1] J. H. Van Vleck, *Theory of Electric and Magnetic Susceptibilities.* Oxford University Press, Oxford, 1932, p. 275.

[2] G. G. Havens, *Phys. Rev.*, **43**, 992 (1933).

[3] E. Witmer, *ibid.*, **48**, 380 (1935); 51, 383 (1937).

experiment. A similar theoretical calculation[4] for molecular deuterium gives $\chi_M = -3.93 \times 10^{-6}$. Somewhat more recently the calculations for hydrogen have been considered by Koppe,[5] by Steensholt,[6] and by Ishiguro and Koide.[7]

Theoretical calculation of susceptibilities of molecules more complex than hydrogen is in a rudimentary state. A very rough approximation may be made by a method similar to that indicated for atomic hydrogen, by use of appropriate screening constants and effective quantum numbers.[8]

The scarcity of theoretical results on diamagnetic susceptibilities of molecules is due to lack of knowledge about reliable wave-functions. An attempted calculation for molecular nitrogen by the Thomas-Fermi statistical method[9] yields a molar diamagnetic susceptibility of nearly twice the observed value of about -13.3×10^{-6}. For methane, the self-consistent field method has been explored by Buckingham, Massey, and Tibbs,[10] and the molecular-orbital and electron-pair approximate wave-functions by Coulson.[11] The first method yields a molar susceptibility of -32.2×10^{-6}, as compared with about -18×10^{-6} observed. It is obvious that the calculated electron distributions are too diffuse. The authors believe that if the theory were extended to include exchange effects, the gain would be worthwhile. The method can be applied to other molecules which possess tetrahedral or octahedral symmetry. This and related methods are discussed by Allard.[12]

Coulson reports that the susceptibility found by the electron-pair method is close to that by the molecular-orbital method, and although both are less than the self-consistent field value, they are still twice the experimental value. The deviation is attributed to approximations in the wave-functions. The largest influence is shown to come from the outer parts of the molecule for which the detailed form of the wave-function is known with least reliability.

Attempts to compare theoretical with experimental diamagnetic susceptibilities of molecules more complex than these have led to some interesting anomalies. Farquharson[13] has measured the susceptibilities of

[4] E. Witmer, *ibid.*, **58**, 202 (1940).

[5] H. Koppe, *Z. Physik*, **121**, 614 (1943).

[6] G. Steensholt, *Phil. Mag.*, **38**, 748 (1947).

[7] E. Ishiguro and S. Koide, *Phys. Rev.*, **94**, 350 (1954).

[8] E. C. Stoner, *Magnetism and Matter*. Methuen and Company, Ltd., London, 1934, p. 467.

[9] J. V. Bonet and A. V. Bushkovitch, *J. Chem. Phys.*, **21**, 2199 (1953).

[10] R. A. Buckingham, H. S. W. Massey, and S. R. Tibbs, *Proc. Roy. Soc. (London)*, **A178**, 119 (1941).

[11] C. A. Coulson, *ibid.*, **54**, 51 (1942).

[12] G. Allard, *Bull. soc. chim. France*, **1949**, D469.

[13] J. Farquharson, *Phil. Mag.*, **14**, 1003 (1932).

several sulfur compounds and compared the results with theoretical values obtained by the Pauling and Slater methods. In practically every case, increasing complexity and decreasing symmetry are attended with a diminution of diamagnetism. The sum of the molar diamagnetic susceptibilities of water and of sulfur trioxide is $-(12.96 + 28.54) \times 10^{-6} = -41.50 \times 10^{-6}$, but χ_M for sulfuric acid is -39.00×10^{-6}, a fall in diamagnetism of 2.5×10^{-6} unit.

A more striking example is given by Henkel and Klemm,[14] who measured the magnetic behavior of some liquid fluorides. The experimental data are compared with Angus's[15] modification of Slater's theoretical susceptibilities in Table IV. Starting with molybdenum hexafluoride the observed susceptibilities become markedly less diamagnetic than the calculated, until with uranium hexafluoride the temperature-independent paramagnetism becomes dominant and the susceptibility becomes positive.

TABLE IV

Magnetic Susceptibilities of Some Liquid Fluorides

Compound	$\chi_M \times 10^6$	
	Observed	Calculated
SF_6	-44	-45
SeF_6	-51	-51
TeF_6	-66	-61
MoF_6	-26	-55
WF_6	-40	-66
UF_6	$+43$	~ -70

It should be pointed out that this paramagnetism is still quite small. For substances with a permanent magnetic moment, the molar paramagnetism may be of the order of 5000×10^{-6}. Nevertheless, the difficulty of calculating theoretical diamagnetic susceptibilities will be obvious. Some progress in this direction may be possible on the basis of Ehrlich's[16] experimental data on the susceptibilities of liquid and solid hydrogen halides. It should be emphasized that there is no essential difference between diamagnetic and weakly paramagnetic substances. The sign of the susceptibility depends simply on whether the negative or positive term is the larger.

25. Water

Such frequent use is made of water for calibration purposes and as a solvent in magnetic studies that some discussion of its susceptibility is

[14] P. Henkel and W. Klemm, Z. anorg. u. allgem. Chem., 222, 70 (1935).

[15] W. R. Angus, Proc. Roy. Soc. (London), A136, 569 (1932).

[16] P. Ehrlich, Z. anorg. u. allgem. Chem., 249, 219 (1942).

justified. There have been several absolute determinations of the susceptibility of water. The two which seem to the writer to be most impressive are those of Piccard and Devaud[17] and of Auer.[18] The former find $\chi_{20°} = -0.71992 \times 10^{-6}$ with an estimated error of 1.1 in 10,000. Auer finds $\chi_{20°} = -0.7218 \times 10^{-6}$ with an estimated error of about 7 in 10,000. Unfortunately, the agreement is not quite as close as might be desired. But there are few cases in which susceptibilities must be known to four significant figures, except for certain dilute solutions in which the relative susceptibility of solvent and solution should be known to at least four figures. Many workers arbitrarily set the gram susceptibility of water at 20°C. at -0.7200×10^{-6} for calibration purposes.

Most investigators agree that the susceptibility of water has a temperature coefficient, but there have been some astonishing disagreements as to the magnitude, and even the sign, of the coefficient. At one time it was thought that the susceptibility of water depended on its thermal history, but this has been shown to be not true. The temperature coefficient has been studied by Mathur,[19] Johner,[20] Cabrera and Fahlenbrach,[21] Auer,[18] Wills and Boeker,[22] and Seely.[23] The work of Auer is particularly impressive. Using an elaborate modification of the Quincke method, he obtains the data shown in Table V. The temperature coefficient $1/\chi_T \cdot d\chi/dT$ falls regularly from 2.9×10^{-4} at 5°C. to 0.62×10^{-4} at 70°C.

TABLE V

Mass Susceptibility of Water (after Auer)

Temp., °C.	$-\chi \times 10^6$
1	0.71896
5	0.71982
10	0.72067
15	0.72131
20	0.72183
25	0.72224
30	0.72258
40	0.72286
50	0.72361
60	0.72406
70	0.72454

[17] A. Piccard and A. Devaud, *Arch. sci. phys. et nat.*, [5], **2**, 455 (1920).
[18] H. Auer, *Ann. Physik*, **18**, 593 (1933).
[19] R. N. Mathur, *Indian J. Phys.*, **6**, 207 (1931).
[20] W. Johner, *Helv. Phys. Acta*, **4**, 238 (1931).
[21] B. Cabrera and H. Fahlenbrach, *Anales soc. españ. fís. quím.*, **31**, 401 (1933); *Z. Physik*, **82**, 759 (1933).
[22] A. P. Wills and G. F. Boeker, *Phys. Rev.*, **46**, 907 (1934).
[23] S. Seely, *ibid.*, **52**, 662 (1937).

Wills and Boeker represent the susceptibility of water by the expression

$$\chi_T/\chi_{20} = 1 + (1.3 \times 10^{-4})\,(T - 20) - (0.7 \times 10^{-6})\,(T - 20)^2$$

The value of $1/\chi \cdot d\chi/dT$ at $20°$ is 1.30×10^{-4}, which is slightly higher than that reported by most others. They also suggest an anomalous region between $35°$ and $55°C$. This is supported by Seely who finds a continuous though irregular change of susceptibility with temperature, with a marked change in slope at $45°C$. His results agree with those of Wills and Boeker except at higher temperatures. Cabrera and Fahlenbrach[24] extend the susceptibility of water to $140°C$. where $\chi = -0.727 \times 10^{-6}$, but this value is based on Cabrera's use of the rather high value -0.7220×10^{-6} for water at $20°C$.

Reasons for the peculiar temperature coefficient of susceptibility for water have been examined by Cabrera and Fahlenbrach, Tammann,[25] Sibaiya,[26] and Cabrera.[27] The consensus is that depolymerization of water molecules is responsible for the change. This view is supported by the observation that potassium iodide solutions all have susceptibilities slightly higher than those calculated by the additivity law.

Again using as standard the rather high value $\chi_{20°} = -0.7220 \times 10^{-6}$, Cabrera and Fahlenbrach report the susceptibility of water at $0°C$. as -0.7177×10^{-6} and of ice at the same temperature as -0.7019×10^{-6}. There is considerable doubt as to the temperature coefficient of susceptibility for ice.

The diamagnetism of heavy water, D_2O, has been measured by several groups of investigators.[28-32] The susceptibility is about -0.647×10^{-6} with thermal properties similar to but not identical with those of ordinary water. Higher accuracy claimed by some investigators is not justifiable on the basis of densities believed to be accurate at the time the work was done. Gray and Cruickshank claim that there is a time lag in the establishment of the susceptibility when either heavy or ordinary water is freshly formed from ice. The susceptibilities of mixtures of ordinary water and heavy water are linear with concentration.[32]

[24] B. Cabrera and H. Fahlenbrach, *Anales soc. españ. fís. quím.*, **32**, 525 (1934).
[25] G. Tammann, *Z. Physik*, **91**, 410 (1934).
[26] L. Sibaiya, *Current Sci.*, **3**, 421 (1935).
[27] B. Cabrera, *J. chim. phys.*, **38**, 1 (1941).
[28] B. Cabrera and H. Fahlenbrach, *Naturwissenschaften*, **22**, 417 (1934); *Anales soc. españ. fís. quím.*, **32**, 538 (1934).
[29] F. W. Gray and J. H. Cruickshank, *Nature*, **135**, 268 (1935).
[30] F. E. Hoare, *ibid.*, **137**, 497 (1936).
[31] V. C. G. Trew and J. F. Spencer, *ibid.*, **137**, 706, 998 (1936).
[32] O. E. Frivold and N. G. Olsen, *Arch. Math. Naturvidenskab*, **44**, 115 (1941).

26. Temperature Dependence of Molecular Diamagnetism

Neither classical nor quantum theories suggest that diamagnetism should be anything but independent of temperature. But as has already been pointed out for water, the temperature coefficient of diamagnetic susceptibility may sometimes be appreciable. Havens[2] has shown that the common diamagnetic gases, such as hydrogen, helium, neon, and argon, have the same susceptibility at liquid air temperature as at 20°C. There is some divergence of opinion regarding the temperature dependence of susceptibility for liquids and solids. Johner[20] and Mathur[19] report positive though small temperature coefficients for aliphatic alcohols, and negative coefficients for several alkyl and aryl iodides. Some of these results are supported by Khanna,[33] but Cabrera and Fahlenbrach[34,35] show that the temperature coefficient is practically zero for a large group of aliphatic alcohols, excepting n-octyl, dodecyl, and especially cetyl alcohol. Slight changes are observed for nitrobenzene and for m-cresol. Rather marked changes are observed on going from liquid to solid. These changes will be discussed in the next section. The susceptibility of supercooled liquids has been examined by Cabrera and Fahlenbrach who find that for o- and p-cresol the diamagnetism follows a normal extension of the susceptibility-temperature curve for the liquid.

One of the most careful examinations in this field was conducted by Boeker[36] who found no temperature dependence of susceptibility exceeding 0.5% for carbon tetrachloride, benzene, and toluene over the temperature range 10° to 50°C. The liquids were not subjected to special purification, and the writer's experience is that dissolved water may appreciably alter the apparent temperature coefficient of susceptibility for nonpolar organic solvents. Boeker's work is, however, supported by that of Bhatnagar, Nevgi, and Khanna[37] on the susceptibilities of diamagnetic aromatic liquids.

The situation regarding temperature dependence of diamagnetism may be summed up about as follows: In diamagnetic gases there is no measurable dependence. In nonpolar liquids the coefficient is very small except possibly near the melting and boiling points. In polar liquids and in solids, so far as is known, the temperature coefficient is generally positive, but it seldom exceeds 1% change over a 50-degree temperature change, Such changes as are observed are probably not due to any fault in the modern theory of magnetism but rather to slight redistributions of electron density attendant on the formation of polymers and addition compounds.

[33] M. L. Khanna, J. Sci. Ind. Research (India), 6, No. 1, B10 (1947).

[34] B. Cabrera and H. Fahlenbrach, Z. Physik, 85, 568 (1933); 89, 682 (1934).

[35] B. Cabrera, J. chim. phys., 37, 86 (1940).

[36] G. F. Boeker, Phys. Rev., 43, 756 (1933).

[37] S. S. Bhatnagar, M. B. Nevgi, and M. L. Khanna, Z. Physik, 89, 506 (1934).

Condensed aromatic rings form a special class which will be described in Chapter VII.

27. Different Physical States

Considerable success has been achieved in calculating susceptibilities additively from what are known as Pascal's constants. The fact that such calculations are possible suggests that diamagnetism is independent of physical state. Oxley[38] has measured the susceptibilities of a large number of organic compounds over a temperature range and found for many substances a decrease in diamagnetism of from 3 to 13% on crystallization. Mere supercooling, even to the vitreous state, does not produce any comparable diminution of diamagnetism. If Oxley's results are correct, then

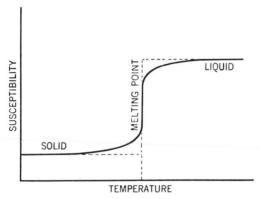

Fig. 51. Relationship between susceptibility and temperature often found for a diamagnetic substance near the melting point.

it becomes difficult to understand the success of Pascal's constants, which frequently yield susceptibilities accurate to 1%. Cabrera and Fahlenbrach[34] support Oxley's results and in some cases find even greater changes on crystallization. They show that for many diamagnetic substances, the susceptibility-temperature relation may be represented by a curve of the form shown in Fig. 51. The susceptibility of the solid is substantially independent of temperature until near the melting point where it begins to rise increasingly sharply as the substance melts. Finally, the susceptibility of the liquid does not reach its full value until several degrees above the melting point. This surprising effect has apparently been observed both with rising and with falling temperatures, and it is reminiscent of Trew

[38] A. E. Oxley, *Phil. Trans. Roy. Soc. (London)*, **A214**, 109 (1914); **A215**, 79 (1915); **A220**, 247 (1920).

and Spencer's claim that there is a time lag in the establishment of the correct susceptibility when water is freshly formed from ice. The effect is not inconsistent with what is known of the structure of certain liquids, notably water, near their freezing points. According to all workers in the field, the liquids are invariably more diamagnetic than the solids, provided any change occurs. Cabrera and Fahlenbrach suggest that there is a relationship between the dipole moment of the compound and the magnitude of the change on melting.

The change of susceptibility on melting is also supported for benzophenone and p-nitrotoluene,[39] but Bose[40] has reached the opposite conclusion. He has measured susceptibilities of several organic compounds in the molten and dissolved states. The data are compared with crystal powder data of Pascal, with average susceptibilities calculated from the known principal susceptibilities, and with additive values from Pascal's constants. Bose reaches the conclusion that, within the limits of experimental error (about 1%) the diamagnetism of a compound is independent of its physical state, that is, whether it is a single crystal, molten liquid, or in solution. This is directly contradictory to Oxley and to some others. It should be pointed out that Bose did not actually measure both liquid and solid states himself, but relied on Pascal's measurements for the solids. Also, in those cases where Bose actually compared liquid and solution values, data are given for only seven of the 27 compounds investigated, and in these seven cases the differences of susceptibility amount to over 3%.

A possible explanation of Oxley's results may be that owing to the diamagnetic anisotropy of most organic crystals, preferential orientation of the microcrystals may have taken place. Such orientation would naturally result in the smallest principal diamagnetic susceptibility lying along the lines of force. But a difficulty with this explanation is that both Oxley, and Cabrera and Fahlenbrach, found no difference in susceptibility between liquid and solid benzene, single crystals of which are markedly anisotropic. Taking everything into consideration, the writer feels that a change of diamagnetism on crystallization probably does occur. What the magnitude of that change may be cannot yet be stated.

The question of possible changes in magnetization on vaporization has until recently been poorly studied. Vaidyanathan,[41] with the aid of a sensitive torsion balance, investigated the vapors of a number of organic compounds. In all but two cases, carbon disulfide and benzene, the susceptibility of the vapor is reported as the same as that for the liquid,

[39] K. C. Subramanian, *Proc. Indian Acad. Sci.*, **3A**, 420 (1936).
[40] A. Bose, *Phil. Mag.*, **21**, 1119 (1936).
[41] V. I. Vaidyanathan, *Phys. Rev.*, **30**, 512 (1927).

within the rather large experimental error. Yanus and Shur[42,43] express the opinion that Vaidyanathan's anomalous results for carbon disulfide and benzene are due to experimental error.

The careful and ingenious experiments of Reber and Boeker[44] seem to establish that for benzene and carbon tetrachloride the susceptibilities (per gram) of vapor and liquid phases are the same. The vapor susceptibilities reported by them are $\chi \times 10^6$ for C_6H_6, -0.697; for CCl_4, -0.432. The average values collected by Seely[45] from earlier work on the liquids are for C_6H_6, -0.7038; for CCl_4, -0.4308. So far, therefore, as is known with certainty, there is no very significant change of susceptibility on the vaporization of a diamagnetic liquid, unless there is some rather obvious chemical change.

It should perhaps be mentioned that there is some evidence for decrease of diamagnetism with decreasing particle size. This seems to be true of quartz,[46] and is definitely true of graphite. This effect is not unlikely, because the electron distributions and hence the diamagnetic susceptibility of an atom on or near a surface might be expected to be different from those of one in the interior of a crystal.

More important, for anisotropic solids, such as graphite, there is a definite decrease of diamagnetic susceptibility when the particle size begins to approach the effective electronic radius of the free, or quasi-free, electrons in such systems.[47] This matter will be discussed more fully in the following chapter.

28. Pascal's Constants[48]

From measurements on a very large number of compounds, Pascal concluded that magnetic susceptibilities could be represented by the expression

$$\chi_M = \Sigma n_A \chi_A + \lambda$$

where n_A is the number of atoms of susceptibility χ_A in the molecule, and λ is a constitutive correction depending on the nature of the bonds between the atoms. In this expression χ_A is not the theoretical atomic susceptibility

[42] R. I. Yanus and I. Shur, *Nature*, **134**, 101 (1934).

[43] I. Shur, *Physik Z. Sowjetunion*, **11**, 194 (1937).

[44] R. K. Reber and G. F. Boeker, *J. Chem. Phys.*, **15**, 508 (1947).

[45] S. Seely, *Phys. Rev.*, **49**, 812 (1936).

[46] Y. Shimizu and N. Takatori, *Science Repts. Tôhoku Imp. Univ., K. Honda Anniversary Vol., First Ser.*, **1936**, 306.

[47] A. Pacault, *J. chim. phys.*, **49**, 585 (1952).

[48] P. Pascal, *Ann. chim. phys.*, **19**, 5 (1910); **25**, 289 (1912); **24**, 218 (1913). *Compt. rend.*, **147**, 56, 242, 742 (1908); **148**, 413 (1909); **150**, 1167 (1910); **152**, 862, 1010 (1911); **156**, 323 (1913); **158**, 37 (1914); **173**, 144 (1921); **176**, 1887 (1923); **177**, 765 (1923); **180**, 1596 (1925); and others.

to which reference was made in the previous chapter, but is a purely empirical constant derived from the measured susceptibilities. At first glance, this whole procedure looks rather dubious, especially in connection with λ. It cannot be denied, however, that considerable success has been achieved by use of Pascal's constants, and that they often afford means of estimating susceptibilities where no other methods are available. For instance, in free radicals such as the triarylmethyls, there is a substantial diamagnetic correction to be made, but there is no direct way to measure this correction. In such cases, Pascal's method may be helpful.

Basic values for Pascal's constants are derived from the halogens. The constant for Cl is one-half the molar susceptibility of Cl_2. All of Pascal's earlier original data refer to the susceptibility of water as -0.75×10^{-6} as standard. Values given here are multiplied by $72/75$ to correct his data to the modern value for water, whenever necessary.

The method will be illustrated by a simple example: for ethyl bromide, C_2H_5Br, the molar susceptibility is given by $2\chi_C + 5\chi_H + \chi_{Br} + \lambda$. In this case λ is the constitutive correction for the C—Br bond. The magnitude of these quantities is as follows:

$$\{ -[(2 \times 6.00) + (5 \times 2.93) + 30.6] + 4.1 \} \times 10^{-6} = -53.1 \times 10^{-6}$$

The observed molar susceptibility is -53.3×10^{-6}. It should, however, be pointed out that more recent data from Pascal's laboratory indicate a somewhat poorer agreement than that indicated. Pascal's constants for the elements are given in Table VI and a list of constitutive correction constants in Table VII. Pascal found that the position of oxygen with respect to carbon atoms in the molecule introduced another constitutive correction. He referred to "tertiary" and "quaternary" (C_3 and C_4) carbon atoms as those in which three or four valences respectively are

TABLE VI

Pascal's Constants for the Elements ($\times 10^6$)

H	-2.93	Cl	-20.1
C	-6.00	Br	-30.6
N (open chain)	-5.55	I	-44.6
N (ring)	-4.61	S	-15
N (monamide)	-1.54	Se	-23
N (diamide, imide)	-2.11	B	-7
O (alcohol, ether)	-4.61	Si	-13
O (aldehyde, ketone)	$+1.72$	P	-10
O (carboxyl group*)	-3.36	As	-21
F	-6.3		

* In later publications from Pascal's laboratory the combined value for the two oxygens in acids and esters is given as -7.95, and for the three oxygens in acid anhydrides as -11.23.

attached to carbon, regardless of the actual number of surrounding carbon atoms. For instance, a tertiary carbon atom is the one designated (*) in the group,

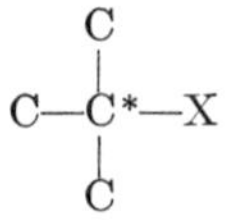

$$
\begin{array}{c}
\text{C} \\
| \\
\text{C}-\text{C}^*-\text{X} \\
| \\
\text{C}
\end{array}
$$

a quaternary carbon atom

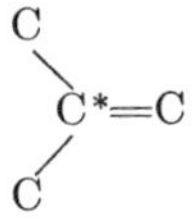

$$
\begin{array}{c}
\text{C} \\
\diagdown \\
\text{C}^*\!\!=\!\!\text{C} \\
\diagup \\
\text{C}
\end{array}
$$

A tertiary carbon atom in the *alpha* position with respect to an oxygen group is designated C_3^α. This notation, which is not common to organic chemistry, is used in Table VII and in the following discussion.

TABLE VII

Some Constitutive Correction Constants (λ)

C=C	+5.5
C=C	+0.8
C=C—C=C	+10.6
N=N	+1.85
C=N—	+8.15
—C≡N	+0.8
Benzene	−1.4
Cyclohexane	−3.0
C_3^α, C_3^γ, C_3^δ, C_3^ϵ	−1.3
C_4^α, C_4^γ, C_4^δ, C_4^ϵ	−1.55
C_3^β, C_4^β	−0.5

A calculation for benzoyl chloride will show some of the uses of these constants.

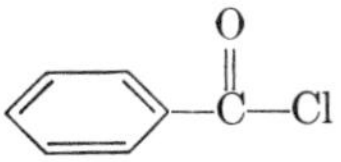

$$
\begin{array}{c}
\text{O} \\
\|\\
\text{C}_6\text{H}_5\text{—C—Cl}
\end{array}
$$

7C		-42.0×10^{-6}
5H		−14.6
O (ketone)		+ 1.7
Cl		−20.1
Benzene		− 1.4
C_4^α		− 1.5
	(calc.)	−77.9
	(obs.)	−77.9

It will be noted that the calculated susceptibilities are like calculated molar refractivities, and are about as accurate.

An extensive discussion of Pascal's constants is given by Bhatnagar and Mathur.[49] Tables and critical discussion are given by Gray and Farquharson,[50] and Pacault[51] has prepared an exhaustive review which no serious student of Pascal's constants can afford to miss.

It may be predicted that a homologous series of organic compounds should have a susceptibility which is a linear function of the number of methylene groups. This is approximately true as found for many such series by Pascal, and more recently by Woodbridge[52] for a group of alkyl acetates, and by Bhatnagar and Mitra[53] for 15 hydrocarbons, and for 29 oxygenated, 13 halogenated, 19 nitrogenous, and five acetylenic compounds. Farquharson and Sastri[54] have measured the susceptibilities of butyric, valeric, caproic, heptylic, and caprylic acids. Pascal's original constant for the $-CH_2-$ group was -11.86 ($\times 10^{-6}$), but Bhatnagar and Mitra favor -11.36. Farquharson and Sastri recommend -11.64, Angus[55,56] gives -11.68, and French[57] gives -11.47. The point is further exhaustively discussed by Pascal and Pacault,[58] and by Pacault.[51] For most purposes a value of -11.8 for the methylene increment is adequate and certainly is not far from the truth. It is perhaps scarcely valid to draw conclusions from measurements on one particular homologous series or even from one class of compounds. The problem is further discussed by Prasad[59] and by Sacconi.[60]

Certain classes of isomeric organic compounds might be expected to have identical molar susceptibilities. This problem has received some careful attention, and it is now possible to draw some definite conclusions. Angus and Hill[61] have summarized the earlier literature in which it is definitely indicated that not all isomers have identical susceptibilities. These workers have examined a substantial number of compounds, most

[49] S. S. Bhatnagar and K. N. Mathur, *Physical Principles and Applications of Magnetochemistry.* MacMillan and Company, Ltd., London, 1935, p. 67.

[50] F. W. Gray and J. Farquharson, *Phil. Mag.*, **10**, 191 (1930).

[51] A. Pacault, *Rev. Sci.*, **82**, 465 (1944); **86**, 38 (1948).

[52] D. B. Woodbridge, *Phys. Rev.*, **48**, 672 (1935).

[53] S. S. Bhatnagar and N. G. Mitra, *J. Indian Chem. Soc.*, **13**, 329 (1936).

[54] J. Farquharson and M. V. C. Sastri, *Trans. Faraday Soc.*, **33**, 1472 (1937).

[55] W. R. Angus, *Ann. Repts. on Progr. Chem.*, **1941**, 32.

[56] W. R. Angus and W. K. Hill, *Trans. Faraday Soc.*, **39**, 190 (1943).

[57] C. M. French, *ibid.*, **43**, 356 (1947).

[58] P. Pascal and A. Pacault, *Compt. rend.*, **222**, 619 (1946).

[59] M. Prasad, S. S. Dharmatti, D. D. Khanolkar, and S. P. Walvekar, *Proc. Indian Acad. Sci.*, **32A**, 313 (1950).

[60] L. Sacconi and R. Cini, *Atti accad. nazl. Lincei*, **16**, 237 (1954).

[61] W. R. Angus and W. K. Hill, *Trans. Faraday Soc.*, **39**, 197 (1943).

of which are aliphatic alcohols, acids, or esters. The differences in susceptibilities found are not large. For instance, the four butyl alcohols give the following values: *tert*, -57.42; *sec*, -57.30; *iso*, -57.21; *n*, -56.15. This diminution of diamagnetism in the sequence *tert-*, *sec-*, *iso-*, and *n-* seems generally to be true for all classes of compounds. For several pairs of compounds investigated the difference in susceptibility between *iso-* and *n-*compounds seems to be almost constant. A comparison of isomeric acids and esters yields the information that the acid is always about one unit more diamagnetic than the ester. Similar studies[62] on aldehyde-ketone isomers show that the aldehyde is slightly more diamagnetic than the ketone. These consistent differences have led Angus to the view that the greatest usefulness of diamagnetism in problems of molecular structure will be found in the assignment of constants to groups of atoms rather than to individual atoms, as is done by Pascal.

Further ample evidence for the slight but definite differences in susceptibilities of isomers has been given by Anderson, Bedwell, and LeFevre[63] for isomeric cyanides and isocyanides; by French[64] for isomeric disubstituted benzenes; and by Hazato,[65] by Pacault and Guy,[66] and by Byerly and Selwood[67] for *cis-* and *trans*-selenophthene, cinnamic acid, and decahydronaphthalene, respectively. Similar evidence has been obtained on paraffin hydrocarbons[68] and on pyridones and their isomeric derivatives.[69] This problem has been reviewed by Angus.[70] For many substances the more diamagnetic isomer has the lower boiling point, lower refractive index, and lower parachor.

It might be expected that optical isomers would show no differences in magnetic susceptibilities. The data available indicate that such, at least, is the case for the *levo* and *dextro* forms of camphor and borneol, and of several camphor derivatives.[71,72]

29. Interpretations of Pascal's Constants

Pascal's method has given many indications of its reliability. It fits

[62] W. R. Angus and G. Stott, *Nature*, **158**, 705 (1946).

[63] D. Anderson, M. E. Bedwell, and R. J. W. LeFevre, *J. Chem. Soc.*, **1947**, 457.

[64] C. M. French, *Trans. Faraday Soc.*, **41**, 676 (1945).

[65] G. Hazato, *J. Chem. Soc. Japan*, **63**, 1685 (1942).

[66] A. Pacault and J. Guy, *Compt. rend.*, **226**, 723 (1948).

[67] W. Byerly and P. W. Selwood, *J. Am. Chem. Soc.*, **64**, 717 (1942).

[68] R. Manzoni-Ansidei, *Boll. sci. facolta chim. ind. univ. Bologna*, **5**, 5 (1944–47).

[69] A. Pacault and J. Chauvelier, *Bull. soc. chim. France*, **1950**, 367.

[70] W. R. Angus, *ibid.*, **1949**, D483.

[71] B. K. Singh, S. L. Aggarwal, S. Singh, and M. Singh, *Proc. Lahore Philosophical Soc.*, **6**, 1 (1944).

[72] B. K. Singh, S. L. Aggarwal, and M. Singh, *Proc. Natl. Acad. Sci. India*, **Sec. A**, **14**, 72 (1944). *Proc. Indian Acad. Sci.*, **29A**, 309 (1949).

well into a system, and in many cases his results have been confirmed by experimental methods entirely different in character. The usefulness of the constants is undeniable, and yet the whole system is empirical. It is not surprising that efforts have been made to put the constants on a theoretical basis. Such an attempt has been made by Gray and Cruikshank[73] who relate Pascal's constants to Pauling's theoretical atomic susceptibilities and the constitutive correction in part to Van Vleck's temperature-independent high-frequency paramagnetism. The method gives promise and has been applied successfully to certain structural problems, one of which will be described.

The method, in brief, consists of comparing experimental susceptibilities with those derived theoretically from different possible structures. Most of the applications of this method are due to Clow.[74] The nature of the calculations will be indicated by reference to urea and its derivatives. It is first necessary to estimate the residual charges on the atoms due to unequal sharing of bond electrons. This may be done as described by Sidgwick.[75] For the carbamide structure of urea, the atoms are found to have the following residual charges: C $+0.54$, H $+0.29$, O -0.42, N -0.64. Gray and Cruikshank assign to these numbers the following significance, namely, that they represent the fraction of time in which the atom has the neighbor-

$$H_2N:C:NH_2$$
$$\overset{..}{\underset{..}{O}}:$$

ing whole-number charge. For instance, carbon with a residual charge $+0.54$ is equivalent to a carbon atom being 54% of the time in a C^+ state and 46% in a $C°$ state. The atomic susceptibility may then be calculated by the method of Pauling,[76] the terms having their usual significance.

$$\chi_A = -1.976 \times 10^{-6} \sum_k \frac{n_x^4}{(Z - s_r)^2} \left[1 - \frac{3l_x(l_x + 1) - 1}{5n_x^2} \right]$$

This gives for the carbamide structure of urea a molar susceptibility of -43.58×10^{-6} which, however, neglects the depression of diamagnetism equal to 16.12×10^{-6} unit, which takes place on bond formation, as follows:

$$1(C::O) = 10.28; \quad 2(C:N) = 3.56; \quad 4(N:H) = 2.28, \text{ all} \times 10^{-6}$$

giving a theoretical molar susceptibility for the carbamide structure of

[73] F. W. Gray and J. H. Cruikshank, *Trans. Faraday Soc.*, **31**, 1491 (1935).

[74] A. Clow, *ibid.*, **33**, 381 (1937).

[75] N. Sidgwick, *Covalent Link in Chemistry*. Cornell University Press, Ithaca, 1933, p. 154.

[76] L. Pauling, *Proc. Roy. Soc. (London)*, **A114**, 181 (1927).

-27.46×10^{-6}. An alternative structure for urea is the resonating zwitterion formula

$$H \colon \ddot{N} \colon \colon C \colon \ddot{O}^- \qquad \text{and} \qquad H \colon \ddot{N}^- \colon \colon \colon C^+ \colon \ddot{O}^- \colon$$

$$NH_3{}^+ \qquad\qquad\qquad NH_3{}^+$$

For the first of these structures, the theoretical susceptibility is -27.90×10^{-6}; for the second, -38.80×10^{-6}. The average -33.35×10^{-6} is in excellent agreement with experiment. Thus the magnetic evidence, interpreted in this way, is that the parent urea molecule is represented by the resonating zwitterion. (For criticism of this view, see Pacault.[51]) Other possible resonance or tautomeric forms are believed by Clow to be of minor importance.

Further support for the method is given by the excellent agreement between observed susceptibilities of tetra-substituted ureas and calculated values for the normal carbamide structures of these compounds. Similarly successful arguments are applied by Clow to many substituted ureas, carbon dioxide, carbon oxysulfide, carbon disulfide, several thioureas, and a rather large number of sulfur compounds.[77-79] The method has also been applied with some success to dicyandiamide, acetamide, and cyanuric acid.[80] Some idea of what may be achieved by juggling empirical susceptibilities among assumed structures (of quite arbitrary form) may be found in a paper by Yang.[81] Other related studies are indicated below.[82-92]

[77] A. Clow and J. M. C. Thompson, *Trans. Faraday Soc.*, **33**, 894 (1937).

[78] A. Clow, *ibid.*, **34**, 457 (1938).

[79] A. Clow, H. M. Kirton, and J. M. C. Thompson, *ibid.*, **36**, 1018 (1940).

[80] S. K. Siddhanta and P. Rây, *J. Indian Chem. Soc.*, **20**, 359 (1943).

[81] Tai-Yuan Yang, *J. Chem. Phys.*, **16**, 865 (1948).

[82] R. Manzoni-Ansidei and A. M. Ghe, *Boll. sci. facolta chim. ind. univ. Bologna*, **5**, 8 (1944–47). (Pyridine, naphthalene, quinoline and derivatives.)

[83] R. Manzoni-Ansidei, *ibid.*, **5**, 70 (1944–47). (Dimethylfurazan and dimethyloxadiazole.)

[84] M. Prasad, S. S. Dharmatti, C. R. Kanekar, and N. S. Birdar, *J. Chem. Phys.*, **17**, 813 (1949). (Hydrates.)

[85] Nguyen-Quang-Trinh, *Bull. soc. chim. France*, **1949**, D397. (Aromatic chlorine derivatives.)

[86] B. K. Singh, K. M. S. Manhas, M. Singh, and V. Puri, *Proc. Indian Acad. Sci.*, **30A**, 103 (1949). (Phthalic acid and phthalic anhydride.)

[87] F. G. Baddar and H. Mikhail, *J. Chem. Soc.*, **1949**, 2927. (Picric acid, naphthalene, and naphthalene picrate.)

[88] J. Metzger, *Bull. soc. chim. France*, **1949**, D466. (Fused aromatic rings.)

[89] M. Séguin, *Compt. rend.*, **228**, 839 (1949). (Diols and derivatives.)

[90] F. G. Baddar and S. Sugden, *J. Chem. Soc.*, **1950**, 308. (Nitro groups.)

[91] J. R. Lacher, R. E. Scruby, and J. D. Park, *J. Am. Chem. Soc.*, **72**, 333 (1950). (Halogen derivatives of methane.)

[92] J. R. Lacher, J. W. Pollock, W. E. Johnson, and J. D. Park, *ibid.*, **73**, 2838 (1951). (Methyl derivatives of methane and of ethylene.)

30. Miscellaneous Structural Problems

In this section there will be grouped, and mentioned briefly, a considerable number of structural problems for which susceptibility measurements have given some measure of success.

Farquharson and Sastri[93] have investigated the effect of ring closure on magnetic susceptibility. Constitutive corrections for various rings are given by Pascal, but for one reason or another their reliability has been questioned. The difference in diamagnetism between saturated cyclic compounds and corresponding saturated open chains must be due to: (a) loss of two H atoms; (b) loss of two C—H bonds; (c) formation of one C—C bond; (d) possible distortion of tetrahedral symmetry, change of C—C bond distance, etc. The change may be represented

$$\chi_{\text{cyclic}} = \chi_{\text{open}} - 2\chi_{\text{H}} + \lambda$$

Measurements were made on n-hexane, cyclopropanecarboxylic acid, cyclobutanecarboxylic acid, cyclopentanecarboxylic acid, cyclohexanecarboxylic acid, cyclohexane, cyclohexanol, cyclohexanone, and cycloheptanone. The following constitutive corrections are calculated. Reference should, however, be made to Pacault's review.[51]

Ring

| λ | 4.1 | 3.05 | − 0.98 | 0.86 |

A somewhat similar problem is ring closure by hydrogen bonding. A preliminary report on diamagnetism and the hydrogen bond has been made by Angus and Hill.[94] They have measured various concentrations of benzoic, salicylic, p- and m-hydroxybenzoic acids, and nitrophenol, in benzene, chloroform, ethanol, and ethyl acetate solutions. The results are rather inconclusive, but seem to indicate that ring-formation is attended with a decrease of diamagnetism, while open-chain addition compounds are formed with an increase of diamagnetism. The interpretation is criticized by Lonsdale and by Venkataramiah,[95] and the experimental results are somewhat at variance with those reported by Anantakrishnan and Varadachari.[96] Investigation of a substantial group of organic compounds by Rumpf and Séguin[97] seems to show that no appreciable change of molar diamagnetism occurs on formation of hydrogen bonds.

[93] J. Farquharson and M. V. C. Sastri, *Trans. Faraday Soc.*, **33**, 1474 (1937).

[94] W. R. Angus and W. K. Hill, *ibid.*, **36**, 923 (1940).

[95] H. S. Venkataramiah, *J. Mysore Univ., Sect. B, Contrib. 10 in Phys. 3, Part 4*, 19 (1942).

[96] S. V. Anantakrishnan and P. S. Varadachari, *Proc. Indian Acad. Sci.*, **20A**, 128 (1944).

[97] P. Rumpf and M. Séguin, *Bull. soc. chim. France*, **1949**, D366; **1950**, 177, 542.

Another question relates to the diminution of diamagnetism associated with unsaturation, or to put it another way, why unsaturation leads to positive Pascal correction factors. The rather remote possibility that this might be related to unpairing of electrons, giving a slight amount of paramagnetism, has been investigated by Müller.[98] Such compounds have no significant temperature coefficient of magnetic susceptibility. The same is true of cyclooctatetraene.[99]

These and related effects in conjugated structures, especially those in which resonance possibilities are great, have been investigated by Pacault.[100,101] In some cases it may be possible to relate certain physiological properties to the electron distribution as determined by magnetic measurements. The matter is more fully discussed in the next chapter.

It has been known for some time that polyhalogenated organic compounds show rather large deviations when the experimental susceptibilities are compared with those calculated from Pascal's constants. Pascal[102] himself has attributed these deviations to mutual deformation of electron clouds produced by halogens in effective contact, and he has extended his observations and explanation to a rather large group of other polyhalides, such as the chlorides of boron, phosphorus, silicon, antimony, and tin.[103] Similar observations have been made by French and Trew,[104] with a qualitative explanation of mutual polarization between halogen atoms. Lacher[105] has extended this idea into a semiquantitative method for calculating the susceptibilities of these compounds.

Magnetic measurements on p-benzoquinone, hydroquinone, and quinhydrone have been made by Mikhail and Baddar[106] and by others.[107] Their results, which are in reasonably good agreement and differ from earlier results on quinhydrone, support the resonance structure for quinone and an additive structure for hydroquinone.

Susceptibility measurements have often been used, especially by the French school, in conjunction with Pascal's constants to obtain evidence on the relative proportions of tautomers, especially of the keto-lactol type.

[98] E. Müller, Z. Elektrochem., 45, 593 (1939).
[99] F. R. M. McDonnell, R. C. Pink, and A. R. Ubbelohde, Trans. Faraday Soc., 46, 156 (1950).
[100] A. Pacault, Ann. chim., [12] 1, 527 (1946).
[101] H. Lumbroso, A. Pacault, and B. Pullman, Bull. soc. chim. France, 1950, 34. (Substituted fulvenes.)
[102] P. Pascal, Compt. rend., 217, 657 (1943).
[103] P. Pascal, ibid., 218, 57 (1944).
[104] C. M. French and V. C. G. Trew, Trans. Faraday Soc., 41, 439 (1945).
[105] J. R. Lacher, J. Am. Chem. Soc., 69, 2067 (1947).
[106] H. Mikhail and F. G. Baddar, J. Chem. Soc., 1944, 590.
[107] Sunder Lal and Noor-ul-Haq Khan, Current Sci., 13, 312 (1944).

For instance, ethyl benzoylacetate may be shown in this way to exist principally in the enol form. Pacault[108] has made such determinations for D-glucose, β-formylpropionic acid, maleic acid, opianic acid, naphthalaldehydic acid, methyl-o-benzoylbenzoate, and o-(2,5-dimethoxybenzoyl)-benzoic acid. Similar calculations and measurements have been made by Séguin[109] for the o-hydroxyquinolates, but it is not likely that such a method can compete with nuclear magnetic resonance[110] by which, as pointed out in Chapter 4, the hydrogen atoms in different molecular environments (such as in C—H or in O—H bonding) may be separately detected and estimated.

It will be recalled that the position of combined oxygen in Pascal's system is somewhat anomalous, not only because different constants have to be used for oxygen in different types of binding, but because oxygen seems to affect the constants for other atoms situated some distance away in the molecule. This difficult problem has been further studied and clarified by Pacault[111] and has also been studied with reference to heterocyclic ring-formation.[112]

Further studies on the applicability of Pascal's constants have been made by several groups. These include the work of Trinh and Séguin[113] on alkyl sulfates, that of Bonino and Manzoni-Ansidei[114] on pyrrole, thiophene, furan, thiazole, and their derivatives, and Dharmatti's study on a rather large number of sulfur, selenium, and tellurium compounds, including chlorides, acids, and some alkyl halides of these elements.[115-117] Mulay[118] has studied the susceptibilities of several isoelectronic groups of compounds. It might be expected that in such substances the susceptibility would vary as the square of the molecular radius. This appears actually to be the case for sets such as phenol, aniline, and toluene; but not the case for other sets such as antimony trichloride and thallous cyanate.

Listed below are a few of the many papers published in recent years on related topics.[119-133]

[108] A. Pacault and Buu-Hoï, *J. phys. radium*, **6**, 277 (1945).

[109] M. Séguin, *Bull. soc. chim. France*, **1946**, 566.

[110] H. S. Jarrett, M. S. Sadler, and J. N. Shoolery, *J. Chem. Phys.*, **21**, 2092 (1953).

[111] A. Pacault, *Compt. rend.*, **22**, 1089 (1946).

[112] B. K. Singh, K. M. S. Manhas, S. L. Aggarwal, Noorul Haq, and Mahan Singh, *Proc. Indian Acad. Sci.*, **22A**, 163 (1945).

[113] Nguyen-Quang-Trinh and M. Séguin, *Compt. rend.*, **226**, 334 (1948).

[114] G. B. Bonino and R. Manzoni-Ansidei, *Ber.*, **76**, 553 (1943).

[115] S. S. Dharmatti, *Proc. Indian Acad. Sci.*, **13A**, 359 (1941).

[116] M. Prasad and S. S. Dharmatti, *ibid.*, **12A**, 185 (1940).

[117] S. S. Dharmatti, *ibid.*, **12A**, 212 (1940).

[118] L. N. Mulay, *ibid.*, **34A**, 245 (1951).

[119] I. Kadomtzeff, *Bull. soc. chim. France*, **1949**, D394. (Alkyl tin, lead, and mercury compounds.)

According to Pascal's method, the susceptibilities of the diamagnetic anhydrous salts should equal those of the same atomic groups in hydrates or in solution. Measurements by Pascal, Pacault, and Jamet[134] on a considerable number of chlorates, bromates, and iodates show that this is so. But considerable deviations are reported by Prasad et al.[135] for several sulfates, halides, and related salts.

In an earlier chapter it was pointed out that small, highly charged, dissolved ions probably exert a measurable influence on the susceptibility of water. Prasad et al.[136] have found that for a series of hydrated borates the observed diamagnetic susceptibility is generally appreciably greater than the sum of susceptibilities obtained for the anhydrous salt plus the appropriate number of water molecules. The same is apparently true of adsorbed water as, for instance, on silica gel.[137] It should be mentioned, in this connection, that nuclear magnetic resonance is likely to solve many problems concerning crystalline hydrates and adsorbed water.[138]

The question of phototropy and photochemical isomerism has been studied from the magnetic standpoint by Bhatnagar, Kapur, and Hashmi.[139]

[120] P. Pascal, A. Pacault, and T. Tchakirian, Compt. rend., 226, 849 (1948). (Organo-germanium compounds.)

[121] M. Prasad, C. R. Kanekar, and L. N. Mulay, J. Chem. Phys., 19, 1051, 1440 (1951); 20, 201 (1952). (Inorganic and organic arsenic, antimony, and bismuth.)

[122] A. Neiding and I. A. Kazarnovskii, Zhur. Fiz. Khim., 26, 1167 (1952). (Hydrogen peroxide.)

[123] J. R. Lacher, J. W. Pollock, and J. D. Park, J. Chem. Phys., 20, 1047 (1952). (Cyclopropane and other 3-membered rings.)

[124] M. Prasad, C. R. Kanekar, and L. S. Kamat, J. Phys. & Colloid Chem., 55, 1534 (1951). (Boron compounds.)

[125] D. Voigt, Ann. chim., 4, 393 (1949). (Esters of sulfur and phosphorus acids.)

[126] H. Mikhail, J. Chem. Phys., 21, 1004 (1953). (Nitroanilines.)

[127] G. Sauret and R. Lalande, Compt. rend., 236, 2066 (1953). (Nitriles.)

[128] R. Perceau, ibid., 236, 76 (1953). (Amino acids.)

[129] C. M. French, Trans. Faraday Soc., 47, 1056 (1951). (Pyridine and homologs.)

[130] R. Perceau, Compt. rend., 239, 170 (1954). (Organic fluorine.)

[131] U. Croatto, A. Fava, and V. Scatturin, Gazz. chim. ital., 82, 552 (1952). (Inorganic polysulfides.)

[132] A. Fava and A. Iliceto, Ann. chim., 43, 509 (1953). (Organic polysulfides.)

[133] A. Pacault and Ch. Marschalk, Bull. soc. chim. France, 1952, 141. (Organic sulfides.)

[134] P. Pascal, A. Pacault, and C. Jamet, ibid., 1948, 324.

[135] M. Prasad, S. S. Dharmatti, and N. S. Birdar, Current Sci. (India), 17, 324 (1948).

[136] M. Prasad, C. R. Kanekar, and L. S. Kamat, J. Chem. Phys., 19, 686 (1951).

[137] W. O. Milligan and H. B. Whitehurst, J. Phys. Chem., 56, 1073 (1952).

[138] G. E. Pake, J. chim. phys., 50, C 104 (1953); this is one of several papers presented before a symposium on this topic of structure in crystalline hydrates.

[139] S. S. Bhatnagar, P. L. Kapur, and M. S. Hashmi, J. Indian Chem. Soc., 15, 573 (1938).

They investigated 23 organic compounds which undergo reversible phototropic changes on exposure to light. In most cases there was no change of magnetic susceptibility, but thiophosgene and cinnamylidenemalonic acid showed definite changes. For the former, for instance, the original red substance had a susceptibility of -0.4401×10^{-6}, while after exposure to light the white compound had a susceptibility of -0.3914×10^{-6}. No evidence was obtained, however, for a paramagnetic free biradical,

$$S-C\underset{\vdots\quad\vdots}{\diagdown}\overset{Cl}{\underset{Cl}{}}$$

as an intermediate product. From what is now known about biradicals, the formation of such a compound as that above is improbable. The authors lean to the "change of aggregation" theory as responsible for the change of color. Other theories are discussed. Other magnetic studies of reversible phototropic change have been made on 4-hydroxy-α-naphthyliminocamphor,[140] and on p-dimethylamino- and p-diethylaminophenyliminocamphor,[141] and related compounds.[142] The possible presence of free radicals in phototropic and thermotropic changes lends itself to study by the method of paramagnetic resonance. This will be referred to again in a later chapter.

Diamagnetic susceptibilities have had some application to reaction mechanisms, including products and velocities. Savithri[143] has studied the reaction $AsBr_3 + Br_2 \rightarrow AsBr_5$. The possibility of studying such reaction *in situ* has been pointed out by Spencer.[144] The applicability of such methods is, however, much less than in corresponding studies on paramagnetic substances.

The change of diamagnetism on the death of living cells is discussed by Bauer and Raskin.[145] Bauer has suggested that life depends on an excited state of protein molecules in the protoplasm. Hence, on death the paramagnetic component of susceptibility should diminish. Actually in yeast cells and in certain bacteria, (*B. coli* and *B. proteus*), an increase of diamagnetism amounting to 4% was found. This change is independent of the way the cells are killed. Cooling with liquid air produced the same effect. Denaturation of native protein did not affect the magnetic susceptibility. If these observations can be substantiated, they suggest an approach to a very fundamental problem. This, and the possibility that

[140] M. Singh and A. Singh, *ibid.*, **17**, 604 (1940).
[141] M. Singh and T. R. Datt, *ibid.*, **19**, 130 (1942).
[142] S. L. Aggarwal and M. Singh, *Proc. Lahore Phil. Soc.*, **6**, 24 (1944).
[143] K. Savithri, *Proc. Indian Acad. Sci.*, **16A**, 196 (1942).
[144] J. F. Spencer, *J. Soc. Chem. Ind.*, **50**, 37T (1931).
[145] E. Bauer and A. Raskin, *Nature*, **138**, 801 (1936).

such changes, if they are real, are due to free-radical formation in the living cell are additional areas in which paramagnetic resonance techniques may be expected to yield noteworthy results.

31. Magnetic Studies on Polymerization

The dimerization of free radicals and of other paramagnetic molecules has been one of the most fruitful fields for magnetochemical research.   But another field, the polymerization of diamagnetic molecules, has received comparatively little attention.   Work in this area has been done by Farquharson[146] who has shown that in some cases magnetic measurements may be used to determine the degree of polymerization.

When polymerization takes place between two molecules $2B \rightarrow B_2$, the molar susceptibility of the dimer $\chi_M = 2\chi_B + \lambda$, where λ is Pascal's

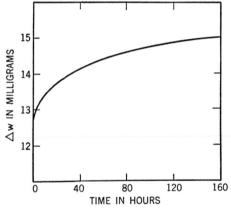

Fig. 52. Polymerization of 2,3-dimethylbutadiene; apparent change in weight on application of the magnetic field *versus* time.

constitutive constant for the formation of a new bond.   If n molecules react to form B_n, then $\chi_M = n\chi_B + (n-1)\lambda$, and the relationship between χ_M and n will be a straight line.   The mass susceptibility of the complex is

$$\chi = \frac{n\chi_B + (n-1)\lambda}{nM_B}$$

where M_B is the molecular weight of the monomer.   The curve for change of χ with n will then be a hyperbola.   For certain compounds, notably 2,3-dimethylbutadiene, this is actually the case.   If something is known regarding the mode of formation of the polymer, λ may be estimated from

[146] J. Farquharson, *Trans. Faraday Soc.*, **32**, 219 (1936).

Pascal's data. Hence, by measurements of susceptibility it is possible to find n, the number of molecules in the polymer. Where n is not large, its value may be found with considerable accuracy. Farquharson's results for 2,3-dimethylbutadiene are shown in Fig. 52. The initial susceptibility of the monomer is -0.670×10^{-6} and the final, after polymerization, -0.7305×10^{-6}. The general shape of the curve is consistent with other evidence as to the course of polymerization.

Another compound investigated is cyclopentadiene, the susceptibility of which changes from -0.717×10^{-6} to -0.680×10^{-6} after $41\frac{1}{2}$ hours of heating. Whether the change of diamagnetism on polymerization is positive or negative depends, of course, on the nature of the bonds ruptured and formed during the reaction. Results are also given by Farquharson for cyanogen chloride and for nitrosobenzene.

A further investigation by Farquharson[147] has been made on the mechanism of formation of polyoxymethylenes. The formula previously given for the mass susceptibility of the complex may also be written

$$\chi = \frac{\chi_B + (n-1)\chi_c}{nM_B}$$

where χ_c is the susceptibility of the group which is added each time to give the next higher polymeride. This is true because λ, the constitutive bond correction, is simply $\chi_c - \chi_B$. In a homologous series, nM_B becomes $M_B + (n-1)M_c$ where M_B is the molecular weight of the first member of the series, and M_c the molecular weight of the added group. The mass susceptibilities of a homologous series are then given by

$$\chi = \frac{\chi_B + (n-1)\chi_c}{M_B + (n-1)M_c}$$

Hence, for polymerization proceeding by regular addition of a known group, it should be possible to estimate n from magnetic data. Farquharson has determined the Pascal constant of the $-CH_2O-$ group as -14.9×10^{-6} from measurements on the oxymethylene diacetates. The mass susceptibility of the $-CH_2O-$ group is then -0.496×10^{-6}.

If the polyoxymethylenes are long chains of the form

$$H-O-CH_2-O-CH_2-O-CH_2-O \cdots CH_2OH$$

made up of many $-CH_2O-$ units, then with increasing polymerization the susceptibility should approach the value -0.496×10^{-6}. Good (to whom reference is made by Farquharson) has measured the magnetic susceptibilities of several polyoxymethylenes and obtained the values shown in Table VIII. Farquharson concludes from these data that only the α- and

[147] J. Farquharson, *ibid.*, **33**, 824 (1937).

TABLE VIII
Magnetic Susceptibilities of Polyoxymethylenes

	$-\chi \times 10^6$
α-Polyoxymethylene	0.503
β-Polyoxymethylene	0.501
γ-Polyoxymethylene	0.467
δ-Polyoxymethylene	0.417

β-polyoxymethylenes are long-chain compounds of this type, and that the others are probably fundamentally different. Estimates of the number of molecules in the polymer give for the α-polyoxymethylene, $n = 32$; for the β, $n = 44$.

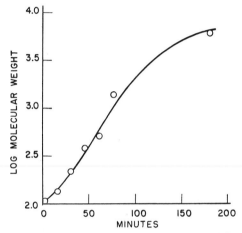

Fig. 53. Average molecular weights in polymerizing methyl methacrylate, obtained from susceptibility measurements.

A change of diamagnetism has also been reported for polymerizing vinyl acetate by Tanaevsky.[148] She finds that polymerization induced by exposure to ultraviolet light in vacuum leads to an increase of diamagnetism from -46.4 to -47.6 ($\times 10^{-6}$) calculated as susceptibility per mole of monomer. In the presence of oxygen the susceptibility remains virtually constant over long periods of time.

Bedwell[149] has used Farquharson's relation, given above, in an attempt to obtain average molecular weights in polymerizing methyl methacrylate. The reaction was catalyzed by benzoyl peroxide at 80°C., samples being removed from time to time for magnetic measurements. The results,

[148] O. Tanaevsky, *Compt. rend.*, **225**, 1069 (1947).
[149] M. E. Bedwell, *J. Chem. Soc.*, **1947**, 1350.

shown in Fig. 53, are in good agreement with those obtained by Bedwell by magneto-optical rotation, and seem to be in fair agreement with molecular weights obtained on systems under similar conditions by other methods. It will be noted, however, that the accuracy drops rapidly with increasing molecular weight. The small differences of susceptibilities encountered and the effects of isomerism, hydrogen bonding, and impurities make it seem unlikely that the magnetic methods can compete with standard procedures in polymer chemistry. There are, to be discussed later, some magnetic methods which have unique advantages in the study of polymers and polymerization, but the determination of molecular weights does not seem to be one of them. Equally pessimistic conclusions have been reached by Pacault and Souchay[150] with respect to the use of susceptibility methods in the study of *iso*-poly and *hetero*-poly acids and salts of phosphorus, vanadium, molybdenum, and tungsten; and by Hoarau[151] who studied monomers and polymers of cyclopentadiene, 2,3-dimethyl-1,3-butadiene, styrene, and methyl methacrylate.

Other diamagnetic dimerizing or polymerizing systems which have been studied include anthracene, anthracene derivatives,[151a] benzaldehyde, furfural, acetylcyanide,[152-154] polyindene,[155] cyanamide,[156] and persulfate ion.[157] A few papers have appeared on the magnetic properties of silicones.[158-160] Efforts have been made to draw conclusions about the degree of ionic character in the bonded silicon, but Pacault points out that not enough is yet known about the magnetic behavior of silicon in these substances to warrant much confidence in the results. Other magnetic studies of polymerization, involving actual or suspected paramagnetic components, are described in Chapter XI.

It should be mentioned that applications of techniques in nuclear

[150] A. Pacault and P. Souchay, *Bull. soc. chim. France*, **1949**, D377.

[151] J. Hoarau, *Bull. soc. chim. France*, **1950**, 1153.

[151a] R. Calas, J. Hoarau, R. Lalande, and A. Pacault, *Compt., rend.*, **241**, 407 (1955).

[152] S. S. Bhatnagar, M. B. Nevgi, and R. N. Mathur, *Z. Physik*, **100**, 141 (1936).

[153] S. S. Bhatnagar, P. L. Kapur, and G. Kaur, *J. Indian Acad. Sci.*, **10A**, 468 (1939).

[154] J. Farquharson and M. V. C. Sastri, *Current Sci. (India)*, **9**, 135 (1940).

[155] W. Schutzner, *Nature*, **164**, 364 (1949).

[156] J. Ploquin and C. Vergneau-Souvray, *Compt. rend.*, **234**, 97 (1952).

[157] P. Pascal, C. Duval, J. Lecomte, and A. Pacault, *ibid.*, **233**, 118 (1951).

[158] K. Asai, *Science Repts. Research Insts., Tôhoku Imp. Univ.*, **2**, 205 (1950).

[159] A. Pacault, *Compt. rend.*, **232**, 1352 (1951).

[160] K. Abe and M. Toyoda, *Bull. Inst. Chem. Research, Kyoto Univ.*, **25**, 59 (1951); the original of this paper was not available to the author.

magnetism offer considerable promise of new structural knowledge in the field of polymers as well as in other branches of chemistry.[161,161a]

32. Molecular Mixtures

The magnetic susceptibility of a mixture may in general be represented by Wiedemann's additivity law

$$\chi = \chi_1 p_1 + \chi_2 p_2 + \ldots \chi_n p_n$$

where χ is the susceptibility of the mixture; χ_n, p_n, are susceptibilities and weight fractions respectively for the components.

For mechanical mixtures this law is obeyed closely; but for solid solutions containing paramagnetic ions the law may bear no relation to reality. Our concern at the moment is with liquid diamagnetic mixtures, over which considerable controversy has raged. Reviews in this field have been published by van Aubel,[162] Stoner,[163] von Rautenfeld and Steurer,[164] and Angus and Tilston.[165] The last named have examined the data on 69 binary mixtures for which susceptibility data are available. Other published work in the same field includes that of Venkatamaran[166] on pyridine-acetic acid mixtures; and of Hatem[167] for mixtures of several alcohols and cyclic amines. One of the most careful studies of this problem is that of Seely,[168] who investigated binary combinations of carbon tetrachloride, benzene, and nitrobenzene. The mixture benzene-nitrobenzene is reported as showing no deviations within the experimental error, but the other two mixtures apparently show deviations amounting to over 0.5%.

These results and a large proportion of all other results listed above have been subjected to careful study by Angus and Tilston,[165] who have examined the effect of various types of errors on the published data. Their viewpoint is enlightening. They conclude that the real magnitude of any supposed deviations from linearity cannot be readily ascertained on the basis of published data. Many rather small, and apparently consistent, deviations are shown to be due to experimental errors, or to errors in the method of computation. There are, of course, some cases in which un-

---

[161] E. M. Purcell, *Science*, 107, 433 (1948).

[161a] V. R. Honnold, F. McCaffrey, and B. A. Mrowca, *J. Applied Phys.*, 25, 1219 (1954).

[162] E. van Aubel, *Nature*, 128, 455 (1931).

[163] E. C. Stoner, *Magnetism and Matter*. Methuen and Company, Ltd., London, 1934, p. 474.

[164] F. von Rautenfeld and E. Steurer, *Z. physik. chem.*, B51, 39 (1941).

[165] W. R. Angus and D. V. Tilston, *Trans. Faraday Soc.*, 43, 221 (1947).

[166] S. Venkatamaran, *J. Indian Chem. Soc.*, 17, 297 (1940).

[167] S. Hatem, *Compt. rend.*, 225, 296, 332 (1947).

[168] S. Seely, *Phys. Rev.*, 49, 812 (1936).

doubted deviations from linearity occur. Such deviations are measures of chemical or physical reaction in the mixture. It may then be concluded that deviations from linearity in mixtures of diamagnetic liquids are, in general, not large; and that where obvious chemical or physical changes take place, some deviations may occur.

Recent studies of the use of susceptibilities as an analytical tool have been made by Kronig[169] on mixtures of saturated hydrocarbons; by Pacault and Seris[170] on a large group of alcohol mixtures; by Bennett, Pritchard, and Simonsen[171] on dinitrobenzanthrone and related compounds, and by Broersma[172] on saturated hydrocarbons and various other organic compounds. Such studies are based on the assumption that the additivity law is obeyed, as is presumably the case in such applications.

On the other hand, deviations from additivity have been used to study the structure of molecular compounds formed in binary mixtures of nitrobenzenes and nitrochlorobenzenes together with a group of hydrocarbons, phenols, and amines.[173,174] Similar studies have been made on alcohol-cyclic amine mixtures,[175] and formaldehyde solutions.[176]

Acids and acid-water solutions have been studied by Frivold and Olsen[177] and by Pacault and Chédin.[178] For slightly ionized and for strongly ionized acids, it might be expected that the susceptibilities would be linear with concentration, and this appears to be the case. But as the proton has a zero susceptibility, it appears that ionized acids should have the same susceptibility as the molecular form except for possible slight distorting effects produced by the proton on its environment. Thus Pacault finds that acid-water mixtures in general follow the additivity law. His results for formic acid are in sharp disagreement with those reported by Yang[179] who, probably erroneously, found the water to change its susceptibility sharply with changing acid-water concentration.

The diamagnetism of phosphorus in solution has been studied by Rao and Aravumathachari.[180] They examined solid white phosphorus and

[169] R. Kronig, *Bull. soc. chim. belges*, **57**, 182 (1948).

[170] N. Pacault and G. Seris, *Compt. rend.*, **224**, 1353 (1947).

[171] D. J. Bennett, R. R. Pritchard, and J. L. Simonsen, *J. Chem. Soc.*, **1943**, 31.

[172] S. Broersma, *J. Chem. Phys.*, **17**, 873 (1949).

[173] R. C. Sahney, S. L. Aggarwal, and M. Singh, *J. Indian Chem. Soc.*, **23**, 335 (1946).

[174] B. Puri, R. C. Sahney, M. Singh, and S. Singh, *ibid.*, **24**, 409 (1947).

[175] S. Hatem, *Bull. soc. chim. France*, **1949**, 599, 601.

[176] R. Sauterey, *Compt. rend.*, **229**, 884 (1949).

[177] O. E. Frivold and N. G. Olsen, *Avhandl. Norske Videnskaps-Akad. Oslo I. Mat.-Naturv. Klasse*, **1944**, No. 7, 30 pp. (1945).

[178] A. Pacault and J. Chédin, *Bull. soc. chim. France*, **1950**, 766.

[179] Tai-Yuan Yang, *J. Chem. Phys.*, **19**, 647 (1951).

[180] S. R. Rao and S. Aravamuthachari, *Proc. Indian Acad. Sci.*, **12A**, 361 (1940).

solutions of phosphorus in carbon disulfide ranging from 3 to 22% by weight. The susceptibility of the solutions is greater than that calculated from the additivity law.

The diamagnetism of iodine solutions of various colors has been studied by Courty[181] who finds that violet and brown solutions of iodine in organic solvents obey the additivity rule, while red and red-brown solutions do not. Iodine dissolved in cyclohexane is reported to have a much smaller diamagnetic susceptibility than it has in other solvents, such as benzene.[182] This appears to be true of other halogens as well.[183]

Diamagnetic solid solutions have been less thoroughly investigated. An example of such studies is to be found in the work of Nikol'skaya and Regel on the systems containing mercuric sulfide, selenide and telluride.[183a]

[181] C. Courty, *Bull. soc. chim. France, Mém.*, **5**, 84 (1938).

[182] S. S. Bhatnagar and C. L. Lakra, *Indian J. Phys.*, **8**, 43 (1933).

[183] S. R. Rao and S. R. Govindarajan, *Proc. Indian Acad. Sci.*, **15A**, 35 (1942).

[183a] E. I. Nikol'skaya and A. R. Regel, *Zhur. Tekh. Fiz.*, **25**, 1347 (1955).

CHAPTER SEVEN

MOLECULAR DIAMAGNETIC ANISOTROPY

33. Principal Molecular Susceptibilities

In crystals of low symmetry, there are three mutually perpendicular directions known as the axes of principal magnetism. The magnetic susceptibilities along these axes are called principal susceptibilities. Cubic crystalline matter is isotropic, but if a sample of noncubic matter is suspended in a magnetic field, it will tend to orientate so that the axis of maximum (algebraic) susceptibility in the plane of rotation lies along the lines of force. In orthogonal crystals, the axes of principal susceptibility coincide with the crystal axes. In the monoclinic system, one principal magnetic axis coincides with the symmetry axis of the crystals.

The additivity of average susceptibilities of organic compounds shows that, even in the solid state, the mutual influence of neighboring molecules on the magnetic susceptibility must be negligible. (This is not always true for paramagnetic substances.) It follows that the anisotropy of a single crystal must be due to the anisotropy of the unit cell, and that this, in turn, depends only on the resultant anisotropy of the individual molecules in the cell. If the molecule is essentially magnetically isotropic, then the crystal will show little or no anisotropy. But if the molecule is anisotropic, then the resultant anisotropy of the crystal depends only on the relative orientation of the molecules. If the molecules are arranged in layers, then the resultant crystal anisotropy will be large, but if the molecules are arranged haphazardly, or so that their anisotropies cancel each other, then the crystal will be isotropic.

Determination of principal susceptibilities in the crystal is a useful tool in structural chemistry. This is particularly true for aromatic compounds, which often show striking magnetic anisotropy. The information obtainable from magnetic data sometimes simplifies determination of crystal structures by x-ray methods. The anisotropy which is observed experimentally is due, first, to the anisotropy of the individual molecules, and second, to their orientation in the crystal. If any two of these properties is known, or can be estimated, the third can be found, except in crystal classes of high symmetry.

The largest diamagnetic anisotropies are shown by graphite and by aromatic compounds whose molecules contain benzene, cyanuric or phthalocyanic rings. Carbon in the cubic (diamond) form is isotropic with a gram-atomic susceptibility of -6×10^{-6}. But the principal susceptibility in graphite parallel to the hexagonal axis (perpendicular to the rings) is about -260×10^{-6} per gram-atom of carbon. This is over 40 times greater than the diamagnetism normal to the hexagonal axis.

It is believed that this very large diamagnetism along the hexagonal axis is, at least in part, due to one free electron per carbon atom, and that this electron is free in the basal plane but highly restricted in the perpendicular direction. Each layer of carbon atoms may be thought of as a giant aromatic molecule. This interpretation is based on the fundamental concept of the resonance theory as applied to such substances.

It was first observed by Raman and Krishnan[1] that the principal susceptibility of benzene normal to the plane of the ring is more than twice that in the plane. In the following discussion, relations will be developed between the principal *molar* susceptibilities, χ_1, χ_2, χ_3, as found experimentally on single crystals, and the principal *molecular* susceptibilities, K_1, K_2, K_3, which refer to the magnetic properties of the single molecule. For naphthalene and anthracene, the principal molar susceptibilities are:

Principal Molar Susceptibilities ($\times 10^6$) for Single Crystals

	$-\chi_1$	$-\chi_2$	$-\chi_3$
Naphthalene	56.0	146.4	76.6
Anthracene	75.5	211.8	102.9

For many organic compounds, the complete structure has been determined by x-ray diffraction studies, and the orientations of the molecules in the unit cell are known. It is possible to deduce the principal molecular susceptibilities from the principal molar susceptibilities and the molecular direction cosines. Principal molecular susceptibilities for naphthalene and anthracene are shown below:

Principal Molecular Susceptibilities ($\times 10^6$)

	$-K_1$	$-K_2$	$-K_3$
Naphthalene	56.1	53.9	169.0
Anthracene	75.8	62.6	251.8

An example of these calculations will be given below. Interpretation of magnetic anisotropy in terms of crystal structure is due to Krishnan[2,3] and to Lonsdale.[4,5] The example will be naphthalene.

[1] C. V. Raman and K. S. Krishnan, *Proc. Roy. Soc. (London)*, **A113**, 511 (1927).

[2] K. S. Krishnan, *Nature*, **130**, 313, 698 (1932).

[3] K. S. Krishnan, B. C. Guha, and S. Banerjee, *Phil. Trans. Roy. Soc. (London)*, **A231**, 235 (1933).

[4] K. Lonsdale and K. S. Krishnan, *Proc. Roy. Soc. (London)*, **A156**, 597 (1936).

[5] K. Lonsdale, *ibid.*, **A159**, 149 (1937).

Naphthalene belongs to the monoclinic class. The crystalline and magnetic axes of a monoclinic crystal are shown in Fig. 54, and Fig. 55 shows the relation of a naphthalene molecule to these axes. Two of the principal magnetic axes lie in the (010) or ac plane; the magnetic susceptibilities along these axes are χ_1 and χ_2. The angle ψ which the χ_1 axis makes with the c-axis of the crystal, taken as positive toward the obtuse angle β

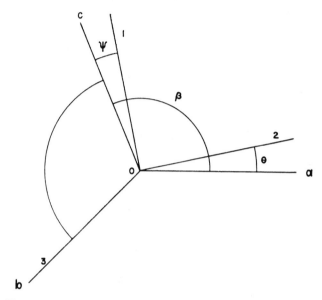

Fig. 54. Principal crystal (a,b,c) and magnetic (1,2,3) axes in a monoclinic crystal.

between the c- and a-axes, determines the positions of the two magnetic axes. The angle θ is connected with ψ by the relation $90° + \theta + \psi =$ obtuse β. The third magnetic axis is along the b-axis and the susceptibility along it is χ_3.

X-ray studies show that the unit cell of naphthalene contains two molecules, for each of which the structure is plane. Both molecules have their lengths, the lines which join centers of constituent rings, almost in the (010) plane, making an angle of 12° with the c-axis. Considerations of symmetry show that the long axis of the naphthalene molecule must be one of its magnetic axes. The above direction in the crystal is expected to be one of the magnetic axes of the crystal. Direct observation of the magnetic axes confirms this view, and the angle ψ is actually found to be 12°. The other two magnetic axes are along the breadth of the molecule in the plane of the rings, and along the normal to the plane of the rings, respectively.

X-ray studies show that the planes of the molecules are inclined at $+65°$ and $-65°$, respectively, to the (010) plane. This completes all the information necessary to find the principal molecular susceptibilities.

$$\chi_1 = K_1$$
$$\chi_2 = K_2 \cos^2 65° + K_3 \sin^2 65°$$
$$\chi_3 = K_2 \sin^2 65° + K_3 \cos^2 65°$$

Substituting the experimentally determined values for χ', χ_2, χ_3, the numerical values for K_1, K_2, K_3 given above are obtained.

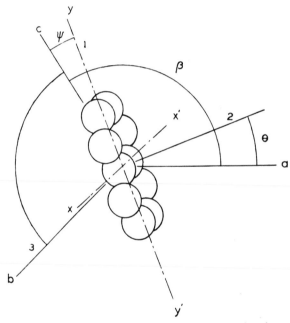

Fig. 55. Position of naphthalene molecule relative to crystal and magnetic axes.

34. Theories of Aromatic Anisotropy

It was mentioned above that the large diamagnetic anisotropy shown by graphite and by aromatic compounds is related to a certain freedom of electron motion in the rings. Several authors, including Hückel[6] and Pauling,[7] have developed an explanation by means of the hypothesis that in aromatic compounds the diamagnetic currents are not limited as or-

[6] E. Hückel, Z. Physik, **83**, 632 (1933).
[7] L. Pauling, J. Chem. Phys., **4**, 673 (1936).

dinarily to individual atoms, but circulate from one atom to another in relatively extended orbits, as around the rings of aromatic compounds.

A very simple and instructive calculation of these extended orbit radii may be made, using Langevin's relation (p. 70):

$$\chi_A = -2.832 \sum \bar{r}^2 \times 10^{10}$$

Thus the average effective radius of the *normal* valence electrons in benzene and its derivatives, calculated from principal susceptibilities parallel to the rings, is 0.70 to 0.78 A., which is in reasonable agreement with the atomic radii found from x-ray studies. But normal to the molecular plane, the susceptibility indicates an average effective radius of the π electrons, which take part in conjugation, as being 1.5 to 1.6 A. in the single benzene nucleus, and rising to 5.3 A. in the inner phthalocyanine nucleus, and to about 7.8 A. in graphite. This corresponds to an average orbital area, in the graphite layers, equal to about 30 benzene nuclei. The condensed aromatic ring compounds are more strongly diamagnetic than would be expected from a strict additivity rule, but the average orbital area in the plane of the molecule corresponds to a value between the area of the single benzene nucleus and that of the whole condensed nucleus. This is as if a large proportion of the π electrons were occupying orbits equal in area to the single benzene ring, with only a few occupying larger orbits.

Pauling's semi-empirical theory of magnetic anisotropy in aromatic systems is easy to understand and is helpful in obtaining a grasp of the subject. Elements of his theory are as follows: of the 42 electrons in benzene, only six give an abnormally large and anisotropic contribution to the susceptibility. Calculations by quantum mechanics show that the probability-distribution function for these electrons is large only in two ring-shaped regions, one above and one below the carbon hexagon. The contribution of an electron to the susceptibility is given by the Pauli expression $\chi_M = -(Ne^2/4mc^2)(\rho^2)_{av}$ where $(\rho^2)_{av}$ is the mean square of the distance of the electron from an axis passing perpendicularly through the nucleus. On the basis of the assumed electron distribution one may use for $(\rho^2)_{av}$ the square of the distance from the hexagonal axis of the molecule to the carbon nuclei, or $(1.39 \text{ A.})^2$. This gives the desired large diamagnetism along the axis perpendicular to the plane of the molecule, and a calculated anisotropy of -49.2×10^{-6} per mole as compared with the experimental value of -54×10^{-6}. Applied to fused ring hydrocarbons, Pauling's method is equivalent to calculating the magnetic effect of the currents induced in a conducting network possessing the form and dimensions of the molecule.

A comprehensive, quantitative theory of diamagnetic anisotropy in aromatic compounds, based on the above qualitative hypothesis, has been given by London.[8-10] London's theory may be said to be reasonably satisfactory, but there is a difficulty. It is important to note that the existence of a large diamagnetic susceptibility normal to the plane of the conjugated bonds applies to open chains as well as to aromatic rings and is, therefore, not dependent on the existence of closed rings. In view of this difficulty, and others, several attempts have been made to place the calculations on a more satisfactory basis. This interest has been stimulated in part by developments in connection with the physiological activity of certain hydrocarbons, and to a greater degree by interest in the processes by which carbonaceous matter may be progressively converted by heat to coke and to graphite. In particular, molecular-orbital methods have been examined by McWeeny[11] and others.[12] Reference to some of the results, which are on the whole satisfactory, will be made in later sections.

35. Structural Information from Principal Susceptibilities

In this section there will be surveyed the chief applications of diamagnetic molecular anisotropy to structural chemistry. Graphite and the general subject of high polymers will be discussed in later sections.

Previously, it was shown that principal molecular susceptibilities may be obtained from principal molar susceptibilities and some knowledge of the unit cell structure. Conversely, if the principal molecular susceptibilities are known or can be estimated, and if the anisotropy of the crystal is measured, it is then possible in favorable cases to find the arrangement of molecules in the unit cell. In other words, the magnetic anisotropy may sometimes be used for a complete structure determination. More often, the anisotropy is of use in simplifying structural determinations by x rays.

Biphenyl will be chosen as an example to illustrate the type of calculation in which the anisotropy is used to find the orientation of molecules in the unit cell. It will be assumed that the rings in biphenyl have the same structure as in benzene and that the molecule is planar. The average (powder) molar susceptibility of biphenyl is -102.9×10^{-6}, which is numerically less than twice that of benzene by 7.7×10^{-6}. This difference is obviously the contribution of the two hydrogen atoms which have been dropped. As a first approximation, it is assumed that this diminution is the same along the three principal axes of the molecule. The principal

[8] F. London, *J. phys. radium*, **8**, 397 (1937).

[9] F. London, *J. Chem. Phys.*, **5**, 837 (1937).

[10] H. Brooks, *ibid.*, **8**, 939 (1940); **9**, 463 (1941).

[11] R. McWeeny, *Proc. Phys. Soc. (London)*, **64A**, 261, 921 (1951); **65A**, 839 (1952); **66A**, 714 (1953).

[12] M. Mayot, G. Berthier, and B. Pullman, *J. phys. radium*, **12**, 652, 717 (1951); **13**, 15 (1952); *J. chim. phys.*, **50**, 176 (1953).

susceptibilities for the benzene molecule are $K_1 = -37.3$, $K_2 = -37.3$, $K_3 = -91.2$ ($\times 10^{-6}$). There is then obtained for the principal molecular susceptibilities of biphenyl:

$$K_1 = K_2 = -(2 \times 37.3) + 7.7 = -66.9 \ (\times 10^{-6})$$
$$K_3 = -(2 \times 91.2) + 7.7 = -174.7$$

The principal molar susceptibilities for the biphenyl crystal are

$$\chi_1 = -63.4 \times 10^{-6}$$
$$\chi_2 = -146.5$$
$$\chi_3 = -98.9$$

and the angle ψ is 20.1°.

There are two molecules in the unit cell. Place both molecules with their planes parallel to (100) and their lengths along the c-axis. To bring the molecules to their actual orientations, they are given the following rotations:

First, a rotation about the c-axis of one of the molecules through an angle λ, and of the other through an angle $-\lambda$.

Second, a rotation of both molecules about the b-axis through an angle ζ, the positive direction of the rotation being defined as from the c-axis to the a-axis, through the obtuse angle β.

Third, a rotation of the molecules through $+\nu$ and $-\nu$ respectively, about the normal to the plane which contains the b-axis and the direction of lengths of the molecules after the second rotation has been performed.

It is clear that $\zeta = \psi = +20.1°$, and λ and ν can be obtained from the following relationships:

$$\chi_1 = K_1 \cos^2 \nu + (K_2 \cos^2 \lambda + K_3 \sin^2 \lambda) \sin^2 \nu$$
$$\chi_2 = K_2 \sin^2 \lambda + K_3 \cos^2 \lambda$$
$$\chi_3 = K_1 \sin^2 \nu + (K_2 \cos^2 \lambda + K_3 \sin^2 \lambda) \cos^2 \nu$$

It has already been assumed that $\chi_2 + \chi_2 + \chi_3 = K_1 + K_2 + K_3$; therefore, only two of the above relationships are independent.

Solving, it is found that

$$\lambda = 31°, \qquad \nu = 0°$$

The lengths of the molecules lie in the (010) plane in the obtuse angle β at 20.1° to the c-axis, while the planes of the molecules are inclined at plus and minus 31°, respectively, to the b-axis. This structure determination is confirmed by x-ray analysis ($\psi = 20°$, $\lambda = 32°$, $\nu = 0°$).

In the above analysis, there have been evaluated the principal molecular susceptibilities from structure considerations which may not be applicable for molecules more complicated than biphenyl. In such cases it may be possible to obtain the molecular susceptibilities from measurements of magneto-optical rotation, according to methods described by Raman and Krishnan.[13]

The structural determination given for biphenyl is, unfortunately, not generally applicable to organic solids. The simplicity of the derivation comes from the special case of $\nu \approx 0$. For other classes of substances, the information obtainable from magnetic anisotropy is often less, but any aid from such a source is welcome if it lessens the labor of complete structural determinations from x-ray data. The general applicability of the magnetic method is described by Lonsdale and Krishnan,[4,5] from whose publications this material is taken. It may be summarized as follows: In the triclinic system, magnetic anisotropy measurements give the molecular orientations directly; in the monoclinic and orthorhombic systems, the magnetic method is of aid in structural determinations, especially so in a few cases; in crystals of high symmetry, the magnetic measurements are of little or no use.

Principal susceptibilities have been obtained for a substantial number of aromatic compounds. But a general understanding of all the phenomena encountered is still incomplete. For instance, the substitution of resonating groups, such as nitro, in the benzene ring leads to anisotropies somewhat difficult to understand.[14] It will be clear also that further development of the idea of Pascal's constants must take the molecular anisotropy into account. A step in this direction has been made by Pacault.[15]

The carbonate and carboxyl groups have molar anisotropies of the order of 5×10^{-6}. This is quite small as compared with the anisotropies of benzene or especially of graphite, but it is indicative of resonance broadening of electron orbits in the plane of the group. Most of the work on this field and on the substances described below has been done by Krishnan[16,17] and by Lonsdale.[4,5,35,37-40]

Aliphatic compounds show quite different magnetic properties, depending on whether or not they possess double bonds. Even when there is no obvious cause for anisotropy of the electron orbits, the shape and arrangement of the molecules in the crystal affect the anisotropy of the crystal as a whole.[18] For organic compounds containing few or no multiple bonds, the maximum diamagnetic susceptibility and maximum refractivity cor-

---

[13] C. V. Raman and K. S. Krishnan, *Proc. Roy. Soc. (London)*, **A113,** 511 (1927).

[14] A. Pace, *Abstracts of Doctoral Dissertation.* Ohio State University, Columbus, 1943.

[15] A. Pacault, *Bull. soc. chim. France,* **1949,** D371.

[16] K. S. Krishnan, *Phys. Rev.,* **38,** 833 (1931).

[17] K. S. Krishnan and S. Banerjee, *Trans. Roy. Soc. (London)*, **A234,** 265 (1935).

[18] W. A. Wooster, *Z. Krist.,* **80,** 495 (1931).

respond to the greatest dimension of the molecule. This effect must be due to a departure from spherical symmetry of electron distribution of separate atoms. The anisotropy of a single carbon atom, together with its singly attached hydrogen or oxygen atoms, is of the order of 1.5 to 1.75 anisotropy units.[19]

The presence of double bonds, and possibly of triple bonds, especially in a state of resonance, introduces a diamagnetic anisotropy of opposite sign, which leads in aromatic compounds to the effects described in the preceding section. In aliphatic compounds, such as those containing ethylenic bonds, the atomic groups tend to lie in a plane. They show their largest diamagnetism (and *smallest* refractive index) normal to the plane. The probability is that the existence of such bonds implies a force constraining certain electrons to occupy plane orbits the effective area of which is larger than for normal atomic radii.

In general, the magnetic anisotropy of diamagnetic ionic crystals is not large, but there are some notable exceptions. For instance, the principal susceptibilities of zircon[20] are -0.170 and -0.732×10^{-6}. Raman and Krishnan[21] have measured the magnetic anisotropy of several inorganic salts. Nitrates, carbonates, and chlorates all exhibit moderately large values of the magnetic anisotropy, in contrast to the almost complete isotropy of sulfates.[22] This is attributed to the intrinsic anisotropy of the NO_3^-, CO_3^{2-}, and ClO_3^- ions, and their parallel arrangement in the crystals.

The temperature dependence of magnetic anisotropy sometimes yields evidence which is supplementary to x-ray crystallographic studies. For instance, Nilakantan[23] has measured the temperature variation of the magnetic anisotropy of ammonium nitrate. Powder measurements [24] on this substance show only a slight and not very informative increase of susceptibility with increasing temperature. Nilakantan's work shows a marked step-wise change of magnetic anisotropy at $32°$, $84°$, and $125°C$. corresponding to the x-ray findings of Hendricks, Posnjak, and Kracek.[25] At $125°C$. the anisotropy falls to zero, confirming Hendrick's postulate of free rotation and spherical symmetry of the nitrate ion above this temperature.

[19] K. Lonsdale, *Proc. Roy. Soc. (London)*, **171**, 541, (1939).

[20] W. Voigt and S. Kinoshita, *Ann. Physik*, **24**, 492 (1907).

[21] C. V. Raman and K. S. Krishnan, *Proc. Roy. Soc. (London)*, **A113**, 511 (1927).

[22] K. S. Krishnan, B. C. Guha, and S. Banerjee, *Phil. Trans. Roy. Soc. (London)*, **A231**, 235 (1933).

[23] P. Nilakantan, *Phys. Rev.*, **52**, 383 (1937).

[24] G. E. R. Schulze, *Z. physik. Chem.*, **B40**, 308 (1938).

[25] S. B. Hendricks, E. Posnjak, and E. C. Kracek, *J. Am. Chem. Soc.*, **54**, 2766 (1932).

A comprehensive review of magnetic anistropy measurements on diamagnetic ionic crystals has been given by Nilakantan.[26]

The problem of temperature variation of magnetic anisotropy of organic crystals has received little attention. Nilakantan[27] reports that the anisotropy of resorcinol decreases slowly from 26° to 95°, then rapidly to zero at the melting point, 110°C. More recently[28] it has been claimed that several monoclinic* single crystals, of which naphthalene is one, show fairly large changes of anisotropy at liquid air temperature as compared with room temperature. The average (powder) susceptibilities are apparently independent of temperature, which means that a loss of diamagnetism along one axis must be compensated by an increase along another. The data suggest slight changes in molecular orientation as a function of temperature.

There are listed in Table IX some diamagnetic substances for which direct measurements of principal susceptibilities have been reported. These are in addition to those mentioned elsewhere in this chapter. No claim for completeness is made, but a reasonably thorough search of the literature has been made through the year 1954. It will be shown below that an estimate of magnetic anisotropy may sometimes be made without recourse to actual measurement of the principal susceptibilities.

For many aromatic compounds, two of the principal molecular susceptibilities, K_1 and K_2, are equal, or nearly so, while the third, K_3, is quite different. This makes it possible to estimate the magnetic anisotropy of such substances without the tedious and rather difficult direct measurement of principal susceptibilities.[46,47] A liquid or a powdered solid is, of course, effectively isotropic, so that:

$$\chi_{av} = K_{av} = \frac{1}{3}(K_1 + K_2 + K_3)$$

This is faintly reminiscent of the powder method for x-ray diffraction, and is true because in such substances all possible molecular orientations are present at random.

The method of Pascal's constants tacitly assumes that the molecule itself is isotropic. This is not true for aromatic and for some other substances, but it is approximately true that the calculated (Pascal) susceptibility is

$$K_p = K_1 = K_2$$

[26] P. Nilakantan, *Quart. J. Indian Inst. Sci.*, **3**, No. 2 (1940).
[27] P. Nilakantan, *Nature*, **140**, 29 (1937).
[28] N. Lumbroso and H. François, *Compt. rend.*, **236**, 2308 (1953).

TABLE IX

References to Some Diamagnetic Anisotropies

Acenaphthene[22,32]	Duodecahydrotriphenylene[34]
Acetic acid[41]	Durene[17]
p-Acetotoluide[34]	i-Erythritol[19]
p-Acetoxybenzaldehydrazine[98]	Fluoranthrene[17]
Alizarin[34]	Fluorene[17]
p-Anisylideneaminoazobenzene[98]	Fluorene alcohol[34]
Anthraquinone[34]	Fluorenone[17]
Artostenone[36]	Guanidine carbonate[36]
Azobenzene[19,22,28,34,35]	Hexachlorobenzene[17]
Behenolic acid[19]	Hexaethylbenzene[30]
Benzamide[36]	Hexamethylbenzene[17]
α-Benzenehexachloride[34]	Hydrazobenzene[22]
Benzidine[34]	Hydroquinol[17]
Benzil[22,37]	Ice[45]
p-Benzoquinone[17,28]	Iodine[43]
Benzophenone[19,22]	Isobutyric acid[41]
1,2-Benzpyrene[34]	Maleic acid[19]
γ-Biphenol[34]	Maleic anhydride[19]
Biphenyl[22]	D-Mannitol (B)[19]
Bromanil[34]	Methoxycinnamic acid[98]
Butyric acid[41]	trans, trans-Methyl fumarate[42]
Catechol[29]	trans, trans-Methyl muconate[42]
Chloranil[34]	Naphthacene[34]
Chrysene[17]	Naphthalene tetrachloride[34]
trans-Cinnamic acid[19]	Naphthazarin[34]
Coronene[44]	α-Naphthol[17]
Cyanuric acid[39]	β-Naphthol[22]
Cyclodiketone[19]	1,4-Naphthoquinone[17]
Decahydro-β-naphthol[36]	α-Naphthylamine[17]
Dianisylidenebenzidine[98]	m-Nitroaniline[17]
Dianthracene[34]	Nonacosane[19]
1,2,5,6-Dibenzanthracene[29]	Pentaerythritol[19]
Dibenzyl[19,22,28]	Pentaerythritol tetraacetate[19]
Dibenzylidenebenzidine[98]	Pentaerythritol tetranitrate[19]
p-Dibromobenzene[17,28]	Pentaerythritol tetraphenylether[19]
p-Dichlorobenzene[17]	Perylene[34,46]
4,4-Dibromodiphenyl[17]	Phenanthrene[17]
4,4-Dichlorodiphenyl[17]	Phloroglucinol dihydrate[34]
Dihydroanthracene[34]	Phthalocyanine (metal-free)[35]
Dimesityl[17]	Pyrene[17]
Dimethylbenzphenanthrene[34]	Picric acid[14]
Dimethyl terephthalate[88]	Picryl chloride[14]
Dinitrobenzene (o, m, p)[14,17,34,36]	Propionic acid[41]
Diphenic acid[17]	Quaterphenyl[17]
Diphenyldiacetylene[38]	Quinhydrone[34]
Diphenylamine[34]	Retene[34]
1,2-Diphenylbenzene[31]	Salol[22]

TABLE IX (*Continued*)

Sorbic acid[40]	p-Toluidine[34]
Stearic acid[19]	Trimethylenetrinitramine[14]
Stearolic acid[19]	s-Trinitroanisole[14]
Stilbene[19,22,28,34,35]	s-Trinitrobenzene[14,34]
Succinic acid[19]	Trinitromesitylene[14]
Succinic anhydride[19]	s-Trinitrotoluene[14]
Sulfur[33]	1,3,5-Triphenylbenzene[17]
Terphenyl[17]	Triphenyl carbinol[17]
1,2,4,5-Tetrabromobenzene[34]	Triphenylmethane[34]
1,2,4,5-Tetrachlorobenzene[17]	Urea[39]
Thianthrene[34]	Urea nitrate[39]
Tolane[19,34,35]	Urea oxalate[39]
o-Toluidine[17]	

Hence, we write

$$3K_{av} = 2K_p + K_3$$

The anisotropy of interest is $K_3 - K_1 = K_3 - K_p$, so that $K_3 - K_1 = 3(K_{av} - K_p)$, the anisotropy being simply three times the difference between observed and Pascal values. If it is so desired, the results may be expressed as the ratio of anisotropy in the substance under investigation to that in benzene.

This method is quite simple and convenient, although naturally less accurate than a direct determination of principal susceptibilities. Some applications of the method will be mentioned. It may be shown[48] that the anisotropy obtained in the above manner is not exactly the same as that

[29] K. S. Krishnan and S. Banerjee, *Z. Krist.*, **91**, 173 (1935).
[30] N. Ganguli, *ibid.*, **93**, 42 (1936).
[31] C. J. B. Clews and K. Lonsdale, *Proc. Roy. Soc. (London)*, **A161**, 493 (1937).
[32] J. Shanker and M. Prasad, *Current Sci.*, **6**, 554 (1938).
[33] P. Nilakantan, *Proc. Indian Acad. Sci.*, **4A**, 419 (1936).
[34] S. Banerjee, *Z. Krist.*, **100**, 316 (1938).
[35] K. Lonsdale, *J. Chem. Soc.*, **1938**, 364.
[36] K. Banerjee and J. Bhattacharjya, *Z. Krist.*, **100**, 420 (1939).
[37] I. E. Knaggs and K. Lonsdale, *Nature*, **143**, 1023 (1939).
[38] K. Lonsdale, *ibid.*, **145**, 148 (1940).
[39] K. Lonsdale, *Proc. Roy. Soc. (London)*, **A177**, 272 (1941).
[40] K. Lonsdale, J. M. Robertson, and I. Woodward, *ibid.*, **A178**, 43 (1941).
[41] A. Piekara, *Compt. rend.*, **199**, 527 (1934).
[42] I. E. Knaggs and K. Lonsdale, *J. Chem. Soc.*, **1942**, 417.
[43] S. R. Rao and H. S. Venkataramiah, *Current Sci.*, **14**, 195 (1945).
[44] M. T. Rogers, *J. Am. Chem. Soc.*, **69**, 1506 (1947).
[45] K. Lonsdale, *Nature*, **164**, 101 (1949).
[46] H. Shiba and G. Hazato, *Bull. Chem. Soc. Japan*, **22**, 92 (1949).
[47] A. Pacault, *Bull. soc. chim. France*, **40**, 371 (1949).
[48] A. Pacault, *Experientia*, **10**, 41 (1954).

found by direct measurement of principal susceptibilities, but the method will suffice for a comparison with theoretical values. This has been done for a substantial group of substances.[49-53] It is often possible to draw conclusions from these data as to the electronic configurations of the compounds. For instance, Shida and Fujii are able to relate the weak resonance character of cyclooctatetraene to a small observed magnetic anisotropy. Pacault[54] has suggested a possible relation between magnetic anisotropy and cancer-producing properties. This is supported by some degree of correlation between increasing anisotropy and increasing activity in the production of skin cancer by certain classes of hydrocarbons. It is not impossible that such a relation involving the resonance character of the molecule should exist. Another area of attempted application of anisotropy is determination of the composition of petroleum.[55]

It may be mentioned in closing this section that if anisotropic compounds are allowed to crystallize in a magnetic field, they tend to assume a preferred orientation, with the largest algebraic susceptibility parallel to the applied field.[56]

36. Graphite

Ganguli and Krishnan[57] have determined the magnetic anisotropy over a wide temperature range for some exceptionally good crystals of natural Ceylon graphite. Perpendicular to the hexagonal axis $\chi_\perp$ is about -0.5×10^{-6}, or nearly the same as for diamond. But along the hexagonal axis $\chi_{||} = -21.5 \times 10^{-6}$ at room temperature. Variation of the anisotropy with temperature is shown in Fig. 56, where $\chi_{||} - \chi_\perp$, that is, the difference in diamagnetism along the hexagonal axis and perpendicular to it is plotted against reciprocal temperature. With decreasing temperature, there is a marked increase of the diamagnetic susceptibility along the principal axis, and of the anisotropy, which changes from 7.8×10^{-6} per gram at $1270°K$. to 29.0×10^{-6} at $90.1°K$.[58] The temperature coefficient of anisotropy for graphite suggests an increasing effective π-electron area, as the tempera-

[49] E. D. Bergmann, J. Hoarau, A. Pacault, A. Pullman, and B. Pullman, *J. chim. phys.*, 49, 474 (1952).

[50] H. Honda and K. Ouchi, *Bull. Chem. Soc. Japan*, 24, 181 (1951).

[51] H. Akamatsu and Y. Matsunaga, *ibid.*, 26, 364 (1953).

[52] G. Hazato, T. Ikenove, Y. Kitahara, T. Nozoe, J. Maruha, and T. Miura, *Science Repts. Research Inst. Tôhoku Imp. Univ.*, Ser. A5, 278 (1953).

[53] S. Shida and S. Fujii, *Bull. Chem. Soc. Japan*, 24, 173 (1951).

[54] A. Pacault and J. Hoarau, *Compt. rend.*, 233, 689 (1951).

[55] H. Honda, *J. Fuel Soc. Japan*, 33, 134 (1954).

[56] E. Gallico and G. Mayr, *Rend. ist. lombardo sci.*, 83, 43 (1950); this paper was not available to the author.

[57] N. Ganguli and K. S. Krishnan, *Proc. Roy. Soc. (London)*, A177, 168 (1941).

[58] K. S. Krishnan and N. Ganguli, *Z. Krist.*, A100, 530 (1939).

ture is lowered and thermal vibrations die down.[59] But the magnitude of the diamagnetic susceptibility perpendicular to the graphitic layers is so great that the usual closed-shell diamagnetism, which is adequate to explain the anisotropy in aromatic compounds, no longer suffices for graphite. It has, therefore, been proposed that in graphite there is an additional Landau diamagnetism due to free electrons. This has been discussed by Mrozowski[60] and McWeeny.[61]

Several studies have shown that the average susceptibility of graphite powder is a function of particle size.[62] Ganguli[63] has measured the mag-

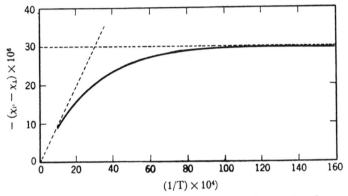

Fig. 56. Diamagnetic anisotropy, $\chi_\| - \chi_\perp$ *versus* temperature for a graphite single crystal.

netic anisotropy of finely powdered graphite. He finds that the principal susceptibility parallel to the hexagonal axis diminishes to about -0.9×10^{-6} per gram in particles of less than 2 microns diameter. This experiment is based on a method described by Goetz,[64,65] in which the microcrystals are suspended in liquid gelatin or paraffin wax which is allowed to solidify in a rather powerful, rotating magnetic field. More recently, there have been several studies[66-68] of the magnetic changes which occur in

[59] K. Lonsdale, *Bull. soc. chim. France*, 1949, D476.

[60] S. Mrozowski, *Phys. Rev.*, 85, 609 (1952).

[61] R. McWeeny, *Proc. Phys. Soc. (London)*, 66A, 714 (1953).

[62] R. Rao, *Indian J. Phys.*, 6, 241 (1931).

[63] N. Ganguli, *Phil. Mag.*, 21, 355 (1936).

[64] A. Goetz and A. Faessler, *Phys. Rev.*, 40, 1053A (1932).

[65] A. Goetz, *ibid.*, 45, 282 (1934).

[66] W. F. Wynne-Jones, H. E. Blayden, and R. Iley, *Brennstoff-Chem.*, 33, 268 (1952).

[67] H. Honda, K. Ouchi, and K. Nagata, *J. Chem. Soc. Japan*, 74, 720 (1953); not read in original.

[68] H. T. Pinnick, *Phys. Rev.*, 94, 319 (1954).

carbon during graphitization, and also during the process of carbonization from a variety of carbonaceous materials. With decreasing particle size, or more precisely with decreasing crystallite diameter perpendicular to the hexagonal axis, the powder diamagnetic susceptibility changes from about -7.8×10^{-6} to -0.5×10^{-6}. Almost all the change takes place in the diameter range 150 A. to 50 A. Particle dimensions naturally increase as the temperature of carbonization increases. Hence, the diamagnetism increases with increasingly severe heat treatment. There may, however, be irregularities caused by the evolution of adsorbed gases, and possibly

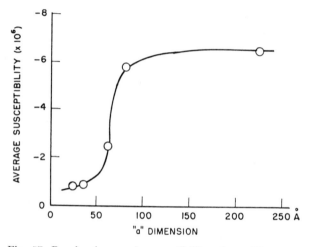

Fig. 57. Powder (average) susceptibility of graphite *versus* "a" diameter of particles.

by the transitory formation of free radicals. From these results, it may be expected that amorphous carbon would show little or no dependence of susceptibility on temperature. Marchand[69] has shown that this is actually the case.

Figure 57 shows the approximate susceptibility of carbon as a function of average particle diameter in the a direction (perpendicular to the hexagonal axis), and Fig. 58 shows the temperature dependence of susceptibility for several samples of different diameter.

The electrons which are effectively free in two dimensions in graphite exhibit spin resonance in paramagnetic resonance experiments. As anticipated, the width of the absorption depends on heat treatment of the specimen.[70]

[69] A. Marchand, *Compt. rend.*, **238**, 1645 (1954).
[70] J. G. Castle, Jr., *Phys. Rev.*, **95**, 846 (1954).

The abnormal diamagnetic anisotropy of graphite is largely destroyed by partial oxidation in nitric plus sulfuric acids to form "blue graphite."[71] This, of course, results in a substantial decrease of the average, powder, diamagnetic susceptibility similar to that shown with decreasing particle size.   Similar algebraic increases of susceptibility occur in graphite during the adsorption of gases, provided that the gas molecules intercalate between the carbon atomic planes.   This behavior is shown by bromine,[72-77] fluorine,[77,78] ferric chloride,[79] nitrogen dioxide,[76] oxygen,[72,75] and other substances.[80,81]   The paramagnetic adsorbates will be described later.

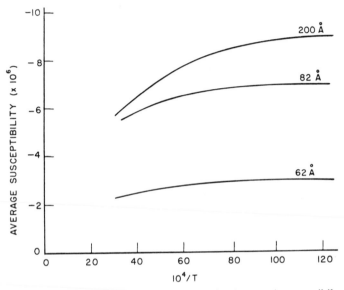

Fig. 58. Temperature dependence of powder (average) susceptibility in graphite of several particle diameters.

Magnetic susceptibility isotherms for the bromine-graphite system are given in Fig. 59.   The amount of bromine adsorbed at saturation pressure

[71] K. S. Krishnan and N. Ganguli, *Current Sci.*, **3**, 472 (1935).
[72] R. Juza, R. Langheim, and H. Hahn, *Angew. Chem.*, **51**, 354 (1938).
[73] W. Rudorff, *Z. anorg. u. allgem. Chem.*, **245**, 383 (1941).
[74] R. Juza, H. Lubbe, and L. Heinlein, *Z. anorg. Chem.*, **258**, 105 (1949).
[75] R. Juza, *Chem.-Ztg.*, **74**, 55 (1950).
[76] L. H. Reyerson and J. E. Wertz, personal communication.
[77] M. Goldsmith, *J. Chem. Phys.*, **18**, 523 (1950).
[78] O. Ruff and O. Bretschneider, *Z. anorg. u. allgem. Chem.*, **217**, 1 (1934).
[79] W. Rudorff and H. Schulz, *ibid.*, **245**, 121 (1940).
[80] A. Schleede and M. Wellman, *Z. phys. Chem.*, **B18**, 1 (1932).
[81] V Hoffman, A. Frenzel, and E. Czalan, *Ann.*, **510**, 1 (1934).

ranges from 0.5 g. per g. to 1.6 g. per g. as reported by various investigators. After the initial adsorption, the susceptibility seems to change reversibly and is a function of bromine content only.   It is clear that the substantial decrease of diamagnetism with increasing concentration of intercalated adsorbate must be related to restriction of the electron which normally

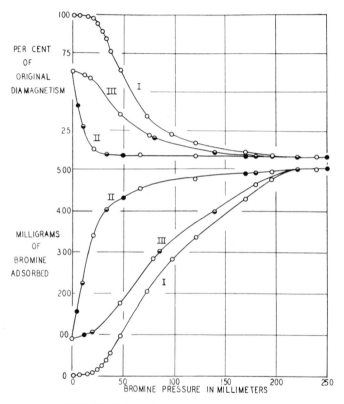

ADSORPTION OF BROMINE ON GRAPHITE

Fig. 59. Isotherms for susceptibility of the bromine-graphite system.

circulates freely in the basal plane.   The precise mechanism by which bromine and other intercalated substances cause this restriction is not clear at the time of writing, although a recent paper by Hennig throws some light on the subject.[81a]   It appears, however, that relatively small perturbations of the "pure benzene" structure in aromatic compounds may cause a rapid decrease in diamagnetic anisotropy.[82]   This view is supported

[81a] G. R. Hennig, *J. Chem. Phys.*, **23**, 1431 (1955).

[82] M. G. Evans, J. de Heer, and J. Gergely, *Proc. Phys. Soc.* (*London*), **62A**, 505 (1949).

by Ubbelohde[83] who made measurements on C_8K and C_8Br, and on a substance of uncertain structure approximating C_4F. The problem is discussed further by Smoluchowski.[84] The paramagnetic resonance absorption observed in graphite, and which corresponds to a concentration of about 10^{-4} spin center per carbon atom, is destroyed by small amounts of various impurities. But, at least for "graphite bisulfate," other resonances appear at higher "impurity" levels.[85]

37. High Polymers

It will be clear that the anisotropy obtained by Krishnan's method is that which exists in the plane of rotation. The third principal susceptibility may be studied by reorienting the crystal so that one of the magnetic axes formerly in the plane of rotation now lies parallel to the torsion axis. One of the applications of magnetic anisotropy is to high polymers. A drawn fiber of a high polymer resembles a uniaxial crystal in that there are only two unique axes, one along the fiber and one across. For work on drawn high-polymer fibers, it may be necessary to assemble bundles of fibers large enough to handle. In this, as in all work on magnetic anisotropy, it is important to note whether the sample, free from torsional restraint, hangs parallel to or perpendicular to the lines of the magnetic field. There is no doubt that the method is a sensitive one for detecting molecular orientation in polymer systems containing aromatic or unsaturated aliphatic groups. It is rather surprising that the method has not had more application.

The magnetic anisotropy of various natural substances, several of them of a polymeric nature, has been investigated by Nilakantan.[26,86] He derives, for instance, the crystalline character and probable crystal orientations in egg shells, shells of molluscs, and related material. He has also studied wood, cellulose, hemicellulose, and lignin. Wood is slightly anisotropic, apparently because of a molecular anisotropy in the cellulose molecule and the more or less regular orientation of these molecules along the fiber axis. Lignin and the hemicelluloses are amorphous. The greatest diamagnetism of cellulose fibers is along the fiber axis, which is presumably along the length of the molecule. Cellulose fibers from various sources have also been investigated by Cotton-Feytis.[87] The anisotropies are in all cases very small and for several specimens are different in orien-

[83] F. R. M. McDonnell, R. C. Pink, and A. R. Ubbelohde, *J. Chem. Soc.*, **1951**, 191.
[84] R. Smoluchowski, *Revs. Modern Physics*, **25**, 178 (1953).
[85] G. R. Hennig, B. Smaller, and E. L. Yasaitis, *Phys. Rev.*, **95**, 1088 (1954).
[86] P. Nilakantan, *Proc. Indian Acad. Sci.*, **7**, 38 (1938).
[87] E. Cotton-Feytis and E. Fauré-Frémiet, *Compt. rend.*, **214**, 996 (1942).

tation from those reported by Nilakantan. Cotton-Feytis has reported
small anisotropies in silk, keratin, and collagen, each derived from several
sources.

The anisotropy of a stretched methyl methacrylate polymer is mentioned by Cotton-Feytis, but no data are given. Other studies on the
magnetic anisotropy of synthetic high polymers have been made on polyethylene terephthalate[88] and on polystyrene and substituted polystyrenes.[89]

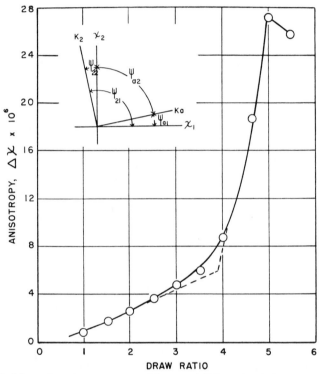

Fig. 60. Magnetic anisotropy *versus* "draw ratio" for polyethylene terephthalate fibers. The relation of fiber and magnetic axes is also shown.

The problem of evaluating molecular orientation in a substantially amorphous polymer appears to be susceptible to attack by this method. The
method in essence is to determine the anisotropy of the monomer, or of the
repeating unit, as may be possible from magnetic and x-ray measurements
on relatively simple compounds, and then to interpret the anisotropy of the
polymer in terms of specific orientation of the molecular magnetic axes.

[88] P. W. Selwood, J. A. Parodi, and A. Pace, Jr., *J. Am. Chem. Soc.*, **72**, 1269 (1950).
[89] E. M. Weir and P. W. Selwood, *ibid.*, **73**, 3484 (1951).

Polyethylene terephthalate is promising for this kind of study because of the aromatic groups present in the chain. In the work described below, it was not possible to carry the determination of molecular orientation through to completion , but this was not due to any fault of the magnetic method, but rather to lack of x-ray data on the nearest monomer analog, dimethyl terephthalate.

Filaments of drawn polymer were available in several draw ratios; i.e., the ratio of final length to the length of the undrawn fiber. These filaments were made into little bundles, large enough for measurements. This procedure is justifiable because each fiber acts as a uniaxial crystal. Anisotropy measurements were made first, as a function of draw ratio; then, for each draw ratio, measurements were made as a function of annealing temperature, both with and without shrinkage being allowed. The first of this series of studies will be described here.

All fiber samples were suspended with the filament axis horizontal. The unique axis of symmetry then assumed an equilibrium position parallel to the field. Results of the anisotropy measurements are shown in Fig. 60. A cylinder of unoriented polymer gave an average susceptibility, $(\chi_1 + \chi_2 + \chi_3)/3$, of -97×10^{-6} per mole of dimethylene terephthalate. This is in reasonably good agreement with the value -101.6×10^{-6} per mole of dimethylene terephthalate, obtained by measurements on a powdered sample of dimethyl terephthalate, after correction for two hydrogen atoms.

If it is assumed that the monomer units are magnetically identical with dimethylene terephthalate, the principal molecular susceptibilities of dimethyl terephthalate and the magnetic anisotropies of polyethylene terephthalate may be used to calculate the average orientation of the aromatic plane (and hence the molecular chain) to the filament axis. Although this calculation must wait for the completion of x-ray studies on dimethyl terephthalate, the method will be indicated.

The fiber acts as a uniaxial crystal, presumably because there is random orientation of the aromatic planes about the fiber axis. In the hypothetical case where all the aromatic planes are parallel to the filament axis, the susceptibility normal to the axis equals the average of the molecular susceptibility perpendicular to the aromatic plane (K_1) and that in the plane normal to the fiber axis (K_3), i.e.:

$$\chi_\perp = (K_1 + K_3)/2 = K_a$$

and

$$\chi_{||} = K_2$$

With the aid of Fig. 60 it is seen that

$$\psi_{22} = \psi_{a1} = \psi$$

$$\psi_{a2} = 90° - \psi$$

and

$$\psi_{21} = 180° - \psi$$

Hence,

$$\chi_\perp = \cos^2 \psi K_a + \sin^2 \psi K_2$$

and

$$\chi_{||} = \sin^2 \psi K_a + \cos^2 \psi K_2$$

from which it is easily shown that

$$\cos 2\psi = (\chi_\perp - \chi_{||})/(K_a - K_2)$$

where ψ is the angle which the aromatic nucleus makes with the filament axis.

The data in Fig. 60 show that there is a linear relation between anisotropy and draw ratio for values of the latter up to 3.0, and that the increase in anisotropy with draw ratio is relatively small. Beyond this value, in the neighborhood of 4.0, the magnetic anisotropy begins to increase very rapidly, with increasing draw ratio, through a maximum of 27.4 anisotropy units at a draw ratio of 5.0. Extrapolation of both sections of the curve (Fig. 60) locates this critical point at 3.8.

These results may be interpreted in the following way: as the amorphous polymer is subjected to increasing tension, the chains tend to straighten out and the segments tend to become more perfectly aligned relative to one another. This process of unkinking the chains reduces the distance between the constituent groups of adjacent chains to the point where short-range van der Waals forces begin to be effective. At about 3.8, these forces become so strong that it requires but little more externally applied force in the form of stretching to cause the segments to snap into positions of minimum potential energy. In the region of high and preferred orientation (4.0 to 5.0), the fibers should tend to become crystalline; that is, there should be a number of crystallites, separated by amorphous regions, distributed at random along the length of the fiber. This apparently agrees with inferences from observations on other properties of the polymer. However, none of these physical properties pertaining to the crystallinity and close-packing of the chains shows a more pronounced change than the plot of magnetic anisotropy.

In polystyrene the situation is somewhat different. If all the aromatic groups were aligned with the planes of the rings perpendicular to the direction of molecular orientation in a drawn fiber, the largest diamagnetism would be along the unique axis.   Actually, polystyrene shows only a small diamagnetic anisotropy even at great fiber draw ratios.   This must mean that the aromatic groups in this polymer are randomly oriented, or perhaps are freely rotating.   If, now, the styrene is substituted as in poly-2,5-dichlorostyrene, the anisotropy developed on stretching becomes quite large.   This effect, which supports x-ray studies, indicates that in *ortho*-substituted polystyrenes, the freedom of rotation of the aromatic group must be greatly restricted.   Weir and Selwood[89] have also investigated the anisotropy of polyethylene.

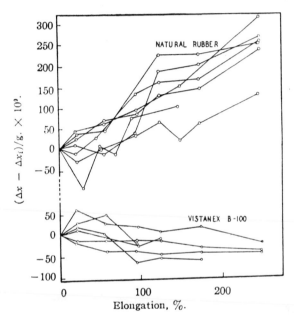

Fig. 61. Magnetic anisotropy *versus* % elongation for several samples of natural rubber and of polyisobutylene (Vistanex B-100 is a B. F. Goodrich Co. product).

The magnetic anisotropy of rubber in several forms has been studied also by Cotton-Feytis.[90,91]   Unoriented rubber seems to have a slight anisotropy for reasons which are not clear, but which are possibly related to the direction of rolling in preparation of the sample.   Stretched crude rubber has a moderately high anisotropy with the largest diamagnetism perpendicular to the magnetic field and to the direction of stretch. In other words, the sample tends to lie with the direction of stretch parallel to the field.   This is the situation to be expected in a long molecule oriented

[90] E. Cotton-Feytis, *Compt. rend.*, **214**, 485 (1942); 215, 299 (1942).

[91] E. Cotton-Feytis, *Rev. gén. caout.*, 21, 27 (1944).

in the specimen, provided the molecule has sufficient double bonds, as the crude rubber molecule apparently has. When crude rubber is stretched, the anisotropy increases, but tends toward a limit. This parallels the effects observed with x rays and suggests more or less complete molecular orientation in one direction at high elongations.

These results have been extended in the author's laboratory, and by Isihara *et al.*, to a variety of natural and synthetic rubbers[92,93] under variable stretching at room temperature, and under fixed stretching over a range of temperature. It is confirmed that unsaturated rubbers under tension have a fairly large principal susceptibility perpendicular to the direction of stretching and hence orientate in the magnetic field with the direction of stretching parallel to the field. This is no doubt due to the presence

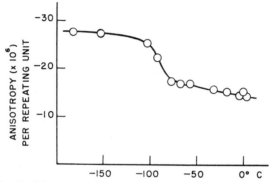

Fig. 62. Magnetic anisotropy of rubber *versus* temperature.

and intrinsic anisotropy of the olefinic bonds, but cross-linking may hinder alignment of the long molecules and thus destroy part of the anisotropy. Stretched saturated rubbers show a rather small anisotropy opposite in sign to those with unsaturated groups. These consequently orientate perpendicular to an applied field. Figure 61 shows some anisotropy data for a polyisobutylene and for a sample of natural rubber. The magnetic anisotropy of natural stretched rubber shows a rather strong dependence on temperature. Figure 62, from the work of Isihara *et al.*, shows that the anistropy drops rather sharply when the temperature is raised through −73°C. This effect is doubtless related to a second-order transition at this temperature. The study of such transitions is also possible by nuclear magnetic resonance.[94]

[92] E. W(eir) Toor and P. W. Selwood, *J. Am. Chem. Soc.*, **74**, 2364 (1952).

[93] A. Isihara, H. Kusumoto, H. Nagano, and K. Oshima, *J. Chem. Phys.*, **21**, 1909 (1953).

[94] L. V. Holroyd, R. S. Codrington, B. A. Mrowca, and E. Guth, *J. Applied Phys.*, **22**, 696 (1951).

38. Liquid Crystals

There have been very few studies on the magnetic properties of substances in the mesomorphic state, although there have been several studies of the phenomenon discovered by Mauguin[95] that the optic axis of substances in this state tends to set itself parallel to the lines of force of a magnetic field of sufficient intensity.

Foëx[96,97] has found that a typical substance such as p-azoxyanisole has in the crystalline state the following principal susceptibilities per gram,

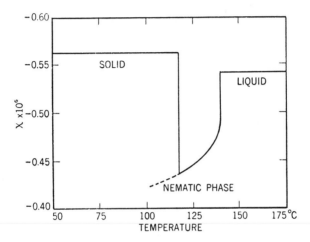

Fig. 63. Susceptibility of p-azoxyanisole in the neighborhood of the "liquid crystal" transition.

$\chi_1 = -0.665$, $\chi_2 = -0.634$, and $\chi_3 = -0.408$, all times 10^{-6}. This anisotropy is not particularly large; in fact, it is much less intense than for substances such as naphthalene which do not occur in the mesomorphic state. The average susceptibility of powdered p-azoxyanisole is -0.565×10^{-6}; the nematic phase is formed at 116°C. at which temperature the susceptibility falls rapidly to -0.457×10^{-6}. As the temperature rises, the diamagnetism also rises slowly until above 133°C. the substance becomes an isotropic liquid for which $\chi = -0.545 \times 10^{-6}$. If, now, the temperature is lowered, the reverse change occurs, except that the nematic phase may persist considerably below 116°C. These changes are shown in Fig. 63. Analogous curves are followed by azoxyphenetol, azoxyanisolephenetol, and anisaldazine. The reason for these peculiar curves is that the long

[95] C. Mauguin, *Compt. rend.*, **152,** 1680 (1911).
[96] G. Foëx, *J. phys. radium,* **10,** 421 (1929).
[97] G. Foëx, *Trans. Faraday Soc.,* **29,** 958 (1933).

dimension of the molecule is the least diamagnetic and hence orientates to lie in the lines of force. If the substance is crystallized in a magnetic field, a strong anisotropy exists, with the smallest diamagnetism along the lines of force. Foëx also reports on measurements of principal susceptibilities over a temperature range.

Substances such as ethylazoxybenzoate which occur in the smectic phase show, in general, only a small and irregular increase of diamagnetism on passing from solid to liquid. If, however, a field is present during cooling to the smectic state, orientation sets in with a strong decrease of diamagnetism.

Some further studies of magnetic anisotropy in liquid crystals have been reported by Tsvetkov and Sosnovskii.[98]

[98] V. Tsvetkov and A. Sosnovskii, *Acta Physicochim.* (*U.R.S.S.*), **18**, 358 (1943); *J. Exptl. Theoret. Phys.* (*U.S.S.R.*), **13**, 353 (1943).

CHAPTER EIGHT

ATOMIC PARAMAGNETISM

39. Theories of Atomic Paramagnetism

An atom may or may not have a permanent magnetic moment. If it does not, application of a magnetic field to the atom leads to an induced moment of sign opposite to that of the applied field, and the atom is said to be diamagnetic. But if the atom has a permanent magnetic moment, application of a field leads to orientation of the moment, and the atom is said to be paramagnetic. An atom will have a permanent magnetic moment if it has an odd number of electrons, or if all the electrons are not paired off. All atoms are subject to induced magnetization, but when paramagnetism is present it is generally at least 10 times greater than the diamagnetism.

The classical theory of paramagnetism was developed by Langevin[1,2] on the assumptions that each atom is a little permanent magnet, and that these atomic magnets tend to line up parallel to an applied magnetic field, but that the alignment is resisted by the thermal agitation of the atoms. There is an obvious identification of the hypothetical atomic magnets with the magnetic moments caused by orbital electronic motion.

The expression deduced by Langevin for the molar paramagnetism is

$$\chi_M = N\mu^2/3kT$$

where N is Avogadro's number, μ is the permanent moment, k the Boltzmann constant, and T the absolute temperature. A precise expression will also include a term for the relatively small diamagnetic part of the susceptibility. The above expression is applicable only to cases where molecular interactions are negligible. It will be seen that paramagnetism, in sharp contrast to diamagnetism, is inversely proportional to the absolute temperature. This theoretical prediction is fulfilled experimentally for a large number of substances. In fact, the experimental discovery of what is known as Curie's law,[3] $\chi = C/T$, preceded Langevin's work by some

[1] P. Langevin, J. phys., **4**, 678 (1905).

[2] P. Langevin, Ann. chim. phys., **5**, 70 (1905).

[3] P. Curie, Ann. chim. et phys., **5**, 289 (1895), et seq.

years. This expression is approximately true for many solids and liquids, as well as for at least the first named of the two well-known paramagnetic gases, oxygen and nitric oxide. Unfortunately, the more accurate magnetic measurements become, the more deviations from Curie's law are discovered.

The quantum mechanics in the hands of Van Vleck[4] yields the analogous expression

$$\chi_M = N\bar{\mu}^2/3kT + N\bar{\alpha} \tag{1}$$

where $\bar{\mu}^2$ is the square of the low-frequency part of the magnetic moment vector, averaged over time, and this average being itself averaged over the various normal states appropriately weighted according to the Boltzmann factor. $N\bar{\alpha}$ is the combined temperature-independent contribution of the high-frequency elements of the paramagnetic moment and of the diamagnetic part.

A convenient unit of atomic magnetic moment is the Bohr magneton, the magnitude of which is given by

$$\beta = eh/4\pi mc = 0.917 \times 10^{-20} \text{ erg oersted}^{-1}$$

Equation (1) then becomes

$$\chi_M = N\left(\frac{\beta^2\bar{\mu}_B^2}{3kT} + \bar{\alpha}\right) \tag{2}$$

where μ_B is the low-frequency part of the magnetic moment expressed in Bohr magnetons.

In general, the magnetic moment of an atom consists of two parts, the orbital contribution and the electron-spin contribution. In different normal states of the atom, the inclination of the orbital and spin contributions may be different. Hence, while one speaks of the "permanent" magnetic moment, one must remember that it may not be invariant with temperature, although for many cases it appears to be so. Also, in most if not all cases of "molecular" paramagnetism as contrasted with "atomic" paramagnetism, the orbital contribution appears to be quenched out. This fact aids greatly in the interpretations to be given in a later chapter.

In evaluating $\bar{\mu}^2$ and $\bar{\alpha}$ in terms of experimentally-determinable quantities, there are three cases for which different equations are required. First, there are the two limiting cases of spin multiplets very narrow or very wide compared to kT, and then there is the general case of multiplet intervals comparable to kT.

(a) Multiplet intervals small compared to kT:

[4] J. H. Van Vleck, *The Theory of Electric and Magnetic Susceptibilities*. Oxford University Press, Oxford, 1932.

The high-frequency elements of the paramagnetic moment are absent (neglecting the diamagnetic part). Equation (2) then becomes

$$\chi_M = \frac{N\beta^2}{3kT} [4S(S + 1) + L(L + 1)] \tag{3}$$

where S and L are the resultant spin and orbital moments, respectively.

(b) Multiplet intervals large compared to kT:

$$\chi_M = \frac{Ng^2\beta^2 J(J + 1)}{3kT} + N\alpha \tag{4}$$

where, following the usual spectral notation, J is the vector sum of L and S; g, the Landé splitting factor, is given by

$$g = 1 + \frac{S(S + 1) + J(J + 1) - L(L + 1)}{2J(J + 1)}$$

The term α no longer has the value zero (neglecting the diamagnetic part) but is given by

$$N\alpha = \frac{N\beta^2}{6(2J + 1)} \left[\frac{F(J + 1)}{h\nu(J + 1; J)} - \frac{F(J)}{h\nu(J + 1; J)} \right]$$

where

$$F(J) = \frac{1}{J} [(S + L + 1)^2 - J^2][J^2 - (S - L)^2]$$

Equation (4) is used for most ions of the rare earth elements, as will be shown in a later section.

(c) Multiplet intervals comparable to kT:

This case involves summation of the contributions of atoms with different values of J. The number N_J, that is the number of atoms in a mole with a given value of J, is determined by the Boltzmann temperature factor

$$\chi_M = N \sum_{J=|L-S|}^{L+S} \frac{\left\{ [g_J^2\beta^2 J(J + 1)/3kT] + \alpha_J \right\}(2J + 1)e^{-W_J{}^\circ/kT}}{\Sigma(2J + 1)e^{-W_J{}^\circ/kT}} \tag{5}$$

It is clear from the above that when the multiplet intervals are small or large compared to kT, the Curie law should be obeyed, except for the relatively small temperature-independent high-frequency elements. But where the multiplet intervals are comparable to kT, one obtains a Boltzmann distribution of the various "normal" states, together with some rather striking departures from the Curie law.

The modern theory of paramagnetism, by far the greater part of which is due to Van Vleck, is, on the whole, very satisfactory. A few new phenomena have been discovered, and the theory has undergone considerable elaboration, especially in the field of complex compounds. The present status of the theory is described by Van Vleck himself.[5]

40. Monatomic Paramagnetic Gases

Unfortunately, direct experimental test of all the equations given above is difficult. The theory applies to substances in which mutual molecular interactions are negligible, namely to gases. But the only common monatomic gases are diamagnetic. There are, of course, substances the vapors of which should be monatomic and paramagnetic, but these are difficult to handle. The alkali metal vapors ought to be paramagnetic because their molecules contain an odd number of electrons. But the vapor pressures are not high at any reasonably attainable temperature, the paramagnetism of such substances is not large at high temperature, a certain degree of association to double molecules must occur, and it is difficult to find suitable containers for these vapors. Gerlach[6] has reported on the susceptibility of potassium vapor between 600° and 800°C., corresponding to vapor pressures of from 0.5 to 30 mm. Within the rather large experimental error, the susceptibility obeys the Curie law and is of about the correct magnitude. As Van Vleck (*op. cit.*,[4] p. 239) points out, it would be of interest if Gerlach's measurements could be refined and extended to other alkali metals. Such measurements would also serve as a sensitive test for molecular association, as magnetic measurements do for free radicals. But so far the experimental difficulties have proved insurmountable.

Another possibility is thallium vapor which has been reported to be paramagnetic.[7] Probably precise measurements on this vapor would be subject to the same or even greater difficulties than those on the alkali metals.

The problem has been attacked by Scott and Cromwell[8] through the study of atomic iodine. Susceptibilities were measured as a function of temperature by the Gouy method. Measurable concentrations of atomic iodine were not obtained below 1000°C., corresponding to three atmospheres of pressure. The experiment is of no less difficulty than that of

[5] J. H. Van Vleck, *Ann. Inst. Henri Poincaré*, 10, No. 2, 57 (1947). Also in *Le Magnétisme*, **Vol. III.** Proceedings of the Strasbourg Congress on Magnetism, 1939, pp. 103–151.

[6] W. Gerlach, *Atti congresso intern. fisici*, 1, 119 (1927).

[7] M. B. Nevgi, *J. Univ. Bombay*, **7**, Pt. 3, 19 (1938).

[8] A. B. Scott and T. M. Cromwell, *J. Am. Chem Soc.*, **70**, 3981 (1948).

Gerlach on alkali metal vapor, but within the rather large experimental error, the results are consistent with theory.

It may be added that the susceptibility of atomic oxygen has been calculated by Wohlfarth.[9] These calculations give atomic oxygen a greater paramagnetism than molecular oxygen. This surprising result seems to be based on sound premises and methods, but there are no direct experimental data available for atomic oxygen and it is not clear how such data could be obtained.

41. The Stern-Gerlach Experiment

Although monatomic paramagnetic gases are difficult to obtain, there is ample evidence that many atoms have permanent magnetic moments.

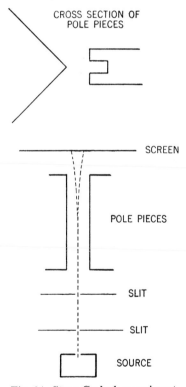

Fig. 64. Stern-Gerlach experiment.

The most direct experimental proof of this condition is known as the Stern-Gerlach experiment, a brief description of which will be given.

[9] E. P. Wohlfarth, *Proc. Leeds Phil. Lit. Soc.*, **4,** 315 (1946).

If a magnet is placed in a uniform magnetic field, it will be oriented but it will suffer no lateral force either parallel or perpendicular to the field. But if the field be made inhomogeneous, then the magnet will be not only oriented but will be deflected toward the region of maximum intensity. Similarly, if an atom possessing a permanent magnetic moment is placed in an inhomogeneous field, it will be deflected, although the nature of the deflection is rather complicated.

The Stern-Gerlach experiment consists of passing an atomic (or molecular) beam through an inhomogeneous magnetic field. The beam is deflected, and from the magnitude of the deflection it is possible to compute the magnitude of the magnetic moment. An inhomogeneous field may be produced with the aid of two specially-prepared pole-pieces, one wedge-shaped, the other slotted. The apparatus is shown diagrammatically in Fig. 64. The atomic beam, after deflection, impinges on a target from which an image may be developed. The image so formed consists generally of a bow-shape; that is, atoms are deflected both toward and away from the region of maximum intensity. This effect is due to space quantization, or the ability of the atoms to take up only certain discrete orientations in space.

The theory of the Stern-Gerlach experiment lies outside the scope of this book. It must suffice to say that for atoms such as those of hydrogen or of silver, the atomic magnetic moment is in satisfactory agreement with theory. An authoritative account of the technique and applications of the molecular-ray method is given by Fraser.[10] The method is by no means limited to atomic beams.[11]

42. The Rare Earths

Failing to find monatomic paramagnetic vapors with which to make tests of Van Vleck's equations, we turn now to paramagnetic salts and their solutions. It is to be hoped that in at least some cases the mutual interactions of the ions will be negligible. In most cases this is not true, but the rare earth elements are unique in this respect, that the electrons responsible for the paramagnetism are to a great degree shielded from external influence. The electronic configuration for the rare earth elements is

$$\ldots 4f^{0-14}\ 5s^2\ 5p^6\ 5d^{0-1}\ 6s^2$$

These elements are generally trivalent, losing their $6s$ and $5d$ electrons. Evidence that the $4f$ electrons, responsible for the paramagnetism, are

[10] R. G. J. Fraser, *Molecular Rays*. Cambridge University Press, Cambridge 1931.
    [11] R. Schnurmann, *J. phys. radium*, **6**, 99 (1935).

relatively free from external influence is given by the fact that most of the rare earths are astonishingly alike chemically and that their absorption bands and magnetic susceptibilities are little affected by change of ionic environment, such as by change of compound or of solvent. These fortunate circumstances lead to very satisfactory confirmation of the Van Vleck theory.

The relation

$$\chi_M = \frac{Ng^2\beta^2 J(J + 1)}{3kT}$$

which is the first part of equation (4), was obtained in the old quantum theory. As is realized now, this is simply equivalent to assuming that the multiplets are all very wide compared to kT. This relationship was used by Hund[12] in his calculation of the magnetic moments of the rare earths, in which, with some exceptions, good agreement with experiment was obtained. As Hund had available no direct spectroscopic evidence as to the spectral terms of the rare earth ions, it may be of interest to show how he evaluated L, S, and J.

Whenever there are several equivalent electrons, the Pauli exclusion principle severely limits the possible spectral terms. It was assumed by Hund that the lowest energy is possessed by the spectral term of highest multiplicity. If, when the multiplicity $2S + 1$ has its maximum value, there are several possible values of L, then the least energy is assumed to be given by the greatest L consistent with this S. Other possible states are assumed to be not normal, because they have so much more energy For instance, for praseodymium with two equivalent f electrons, the following terms are admitted by the Pauli exclusion principle, ^1S, ^3P, ^1D, ^3F, ^1G, ^3H, ^1I, and the ^3S, ^1P, ^3D, ^1F, ^3G, ^1H, and ^3I states are excluded. Under Hund's assumptions, of the first group of terms only the ^3H term is a normal state. The correctness of Hund's assumptions is demonstrated by the magnetic theory itself.

It is, of course, necessary to know whether equation (3), (4), or (5) should be used for calculating the susceptibilities. This is done by supposing that the normal state is the one whose component has a minimum or maximum J, depending on whether the multiplet is "regular" or inverted. For less than seven $4f$ electrons, the multiplet is "regular"; for more, inverted. The trivalent ion of gadolinium, with seven $4f$ electrons, is in an S state. For europium, samarium, and to a slight degree neodymium, the general equation (5) must be used, as will be described below.

[12] F. Hund, Z. Physik, 33, 855 (1925).

A convenient comparison of theoretical with observed susceptibilities is done by the aid of "effective Bohr magneton numbers" instead of susceptibilities. These are defined as

$$u_{\text{eff}} = \sqrt{\frac{3k\chi_M T}{N\beta^2}} = 2.84\sqrt{C}$$

This quantity is a function of temperature, unless Curie's law is obeyed.

Theoretical effective Bohr magneton numbers calculated from the appropriate equations of Van Vleck are in good agreement with observed values. In Fig. 65 the averages of experimental values at room temperature have been shown and compared with Van Vleck's results.

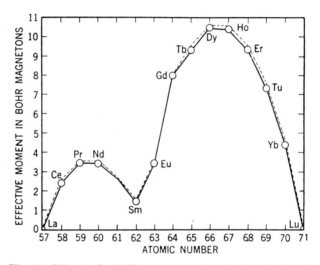

Fig. 65. Effective Bohr Magneton numbers for the trivalent ions of the rare earths at room temperature. The dotted line shows theoretical numbers calculated from the appropriate equations of Van Vleck.

Some remarks may be made concerning the experimentally determined susceptibilities of the trivalent rare earth ions. Although there has been a great accumulation of data in this field, it must be remembered that most of the material used, until quite recently, came from only three or four laboratories where fractional crystallization of rare earths was carried on. Interpretation of experimental results should be weighted somewhat by considerations of source and purity of material. Furthermore, as will be shown later, the ionic environment is not without influence on the susceptibility of rare earth ions, in spite of the shielding of the $4f$ electrons. Most weight is generally given to measurements on hydrated, "magnetically dilute" crystals. By "magnetically dilute" crystals is meant crystals in which the paramagnetic ions do not form a large proportion of the whole; that is, they are so dispersed that their magnetic interactions are relatively small. There is another difficulty and that is that no uniform method has been adopted for reporting ionic susceptibilities. Most workers properly correct for the diamagnetism of solvent and of anion and water of hydration. Few correct for the underlying diamagnetism of the paramagnetic ion itself.

In spite of these difficulties, the agreement between theory and experiment is very satisfactory. Lanthanum and lutetium are diamagnetic. The susceptibilities of the other rare earth trivalent ions lie on two curves, the oxides Dy_2O_3 and Ho_2O_3 being among the most powerfully paramagnetic substances known. The susceptibilities of these ions follow the Curie law with a fair degree of accuracy, except for samarium and europium which are entirely different.

It may be mentioned that several observers have reported magnetic moments in terms of "Weiss magnetons." The Bohr magneton is equal to 4.95 Weiss magnetons.

In addition to the reviews given by Van Vleck (op. cit.[4]) and by Stoner,[13] excellent summaries of experimental work on the rare earths are given by Gorter,[14] and by Cabrera.[15] Some of the more important papers which have appeared since those dates will be mentioned here, together with a few earlier papers.

Dilute solutions of rare earth salts would appear to be the most favorable case for obtaining ionic moments free from complication by mutual interaction. But there have been relatively few measurements made on solutions, and very few over a temperature range. The most extensive work in this field is that of Decker[16] who measured the susceptibilities of aqueous solutions of nitrates or sulfates of all the rare earth elements. The writer[17] measured the susceptibility of neodymium nitrate solutions over a range of concentration. The susceptibility seems to decrease slightly with increasing concentration. The writer also measured the susceptibility of neodymium nitrate in ethyl alcohol solution over a range of temperature.[18] Some unpublished work suggests that the magnetic susceptibilities of rare earth salts in dilute nonaqueous solvents show deviations from additivity. Salts of trivalent cerium in aqueous and in alcoholic solutions

[13] E. C. Stoner, *Magnetism and Matter*. Methuen and Company, Ltd., London, 1934.

[14] C. J. Gorter, *Arch. du Musée Teyler*, **7**, 183 (1932).

[15] B. Cabrera, *Le Magnétisme*, **Vol. III**. Report of the Strasbourg Congress on Magnetism, 1939, pp. 153–186.

[16] H. Decker, *Ann. Physik*, **79**, 324 (1926). A good bibliography is included.

[17] P. W. Selwood, *J. Am. Chem. Soc.*, **53**, 1799 (1931).

[18] P. W. Selwood, *ibid.*, **55**, 3161 (1933).

have been studied over a temperature range by Haenny and Dupouy[19] and by Liquier-Milward.[20] The susceptibility is roughly inverse as the absolute temperature, but there are some irregularities yet to be cleared up. Cabrera, Sanchez, and Menendez[21] report on neodymium chloride solutions over a temperature range, while Dupouy[22] gives data on aqueous solutions of praseodymium, neodymium, samarium, europium, and gadolinium salts over a temperature range. Sanchez[23] has reported on aqueous solutions of praseodymium chloride and neodymium chloride over a temperature range, and Douglas and Yost[24] have reported on europium chloride.

Next to dilute solutions, the octahydrated sulfates of the rare earths are probably most satisfactory. They are fairly easy to prepare in stoichiometrically accurate form. They crystallize well, are readily handled, and are magnetically dilute. Some of the classical low-temperature work has, for instance, been done on $Gd_2(SO_4)_3 \cdot 8H_2O$. Woltjer and Onnes[25,26] measured the susceptibility of this compound down to 1.48°K. over a large range of field strength, and were the first to show that the Langevin formula is obeyed at extremes of cold, even though the fundamental assumptions of the Langevin theory may be shown to be inapplicable. Zernike and James[27] measured the temperature coefficient of susceptibility of all the octahydrated rare earth sulfates except europium, dysprosium, and thulium. De Haas, Wiersma, and Capel[28] report on erbium sulfate octahydrate from 14° to 285°K. Kürti[29] gives magnetic and other data on $Gd_2(SO_4)_3 \cdot 8H_2O$ in the liquid helium region. The susceptibilities of several compounds of praseodymium, neodymium, samarium, and ytterbium at room temperature are given by Rodden.[30] Williams[31] reports on $Gd_2(SO_4)_3 \cdot 8H_2O$ over a temperature range and claims that the susceptibility plotted against reciprocal temperature is a broken line. Velayos[32] gives

[19] C. Haenny and G. Dupouy, Compt. rend., 199, 843 (1934).

[20] J. Liquier-Milward, Proc. Phys. Soc. (London), 47, 559 (1935).

[21] B. Cabrera, A. E. Sanchez, and N. Menendez, Bol. acad. cienc. exactas. fis.-quim. nat. (Madrid), I No. 2, 2 (1955); this paper was not available to the writer.

[22] G. Dupouy, Compt. rend., 202, 646 (1936).

[23] A. E. Sanchez, Rev. acad. cienc. exact., fis. y. nat., Madrid, 34, 202 (1940); this paper was not available to the writer.

[24] D. L. Douglas and D. M. Yost, J. Chem. Phys., 17, 1345 (1949); 18, 1687 (1950).

[25] H. R. Woltjer and K. Onnes, Proc. Acad. Sci. Amsterdam, 26, 626 (1923).

[26] H. R. Woltjer, ibid., 26, 613 (1923).

[27] J. Zernike and C. James, J. Am. Chem. Soc., 48, 2827 (1926).

[28] W. J. de Haas, E. C. Wiersma, and W. H. Capel, Proc. Acad. Sci. Amsterdam, 32, 739 (1929).

[29] N. Kürti, Z. physik. Chem., B20, 305 (1933).

[30] C. J. Rodden, J. Am. Chem. Soc., 56, 648 (1934).

[31] E. H. Williams, Phys. Rev., 46, 133 (1934).

[32] S. Velayos, Anales soc. españ. fis. quim., 33, 297 (1935).

temperature coefficients of susceptibility for the octahydrated sulfates of terbium, dysprosium, holmium, and erbium, while Cabrera, Velayos, and Cabrera[33] give the same for thulium and neodymium. Jackson[34,35] reports on the susceptibilities of octahydrates of ytterbium, dysprosium, erbium, and neodymium over a wide temperature range. Some of the data and conclusions in this paper are later corrected. Some very painstaking researches of Cabrera[36-38] especially on gadolinium, dysprosium, holmium, erbium, and terbium are probably among the most accurate yet performed.

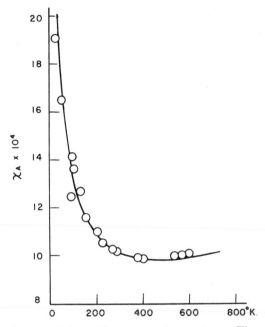

Fig. 66. Ionic susceptibility of Sm^{3+} *versus* temperature. The solid line is the theoretical susceptibility; the points are experimental.

In these papers he describes many of the difficulties of observation and interpretation involved in work on these substances.

Many magnetic measurements have been done on rare earth oxides. These compounds are, of course, easy to prepare once the rare earth itself

[33] B. Cabrera, S. Velayos, and N. Cabrera, *Bol. acad. cienc. Madrid*, **I**, No. **2,** 1 (1935).

[34] L. C. Jackson, *Proc. Phys. Soc. (London)*, **48**, 741 (1936).

[35] L. C. Jackson, *Proc. Roy. Soc. (London)*, **A170**, 266 (1939).

[36] B. Cabrera, *J. phys. radium*, **9**, 209 (1938).

[37] B. Cabrera, *J. chim. phys.*, **36**, 237 (1939).

[38] B. Cabrera, *Anales. soc. españ. fis. quim.*, **35**, 207, (1937).

has been obtained in a state of purity, free from other rare earths.   Because of their high magnetic concentration and the rapidity with which some of them take up carbon dioxide from the air, their susceptibilities are less reliable than those of some other compounds.   Among the many reports on rare earth oxides, those of Velayos[39] on Gd_2O_3, Dy_2O_3, Er_2O_3, Pr_2O_3, and Nd_2O_3, and of Sucksmith[40] on Yb_2O_3, Nd_2O_3, Sm_2O_3, and Eu_2O_3 may be mentioned.

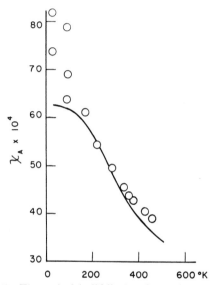

Fig. 67. Theoretical (solid line) and experimental ionic susceptibilities of Eu^{3+} *versus* temperature.   There seems little doubt of a serious discrepancy at low temperatures.

As previously mentioned, compounds of trivalent samarium and europium have temperature coefficients of susceptibility quite different from those of the other rare earths.   The reason for this is that the multiplet levels for these elements are comparable to kT.   A satisfactory agreement with experiment may be obtained by using the general equation (5).   It is, however, not necessary to use the screening constant formula for this calculation, because the multiplet widths for samarium are available and, with a very slight extrapolation, these data may be applied to europium. The results so obtained are in agreement with observed values.

The striking feature about the susceptibilities of samarium and europium is that that of the former is nearly independent of temperature above

[39] S. Velayos, *ibid.*, **31**, 597 (1933); 33, 5 (1935).
[40] W. Sucksmith, *Phil. Mag.*, **14**, 1115 (1932).

about 700°K. while that of europium is nearly independent of temperature below about 100°K. Figures 66 and 67 show such experimental values as are available, toether with Van Vleck's theoretical values.[41–47]

There are no experimental data available on $Eu_2(SO_4)_3 \cdot 8H_2O$ at temperatures much below 100°K. although Fritsch[48] has indicated that the susceptibility is the same at 20° as at 80°K. Trapnell and Selwood[49] have extended measurements on Eu_2O_3 down to liquid hydrogen temperature.

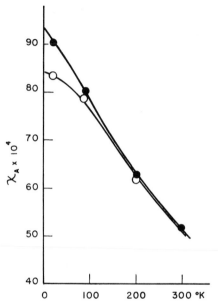

Fig. 68. Susceptibility of Eu^{3+} at low temperatures; ● before and ○ after, exhaustive purification.

The results are shown in Fig. 68 and are not in very good agreement with the Van Vleck theory at 20°K. These observations do, however, offer a rather formidable difficulty. A trace of paramagnetic impurity following the Curie law might have a negligible effect on the apparent susceptibility of europium at room temperature but might have a very great effect at

[41] S. Freed, *J. Am. Chem. Soc.*, **52**, 2702 (1930).

[42] F. H. Spedding, *ibid.*, **54**, 2593 (1932).

[43] E. C. Wiersma and B. H. Schultz, *Physica*, **13**, 171 (1933).

[44] P. W. Selwood, *J. Am. Chem. Soc.*, **56**, 2392 (1934).

[45] O. E. Frivold and L. Lunde, *Physik Z.*, **39**, 571 (1938).

[46] G. Hughes and D. W. Pearce, *J. Am. Chem. Soc.*, **55**, 3277 (1933).

[47] P. W. Selwood, *ibid.*, **55**, 4869 (1933).

[48] H. Fritsch, *Ann. Physik*, **39**, 31 (1941).

[49] B. M. W. Trapnell and P. W. Selwood, *Nature*, **169**, 840 (1952).

temperatures approaching absolute zero. Although the sample of europium sesquioxide was spectroscopically pure, the presence of a trace of gadolinium is difficult to exclude.

Magnetic anisotropy in crystalline rare earth compounds will not greatly concern us, although further reference to the effects of crystalline fields will be made in the next section. Van Vleck[4] points out that paramagnetic crystalline matter may be divided into three groups: (a) crystals in which the electrical fields have little influence on the coupling between the orbital and spin moments; (b) crystals in which the fields are strong enough to break down the spin-orbital coupling but not the Russell-Saunders-coupling between electrons; and (c) crystals in which the fields are large enough to break down the Russell-Saunders coupling.

Compounds of the rare earth elements belong to the first group, but even the influence of the crystalline field is by no means negligible. The result of presence of a local orienting field will be:

(1) A value for the effective moment which will bear no simple relation to the spin and orbital moments. As will be seen in a later section, this effect is marked for ions in which the electrons responsible for paramagnetism are not so well shielded as they are in the rare earths.

(2) A complicated deviation from the Curie law. Even for the magnetically dilute rare earth sulfate octahydrates, the deviations may be appreciable.

(3) Magnetic anisotropy will appear unless the crystal has cubic symmetry. For many rare earth crystals, the anisotropy is somewhat greater than might have been anticipated.

There have been several investigations of the paramagnetic anisotropy of the rare earths. The above conclusions are verified by Krishnan and Mookherji[50] and by others. A good introduction to both theory and experiment is given by Jackson.[51]

The familiar reactions of analytical chemistry have little application to the analysis of rare earth mixtures. Recourse must in most instances be made to physical methods, some of which are unique in this field. In recent years, the absorption spectra have been widely used for analytical purposes, but the history of the rare earths contains many references to analysis by measurement of magnetic susceptibilities. The magnetic method is still not infrequently used and, although it is generally limited to binary mixtures, it is a powerful method. For instance, a mixture of lanthanum oxide and of gadolinium oxide could quickly be analyzed quantita-

[50] K. S. Krishnan and A. Mookherji, Phil. Trans. Roy. Soc. (London), A237, 135 (1938).

[51] L. C. Jackson, Proc. Roy. Soc. (London), A140, 695 (1933).

tively by a susceptibility measurement, although such an analysis would be at best tedious by any other method.

Magnetic analysis of rare earth mixtures has frequently been done on the Curie-Chéneveau balance, although other balances may be used. The method is based on the Wiedemann mixture law, $\chi = \chi_1 p_1 + \chi_2 p_2 + \cdots \chi_n p_n$, where χ is the susceptibility of the mixture and $\chi_1 p_1$ etc. are the susceptibilities and weight fractions of the respective constituents of the mixture. The temperature coefficient of susceptibility for most paramagnetic substances is only about $1/300$ per degree at room temperature. No careful control of temperature is necessary unless accuracy better than 1% is aimed at, and this is not often achieved. Most such analyses are done on the oxides, although the additional trouble of preparing solutions is probably worth while in terms of increased accuracy. Table X shows susceptibilities per gram for the known rare earth sesquioxides at 20°C.

TABLE X

Magnetic Susceptibilities of Rare Earths at 20°C.

Oxide	$\chi \times 10^6$	Oxide	$\chi \times 10^6$
Y_2O_3	-0.2	Tb_2O_3	—
La_2O_3	-0.4	Dy_2O_3	230
Ce_2O_3	—	Ho_2O_3	229
Pr_2O_3	27	Er_2O_3	199
Nd_2O_3	29	Tu_2O_3	133
Sm_2O_3	6	Yb_2O_3	33
Eu_2O_3	29	Lu_2O_3	-0.3
Gd_2O_3	135		

Rare earths were formerly separated by a fractionational-crystallization process. Approaching purity was sometimes determined by plotting magnetic susceptibility against fraction number. A horizontal region in such a plot is evidence for isolation of a pure substance. For the diamagnetic rare earths La_2O_3 and Lu_2O_3, the magnetic criterion of purity may be made quite sensitive by conducting the measurements at low temperature. It will be clear that magnetic analysis of rare earth oxide mixtures is possible only because sequestration of the $4f$ electrons makes interaction effects between adjacent paramagnetic ions negligible, or nearly so.

43. The "Molecular Field"

It is an illuminating fact that the magnetic susceptibility of many substances may be represented by the relation $\chi = C/(T + \Delta)$ much better than by the simple Curie law $\chi = C/T$. On classical theoretical grounds, Weiss[52] obtained this expression by consideration of the mutual interaction

[52] P. Weiss, *J. phys.*, **6**, 661 (1907).

of the elementary magnets or molecular magnetic fields. Although Δ is no longer entirely identified with this supposed field, the name is often retained. We shall refer to Δ as the "Weiss constant." This constant has been discussed at length by Van Vleck,[4] Gorter,[53,54] Kramers,[55,56] and by many others. In fact it has received attention which some consider out of all proportion to its importance. The significance of Δ in the light of present knowledge is threefold.*

First, Δ may appear as an empirical constant from the fact that the multiplet intervals are neither very large nor very small compared with kT. In this case the Curie constant, C, will itself change with temperature, and Δ will have no real significance and probably will not remain constant over a very large temperature interval. This is the case that arises with samarium and europium, as has just been described. But for neodymium, calculation shows that neglect of the multiplet levels adds only 3% to the susceptibility at room temperature. Gadolinium has also received attention in this connection but here, of course, we are not bothered with multiplet structure as the Gd^{3+} ion is in an S state.

The second source of the molecular-field constant is the effect of inhomogeneous electric fields produced by neighboring ions or oriented solvent dipoles on the orbital moment of the $4f$ electrons. Measurements at low temperatures are of special interest because they indicate the size of the interatomic forces tending to orient the $4f$ orbits. Penney and Schlapp[57] have examined theoretically the influence of crystalline fields on the susceptibilities of praseodymium and neodymium, as well as certain other rare earths whose experimental examination has been less thorough. Assuming cubic symmetry for the octahydrated sulfates, they find that the field causes a splitting of the multiplet levels and consequent redistribution of the magnetic moment. At ordinary temperatures, kT is of the same order as the energy separations produced by the field and the susceptibility actually appears to follow the Weiss law over a wide temperature range, although here again Δ has no real significance. At low temperatures, the $1/\chi$, T relationship should bend away from the temperature axis for praseodymium and toward it for neodymium. The theory of Penney and Schlapp is in agreement with Gorter's experimental results on praseodymium and neodymium sulfate octahydrates, but in somewhat less satisfactory agree-

---

* Many authors write the Curie-Weiss law with a negative sign for the Weiss constant, e.g., $\chi = C (T - \theta)$. We have adhered to the convention adopted by Van Vleck.

[53] C. J. Gorter and W. J. deHaas, *Proc. Acad. Sci. Amsterdam*, **34**, 1243 (1931).

[54] C. J. Gorter, *Phys. Rev.*, **42**, 437 (1932).

[55] H. A. Kramers, *Proc. Acad. Sci. Amsterdam*, **35**, 1272 (1932); **36**, 17 (1933).

[56] H. A. Kramers, *Physica*, **1**, 182 (1934).

[57] W. G. Penney and R. Schlapp, *Phys. Rev.*, **41**, 194 (1932).

ment with those of Selwood,[58] Jackson,[59] and others, on the latter compound. Gorter's results on this element have been shown by Van den Handel[60] to be in error. Further studies of the crystalline field and its effect on magnetic properties of the rare earths have been made by Penney,[61] Spedding,[62] and Fritsch.[63] There seems little doubt that, so far as the crystalline fields are concerned, the Weiss constant does not well represent the experimental facts over a wide temperature range and has no simple theoretical significance. The development of paramagnetic resonance has led to some spectacularly successful advances in this area. The reason for this is that the fine structure as observed at high resolution may be directly related to the symmetry of the electric field in which the paramagnetic atom or ion is placed. Whether or not resonance will be observed, and what will be the detailed fine structure, depend on the spectroscopic state of the ion as well as on the crystal-field symmetry. It will also depend on possible interactions between adjacent paramagnetic ions. Such interactions may be observed at effective concentrations far lower than is possible with static susceptibility measurements. For this reason many resonance studies have been made on magnetically dilute compounds such as the rare earth ethylsulfates, or even on dilute solutions of the paramagnetic ethylsulfates in the diamagnetic lanthanum ethylsulfate. This area has not yet attracted great interest on the part of chemists, but it doubtless will do so in view of the rate at which the resonance methods are being adopted in chemical laboratories. An excellent review of the field is given by Bleaney and Stevens.[64]

The third, and final, source of Δ lies in the Heisenberg exchange interaction. When magnetic atoms or ions are very close together, this interaction has the effect of introducing a very strong coupling between the respective spins. This is the effect responsible for ferromagnetism in Heisenberg's theory of that subject. In this discussion, we are interested only in behavior above the Curie point; that is, above the temperature at which ferromagnetism turns into paramagnetism. As a matter of fact, the Curie point often lies below $0°K$. and so is imaginary. We have the relationship

$$\chi_M = \frac{4N\beta S(S + 1)}{3k(T - T_c)} \tag{6}$$

[58] P. W. Selwood, *J. Am. Chem. Soc.*, **55**, 3161 (1933).
[59] L. C. Jackson, *Proc. Roy. Soc. (London)*, **A170**, 266 (1939).
[60] J. van den Handel, *Physica*, **14**, 618 (1949).
[61] W. G. Penney, *Phys. Rev.*, **43**, 485 (1933).
[62] F. H. Spedding, *J. Chem. Phys.*, **5**, 316 (1937).
[63] H. Fritsch, *Ann. Physik*, **38**, 555 (1940).
[64] B. Bleaney and K. W. H. Stevens, *Repts. on Progress in Physics*, **16**, 108 (1953).

where
$$T_c = \frac{2JzS(S + 1)}{3k} \qquad (7)$$

J (following Van Vleck's notation) is here the exchange integral, z is the number of equidistant neighbors with which the atom has exchange coupling. For example, for a linear chain, $z = 2$, for a simple cubic system, $z = 6$. The other terms have their usual significance. Equation (6) is equivalent to $\chi = C/(T + \Delta)$. This relation of the Heisenberg exchange interaction to the temperature coefficient of magnetic susceptibility has proved to be useful in structural inorganic chemistry. A later section will be devoted to this topic. But it must be pointed out that the whole subject of exchange interaction between adjacent or neighboring paramagnetic atoms and ions is in a state of development. This is particularly true with reference to ferromagnetic and to antiferromagnetic substances, which will be discussed in later chapters. Exchange effects are small but not negligible in rare earth compounds.

Turning now to some pertinent experimental data, information is given in Table XI[47,58] for some gadolinium compounds.

TABLE XI

Weiss Constants for Some Compounds of Gadolinium

Compound	$\Delta°C.$
Gd_2O_3	18 ± 2
$GdCl_3$	14
$Gd_2(SO_4)_3 \cdot 8H_2O$	2 (or zero)

For gadolinium there is no multiplet structure so that Δ must here be due solely to exchange forces. The order of compounds written down is almost certainly the order of increasing "magnetic dilution," that is, the Gd^{3+} ions are getting farther apart. It is therefore gratifying to see Δ decreasing until, in the octahydrated sulfate, the exchange forces are presumably negligible. Gadolinium is the only trivalent paramagnetic rare earth in which Δ approaches zero in any compound, and is the only one in an S state.

Neodymium is somewhat more complicated, as shown in Table XII. Here one must contend with both exchange forces and the crystalline-field effect; while the exchange forces become negligible, the crystalline-field splitting produced by oriented-water dipoles remains constant and fairly large, even at the highest magnetic dilution.

As the crystalline field can scarcely be constant in all the compounds used, it would be of interest to know precisely what part of the change from 45° to 59°C. is produced by each effect. This has been done by hold-

TABLE XII

Weiss Constants for Some Compounds of Neodymium

Compound	$\Delta\,^{\circ}$C.
Nd_2O_3	59
NdF_3	54
$Nd(NO_3)_3$	49
$Nd(ClO_4)_3$	48
$Nd_2(SO_4)_3 \cdot 8H_2O$	45
Nd^{3+} in solution	45

ing the crystalline field constant while the magnetic dilution is increased. Solid solutions were made of neodymium oxide in the diamagnetic and structurally similar lanthanum oxide. It was formerly thought that even diamagnetic atoms would have strong mutual magnetic interactions, but both Van Vleck and Slater have shown that atoms or ions with closed shells, and hence diamagnetic, have no exchange interaction. The results obtained are shown in Table XIII.

TABLE XIII

Molecular Field Constant in Solid Solutions of Neodymium Oxide in Lanthanum Oxide

% Nd_2O_3 in La_2O_3	$\Delta\,^{\circ}$C.
50	55
10	32
2	30

Of course, the experimental error is quite large in these measurements, but they show that practically all the change in Δ in the various compounds is due to exchange forces. This work also illustrates the use, apparently for the first time, of the method of diluting paramagnetic substances with diamagnetic isomorphous substances in which the ionic radii are comparable. This technique, to which reference will be made again, has proved useful in the study of many substances in which exchange effects tend to obscure the interpretation. It will be clear that the exchange forces are very small even in the most magnetically concentrated rare earth compound. In fact, it has been shown by Trombe[65] that these forces are small even in rare earth metals, although gadolinium and one or two other rare earth metals become ferromagnetic and thus exhibit strong exchange effects as the temperature is lowered. This emphasizes the remarkable sequestration of the $4f$ electrons in the rare earths. As will be shown later, the situation is very different in the transition elements of the iron series.

[65] F. Trombe, *Compt. rend.*, 219, 182 (1944).

One further point which will be mentioned here is the suggested use of a second arbitrary constant in the Curie-Weiss law. The law then becomes $(\chi + a) = C/(T + \Delta)$. The constant a generally represents a small positive susceptibility which is independent of temperature. Temperature-independent paramagnetism is by no means unknown, and it is true that some experimental results are better represented by inclusion of the constant a. Nevertheless, it seems difficult to find any theoretical basis for some of the cases in which it has been applied. The question is discussed at length by Cabrera[15] and by Foëx.[66]

44. Non-Trivalent Rare Earths

It is well known that certain members of the rare earth family exhibit valences other than three. Cerium is readily oxidized to the ceric, Ce^{4+}, state, praseodymium and terbium form higher oxides, and samarium, europium, and ytterbium may be reduced to the divalent state. Reviews of this field are given by Pearce,[67] by Pearce and Selwood,[68] and by Yost, Russell, and Garner.[69]

The Sommerfield-Kössel rule states that ions with equal numbers of electrons often have very similar properties. The magnetic susceptibility of the Fe^{3+} ion is, for instance, in fair agreement with that of the Mn^{2+} ion. According to this rule, the ceric ion, Ce^{4+}, should be diamagnetic like La^{3+}. Ceric oxide, CeO_2, has not been investigated as thoroughly as might be desired, but measurements tend to show that it has a small, temperature-independent paramagnetism.[70] This view has been supported by Foëx[71] who studied carefully purified $Ce(SO_4)_2 \cdot 4H_2O$. The compound is diamagnetic, but after correction for the diamagnetism of the sulfate group and the water, the molar susceptibility of the ceric ion is 22×10^{-6}. The ion, therefore, shows a slight paramagnetism similar to that shown by certain other transition group elements in the oxidation state in which they have the same number of electrons as an inert gas. This result is a natural consequence of Van Vleck's theory of atomic magnetism in which it is shown that the temperature-independent term may be either positive or negative. It is clear, at least from the magnetic measurements, that ceric oxide is a true dioxide and not a peroxide, but the corresponding

[66] G. Foëx, *Le Magnétisme*, **Vol. III.** Report of the Strasbourg Congress on Magnetism, 1939, p. 187.

[67] D. W. Pearce, *Chem. Rev.*, **16**, 121 (1935).

[68] D. W. Pearce and P. W. Selwood, *J. Chem. Education*, **13**, 224 (1936).

[69] D. M. Yost, H. Russell, Jr., and C. S. Garner, *The Rare Earth Elements and Their Compounds.* J. Wiley and Sons, Inc., New York, 1946.

[70] S. Meyer, *Ann. Physik*, **68**, 325 (1899).

[71] G. Foëx, *Compt. rend.*, **208**, 738 (1939).

sulfides appear to be of polysulfide structure,[72] because the compound CeS_2 (or Ce_2S_4) has about the same susceptibility as Ce_2S_3. If CeS_2 contained tetravalent cerium, the compound would presumably be diamagnetic or at least have a much lower susceptibility.

The higher oxides of praseodymium and of terbium, PrO_2 and TbO_2, are rather difficult to characterize exactly, but early measurements by Meyer seem to indicate that their susceptibilities are at least in rough agreement with the Sommerfeld-Kössel rule, as do measurements on PrO_2 by Klemm[73] and by Cabrera and Duperier.[74] More recently, Rabideau[75] in a study of Pr_2O_3, PrO_2, and of the intermediate oxide Pr_6O_{11}, reports that the praseodymium in PrO_2 follows the Curie-Weiss law with $\Delta = 104°$ and a magnetic moment of 2.48. This is in agreement with the moment expected for the isoelectronic ion Ce^{3+}. The oxide Pr_6O_{11}, in contrast to both Pr_2O_3 and PrO_2, does not follow the Curie-Weiss law. The possibility that this may be related to antiferromagnetism and that PrO_2, like the ferrites, may become ferromagnetic at low temperatures is discussed by Yosida.[76]

The most carefully studied isoelectronic pair is Eu^{2+} and Gd^{3+}. The molar susceptibility[77,78] of Eu^{2+} in the compound $EuSO_4$ at 20°C. is about $25,800 \times 10^{-6}$; Douglas and Yost[79] give $26,250 \times 10^{-6}$ at 25°C. An average value for Gd^{3+} is $25,700 \times 10^{-6}$. By comparison, the susceptibility of the Eu^{3+} ion is only 4940×10^{-6}. Furthermore, far from showing an erratic temperature coefficient like Eu^{3+}, Eu^{2+} follows the law $\chi = C/(T + \Delta)$. From considerations previously discussed, the value $\Delta = 4$ may be regarded as due to exchange forces, because $EuSO_4$ is not a very "dilute" compound, magnetically speaking. It is unlikely that any rare earth ion other than one in an S state could have such a low value for the Weiss constant. It may, therefore, be concluded that the electronic configuration of the Eu^{2+} ion is identical with that of the Gd^{3+} ion. The outer electron grouping of europium is $\ldots 4f^75s^25p^65d^06s^2$. In trivalent europium the two $6s$ and one of the $4f$ electrons are removed. In divalent europium it appears that the extra electron remains in the $4f$ shell (instead of going into the $5d$ level) leaving a structure identical with that of Gd^{3+}, namely, $\ldots 4f^75s^25p^6$.

[72] W. Klemm, K. Meisel, and H. V. v. Vogel, Z. anorg. u. allgem. Chem., **190**, 123 (1930).

[73] W. Klemm, Z. angew. Chem., **44**, 254 (1931).

[74] B. Cabrera and A. Duperier, Compt. rend., **188**, 1640 (1929).

[75] S. W. Rabideau, J. Chem. Phys., **19**, 874 (1951).

[76] K. Yosida, ibid., **20**, 202 (1952).

[77] G. Hughes and D. W. Pearce, J. Am. Chem. Soc., **55**, 3277 (1933).

[78] P. W. Selwood, ibid., **55**, 4869 (1933).

[79] D. L. Douglas and D. M. Yost, J. Chem. Phys., **17**, 1345 (1949).

Klemm and his co-workers[80] have made a thorough study of divalent europium compounds. Europium dichloride, dibromide, and diiodide all give an effective Bohr magneton number of 7.9 for the Eu^{2+} ion, the same as the Gd^{3+} ion. Europous fluoride gives $\mu_{eff} = 7.4$, but this low value may be due to contamination of the compound with EuF_3, or to variations in the lattice. Fair agreement is also obtained from europous sulfide, selenide, and telluride. The large change of susceptibility which occurs during the reaction $Eu^{3+} + \epsilon \rightarrow Eu^{2+}$ makes it possible to study the kinetics of this reaction, *in situ* so to speak, by carrying the reaction

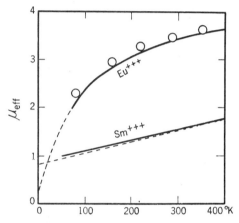

Fig. 69. Effective Bohr Magneton numbers for the ions Sm^{3+}, Sm^{2+}, and Eu^{3+} *versus* temperature. The solid lines are for the trivalent ions as shown. The experimental points are for the divalent, Sm^{2+}, ion.

out in solution in the Gouy balance.[79] There is nothing unique about this because a great variety of similar studies may be made on other reactions, such as the reduction of dichromate ion, of cupric ion, and so forth, all of which involve large susceptibility changes. But it will be recalled (p. 65) that the effect of paramagnetic ions on the proton relaxation time depends on the spin-orbital coupling in the paramagnetic ion. This coupling is strong in Eu^{3+}, but of course absent in Eu^{2+} because the latter, being isoelectronic with Gd^{3+}, must be in an S spectroscopic state. It may, therefore, be expected that the longitudinal proton relaxation time in the presence of Eu^{3+} will suffer a quite large decrease as reduction to Eu^{2+} proceeds as, for instance, when zinc dust is added to a Eu^{3+} aqueous solution containing a little acid. This effect, resulting from a combination of in-

[80] W. Klemm and W. Döll, *Z. anorg. u. allgem. chem.*, **241**, 233 (1939).

creased magnetic moment together with disappearance of spin-orbital coupling, has been observed by Hickmott and Selwood.[81]

Similar considerations apply to the ytterbous ion, Yb^{2+}, which is isoelectronic with the diamagnetic lutetium ion, Lu^{3+}. The compounds $YbSO_4$ and $YbCl_2$ have been studied by Hughes and Pearce[77] and by Klemm and Schüth,[82] respectively. There is still some doubt whether the Yb^{2+} ion is diamagnetic or, like Ce^{4+}, has a small temperature-independent paramagnetism. Hughes and Pearce report a molar susceptibility of 142×10^{-6} for the Yb^{2+} ion. In the trivalent oxide, Yb^{3+} has a molar susceptibility of about 7260×10^{-6}, and it is rather difficult to be sure that all the ytterbium has been reduced. It would be interesting to have accurate data on the temperature coefficient of susceptibility for, say, $YbSO_4$. Some unpublished work by the author suggests that the susceptibility is independent of temperature. Senff and Klemm[83] have studied the selenides and tellurides of bivalent ytterbium. During reduction of Yb_2Te_3 to YbTe the susceptibility drops sharply and may be used to measure the degree of reduction.

Still another isoelectronic pair of rare earths is bivalent samarium, Sm^{2+}, and trivalent europium, Eu^{3+}. Measurements on the compound $SmBr_2$ have been reported by Klemm and Rockstroh[84] and by the author.[78]

Figure 69 shows the effective Bohr magneton numbers for Sm^{3+}, Sm^{2+}, and Eu^{3+}, plotted against temperature. The solid lines are for the trivalent ions of samarium and europium, and the experimental points are for bivalent samarium. The dotted lines show theoretical extension of the data to absolute zero. It is not possible to estimate the Weiss constant with any degree of accuracy, and it is doubtful if it would have any significance even if obtained. But in view of the correspondence at all temperatures investigated, it is probably safe to say that the electronic configurations of the Sm^{2+} and Eu^{3+} ions are also identical.

45. Transition Group Elements and Their Ions

In this section, some general remarks will be made concerning the elements of the first transition group. More detailed discussion of each paramagnetic ion will be given later.

Just as for the rare earths, the main transition group elements possess an incomplete inner electron shell. For these elements the incomplete shell is by no means so effectively shielded from external influence as it is in the rare earths. Generally, this leads to a considerable degree of quench-

[81] T. W. Hickmott and P. W. Selwood, *J. Chem. Phys.*, **20**, 1339 (1952).
[82] W. Klemm and W. Schüth, *Z. anorg. u. allgem. chem.*, **184**, 352 (1929).
[83] H. Senff and W. Klemm, *ibid.*, **241**, 259; **242**, 92 (1939).
[84] W. Klemm and J. Rockstroh, *ibid.*, **176**, 181 (1928).

ing of the orbital contribution to the magnetic moment, and in some cases the results are actually easier to interpret than are those for the rare earths.

The ions of the first transition group, starting with the scandium, Sc^{3+}, ion and ending with the zinc, Zn^{2+}, ion have progressively 0 to 10 electrons in the $3d$ shell. The first and last members are diamagnetic, but all the others with intermediate numbers of electrons are paramagnetic. It might be supposed that these ions would be alternately paramagnetic and diamagnetic, depending on whether they had an odd or an even number of electrons. But, as for the rare earths, the ions are all paramagnetic; the electrons in the incomplete shell do not tend to pair off until they are forced to do so. For instance, in the $3d$ shell there are five orbitals available, each of which may hold two electrons. If six electrons are present they will take one paired and four unpaired places instead of three pairs. The four unpaired electrons will contribute to the paramagnetism. It is, therefore, an easy matter to compute the number of unpaired electron spins in any given ion.

A surprising feature that arises with these ions is in connection with the orbital contribution to the magnetic moment. The orbital moments of such ions are not protected from external influence as they are for the rare earths and yet, on the other hand, they may not be entirely quenched. Various efforts have been made to compute the effective moment of these ions, assuming that the multiplet intervals are infinitely wide compared to kT, or that they are infinitely small compared to kT. Calculations have also been made using the actual multiplet intervals where these are known from spectroscopic data. But the best agreement with experiment is obtained by completely neglecting the orbital moments. The various types of calculations, together with comparison with experiment are given by Van Vleck (op. cit.,[4] p. 285). For ions such as Fe^{3+} or Mn^{2+}, which are in S states, the question of orbital moment does not enter. The result of theoretical calculations for these ions agrees well with experiment. But even for ions which are not in S states, the moments calculated on a spin-only basis are often in excellent agreement with theory. Of course, many of the transition group elements form covalent bonds. When this occurs the magnetism is greatly modified. In fact, as will be shown in Chapter X, the deviation of the susceptibility from the normal has been used to determine the possible covalency of bonds and the spatial configuration of complex molecules.

The paramagnetic part of the susceptibility of a transition group element is approximately represented by the spin-only formula

$$\chi_M = \frac{N\beta^2 4S(S+1)}{3kT}$$

and the effective moment in Bohr magnetons by

$$\mu_{\text{eff}} = 2\sqrt{S(S + 1)}$$

If the multiplicity, $2S + 1$, is known, S may readily be found, or if the number, n, of unpaired electrons is known,

$$\mu_{\text{eff}} = \sqrt{n(n + 2)}$$

It is clear, therefore, that the magnetic susceptibility is not directly proportional to the number of unpaired electrons, but rather to $n(n + 2)$. This is a fact which sometimes has caused confusion because it is erroneously assumed that two unpaired electrons would produce twice the molar paramagnetism of one.   Justification for use of the spin-only formula has been found by consideration of the crystalline fields produced by neighboring ions or oriented solvent dipoles.   In most cases it is possible to assume a field adequate to quench the orbital contribution completely.

Comparison of theoretical magneton numbers with experiment is, for transition group elements, complicated by the possibility of hydrolysis and of other chemical changes which do not occur so readily with the rare earths.   Table XIV gives the various ions in the first transition group with

TABLE XIV

Theoretical and Effective Bohr Magneton Numbers for Ions of First Transition Group

Ion	$3d$ electrons	Term	$\mu_{\text{eff}} = \sqrt{n(n+2)}$	μ_{eff}(obs.)
Sc^{3+} Ti^{4+} V^{5+}	0	$^1S_0$	0.00	0.0
Ti^{3+} V^{4+}	1	$^2D_{3/2}$	1.73	1.77–1.79
V^{3+}	2	$^3F_2$	2.83	2.76–2.85
V^{2+} Cr^{3+} Mn^{4+}	3	$^4F_{3/2}$	3.87	3.68–4.00
Cr^{2+} Mn^{3+}	4	$^5D_0$	4.90	4.80–5.06
Mn^{2+} Fe^{3+}	5	$^6S_{5/2}$	5.92	5.2 –6.0
Fe^{2+}	6	$^5D_4$	4.90	5.0 –5.5
Co^{2+}	7	$^4F_{9/2}$	3.87	4.4 –5.2
Ni^{2+}	8	$^3F_4$	2.83	2.9 –3.4
Cu^{2+}	9	$^2D_{5/2}$	1.73	1.8 –2.2
Cu^{1+} Zn^{2+}	10	$^1S_0$	0.00	0.0

their spin-only theoretical effective Bohr magneton numbers and the best available experimental data.

A few remarks concerning these data may be in order. It must be realized that, owing to crystalline-field and exchange effects, the simple Curie law is rarely obeyed, so that T in the above expression for χ_M must generally be replaced by $T + \Delta$. But deviations from the Weiss law are also common, especially at low temperatures, and it is seldom possible to calculate χ_M accurately over a very wide temperature range. Furthermore, variations of susceptibility with concentration are reported by many experimenters for salts of transition group elements. Oxides and other magnetically concentrated substances are notoriously peculiar in their magnetic properties and little agreement is to be expected from measurements on such compounds. It will also be noticed that the magneton numbers of all ions in an isoelectronic sequence are given as the same. Actually, they should increase slightly with increasing atomic number because the multiplet intervals are increasing. Finally, it will be noticed that the agreement of theory with experiment is slightly better in the first half of the transition series than in the second. This may possibly be due to rather less complete quenching of the orbital component in the second half. But taking everything into consideration, the agreement is satisfactory except for cobalt.

In addition to the rare earths and the first transition series just discussed, there are three other transition series of elements in the periodic table. These include the series beginning with yttrium and ending with cadmium; and the series, of which the rare earths form a sub-series, beginning with lanthanum and ending with mercury. For these the incomplete electron shells are respectively the 4d and the 5d. Actinium through element 101 (not yet named at this writing) form part of another transition sub-series in which the 5f electron shell may be incomplete.

In the following sections the ionic paramagnetism of the various transition group elements will be discussed. Attention in this chapter will be confined to magnetically dilute substances. It must be pointed out that the use of hydrated crystals and aqueous solutions is by no means the only way in which magnetic dilution may be achieved. Supported oxides and colloidal oxides may exhibit surprising degrees of magnetic dilution. The study of such substances and mixtures makes up one of the most important branches of magnetochemistry. Some reference to these will be made in this chapter, but most will be deferred to Chapter 15. Extensive references to the earlier literature will be found in the books of Van Vleck[4] and of Stoner.[13] In addition, the references listed below may be useful.[85-89]

[85] G. Foëx, *Ann. phys.*, 16, 174 (1921).
[86] C. J. Gorter, *Physica*, 11, 171 (1931).

As previously mentioned, there is a method for studying the magnetic properties of transition elements in general and, although so far applied to only a few elements, it has given results of considerable interest. This method consists of preparing solid solutions of a paramagnetic substance in an isomorphous diamagnetic substance and in this way obtaining the susceptibility of the paramagnetic ion at, so to speak, infinite magnetic dilution. Some studies of dissolved metals and of mixed hydrated salts may perhaps fall in this class, but the most useful type of study seems to be that in which a transition metal oxide or fluoride is dissolved in an isomorphous diamagnetic oxide or fluoride, as the case may be. The crystal field in such cases is generally known, and the effect of exchange interaction may be progressively reduced by increasing dilution. The positive ions must have the same radius within about 15% if true solid solutions are to be formed. Solutions such as Cr_2O_3-Al_2O_3, UO_2-ThO_2, and PuF_4-ThF_4 have been studied in this way, and the results will be described below.

46. Elements of First Transition Series

Titanium. If divalent titanium forms any magnetically dilute compounds, they have so far escaped magnetochemical investigation. Trivalent titanium, especially in the alum, ought to have a spin-only moment and to follow the Curie law to very low temperatures.[90] Tetravalent titanium is diamagnetic. There is no question that the Ti^{3+} ion is paramagnetic and that it has a moment corresponding closely to one unpaired electron spin. Several substances and mixtures containing this ion will be referred to in later chapters. Adler and Selwood[91] have studied solid solutions of Ti_2O_3 in the diamagnetic oxide, Al_2O_3. The observations are somewhat difficult because of the low susceptibility and the formation in trace amounts of ferromagnetic impurities. A 14.3% Ti_2O_3 solution gave a moment for Ti^{3+} of 1.1 and $\Delta = 105°$. This is about what is to be expected for a solution of this concentration.

Vanadium. Freed[92] has studied di-, tri-, and tetravalent vanadium and finds the effective Bohr magneton numbers to be respectively 1.745, 2.760, and 3.805 to 3.855. These are in close agreement with the theoretical, assuming complete orbital quenching. Vanadium alum, $V_2(SO_4)_3 \cdot$

[87] W. J. de Haas and E. C. Wiersma, *Rapports et Communications, VI ième Čongr. Intern. Froid*, Buenos Aires. *Communications Kamerlingh Onnes Lab. Univ. Leiden*, **Suppl. No. 74**, 36 (1932).

[88] B. Cabrera, *Inst. Intern. Phys. Solvay, VI ième, Conseil Phys.*, **81** (1932).

[89] G. Foëx, *J. phys. radium*, **4**, 517 (1933).

[90] J. H. Van Vleck, *J. Chem. Phys.*, **7**, 61 (1939).

[91] S. F. Adler and P. W. Selwood, *J. Am. Chem. Soc.*, **76**, 346 (1954).

[92] S. Freed, *ibid.*, **49**, 2456 (1927).

$(NH_4)_2SO_4 \cdot 24H_2O$, has been studied by van den Handel and Siegert.[93,94] Over the range from 293°C. down to liquid helium temperatures, the Curie-Weiss law is obeyed with a moment of 2.62 which is only slightly less than the theoretical spin-only value for trivalent vanadium.

Chromium. The chromous ion, Cr^{2+}, has been studied by Lips[95] in the sulfate hexahydrate, $CrSO_4.6H_2O$. Over the temperature range from 54° to 400°K., he finds the Curie-Weiss law to be obeyed, with a Bohr magneton number of 4.82, in agreement with the spin-only formula. For other chromous compounds studied, the susceptibility is a complicated function of temperature.

The susceptibilities of chromic salts have received considerable attention. The compound $Cr_2(SO_4)_2(OH)_2 \cdot 5H_2O$ has been shown by Gorter, de Haas, and van den Handel[96] to follow the Curie-Weiss law with $\Delta = 36°$ and $\mu = 3.7$ Bohr magnetons. This is close to the theoretical moment for three electron spins. In the compound $[CrCl_2(OH_2)_4]Cl \cdot 2H_2O$ the Weiss constant is only 0.4°, $\mu = 3.8$. The susceptibilities of anhydrous chromic salts seem nearly always to be lower than those of the hydrated salts and are often more difficult to understand.

The magnetic anisotropies of chromic salts have also received attention. Jackson,[97] and Krishnan, Mookherji, and Bose[98] have shown that potassium and ammonium chromioxalates have unusually low magnetic anisotropies. The influence of crystalline fields on the susceptibilities of chromium and other transition group salts is studied theoretically by Schlapp and Penney.[99]

The method of diamagnetic dilution has been used by Thilo and Jander[100,101] and also by the author[102] for the system Cr_2O_3–Al_2O_3. The results, which are in substantial agreement, show the changes which occur in all the systems so far studied by this method. This is a progressive decrease of Weiss constant which becomes effectively zero at infinite dilution. This can only mean that exchange effects have been rendered negligible by this technique. The magnetic moment of the chromic ion at infinite dilution is

[93] A. Siegert, *Physica*, **4**, 138 (1937).

[94] J. van den Handel and A. Siegert, *ibid.*, **4**, 871 (1937).

[95] E. Lips, *Helv. Phys. Acta*, **7**, 537 (1934).

[96] C. J. Gorter, W. J. de Haas, and J. van den Handel, *Proc. Acad. Sci. Amsterdam*, **36**, 168 (1933).

[97] L. C. Jackson, *Proc. Roy. Soc. (London)*, **A140**, 695 (1933).

[98] K. S. Krishnan, A. Mookherji, and A. Bose, *Phil. Trans. Roy. Soc. (London)*, **A238**, 125 (1939).

[99] R. Schlapp and W. G. Penney, *Phys. Rev.*, **42**, 666 (1932).

[100] E. Thilo, J. Jander, H. Seemann, and R. Sauer, *Naturwissenschaften*, **37**, 399 (1950).

[101] E. Thilo and J. Jander, *Forschungen v. Fortschr.*, **26**, 35 (1950).

[102] P. W. Selwood, L. Lyon, and M. Ellis, *J. Am. Chem. Soc.*, **73**, 2310 (1951).

3.8 Bohr magnetons. The effect of dilution is shown by the observation that a 43% Cr_2O_3–Al_2O_3 solution at liquid air temperature has a suscepti- bility twice that of pure, crystalline chromia at the same temperature. The results are shown in Fig. 70. It might have been hoped that these data would show why Cr_2O_3–Al_2O_3 solid solutions dilute in chromia are ruby-colored while those of higher chromia concentration are green. As pointed out by Thilo, this may be due to the fact that below about 8% chromium, exchange interaction is reduced to a minimum because each

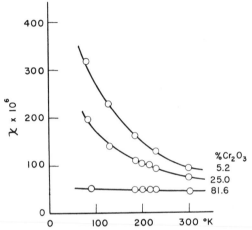

Fig. 70. Susceptibility per g. of Cr^{3+} *versus* temper- ature in a Cr_2O_3-Al_2O_3 solid solution.

chromium is surrounded by aluminum neighbors. Certainly the Weiss constant is greatly reduced at the concentration where the color changes from green to ruby, but the problem is not made simpler by the fact that the color changes from green to ruby at low temperatures, and vice versa. If exchange effects between adjacent chromia produce the green color, it might be expected that these would become stronger, with enhancement of the green color, at low temperatures. But the reverse is actually true. Natural and synthetic ruby owes its color to chromia dissolved in the color- less alumina or sapphire. Rao[103] has shown that the magnetic suscepti- bilities of these substances are consistent with those found for the more concentrated solutions described above.

Chromic ions strongly diminish the proton relaxation time.[104] The chromate ion has only a small paramagnetism which is independent of tem- perature.

[103] S. R. Rao and M. Leela, *Current Sci.*, **22**, 72 (1953).
[104] R. L. Conger and P. W. Selwood, *J. Chem. Phys.*, **20**, 383 (1952).

Manganese. The manganous ion, Mn^{2+}, is in an S state; hence one would expect the theoretical magneton numbers to be in good agreement with experiment. Among measurements on the more "dilute" manganous compounds the following may be mentioned. Krishnan, Chakravorty, and Banerjee[105] have reported on manganous ammonium sulfate which has an exceedingly small anisotropy and for which $\mu = 5.85$ Bohr magnetons, compared with 5.95 for five unpaired electrons. The anisotropy and susceptibility of manganous salts have been studied theoretically by Van

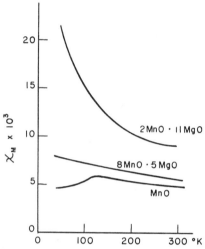

Fig. 71. Susceptibility per mole of MnO *versus* temperature for several concentrations of MnO dissolved in MgO.

Vleck and Penney.[106] Jackson[107] has also studied manganous ammonium sulfate and confirms the results of the Indian workers. The Weiss constant, as anticipated, is small, being only 0.7°. The hydrated and anhydrous sulfates have been studied by Jackson[107] and by Herroun[108] aqueous solutions by Bose,[109,110] and the anhydrous acetate, formate, lactate, and oxalate by Bhatnagar, Nevgi, and Sharma.[111] In all of these, the Curie law is obeyed closely and the spin-only formula gives a close approximation to experiment. It is interesting that crystalline manganous

[105] K. S. Krishnan, N. C. Chakravorty, and S. Banerjee, *Trans. Roy. Soc. (London)*, A232, 99 (1933).

[106] J. Van Vleck and W. G. Penney, *Phil. Mag.*, 17, 961 (1934).

[107] L. C. Jackson, *Proc. Roy. Soc. (London)*, A140, 695 (1933).

[108] E. F. Herroun, *Proc. Phys. Soc. (London)*, 46, 872 (1934).

[109] A. Bose, *Nature*, 133, 213 (1934).

[110] A. Bose, *Proc. Indian Acad. Sci.*, 1A, 605 (1935).

[111] S. S. Bhatnagar, M. B. Nevgi, and R. L. Sharma, *Phil. Mag.*, 22, 409 (1936).

hydroxide, $Mn(OH)_2$, is properly considered as a magnetically dilute compound,[112,113] as apparently also is manganous carbonate.[114]

Bizette and Tsaï[115] have investigated the magnetic susceptibility of solid solutions of manganous oxide in magnesium oxide. Some of the results are shown in Fig. 71. Increasing dilution of the MnO is accompanied by disappearance of the antiferromagnetic Curie point and by a large increase of susceptibility per gram of manganese. At great dilution, the Curie-Weiss law is followed with a Weiss constant close to zero and a moment near that expected for five unpaired electron spins. Similar results have been reported for the solid solution system, MnF_2-ZnF_2.[116]

Paramagnetic resonance studies[117] on solutions of manganous nitrate have shown that exchange effects are operative and measurable even in such magnetically dilute systems. There is, however, an anomaly in that the ratio of spin-lattice to spin-spin relaxation times, which is generally unity in such systems, is about 10 in this solution.[118] This may indicate something unusual about the coordination of water about the manganous ion.

The manganic ion, Mn^{3+}, has been studied in the compound manganic acetylacetonate by Jackson.[119] This compound obeys the Weiss law with $\Delta = 5.5°$ down to $70°K$. below which temperature the susceptibility increases somewhat more rapidly. The Bohr magneton number is 4.98, in good agreement with theory for four unpaired spins, but other studies tend to give a slightly higher moment. Cesium manganic alum similarly shows a normal moment for four unpaired electron spins.[120]

Compounds in which manganese has valences other than two or three belong, for the most part, either to the category of complex compounds, to be treated in Chapter X, or to those in which exchange effects are important. These will be dealt with later. It may be mentioned, however, that the magnetic moments associated with the valences of one, four, six, and seven are consistent with the appropriate number of unpaired electrons in each state, provided that neither covalent bond formation nor exchange demagnetization occurs.

Iron. This element and its compounds have been the subject of almost innumerable magnetic studies. The more magnetically concentrated

[112] W. H. Albrecht, *Z. anorg. u. allgem. Chem.*, **232**, 382 (1937).
[113] T. E. Moore, M. Ellis, and P. W. Selwood, *J. Am. Chem. Soc.*, **72**, 856 (1950).
[114] K. S. Krishnan and S. Banerjee, *Z. Krist.*, **99**, 499 (1938).
[115] H. Bizette and B. Tsaï, *Compt. rend.*, **217**, 444 (1943).
[116] L. Corliss, Y. Delabarre, and N. Elliott, *J. Chem. Phys.*, **18**, 1256 (1950).
[117] M. A. Garstens and S. H. Liebson, *ibid.*, **20**, 1647 (1952).
[118] J. R. Zimmerman, *ibid.*, **22**, 950 (1954).
[119] L. C. Jackson, *Proc. Phys. Soc. (London)*, **47**, 1029 (1935).
[120] J. Zernike, *Rec. trav. chim.*, **71**, 965 (1952).

compounds show anomalies due to exchange effects, leading in several oxides, hydroxides, and other compounds, to ferromagnetism. Magnetically dilute salts, on the other hand, follow the Curie-Weiss law with some accuracy. The earlier literature in this field is reviewed by Stoner (*op. cit.*,[13] p. 325).

Solutions of ferrous sulfate and of ferrous ammonium sulfate have been studied by Weiss[121,122] Foëx,[123] Fahlenbrach,[124] and Nicolau.[125] The Weiss constant is a modest 20°, and the magnetic moment tends to be 5.1 to 5.3 Bohr magnetons, which is only slightly greater than the theoretical value, 4.9, for four unpaired electron spins. Hydrated and anhydrous ferrous salts have been studied by Herroun,[108] and the measurements on $FeSO_4 \cdot 7H_2O$ have been extended by Lyon and Giauque[126] to very low temperatures. The hydrated salts give results not unlike those obtained with solutions, but the anhydrous salts show some deviations, doubtless due at least in part to the increased magnetic concentration in such substances.

The magnetic anisotropy of mixed Tutton salts has been studied by Jogelkar.[127] These salts are of the type $MSO_4 \cdot (NH_4)_2SO_4 \cdot 6H_2O$, similar to Mohr's salt, where M is Fe^{2+}, Co^{2+}, Ni^{2+}, or Cu^{2+}. It is possible to dilute the paramagnetic ion in these crystals by progressive replacement with the diamagnetic magnesium ion, Mg^{2+}, or by Zn^{2+}. In this way Jogelkar found that the order of magnitude of the anisotropy of any given paramagnetic ion is the same at all dilutions. Single crystals containing hexacoordinated ferrous ions have been examined by Bose.[128] Ferrous hydroxide appears to be a magnetically dilute substance although, for obvious reasons, it is difficult to prepare pure.[129]

Bizette and Tsaï[115] have studied FeO-MgO solid solutions with results comparable to those given for MnO-MgO.

Ferric salts in aqueous solution are subject to hydrolysis. Use has been attempted of the deviations from additivity of susceptibility to calculate the degree of hydrolysis of ferric chloride solutions.[130] Nevertheless, studies have been made of dissolved ferric salts by Fahlenbrach[124] on the chloride, and by Bose[131] on the chloride, nitrate, and sulfate. The results

[121] P. Weiss, *J. phys. radium*, **5**, 129 (1924).
[122] P. Weiss and L. Néel, *Congr. internat. d'électricité*, **2**, 227, 249, Paris, 1932.
[123] G. Foëx, *Ann. phys.*, **16**, 174, (1921).
[124] H. Fahlenbrach, *Ann. Physik*, **13**, 265; 14, 521, 524 (1932).
[125] A. Nicolau, *Compt. rend.*, **205**, 557 (1937).
[126] D. N. Lyon and W. F. Giauque, *J. Am. Chem. Soc.*, **71**, 1647 (1939).
[127] M. S. Jogelkar, *Z. Krist.*, **98**, 411 (1938).
[128] A. Bose, *Indian J. Phys.*, **22**, 483 (1948).
[129] J. Zernike and B. C. Sinha, *Rec. trav. chim.*, **72**, 390 (1953).
[130] M. Auméras and M. Mounic, *Bull. soc. chim. France, Mém.*, **4**, 536 (1937).
[131] A. Bose, *Proc. Indian Acad. Sci.*, **1A**, 754 (1935).

are somewhat difficult to interpret, but in some cases, at least, the paramagnetism is approximated by the spin-only formula at great dilution.[132] Much of this difficulty has been resolved[133] by the discovery that such solutions may contain a substantial portion of the iron in the form of a diamagnetic dimeric ion of the probable formula $Fe_2(OH)_2^{4+}$. A solution of ferric perchlorate, say $0.04M$ in total iron and at a pH of about 2, has a magnetic susceptibility about one-half of that for the same solution in

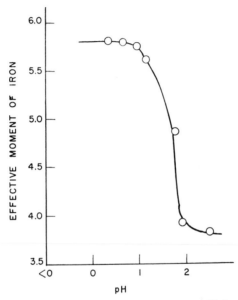

Fig. 72. Effective magnetic moment of iron *versus* pH for an aqueous solution of ferric perchlorate at constant ionic strength.

fairly strong acid. The average magnetic moment of the iron under these circumstances is only about 4.0 Bohr magnetons, as shown in Fig. 72.

The susceptibility of ferric ammonium alum at very low temperatures has been studied by Kürti, Lainé, and Simon,[134] and by Casimir, de Haas, and de Klerk.[135] This compound, although it is magnetically dilute, shows remanence and hysteresis very near the absolute zero. The phenomena are fairly common. They are shown by cesium-titanium and potassium-chromium alums, and by ammonium-manganese, potassium-manganese hydrated double sulfates, and other compounds.

[132] R. Mercier, *Ann. phys.*, **3**, 201 (1935).
[133] L. N. Mulay and P. W. Selwood, *J. Am. Chem. Soc.*, **77**, 2693 (1955).
[134] N. Kürti, P. Lainé, and F. Simon, *Compt. rend.*, **204**, 675 (1937).
[135] H. B. G. Casimir, W. J. de Haas, and D. de Klerk, *Physica*, **6**, 241 (1939).

The magnetic anisotropy of the ferric salts has been studied by Jackson,[136] Forrest,[137] Krishnan and Banerjee,[138] and Krishnan and Mookherji[139] from a theoretical standpoint by Van Vleck and Penney,[140] Siegert,[141] and Guha.[142]   Although the ferric ion is in an S state, like com-

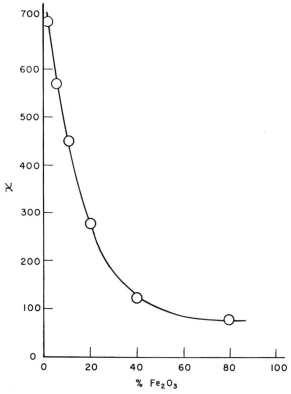

Fig. 73. Susceptibility at 86°K. per g. of Fe^{3+} *versus* concentration in Fe_2O_3-Al_2O_3 solid solutions.

pounds of divalent manganese, its salts show a definite though feeble anisotropy.   This seems to be due in part to the diamagnetic anisotropy of the crystal, and in part to the mutual influence of the magnetic moments and their noncubic arrangement in the crystal lattice.

[136] L. C. Jackson, *Proc. Roy. Soc. (London)*, **A140**, 695 (1933).
[137] J. Forrest, *Phil. Mag.*, **15**, 1153 (1933).
[138] K. S. Krishnan and S. Banerjee, *Trans. Roy. Soc. (London)*, **A235**, 343 (1936).
[139] K. S. Krishnan and A. Mookherji, *ibid.*, **A237**, 135 (1938).
[140] J. H. Van Vleck and W. G. Penney, *Phil. Mag.*, **17**, 961 (1934).
[141] A. Siegert, *Physica*, **4**, 138 (1937).
[142] B. C. Guha, *Proc. Roy. Soc. (London)* **206A**, 353 (1951).

These studies, and those of Amiel et al.[143] on different varieties of ferric sulfate hydrate, emphasize that the examination of magnetically dilute compounds in the presence of water, either as a solvent or in the crystal, is not the ideal way to compare observed with theoretical magnetic properties.

The system Fe_2O_3–Al_2O_3 is somewhat difficult because of the strong tendency toward formation of γ-Fe_2O_3 at lower ignition temperatures and Fe_3O_4 at higher temperatures.[102]   With care these can be avoided and the true paramagnetism of the Fe^{3+} ion can be determined.   Results are shown in Fig. 73.   These results are of considerable interest because the Fe^{3+} ion in hydrous ferric oxide has a moment about 30% lower than the expected value of 6.0.   With increasing magnetic dilution, the Weiss constant in the Fe_2O_3-Al_2O_3 system becomes zero, and the moment slowly rises until at infinite dilution there is no doubt that the moment is at least 5.9. It is probably correct to say, therefore, that the low moment observed in ferric oxide gel is due to interaction between adjacent iron ions and not to some kind of covalent bonding between iron and oxygen.

From a magnetic study of amethyst it is concluded by Leela[144] that the coloring agent is iron in the form of ferric oxide or hydroxide.   But perhaps from what has been said above it may be possible that some of the iron is in the form of dimeric ions.

The remarks above about dimerization in aqueous salt solutions ought to be reflected in the proton relaxation time and also in paramagnetic resonance experiments.   This is not, however, clear from the results on ferric nitrate solution reported by Gabillard.[145]

Oxidation states of iron higher than three will be mentioned in a later chapter.

Cobalt.   The situation with respect to this element is somewhat more confusing.   An extensive series of investigations on aqueous solutions by earlyworkers is described by Stoner (op. cit.,[13] p. 326).   There seems little doubt, as shown by Chatillon,[146] that the apparent moment depends considerably on the previous chemical history of the solution.   This is true even of such relatively simple cobalt compounds as the sulfate.   Other studies by Mercier[147] and Datta[152] confirm these effects which, however, do not greatly surprise any chemist who has investigated the properties of the cobalt ion in solution.   The magnetic changes have been used by Bhatnagar and Kapur[148] who studied the well-known color changes of cobalt

[143] J. Amiel, M. Gourdonneau, and R. Vauthier, Compt. rend., 220, 402 (1945).

[144] M. Leela, Nature, 172, 464 (1953).

[145] R. Gabillard, Rev. sci., 90, 307 (1952).

[146] A. Chatillon, Ann. phys., 9, 187 (1928).

[147] R. Mercier, Helv. Phys. Acta, 6, 240 (1933); Ann. phys., 3, 201 (1935).

[148] S. S. Bhatnagar and P. L. Kapur, J. Indian Chem. Soc., 9, 341 (1932).

chloride from the magnetic standpoint. In all aqueous solutions, they found the Co^{2+} ion to have the same effective moment, but slightly lower results were obtained with solutions of $CoCl_2 \cdot 6H_2O$ in methyl, ethyl, and amyl alcohols. They suggest that the color change from red to blue is due to complex ion formation rather than to the formation of different hydrates.

The most striking feature of magnetically dilute cobalt compounds is that the moments are all higher than predicted by the spin-only formula for three unpaired electrons. The moment differs in various compounds and under diverse conditions of temperature, but it averages about 30% higher than expected. This abnormality is generally attributed to incomplete quenching of the orbital contribution to the magnetic moment, and is a consequence of inverted multiplet levels in this element. $Cobalt^{2+}$ is the only ion of the series in which the effect is large, but moments somewhat higher than the spin-only value are also found for the ions Fe^{2+} and Ni^{2+}. This curious effect in cobalt leads to a fairly high magnetic anisotropy, which has been studied by Bartlett, Krishnan, Bose,[159-162] and others.

It might be expected that the cobaltous ion would lend itself well to the magnetic dilution technique. Bizette[115] has reported briefly on the CoO–MgO system, and Elliott[149] has studied the systems $CoCl_2$–$ZnCl_2$ and $CoCl_2$–$CdCl_2$. The situation is a rather interesting one because manganous chloride has a Weiss constant close to zero and this suggests that any deviation of the isomorphous cobaltous chloride from the Curie law would be due more to crystalline field splitting rather than to spin-spin exchange interaction. The results show that this is probably true. At high dilution the Co^{2+} ion has a moment of 5.37 and Weiss constants of $-10.8°$ and $-20.5°$ in the zinc and cadmium solutions, respectively. It may be mentioned that crystals of these substances are platelike and anisotropic. Some care must, therefore, be taken with them to prevent preferential orientation. A careful, recent study by Elliott[149a] on the system CoO–MgO has shown a moment for the Co^{2+} ion of 5.1. This is independent of concentration. The Weiss constant becomes effectively zero ($\pm10°$) at infinite dilution.

A substance worth further study is so-called cobalt sulfoxylate which may or may not contain Co^{2+} ions. It follows the Curie law with a moment of 3.8. This is, of course, the spin-only moment for Co^{2+}, but it has not been reported in any other compound.[150]

Salts of trivalent cobalt have given anomalous results, and it is not certain if any magnetically dilute ionic compounds are known for the element in this oxidation state. The cobaltic ion in the presence of water[151] is

[149] N. Elliott, *J. Chem. Phys.*, **21**, 890 (1953).
[149a] N. Elliott, *J. Chem. Phys.*, **22**, 1924 (1954).
[150] H. Bode and H. Weiss, *Z. anorg. Chem.*, **267**, 247 (1952).

apparently diamagnetic, but perhaps the possibility of dimerization in this system has not been completely excluded.   It would be quite useful to have some magnetic dilution experiments made on this ion if a suitable diluent can be found.   Zernike[120] reports cobaltic alum to be diamagnetic.   Extensive reference to Co(III) coordination compounds will be made in Chapter X.

Nickel.   Magnetically dilute compounds of nickel have been investigated thoroughly.   The susceptibilities have been determined over a range of temperature for aqueous solutions of the chloride and sulfate by Fahlenbrach,[124] Datta,[152] Nicolau,[125] and Nettleton and Sugden.[153]   Such solutions appear to obey the Curie law and to yield for the nickel ion a magnetic moment of about 2.8 to 3.2 Bohr magnetons, which is in fair agreement with the spin-only formula for two unpaired electrons.

Several workers have reported rather small changes which occur as a function of concentration in aqueous nickel salt solutions.[154]   A procedure sometimes used has been the extrapolation of the data to infinite dilution in order to find the moment of the free ion.   This procedure, as applied to aqueous solutions, has been questioned by Auer.[155]   It is probable that in solution the paramagnetic ions are no less subject to the fields of oriented solvent molecules than they are in hydrated crystals.   Foëx[156] claims that several distinct magnetic states of the ions exist in aqueous solution.

The moments derived from hydrated nickel salts are in general in good agreement with those obtained from solutions.   The sulfate, chloride, and bromide have been studied by Serres,[157] Herroun,[108] and Janes,[158] and are found to be normal, as are most simple and double salts.

The magnetic anisotropies of dilute compounds have been extensively studied.[159-164]   In general, the observed anisotropies for nickel salts are moderate.

[151] H. L. Friedman, J. P. Hunt, R. A. Plane, and H. Taube, *J. Am. Chem. Soc.*, **73**, 4028 (1951).

[152] S. Datta, *Phil. Mag.*, **17**, 585, 1160 (1934).

[153] H. R. Nettleton and S. Sugden, *Proc. Roy. Soc. (London)*, **A173**, 313 (1939).

[154] J. M. Alameda, *Anales soc. españ. fís. quím.*, **43**, 689, 711 (1947).

[155] H. Auer, *Physik Z.*, **33**, 869 (1932).

[156] G. Foëx, *J. phys. radium*, **3**, 337 (1932).

[157] A. Serres, *Ann. phys.*, **20**, 441 (1933).

[158] R. B. Janes, *Phys. Rev.*, **48**, 78 (1935).

[159] B. W. Bartlett, *ibid.*, **41**, 818 (1932); **44**, 687 (1933).

[160] K. S. Krishnan, A. Mookherji, and A. Bose, *Trans. Roy. Soc. (London)*, **A228**, 125 (1939).

[161] A. Mookherji, *Indian J. Phys.*, **20**, 9 (1946).

[162] A. Bose, *ibid.*, **22**, 195, 276 (1948).

[163] J. W. Stout and M. Griffel, *J. Chem. Phys.*, **18**, 1449 (1950).

[164] J. Becquerel, J. van den Handel, and H. A. Kramers, *Physica*, **17**, 717 (1951).

Copper.   The cuprous ion has no incomplete electron shell and hence is expected to be diamagnetic.   This appears to be the case,[165,166] although Perakis and Capatos[167] suggest that it may possess a feeble paramagnetism. If this is true, it can only be of the temperature-independent type.   In measurements on cuprous compounds, the necessity of eliminating the paramagnetic cupric ion is obvious.   The matter is discussed by Sugden.[168]

The cupric ion, Cu^{2+}, has one unpaired electron and generally shows a magnetic moment of 1.8 Bohr magneton or slightly more in magnetically dilute compounds and solutions.[169]   The results are much less irregular than are those on cobalt.   It is well known that copper chloride solutions change color with changing concentration, and this effect has been correlated with magnetic changes,[170,171] but, in general, the results on copper are fairly easy to interpret.   A notable exception is the reported increase in the susceptibility of the cupric ion at low concentrations in a variety of salts in aqueous solution.[172]   For instance, the susceptibility of Cu^{2+} in the perchlorate at concentrations below 0.5% by weight is twice that at higher concentrations.   No explanation for this has been offered.   If the effect is real the cause may be found in a slight change of the susceptibility of water, as described in Chapter VI.

Reekie[173] has measured the susceptibilities of blue vitriol and of several hydrated double sulfates of copper down to 1.6°K.   He finds the Weiss law to be obeyed with a remarkably small value for Δ (less than 1°) and with Bohr magneton numbers averaging about 1.91, with small differences for the different compounds.   Measurements by Bhatnagar, Lessheim, and Khanna,[174] and by Mas[175] are reported on various arsenites, arsenates, and double salts of copper between the temperatures 304° and 368°K.   The effective Bohr magneton numbers range from 1.80 to 2.00 in different compounds.   The fluctuations are ascribed to uncertainties in the correction to be applied to the negative radical.   In any event, there

[165] C. Courty, *Compt. rend.*, **202**, 1929 (1936).

[166] F. Hommel, *Ann. Physik.*, **30**, 467 (1937).

[167] N. Perakis and L. Capatos, *J. phys. radium*, **7**, 391 (1936).

[168] S. Sugden, *J. Chem. Soc.*, **1932**, 161.

[169] J. Amiel, *Compt. rend.*, **213**, 240 (1941).

[170] N. A. Yajnik, R. Chand, A. N. Kapur, and D. C. Jain, *J. Indian Chem. Soc.*, **19**, 357 (1932).

[171] N. A. Yajnik, R. Chand, and D. C. Jain, *ibid.*, **20**, 203 (1943).

[172] P. Berthier, C. Courty, and J. Gauthier, *Compt. rend.*, **233**, 473 (1951); **234**, 604, 2525 (1952); **239**, 241 (1954).

[173] J. Reekie, *Proc. Roy. Soc. (London)*, **A173**, 367 (1939).

[174] S. S. Bhatnagar, H. Lessheim, and M. L. Khanna, *J. Indian Chem. Soc.*, **14**, 445 (1937).

[175] R. Mas, *Ann. chim.*, **4**, 459 (1949).

seems to be little or no contribution from the orbital component.   Amiel[176] reports that the ionic susceptibility of divalent copper is but little influenced by change of organic substituent in a large number of cupritetrachlorides and cupritrichlorides.   On the other hand,[177] the paramagnetism of the Cu^{2+} ion in cupric salts of long open-chain fatty acids is said to be only about half the normal.   This appears to be the first of a series of observations leading to some revised ideas concerning the cupric ion and its magnetic properties.   Subnormal magnetic moments in a variety of cupric salts of fatty acids have been reported by Ploquin and Vergneau[178,179] who showed that the anomaly is absent in the corresponding nickel salts. Guha,[142] in a very thorough study, showed that the apparent moment of the cupric ion in the acetate monohydrate decreases rapidly with decreasing temperature, becoming zero well above absolute zero.   The reason for this anomaly now appears to be that two copper ions in the unit cell lie close together and that exchange interaction reduces the effective moment.[180] This has been confirmed by paramagnetic resonance and by x-ray diffraction studies.   The effect is shown by copper laurate and several other compounds.[181]

It is rather interesting that crystalline cupric hydroxide is a magnetically dilute compound with a normal moment.[182]

In view of the above, it is somewhat surprising to find that crystalline copper sulfate hydrate, $CuSO_4 \cdot 5H_2O$, has an appreciable magnetic anisotropy.   It was pointed out by Jordahl[183] that this could be explained if the crystalline field surrounding the cupric ion had less than cubic symmetry. It had previously been thought that the copper was tetrahedrally coordinated in this compound.   The anisotropy of $CuSO_4 \cdot 5H_2O$ has been studied by Krishnan and Mookherji[184] and, at very low temperatures, by Benzie and Cooke.[185]   The magnetic measurements support the view established by x-ray studies that each Cu^{2+} ion is at the center of an approximate octahedron formed by four water molecules and two oxygen atoms.   But the results indicate that the crystalline field has a rhombic component in addition to the cubic.   The anisotropy is surprisingly large.   Parallel and perpendicular to the tetragonal axis of the crystalline field the effective

[176] J. Amiel, *Compt. rend.*, **206**, 1113 (1938).

[177] J. Amiel, *ibid.*, **207**, 1097 (1938).

[178] J. Ploquin and C. Vergneau, *Bull. soc. chim. France*, **1951**, 757.

[179] C. Vergneau-Souvray, *Compt. rend.*, **233**, 164 (1951).

[180] B. Bleaney and K. D. Bowers, *Proc. Roy. Soc.* (*London*), **A214**, 451 (1952).

[181] A. Gilmour and R. C. Pink, *J. Chem. Soc.*, **1953**, 2198.

[182] L. Chaumeton, *Compt. rend.*, **206**, 1104 (1938).

[183] O. Jordahl, *Phys. Rev.*, **45**, 87 (1934); 46, 79 (1934).

[184] K. S. Krishnan and A. Mookherji, *Phys. Rev.*, **50**, 860 (1936); 54, 533, 841 (1938).

[185] R. J. Benzie and A. H. Cooke, *Proc. Phys. Soc.* (*London*), **64A**, 124 (1951).

Bohr magneton numbers are respectively 2.13 and 1.80. There is practically no temperature dependence of moment. Other copper compounds the anisotropy of which has been measured[186-192] include the potassium double sulfate, some double chlorides of the general formula $2RCl\cdot CuCl_2\cdot 2H_2O$, and cupric selenate pentahydrate.

Oxidation states of copper higher than two will be discussed in Chapter X.

47. Elements of the Second and Third Transition Series

The only elements of these series which have received much study are the palladium-platinum groups. The reason for this is that these are almost the only elements of the series which show appreciable paramagnetism. This is partly due to the somewhat restricted range of oxidation states shown by these elements as compared with the elements of the first transition series, and partly due to the strong tendency on the part of some of these heavier elements to form complex compounds and to exhibit exchange effects, which will be treated later.

Zirconium and hafnium apparently form no appreciably paramagnetic compounds. The usual valence of four is diamagnetic. The situation is similar for the elements niobium and tantalum. Magnetically dilute compounds for valences less than five should be paramagnetic, but this is not necessarily true for such concentrated compounds as the oxides.

Molybdenum and tungsten are in a somewhat different category, because both these elements form large numbers of compounds in which the valence is less than six. Molybdates and tungstates show a small temperature-independent paramagnetism. The lower oxides tend to be diamagnetic, or nearly so, from strong exchange interaction. Sucksmith[193] has studied $MoCl_3$ and $MoCl_5$. Klemm and Steinberg[194] report on $MoCl_3$, $MoCl_5$, $MoBr_5$, and $MoBr_5$. The susceptibilities are all temperature dependent and suggest quenching of the orbital component.

Magnetic properties of the element technetium have been studied by Nelson, Boyd, and Smith.[194a] The $(7+)$ oxidation state shows a small

[186] B. W. Bartlett, *ibid.*, 41, 818 (1932); 44, 687 (1933).

[187] J. C. Hupse, *Physica*, 9, 633 (1942).

[188] D. Polder, *ibid.*, 9, 709 (1942).

[189] D. de Klerk, *ibid.*, 12, 513 (1946).

[190] A. Mookherji, *Indian J. Phys.*, 19, 63 (1945).

[191] W. Opechowski, *Physica*, 14, 237 (1948).

[192] K. S. Krishnan, A. Mookherji, and A. Bose, *Trans. Roy. Soc. (London)*, A238, 125 (1939).

[193] W. Sucksmith, *Phil. Mag.*, 14, 1115 (1932).

[194] W. Klemm and H. Steinberg, *Z. anorg. u. allgem. Chem.*, 227, 193 (1936).

[194a] C. M. Nelson, G. E. Boyd, and W. T. Smith, Jr., *J. Am. Chem. Soc.*, 76, 348 (1954).

temperature-independent paramagnetism; lower states are paramagnetic. There have been a few magnetic studies of rhenium. Schüth and Klemm[195] have measured several rhenium compounds in different valence states. For instance Re_2O, $KReO_4$, and ReO_3Cl show a small temperature-independent paramagnetism which is also shown by ReO_3, ReO_2, ReS_2, $ReCl_3$, and $ReBr_3$. The effect is normal for a valence of seven, but may be due to strong exchange effects in the other compounds. Compounds in which the valence is five, such as $ReCl_5$, have a susceptibility which at high temperatures approaches that for "spin only." The same is true of the valence of four in such compounds as K_2ReCl_6 and Ag_2ReCl_6. The peculiar rhenide ion, Re^-, has been investigated as it occurs in the compound $KRe \cdot H_2O$. The susceptibility per gram-atom of rhenium is only about 250×10^{-6}, less than one-fifth of that expected for one unpaired electron spin. It is scarcely possible to draw any definite conclusions concerning the structure of the rhenide ion from this datum.[196]

The elements of the palladium-platinum group show peculiar magnetic properties in all their compounds. The situation has been summarized by Van Vleck (op. cit.,[4] p. 311) and not very much has been added to the knowledge of these elements during the past quarter century. In brief, the compounds do not obey the Weiss law, although Cabrera[197,198] points out that the susceptibilities may be represented by $(\chi + a)\ (T + \Delta) = C$. The effective Bohr magneton numbers probably have little significance and are all small compared with the theoretical spin-only predictions. Values given by Cabrera and Duperier are shown in Table XV. An extensive and useful survey of these elements is given by Cabrera.[199] It will be noticed that the Pt^{2+} ion is diamagnetic in spite of having an

TABLE XV

Bohr Magneton Numbers for the Palladium and Platinum Group Elements

Ion	μ
Ru^{3+}	2.09
Rh^{3+}	0.06
Pd^{2+}	0.07–0.13
Os^{2+}	0.27–0.50
Ir^{3+}	0.11
Pt^{2+}	0

[195] W. Schüth and W. Klemm, Z. anorg. u. allgem. Chem., 220, 193 (1934).
[196] J. B. Bravo, E. Griswold, and J. Kleinberg, J. Phys. Chem., 58, 18 (1954).
[197] B. Cabrera and H. Fahlenbrach, Ann. Physik, 21, 832 (1935).
[198] B. Cabrera and A. Duperier, Proc. Phys. Soc. (London), 51, 845 (1939).
[199] B. Cabrera, Le Magnétisme, Vol. III.   Proceedings of the Strasbourg Congress on Magnetism, 1939, p. 179.

incomplete electron shell. The divalent palladium ion is stated by Janes[200] to be diamagnetic also. In any event, its paramagnetism is very small. Reasons for these peculiarities are obscure. Probably the elements of these groups do not form salts in the normal sense and the simple theory of ionic paramagnetism must be abandoned in favor of the "complex" theory described in Chapter X. In some cases, there is actually an odd number of electrons in the diamagnetic compounds, as for instance in $Pd(NH_3)_2Cl_2$. The diamagnetism here is possibly to be explained by dimerization to $[Pd(NH_3)Cl_2]_2$, a view which is supported by freezing point data. In any event, there remains much to be learned about these elements. It will be noted that ruthenium is the only element of the group which approaches normal paramagnetism.

The normal silver ion, Ag^+, is diamagnetic. Complex compounds containing divalent (or possibly trivalent) silver are paramagnetic. They will be described in Chapter X. Gold in the oxidation states of one and three is diamagnetic. Magnetic measurements on the substance formed by the action of ozone on gold have given indecisive magnetic results.[201]

48. The "Actinides"

Actinium(III) is presumably diamagnetic like lanthanum(III). Thorium(IV) is also diamagnetic. Certain lower sulfides of thorium may show paramagnetism.[202]

Measurements on various uranium compounds have been made by Sucksmith,[203] Lawrence,[204] Klemm and Steinberg,[205] Nicolau,[206] Haraldsen and Bakken,[207] Bommer,[208] and others. The results obtained by these earlier workers were for the most part on uranium compounds at a single temperature, or for compounds such as the oxide, in which the possibility of exchange effects cannot be ignored. The interesting question as to whether uranium in its magnetic properties most closely resembles the rare earths or the Group VI elements, such as tungsten and molybdenum, could not be answered definitely on the basis of these earlier studies.

[200] R. B. Janes, J. Am. Chem. Soc., **57**, 471 (1935).

[201] H. Schütza and I. Schütza, Z. anorg. u. allgem. Chem., **245**, 59 (1940).

[202] E. D. Eastman, L. Brewer, L. A. Bromley, P. W. Gilles, and N. L. Lofgren, J. Am. Chem. Soc., **72**, 4019 (1950).

[203] W. Sucksmith, Phil. Mag., **14**, 1115 (1932).

[204] R. W. Lawrence, J. Am. Chem. Soc., **56**, 776 (1934).

[205] W. Klemm and H. Steinberg, Z. anorg. u. allgem. Chem., **227**, 193 (1936).

[206] A. Nicolau, Compt. rend., **205**, 654 (1937).

[207] H. Haraldsen and R. Bakken, Naturwissenschaften, **28**, 127 (1940).

[208] H. Bommer, Z. anorg. u. allgem. Chem., **247**, 249 (1941).

It is sometimes stated[209] that magnetic measurements point toward filling of the $5f$ electron shell as anticipated on the basis of the actinide concept. With this statement the writer cannot agree completely, although this is by no means to say that magnetic susceptibility data are inconsistent with f electrons throughout this group of elements.

Careful studies of the temperature coefficient of susceptibility have been made on a variety of halides, double fluorides, and such magnetically dilute compounds as the hydrated(IV) sulfate, the hydrated(IV) oxalate, and the acetylacetonate.[210-214] For the tetrafluoride, for instance, the

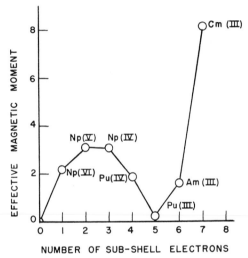

Fig. 74. Effective magnetic moments of some "actinide" ions.

Curie-Weiss law is followed between 90° and 500°K. with a magnetic moment of 3.3 Bohr magnetons and a Weiss constant ∼116°. This is not in good agreement with the spin-only formula for two electrons. On the basis of these and other results on uranium halides, it is not possible to say that uranium(IV) possesses an unfilled d shell rather than an f shell like the rare earths. But even this modest conclusion is dependent on the assumption that the orbital part of the moment for $5f$ electrons would resist

[209] G. T. Seaborg, *The Actinide Elements*. National Nuclear Energy Series, Plutonium Progress Report. McGraw-Hill Book Co., Inc., New York, 1954, Vol. 14A, p. 749.

[210] N. Elliott, *Phys. Rev.*, **74**, 498 (1948); **76**, 431 (1949).

[211] C. A. Hutchison, Jr., and N. Elliott, *J. Chem. Phys.*, **16**, 920 (1948).

[212] L. Sacconi, *Atti. accad. nazl. Lincei*, **6**, 639 (1949).

[213] J. K. Dawson, *J. Chem. Soc.*, **1951**, 429.

[214] R. Stoenner and N. Elliott, *J. Chem. Phys.*, **19**, 950 (1951).

quenching in the same manner as is shown by the $4f$ electrons in the rare earths. On this point there is no assurance.

The results of Hutchison and N. Elliott[211] on the sulfate, oxalate, and acetylacetonate yield moments of 3.52, 3.75, and 3.21 with corresponding Weiss constants of 113°, 168°, and 101°, respectively. These data are in approximate agreement with those expected for f electrons and are interpreted by the authors as proving the presence of f electrons in uranium(IV). But it is clear that such large values for the empirical Weiss constant indicate the inapplicability here of the simple theory which we applied to the first transition series and to the rare earths.

Uranium in the oxidation state 6+ has no unpaired electrons, but the ion, UO_2^{2+}, and the trioxide, UO_3, have a small temperature-independent paramagnetism.

Susceptibilities of the neptunium ions, NpO_2^{2+}, NpO_2^{+}, and Np^{4+} in solution, together with those of several other transuranium elements, have been reported by Howland and Calvin.[215] These results and some others are summarized in Fig. 74. The authors interpret these data as proving the presence of f electrons in neptunium. But it must be pointed out that the measurements were made at one temperature only and that the method used for calculating the magnetic moments is equivalent to assuming the Weiss constant to be zero. Hutchison and Elliott reached the same conclusion for uranium by the use of Weiss constants in excess of 100°. Not only is it impossible to draw any conclusions about electronic configuration from these data, but it is impossible to calculate the actual magnetic moment with any degree of confidence.

The situation is considerably improved by the results of Gruen and Hutchison[216] on Np(VI), Np(V), and Np(IV) as found in the solid compounds, $NaNpO_2(CH_3COO)_2$, $NpO_2C_2O_4H \cdot H_2O$, and $KNpF_5$ respectively. These all give small Weiss constants and magnetic moments which are shown in Fig. 74. In this case there is little doubt about the magnetic moments actually being as given. The only remaining question is the interpretation in terms of electronic configuration.

Plutonium in several oxidation states has also received careful study. Calvin et al.[217] and Dawson[218] have concluded that the magnetic moments of this element in its several oxidation states support the view that f electrons are present. Dawson[219] suggests that Pu(VI) in sodium plutonyl

[215] J. J. Howland, Jr. and M. Calvin, *ibid.*, **18**, 239 (1950).

[216] D. M. Gruen and C. A. Hutchison, Jr., *ibid.*, **22**, 386 (1954).

[217] M. Calvin, M. Kasha, and G. E. Sheline, *The Transuranium Elements*. National Nuclear Energy Series, Plutonium Progress Record. McGraw-Hill Book Co., Inc., New York, 1949, Vol. 14B, p. 632.

[218] J. K. Dawson, C. J. Mandelberg, and D. Davies, *J. Chem. Soc.*, **1951**, 2047.

[219] J. K. Dawson, *ibid.*, **1952**, 2705.

acetate may be an exception, but this is disputed by R. J. Elliott[220] on theoretical grounds, and by Hutchison[221] on the basis of paramagnetic resonance studies.

Almost the only other published work on transplutonium elements is that of Howland and Calvin,[215] except for some magnetic dilution studies to be presented below.   But first some comments will be made on the data already mentioned.

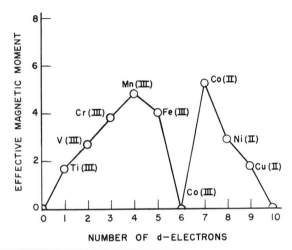

Fig. 75. Effective magnetic moment *versus* number of electrons in ion for several elements of the first transition series.   The purpose of this is to show that by selecting certain data and excluding others it is possible to construct a curve resembling that shown by the rare earths and the "actinides."

In Fig. 74 most of the published work on the "actinides" is represented. This is similar to the figure given by Seaborg (*op. cit.,*[209] p. 748) except that magnetic moments rather than gram-atomic susceptibilities have been plotted.   The resemblance of the double maxima to those shown by the lanthanides (Fig. 65, p. 142) is striking.   This remarkable analogy is often cited as evidence that the magnetic data are in agreement with the "actinide" hypothesis.   We shall point out two difficulties in this interpretation.

First, the magnetic moments to be expected for one or two d electrons (spin-only) are in about as good agreement with published results on uranium and the transuranium elements as are the moments expected for f electrons.   Consequently, so far as U(IV), Np(VI), Np(V), and Pu(VI)

[220] R. J. Elliott, *Phys. Rev.,* **89,** 659 (1953).
[221] C. A. Hutchison, Jr., and W. B. Lewis, *ibid.,* **95,** 1096 (1954).

are concerned, the magnetic data do not enable us to assign electrons uniquely to either configuration.

Second, in Fig. 75 we give observed magnetic moments for some ions of the first transition series in which, by universal agreement, d electrons are present. The analogy with the rare earths is remarkable here, too. If there were no other information available, it would be justifiable to claim the existence of a "scandide" rare earth series. Of course, Fig. 75 has been drawn by selecting certain anomalous cases and special conditions, references to all of which were made in the previous sections. For instance, we choose iron(III) as present in dilute aqueous solution at pH 2, and we ignore iron(II) entirely. The point to be emphasized is that unless one decides *a priori* that the actinides are like the rare earths, no convincing conclusions about the data summarized in Fig. 74 can be drawn.

Fortunately these elements lend themselves well to study by the technique of isomorphous diamagnetic dilution, and there are beginning to be some studies by this method. Trzebiatowski and the writer[222] have investigated the system UO_2–ThO_2. With increasing dilution of the uranium, the Weiss constant falls and becomes zero at infinite magnetic dilution. This behavior thus resembles chromium(III) much more than, say, neodymium(III) and proves the existence of considerable exchange interaction in uranium dioxide. At the same time, the magnetic moment becomes 2.8, in excellent agreement with the expected moment for two spin-only d electrons. This result has been confirmed by Dawson[223] and by N. Elliott.[224] Similar results strongly favoring the presence of d electrons, at least in uranium(IV), have been given by Dawson[225] for the system UF_4–ThF_4. On the other hand, Dawson's results[226] on the plutonium(IV) system, PuF_4–ThF_4, give fairly definite evidence in favor of f electrons, as do the results on the system, PuO_2–ThO_2. Similarly, Crane and Cunningham[227] have developed strong magnetic evidence for f electrons in curium(III) in the system CmF_3–LaF_3. Curium is analogous to gadolinium. Seaborg[209] refers to work by Crane, Wallman, and Cunningham in which solid americium trifluoride is shown to have a rather low susceptibility analogous to europium.

In summary, it may be said that magnetic studies strongly support the idea of f electrons in the transneptunium elements. For uranium(IV)

[222] W. Trzebiatowski and P. W. Selwood, *J. Am. Chem. Soc.*, **72**, 4504 (1950).

[223] J. K. Dawson and M. W. Lister, *J. Chem. Soc.*, **1952**, 5041.

[224] E. Slowinski and N. Elliott, *Acta Cryst.*, **5**, 768 (1952).

[225] J. K. Dawson, *J. Chem. Soc.*, **1951**, 2889; an arithmetical error is corrected in *ibid.*, **1952**, 1185.

[226] J. K. Dawson, *ibid.*, **1952**, 1882.

[227] See Seaborg (*op. cit.*,[209] p. 747).

the evidence favors d electrons, and this view is supported by paramagnetic resonance studies on UF_4.[227a] Actinium(III) and thorium(IV) have neither f nor d electrons. This is essentially the same as the conclusion reached by Seaborg (*op. cit.*), although the argument presented here follows a rather different path. Whether or not the term "actinides" for this series of elements is appropriate becomes, therefore, a problem in nomenclature which does not lie within the scope of this book.

[227a] S. N. Ghosh, W. Gordy, and D. G. Hill, *Phys. Rev.*, 96, 36 (1954).

CHAPTER NINE

SOME APPLICATIONS OF ATOMIC PARAMAGNETISM

49. The Composition and Structure of Glass[1]

Typical glasses which are free from paramagnetic ions, such as Ni^{2+} and Fe^{3+}, are diamagnetic with susceptibilities in the neighborhood of -0.4×10^{-6}. It is doubtful if much useful information may be obtained from magnetic measurements on such systems. The presence of paramagnetic ions may impart paramagnetism to the whole mass. It seems probable that the oxidation state and to some degree the state of aggregation of such ions may be revealed by susceptibility measurements in accordance with principles which have been outlined. At the same time, there is the possibility that something may be learned concerning the structure of the glass network through such measurements. The number of studies which have been reported in this field is quite limited. Some results obtained in the author's laboratory on samples kindly provided by Professor W. A. Weyl are shown in Table XVI. It will be noted that the presence of paramagnetic ions may alter the magnetic susceptibility quite markedly.

TABLE XVI
Magnetic Susceptibilities of Glasses

Glass composition	Magnetic susceptibility ($\times 10^6$)	
	At 25°C.	At −188°C.
$Na_2O \cdot MgO \cdot 4SiO_2$	−0.3	−0.3
$Na_2O \cdot {}^1/_4MgO \cdot {}^3/_4CoO \cdot 4SiO_2$	21.2	72.5
$Na_2O \cdot {}^1/_4MgO \cdot {}^3/_4NiO \cdot 4SiO_2$	13.7	50.6
$Na_2O \cdot CaO \cdot 3SiO_2 + 5\%\ UO_2$	−0.6	+0.13

From the limited available data there seems no doubt that transition group ions present in glasses may generally be said to be at high magnetic

[1] The experimental results described in this section, unless otherwise acknowledged, were obtained in the author's laboratory by Lorraine Lyon. They have not yet been published elsewhere.

182

dilution.   The susceptibility per gram-atom of, say, manganese in a typical glass is much higher than that of manganese in a crystalline oxide such as Mn_2O_3, and this difference becomes increasingly pronounced as the temperature is lowered.

Another question is whether the orbital contribution to the moment will be as fully quenched in glass systems as it is in the salts and oxides with which one is more familiar.   To this question it is scarcely possible to give a complete answer.   For the Co^{2+} ion the orbital component is definitely not fully quenched; for the Fe^{2+}, Ni^{2+}, and Mn^{3+} ions, the observed moment is often somewhat different from that predicted by the spin-only formula.   Other ions seem to give normal spin-only moments, but the measurements on which some of these results are based have been made at room temperature only.

DeJong[2] has made susceptibility measurements on a glass containing 0.25% titanium reported as TiO_2.   This gives an average moment of 1.05 for the titanium, from which it is concluded that 36% of this element is present as Ti^{3+} ions.   In principle this is sound, but no details of the results are given, and to observe such a change at room temperature requires a somewhat higher degree of precision than is indicated.   The result is, however, consistent with the absorption spectrum results.

Reduced chromium glass gives evidence of Cr^{3+} ions at infinite magnetic dilution with a moment of 3.93, according to Bhatnagar.

Bhatnagar[3] has studied a series of sodium borate glasses to which various coloring agents were added and which were subject to oxidizing or reducing action, respectively, by conducting the fusion with free access of air, or by the addition of tartaric acid.   Reduced, decolorized manganese glass follows the Curie-Weiss law over the temperature range of 316° to 473°K.   The magnetic moment of the manganese in this system is 5.99 Bohr magnetons, which is in excellent agreement with the spin-only formula for Mn^{2+}.   The Weiss constant is $-6.5°$ which is probably not significantly different from zero.   One may therefore say that in such a glass, containing about 1% of manganese, the magnetic moment agrees with the chemical evidence for an ion in an S state and, furthermore, it may be said that the manganese is effectively at infinite dilution.   On the other hand, oxidized manganese glasses which presumably contain some tripositive manganese yield susceptibilities which are definitely higher than the calculated spin-only formula.

Somewhat similar results are reported by Bhatnagar for glasses containing iron ions.   For oxidized iron glasses the moment of the iron is

[2] J. deJong, *J. Soc. Glass Technol.*, **38**, 84 (1954).
[3] S. S. Bhatnagar, B. Prakash, and J. C. Maheshwari, *J. Sci. and Ind. Research* (*India*), **4**, 151 (1945).

5.74, which is in fair agreement with the theoretical 5.92. The Weiss constant is again effectively zero, indicating infinite magnetic dilution. For reduced iron glasses the moment tends to be high. This is possibly the cause of the erratic results found by Andresen-Kraft[4] in an effort to use magnetic methods to estimate the Fe^{2+}/Fe^{2+} ratio in glasses. Somewhat similar high moments for reduced iron in glass are reported by Yajnik, Chand, and Jain.[5] The situation in iron-containing glasses is fairly com plicated and has been clarified to some degree by Cole,[6] Moore,[7] Abou-El-Azm,[8] and deJong.[2] The problems of principal interest are: (1) the ratio of Fe^{2+}/Fe^{3+} in various glasses, and (2) the structural configuration (co-ordination) of the iron ions. It is, in general, believed that ions of this sort may either take part in forming the network structure which consists mostly of silicon-oxygen units, or as network modifiers lying in interstices adjacent to the network. In the network, the coordination number of a positive metal ion is four, the surrounding groups being oxide ions. As network modifiers, the coordination number is probably six or even higher. A modification of color and probably of magnetic moment is believed to occur when the proportions of network formers to network modifiers is changed.

The influences which may tend to reveal themselves as a change of magnetic moment in a transition ion in a glass include: (1) oxidation state, (2) coordination number, (3) acidity, and probably (4) interaction between adjacent paramagnetic ions. Abou-El-Azm suggests five different magnetic states of iron in various glasses. It is probable that much more information about glass composition and structure will be revealed as magnetic measurements are extended to lower temperatures where the effects are magnified, and to a range of field strength for the more careful detection of ferromagnetism. It is also certain that paramagnetic resonance will be useful in this field.

The present status of the subject is that in favorable cases the Fe^{2+}/Fe^{3+} ratio may be found with about as much precision as by the use of spectroscopic methods. DeJong, for a typical glass containing 0.08% iron (reported as Fe_2O_3), finds the percentage of Fe^{3+} ions to be 44.5 to 47 from the ultraviolet absorption spectrum, 44 from the infrared spectrum, and 45.5 from the magnetic data. This is done by assuming that the moment for Fe^{3+} is 5.91 and for Fe^{2+} is 4.90 Bohr magnetons, and that the susceptibilities per gram-atom are linear with weight composition.

[4] C. Andresen-Kraft, *Glastechn. Ber.*, 9, 594 (1931).
[5] N. A. Yajnik, R. Chand, and D. C. Jain, *J. Indian Chem. Soc.*, 20, 169 (1943).
[6] H. Cole, *J. Soc. Glass Technol.*, 35, 5, 25 (1951).
[7] H. Moore and S. Kumar, *ibid.*, 35, 58 (1951).
[8] A.-E.-M. Abou-El-Azm, *ibid.*, 38, 101, 146, 197, 244, 271 (1954).

While the result is satisfactory in this particular case, it must be pointed out that higher iron concentrations apparently lead to the formation of colloidal ferric oxide and also to ferromagnetic Fe_3O_4 in colloidal form. Abou-El-Azm points out that iron may also be present in a pink form with a very low susceptibility. He refers to this as a "ferrate" but the possibility of exchange interaction between adjacent iron ions leading to diamagnetic groups cannot be ignored.

Cole has extended these observations to glasses containing iron and sulfur. This situation is a little too complicated for our understanding at the present time.

Cobalt glasses give, according to Bhatnagar, a moment of about 4.88, which is independent of whether the glass is produced under oxidizing or reducing conditions. This moment is about that found in many Co^{2+} compounds. The moment is confirmed by Hüttig and Strotzer,[9] who attempted to use the changing susceptibility with thermal treatment to estimate the activation energy of the glass-forming process. It is not probable that much confidence can be placed in this procedure.

It is well known that cobalt glass may vary from red to blue. The red color is, for instance, found in acidic borate glasses, while in glasses of higher basicity the color is blue. This color change is generally believed to be related to the coordination of the cobalt ion, which is thought to change from a more or less free hexacoordinated red ion to a tetracoordinated blue network former. It will be recalled that Co^{2+} is unique among the transition elements for the large orbital contribution to the magnetic moment. Some evidence that the observed moment is sensitive to the coordination was presented in the preceding chapter, where it was shown that the hexaäquocoordinated ion probably has a somewhat higher effective moment than cobaltous ion in lower coordination, even though no true "penetration" complex is formed. It might be hoped that a similar effect would be found in cobalt glasses, but the experimental evidence is not very clear. Breit and Juza[10] report a definite increase of susceptibility per gram-ion of cobalt amounting to about 7% in going from blue to red. Their compositions ran up to 37 mole % as CoO. But deJong, working at 0.1% CoO, could find no change of susceptibility with color. The only conclusion possible in this case is that the bonding of the ion is ionic in both cases. The great difference in concentration of cobalt may, however, bear some relation to this discrepancy.

In the writer's laboratory, measurements over the temperature range of 84° to 300°K. have been made on a composition $Na_2O \cdot (1 - x)MgO \cdot x$-$CoO \cdot 4SiO_2$ kindly supplied by Professor W. A. Weyl. For cobalt (as Co)

[9] G. F. Hüttig and E. Strotzer, *Z. anorg. u. allgem. Chem.*, **236**, 107 (1938).
[10] K. L. Breit and R. Juza, *Glastech. Ber.*, **27**, 117 (1954).

concentrations from 4 to 15% by weight, the moment of the Co^{2+} ion is 4.6 magnetons, with a small ($\sim 10°$) Weiss constant. Reciprocal suscepti- bilities are plotted against temperature in Fig. 76. These results are fur- ther discussed in the following section.

Bhatnagar gives the very high moment of 3.89 magnetons for nickel in an oxidized glass. In Fig. 76, there are shown reciprocal susceptibilities per gram-atom of nickel over a range of temperature for several nickel concentrations in the glass type $Na_2O·(1 - x)MgO·xNiO·4SiO_2$. The

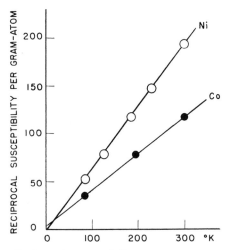

Fig. 76. Reciprocal susceptibility *versus* temperature for cobalt in cobalt glass and for nickel in nickel glass.

nickel-free glass was diamagnetic ($\chi = -0.27 \times 10^{-6}$) at all temperatures studied. From these data, the Weiss constant is seen to be negligible and the magnetic moment to be independent of concentration in the range 4.2 to 15.6% nickel. The moment is 3.6 Bohr magnetons which is somewhat higher than the spin-only value of 2.8. These results were obtained by Mrs. Lyon in the author's laboratory.

The high magnetic moment is only a little higher than that (3.35) reported by Breit and Juza[10] for Ni^{2+} in a series of borate glasses. These authors found that the magnetic moment of the nickel is independent of the color, which may be altered from yellow to violet by altering the potassium content. The colors are generally believed to be due to Ni^{2+} ions (yellow) and NiO_4^{2-} ions (violet). This aspect will be further commented on in the following section.

The case of reduced nickel glasses is interesting. Bhatnagar[3] re- ports that such glasses are ferromagnetic owing to the presence of metallic nickel. This is confirmed by Ham and Coleman[11] who observed a Curie point transition corresponding to pure nickel in a glass containing less than 1% nickel. This is a rather peculiar result because it seems to indicate a remarkable tendency for atoms of nickel to aggregate from a true highly dispersed solid solution to nickel metal aggregates large enough to show ferromagnetism.

Quite apart from the possible development of ferromagnetism, the study of reduced metal ions in glass would seem to be a field worthy of study. For instance, silver atoms in a state of atomic dispersion in glass might be expected to be paramagnetic, while metallic aggregates of silver atoms would be diamagnetic. No evidence of paramagnetism has been found in dispersions of gold in borax glass,[12] but the gold in this system is doubtless in colloidal particles rather than in true solution. The problem is of some interest in connection with the well-known photosensitive glasses.

Other glasses studied in the writer's laboratory include copper, lanthanum, and uranium. Table XVII shows composition, per cent Cu, Weiss constant (Δ), and magnetic moment (μ) for three preparations, all supplied by Professor Weyl.

TABLE XVII

Magnetic Data on Some Copper Glasses[a]

Glass type	Per cent Cu	$\Delta °$	μ
$Na_2O \cdot CuO \cdot 5B_2O_3$	13.0	68	1.8
$K_2O \cdot CuO \cdot 3SiO_2$	18.0	12	1.5
$Na_2O \cdot CuO \cdot 3SiO_2$	19.8	10	1.5

[a] The spin-only moment for Cu^{2+} is 1.7.

A single sample of lanthanum glass $Na_2O \cdot 0.25La_2O_3 \cdot 5.0SiO_2$ proved to be diamagnetic with susceptibility independent of temperature down to $-190°C$. This is, of course, the expected result for lanthanum(III) which has no f electrons. Several samples of uranium glass studied by the writer proved to be diamagnetic in spite of the fact that optical evidence suggested that the uranium was in the 4+ oxidation state, which is certainly paramagnetic in UO_2 and elsewhere. This result has not been explained.

All of the results presented above may be regarded as exploratory. Principal interest is found in the susceptibility results on the iron, nickel, cobalt, and uranium glasses. It may be noted that glass has a very strong solvent, or dispersing effect on these dissolved ions. That is to say, a glass, as is well known, is a much more effective solvent than the

[11] W. R. Ham and H. S. Coleman, *Phys. Rev.*, **65**, 348 (1944).
[12] S. K. Majumdar and G. P. Basu-Chaudhury, *J. Indian Chem. Soc.*, **25**, 301 (1948).

oxides, say alumina or magnesia. A result of this is that there are substantial percentages of nickel or of cobalt in a state of effectively infinite magnetic dilution, whereas if these same oxides were dissolved in magnesia, the state of dilution would be much less; or at least, the difficulty in preparing a homogeneous solution would be much greater.

The chief questions raised by these results concern the magnetic moments of nickel, cobalt, and uranium. The nickel has a magnetic moment which could be explained in either of two ways. The nickel could have an oxidation state of 3+ and if this state yielded a spin-only magnetic moment, this moment would be approximately 3.8. The moment actually observed is fairly close to 3.8. An alternative explanation is that the quenching of the orbital component found in most nickel compounds and in solutions containing nickelous ions is absent in the glass. This is a not unlikely state of affairs which might be taken as indicating that the electrical fields surrounding the nickel ion are much less intense or perhaps more symmetrical than they are in most other environments.

The results obtained on nickel would be easier to understand if those on cobalt did not seem to point in an opposite direction. As shown above, the magnetic moment in cobalt tends to be very high, and the usual explanation given for this is the strong spin-orbital coupling. The cobalt ions in several glasses have a magnetic moment which is substantially less than that normally found in cobaltous compounds or solutions. A possible explanation for this result is that the quenching effect on the orbital component in cobalt is much greater in glass than it is in other environments. But this explanation is exactly the opposite of that advanced for the anomalous moment found in nickel. An alternative explanation is that the cobalt in the glass has an oxidation state of 3+. The spin-only moment for the 3+ cobalt is actually very close to that observed for the cobalt in the glass. It might be expected that any explanation finally found for the results in nickel would be equally applicable for the results on cobalt, but it will be shown below that this is not necessarily true.

The results on uranium glass are even more difficult to understand. The work of Trzebiatowski and Selwood shows that uranium dioxide dissolved in thorium dioxide at concentrations comparable with those of the uranium in the glass samples reported above would have a magnetic susceptibility several times greater than that observed in the glass. From these results one can only conclude either that the glass contains uranium in the 6+ oxidation state or that prevailing views concerning the magnetic moments of transition group ions are completely erroneous. There is the possibility that some coordination effect could greatly modify the magnetic moment of 4+ uranium, but there is certainly not much evidence for this in all the substantial magnetic data available on uranium and its compounds.

50. Magnetic Anisotropy of Glass Filaments

Drawn glass fibers are generally considered to exhibit no anisotropy. But glasses containing paramagnetic ions may become magnetically anisotropic. All the work described in this section was done in the author's laboratory by Dr. Elizabeth Weir Toor who also wrote some of the paragraphs below. This work has not yet been published elsewhere. The work throws some light on the susceptibility data reported in the previous section.

Anisotropy measurements were made on two glass samples similar to those mentioned above. One sample was diamagnetic, with the composition $MgO \cdot Na_2O \cdot 4SiO_2$; the other was paramagnetic with the composition

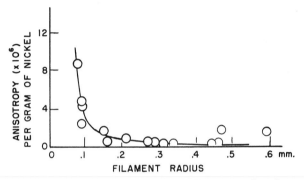

Fig. 77. Magnetic anisotropy *versus* filament radius for a
drawn sample of nickel glass.

$NiO \cdot Na_2O \cdot 4SiO_2$, and contained 15.6% of nickel. These are referred to below as "the magnesium glass" and the "nickel glass." The magnetic moment of the nickel in the nickel glass is given above as 3.6 Bohr magnetons.

Samples were prepared for magnetic anisotropy measurements by melting a portion in an oxy-gas flame, then drawing out a thread with the aid of a quartz rod. Sections of thread a few millimeters long were broken off for measurement. Anisotropy measurements were made by the Krishnan oscillation method. For the finest threads it was necessary to assemble several together in a bundle in the manner already described for anisotropy measurements on high polymers (p. 129). The anisotropy measured was the difference between susceptibilities parallel to and perpendicular to the direction of drawing. Samples were annealed as indicated below.

The magnesium glass proved to be isotropic. The nickel glass filaments, before annealing, proved to be anisotropic with $\Delta\chi$ depending on the filament diameter. The long axis lay parallel to the field, showing that the largest algebraic susceptibility was in the direction of drawing.

In Fig. 77, the magnetic anisotropy per gram of nickel is plotted as a function of filament radius. The maximum effect observed with the magnesium glass was about 1% of that in the nickel glass. Several samples were now annealed at various temperatures up to about 700°C. There was little change of anisotropy, as measured at room temperature, until the annealing temperature exceeded 500°. Above this temperature, the anisotropy dropped slowly and finally became negligible. There was no change of anisotropy when the samples were merely held at room temperature for as long as 60 days.

Since the nickel glass filaments showed anisotropy, it appears that the abnormal magnetic moment in this system is caused by some effect of the crystalline field on the spin-orbital coupling. The subnormal moment of cobalt in glass should be explainable on the same basis. The nickel and cobalt ions must occupy equivalent, or nearly equivalent, positions in these series of glasses, as in isomorphous salts. Furthermore, the low Weiss constant seems to exclude exchange interaction between adjacent paramagnetic ions.

In a position of octahedral symmetry, as in the network-modifying positions in a glass, the lowest Ni^{2+} level is a singlet, which gives a low anisotropy and conformity to the Curie law down to low temperatures. In the same environment, the multiplet levels of Co^{2+} being inverted, the lowest level is a triplet, which yields a larger anisotropy, deviations from the Curie law, and less quenching of the orbital component for the Co^{2+} ion. But in a tetrahedral field, as in the network-forming positions in a glass, the situation is reversed. Under these circumstances, the Ni^{2+} ion will have a magnetic moment in which the orbital component is less effectively quenched than is the case for Co^{2+} ions in a similar environment.

Thus the behavior of cobalt and nickel in glasses can be explained quite satisfactorily by the assumption that the paramagnetic ions are distributed in both octahedral and tetrahedral positions. Even if only a small percentage of the ions are in tetrahedral positions, the moment of cobalt will be lower than normal and that of nickel will be higher. It might be possible to predict the number of ions in tetrahedral positions, at least for cobalt glasses, by comparing the moment of the cobalt in the glass to that of a normal cobalt salt, such as $CoSO_4 \cdot 7H_2O$, and to that for Cs_2CoCl_4. This view is not in agreement with the results obtained by Breit and Juza[10] to which reference was made above. But small changes in composition may greatly modify the color and other properties of a glass. A study by the paramagnetic resonance technique might easily reveal small differences in the proportions of Ni^{2+}, Co^{2+}, and other ions in the several possible coordination position in a glass.   A start in this direction has been made by Sands.[12a]

The second problem is to explain the anisotropy of drawn nickel glass. Nickel salts in which the nickel ions have positions of octahedral symmetry have an anisotropy which is about 3% of the average susceptibility, while isomorphous cobalt salts have anisotropies which are about 20% of the average susceptibility.   Therefore, nickel ions in octahedral positions in glass will have a very small anisotropy, while those in tetrahedral positions will have a much larger anisotropy.   In the unstrained glass network, both the tetrahedral and octahedral positions of the nickel atoms are oriented randomly so that the glass has no resultant anisotropy.

To obtain the anisotropic glass rods, the glass was heated and rapidly drawn out, being allowed to cool rapidly to room temperature.   This procedure must distort the original structure of the glass.   It is possible that the octahedral holes are drawn out along the direction of pulling of the glass fiber.   This would have the overall effect of changing some of the octahedral holes into positions of tetragonal symmetry, with one axis elongated along the direction of drawing.   If this elongation is not too large, the conditions will still correspond to a predominantly cubic field with a weak rhombic field superimposed, which would leave the nickel ion with a small anisotropy, not much different from that of the ion in the strictly octahedral position.   But here all the imposed local fields will be oriented in nearly the same direction, and as a result, the glass will show anisotropy, of the same order as that of $NiSO_4 \cdot 6H_2O$.   On the other hand, if the elongation of the cubic axis parallel to the direction of drawing is large, it is possible that the symmetry of the octahedral holes might change to something approaching tetrahedral symmetry, but this is rather unlikely.

It is more difficult to conceive of a way in which the tetrahedrally coordinated nickel ions in network-forming positions could be oriented in the drawn glass so that there could be a large resultant anisotropy.   Probably such an orientation would lead to a distortion of the tetrahedral symmetry, possibly to a degree which could cause the crystalline fields to become so unsymmetric as to remove all degeneracy in the energy levels, causing the moment to drop to the spin-only value for those particular ions.   Thus it is difficult to account for any large anisotropy which arises in a drawn glass. However, more nickel ions will be present as tetrahedrally coordinated ions when the glass is raised to a high temperature, and also in the unannealed glass.   If there is any orientation of these tetrahedrally coordinated nickel ions in the glass network, there could be quite a substantial anisotropy. Annealing should decrease strain and increase the randomness of orientation

[12a] R. H. Sands, *Phys. Rev.*, **99**, 1222 (1955).

thus decreasing the anisotropy of the glass samples, as was found experimentally.

51. Irradiated Inorganic Solids

Susceptibility measurements and, to a greater degree, paramagnetic resonance are proving to be useful in the study of crystals and glasses subjected to gamma-radiation or to a neutron flux. It is well known that such treatment produces color centers. These color centers have unpaired electrons "trapped" in regions called F centers or V centers, depending on the way the electrons are held. In F centers the electron is essentially uncombined but is trapped in a hole left by a missing anion. In V centers the unpaired electron is thought to be in a neutral atom formed by the loss of an electron from an anion. For this reason, V centers are often called "positive holes." In principle, it is possible to estimate the concentration of such unpaired electrons by magnetic measurements. It is also possible to draw some conclusions about the environment of these electrons. Color centers may be produced by methods other than by irradiation, but all magnetic studies on such systems which have come to the writer's attention are mentioned here.

Jensen[13] has measured the magnetic susceptibility of potassium bromide with color centers. He concludes that there is an increase of volume susceptibility at room temperature amounting to 2.6×10^{-27} times the the number of color centers per cubic centimeter. The molar susceptibility of the color centers is 1.58×10^{-3}, and the effective Bohr magneton number of a color center is 1.93. Some further results on color centers in potassium chloride, together with experimental details, are given by Scott.[14] In these experiments, and those of Heer and Rauch,[15] the excess potassium is introduced by baking pure crystals of potassium chloride with a small piece of metallic potassium. For pure KCl, the susceptibility is independent of temperature, but the colored samples have a susceptibility which is definitely larger (algebraically) than that of the pure salt, and which varies inversely with the temperaure. Heer and Rauch carried the measurements down to 1°K. and showed that the paramagnetism related to the presence of color centers could be broken down into two parts. One part, varying according to the Curie law, is believed to be related to the F centers, and the other, independent of temperature, to color centers near enough to each other to show exchange effects. The number of F centers determined in this way is slightly smaller than the actual excess of potassium which amounted to about 1×10^{19} atoms per cubic centimeter.

[13] P. Jensen, *Ann. Physik*, **34**, 161 (1939).
[14] A. B. Scott, H. J. Hrostowski, and L. P. Bupp, *Phys. Rev*, **79**, 346 (1950).
[15] C. V. Heer and C. Rauch, *Phys. Rev.*, **90**, 530 (1953).

Paramagnetic resonance absorption in irradiated lithium fluoride and potassium chloride has been observed by Hutchison.[16] Strong neutron irradiation produced a resonance intensity equal to one-tenth of that produced by an equal weight of $CuSO_4 \cdot 5H_2O$. Similar experiments have been made by Schneider and England[17] on irradiated KCl, NaCl, and KBr. These authors obtained evidence of exchange effects between adjacent color centers. Nuclear magnetic resonance applied to the study of crystalline imperfections has been reviewed by Pound.[18]

Paramagnetic resonance has recently been applied to irradiated glasses.[19,20] For instance, a series of boron-free glasses showed a strong resonance at a g-factor of 2.00 after 1000 roentgens or more of gamma-radiation. Borosilicate glass showed several resonance peaks thought to be due to boron-11. All glasses except vitreous silica had a strong resonance independent of irradiation, presumably due to some paramagnetic impurity. The irradiation-dependent resonance amplitudes varied linearly with optical density and decreased linearly with bleaching. The most interesting feature of this work, at its present state of development, is the great sensitivity, which is able to detect as little as 2×10^{14} electron spins. This sensitivity is many orders greater than the best classical susceptibility measurement might be capable of at any readily attainable temperature.

The application of magnetic methods to irradiated organic substances will be described in a later chapter.

52. Luminescent Solids and Related Topics

The susceptibility of luminous sulfides has been studied by Rupp[21] and by Sibaiya and Venkataramiah.[22] The susceptibility changes during phosphorescent decay. For instance, for a CaS-Bi phosphor the susceptibility ($\times 10^6$) varied from -0.268 at 0 minutes to -0.250 at 3 minutes and to -0.247 at 12 minutes. This change is parallel to light output. More readily interpreted results have been obtained on phosphors containing a paramagnetic ion such as Mn^{2+} as activator.

Manganese-activated zinc fluoride phosphors have been studied by Johnson and Williams.[23] The apparatus used was an adaptation of the Faraday balance. The susceptibility of the manganese in such systems

[16] C. A. Hutchison, Jr., *Phys. Rev.*, **75**, 1769 (1949).
[17] E. E. Schneider and T. S. England, *Physica*, **17**, 221 (1951).
[18] R. V. Pound, *J. Phys. Chem.*, **57**, 743 (1953).
[19] E. L. Yasaitis and B. Smaller, *Phys. Rev.*, **92**, 1068 (1953).
[20] J. Combrisson and J. Uebersfeld, *Compt. rend.*, **238**, 572 (1954).
[21] E. Rupp, *Ann. Physik*, **78**, 505 (1925).
[22] L. Sibaiya and H. S. Venkataramiah, *Current Sci.*, **9**, 224 (1940).
[23] P. D. Johnson and F. E. Williams, *J. Chem. Phys.*, **17**, 435 (1949).

tends to reach the theoretical spin-only value for Mn^{2+} at low concentrations of manganese. At higher concentrations, exchange effects tend to lower the susceptibility, as described earlier for manganous oxide and manganous fluoride solid solutions. On excitation the susceptibility drops sharply. When the illumination is turned off, the susceptibility rises again, as shown in Fig. 78.

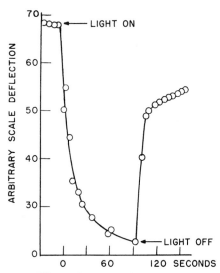

Fig. 78. Effect of illumination on the susceptibility of a manganese phosphor.

This has been interpreted as evidence for the oxidation Mn^{2+} ($\mu = 5.9$) → Mn^{3+} ($\mu = 4.9$) + ϵ taking place during illumination. But later paramagnetic resonance work tends to show that any change of magnetic moment due to change of oxidation state is obscured by the production of photoconductive electrons.

The spin-only moment and the existence of exchange interaction between adjacent manganese ions is further confirmed by Larach and Turkevich[24] on the manganese-activated zinc silicate system. The same authors[24a] have shown that under certain circumstances zinc sulfide phosphors may show a large enhancement of diamagnetism, resembling that shown by irradiated germanium.

There is no question that paramagnetic resonance techniques are exceedingly powerful for this kind of study. Hershberger and Leifer[25]

[24] S. Larach and J. Turkevich, *Phys. Rev.*, **89**, 1060 (1953).
[24a] S. Larach and J. Turkevich, *Phys. Rev.*, **98**, 1015 (1955).
[25] W. D. Hershberger and H. N. Leifer, *ibid.*, **88**, 714 (1952).

show that as little as 10^{-11} gram-atom of Mn^{2+} may be detected in certain classes of host crystals. In favorable cases it is possible to work out the energy level diagram in great detail. On the other hand, some manganese-activated phosphors fail to show any resonance spectrum. This is true also of some phosphors activated by iron, titanium, copper, or the rare earth elements. In some cases, as for instance for copper, this failure may be due to the activator ion being in a nonparamagnetic oxidation state, such as Cu(I).

Paramagnetic resonance is also useful in detecting exchange effects in these systems.[26, 26a] Current theories of phosphor activity have led to discussions of coordination and to the possibility of clustering of the activator ions. Clustering would be expected to increase exchange interaction and this would cause a decrease of resonance line width. The paramagnetic resonance techniques are sufficiently sensitive to detect such effects at very low activator concentrations and to show the influence of added ions, such as beryllium, on the tendency of the activator to cluster.

Two other distantly related studies will be mentioned briefly. Delgery[27] has reported that lead bromide suffers moderate positive change of susceptibility on exposure to light. It is not clear how this could occur. The formation of paramagnetic lead ions seems unlikely, but parallel studies of other light-sensitive systems might be instructive. Perakis[28] has shown that a mixture of silver bromide and silver sulfide heated above 220° develops a paramagnetic phase. The results may have some bearing on a current theory of the production of F centers in the latent photographic image.

[26] E. G. Spencer, M. A. Garstens, C. C. Klick, and J. H. Schulman, *J. Chem. Phys.*, **20**, 1177 (1952).

[26a] K. Oshima, H. Abe, H. Nagano and M. Nagusa, *J. Chem. Phys.*, **23**, 1721 (1955).

[27] I. Delgery, *Compt. rend.*, **225**, 298 (1947).

[28] N. Perakis, *Helv. Phys. Acta*, **26**, 258 (1953).

CHAPTER TEN

COORDINATION COMPOUNDS

53. Magnetic Moment, Bond Type, and Stereochemistry

There are many chemical compounds which contain a central transition atom or positive ion surrounded by neutral or negative atoms or groups of atoms. Such coordination compounds, or Werner complexes, will be discussed in the present chapter. Their study makes up what is possibly the most active single branch of magnetochemistry, although the results have not always been so rewarding as might have been hoped. As always, there is a certain difficulty of classification. There is no sharp dividing line between simple ionic compounds, complex compounds, and molecular compounds. The author has resolved this difficulty rather arbitrarily in some cases.

Since the first edition of this book, there have appeared some comprehensive reviews of complex compounds and their magnetic properties. These reviews[1,2] have greatly simplified the author's task in rewriting the present chapter. Early attempts to interpret magnetic susceptibilities in terms of chemical structure were made by Jackson,[3] Bose,[4] Baudisch and Welo[5,6] and others. Welo and Baudisch[7] and later Sidgwick and Bose expressed essentially the following rule: the magnetic moment of a complex is the same as that of the atom with the same number of electrons as the central atom of the complex, counting two for each electron pair.

Thus Fe^{2+} has 24 electrons; add 12 for six bonds to give 36, the atomic number of krypton; so that the diamagnetism of ferrocyanide is paralleled by that of the rare gases. This number of electrons about the center atom of the complex is often called the "effective atomic number" or E.A.N.

---

[1] R. W. Asmussen, *Magnetokemiske Undersøgelser over Uorganiske Kompleks-forbindelser*. Jul. Gjellerups Forlag, Copenhagen, 1944.

[2] R. S. Nyholm, *Quart. Revs. (London)*, **7**, 377 (1953).

[3] L. C. Jackson, *Phil. Mag.*, **2**, 86 (1926).

[4] D. M. Bose, *Z. Physik*, **43**, 864 (1927).

[5] O. Baudisch and L. A. Welo, *Chem. Rev.*, **15**, 1 (1934).

[6] O. Baudisch, *Ber.*, **68**, 769 (1935).

[7] L. A. Welo and O. Baudisch, *Nature*, **116**, 606 (1925).

But there are many exceptions to this rule.   For instance $Ni(CN)_4{}^{2-}$ is diamagnetic, but the rule would make it paramagnetic, as for $Ni(NH_3)_4{}^{2+}$. Diamagnetic complexes such as $Ni(CN)_4{}^{2-}$ are sometimes referred to as "penetration" complexes, as opposed to normal complexes, such as Ni-$(NH_3)_4{}^{2+}$.

The binding forces within the complex may be due to electrostatic attraction for the surrounding ions or oriented dipoles, or to covalent binding, or to some combination of the types.   Application of magnetic measurements to the study of complex compounds is due largely to Pauling,[8,9] and nearly all recent work on the subject has been interpreted in Pauling's terms.   This procedure will be adhered to here, although it will be pointed out that alternative methods of regarding these structural problems have been suggested.   It will be assumed that the reader is in general familiar with the relative stability and the directional properties of atomic bond orbitals, but the subject will be reviewed very briefly.[10,11]

The order of decreasing stability for atomic bond orbitals is approximately as follows: $1s, 2s, 2p, 3s, 3p, 4s, 3d, 4p, 5s, 4d, 5p, 6s, 4f, 5d, 5p$. The number of orbitals for the s, p, d, f groups is, respectively, 1, 3, 5, and 7. Each orbital may be occupied by one electron, or by two electrons provided these have opposed spins.   It should be noted that electrons first tend to occupy stable orbitals by pairing, but that when several orbitals of the same energy are available the electrons tend to keep their spins parallel and to occupy different orbitals.   One must, of course, distinguish between the orbitals and the electrons which occupy them.   The orbitals are, strictly speaking, the wave-functions associated with the orbital motion of the electrons.   An electron-pair bond may be formed for each stable orbital of the atoms between which bonds exist.   It is clear that for bond formation it is necessary to have two electrons with opposed spins and for each of the bonded atoms to have a stable orbital.

Such bonds, commonly called covalent bonds, are characterized by having definite directions in space.   The bond angles may be found experimentally by electron diffraction and other methods, or they may be found theoretically.   When only s electrons are available for bond formation, as in molecular hydrogen, the bond is spherically symmetrical about the nucleus.   If p electrons are involved in the bond formation, the bonds are at right angles to one another.   In most cases the situation is complicated

[8] L. Pauling, *J. Am. Chem. Soc.*, **53**, 1391 (1931); **54**, 988 (1932).

[9] L. Pauling and M. L. Huggins, *Z. Krist.*, **87**, 214 (1934).

[10] L. Pauling, *Nature of the Chemical Bond*.   Cornell University Press, Ithaca 1939, 2nd ed., 1940.

[11] O. K. Rice, *Electronic Structure and Chemical Binding*.   McGraw-Hill Book Co., Inc., New York 1940.

by "hybridization" which is a combination of s and p and other orbitals. If the structure involves all s and p orbitals, the result will be a tetrahedron. The fact that one s and three p orbitals are involved is indicated by calling them sp^3 bonds.

The structure is a square if it involves all s, all p orbitals of a given level, and one d orbital. This is designated as sp^2d bonding. It might be thought that the proper designation should be sp^3d, but one of the p orbitals is used for a nonbonding combination.

For all s, all p orbitals of a given level, and three or more d orbitals (sp^3d^3) the structure is a tetrahedron.

For all s, all p, and two or more d orbitals (sp^3d^2) the six bonds may form an octahedron.

The use of magnetic susceptibility measurements in the study of complexes arises from the fact that electrons used in covalent bond formation are of necessity paired and so contribute nothing to the permanent magnetic moment of the molecule. It is possible to compute the number of paired and unpaired electrons in a complex because the moment is often given by $\mu = \sqrt{n(n+2)}$, where n is the number of unpaired electrons.

From a knowledge of the number of electrons used in covalent bond formation, it is possible to deduce the nature of the orbitals involved and hence the spatial configuration of the complex. For instance, iron in the compound $(NH_4)_3FeF_6$ has a moment of 5.9 Bohr magnetons, while in $K_3Fe(CN)_6$ it has a moment of about 2.3 Bohr magnetons. The ferric ion, Fe^{3+} has five unpaired d electrons with a theoretical moment of 5.92. It is assumed that the spins only are involved. As pointed out in Chapter VIII, the orbital moments are appreciable for the rare earth elements but are probably not large for other transition group elements, with the exception of cobalt. The moment for the FeF_6^{3-} corresponds therefore to a structure primarily ionic. If, on the other hand, covalent sp^3d^2 bonds are formed, two of the five d orbitals are used up, and only three d orbitals remain for five electrons. These must then pair off so far as possible, leaving only one

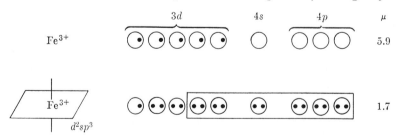

electron unpaired. If such is the case, the complex should have a moment of about 1.7 Bohr magnetons. It would appear that while the FeF_6^{3-}

complex is dominantly ionic, the $Fe(CN)_6^{3-}$ complex is essentially covalent. Magnetic measurements do not contribute much to our knowledge of the spatial configuration of complexes such as the above, because the sp^3d^2 bonds are octahedral, and it may be assumed that ionic bonds would lie at the largest possible angle from one another so that they would also be octahedral. But where the covalent structure leads to a square, or to a tetrahedron involving only three bonds, then the information so obtained may be valuable, as will be indicated for certain nickel compounds.

The divalent nickel atom has two unpaired electrons, with a normal moment of about 2.8 Bohr magnetons. In a tetrahedral complex involving

ionic bonds, or only the $4s$ and $4p$ orbitals in weak covalent bonds, the moment remains unchanged. But for the formation of four planar dsp^2 covalent bonds, there are only four $3d$ orbitals available for eight electrons. The square planar nickel complexes, such as in $K_2Ni(CN)_4$, are therefore

diamagnetic. In this way it is possible, on the basis of magnetic susceptibility measurements, to determine not only bond type but also spatial configuration in numerous complex compounds. The method is most effective for nickel and for iron complexes. The structural information so obtained is in agreement with that derived from x-ray diffraction. Numerous other examples are given below.

Van Vleck[12] has pointed out that Pauling's interpretation in terms of directed wave-functions is not the only possible explanation of the magnetic properties of complex compounds. Alternatives are the crystalline potential model of Penney and Schlapp, and the molecular orbital model of Mulliken. The three approaches give results so similar that it is difficult to establish any preference among them. A somewhat different approach to the problem has been made by Syrkin and Dyatkina[13] who, comparing the energy differences between d, s, and p levels, reach the conclusion that multivalences up to nine are possible in complex-forming atoms. A correlation of these valence states and their various resonance structures may be made with magnetic data and with the stability of various complexes.

The crystal-field theory has already been referred to briefly in several

[12] J. H. Van Vleck, *J. Chem. Phys.*, **3**, 807 (1935).

[13] J. Syrkin and M. Dyatkina, *Acta Physicochim.* (U. R. S. S.), **20**, 137, 273 (1945).

connections.   The physical picture here is that a central atom or ion must lie in an electric field due to coordinated negative ions or oriented dipoles, and that the electrons in the central atom are influenced by the intensity and symmetry of this electric field.   This influence may be pictured as a tendency of electrons to avoid those regions where the crystal field has its greatest intensity.   We have already become accustomed to the "quenching" of the orbital component in many transition ions, but this, so far as it leads to spin-only moments, is only one rather special possibility.   The crystal field may, in general, split the energy levels in the coordinated central atom and may result in removing the degeneracy of the ground state. Precisely how this is done, and the effect on the magnetic properties of the complex, depend in a complicated way on the energy levels of the central atom, and also on the nature of the field itself.   The crystal-field theory leads to the same stereochemical configurations as the Pauling theory, but it does not specifically make use of the terms "ionic" and "covalent" with reference to the valence bonding.

Chemists in general, and those interested in coordination chemistry in particular, have tended to interpret magnetic data on complex compounds exclusively in terms of Pauling's approach.   This seems to have as its principal basis the fact that Pauling's theory is not very difficult to understand and that the essential features may be expressed in language with which the average chemist is familiar.   The crystal-field theory, by contrast, requires a more than average understanding of atomic structure. It is a "physical" rather than a "chemical" theory.

In recent years evidence has accumulated that the classification of valence bonds into "ionic" or "covalent" by the magnetic criterion is not entirely justifiable.   Other methods of determining bond type, by exchange reaction studies or by spectroscopic means, sometimes give different results.   These and related considerations have led Pauling[14] to abandon the idea that the magnetic criterion distinguishes between essentially covalent bonds and essentially ionic bonds.   This abandonment by the author of the theory seems to have had remarkably little effect on many workers in the field, who continue to classify bonds as "essentially covalent" or "essentially ionic" by this criterion.[15]

The present status of the matter seems to be that the magnetic criterion has a definite usefulness in establishing the stereochemistry of those complexes to which the method is applicable.   As will be shown below, the method works best for nickel(II) and iron(II and III), but tells little for chromium(III) and copper(II).   So far as bond type is concerned, the

[14] L. Pauling, *J. Chem. Soc.*, **1948**, 1461.
[15] A. E. Martell and M. Calvin, *Chemistry of the Metal Chelates*.   Prentice-Hall, Inc., New York, 1952, p. 211.

situation is less clear. Pauling expresses the difference as being between "strong covalent bonds, using good hybrid bond orbitals and with the possibility of unsynchronized ionic-covalent bonds, using poor bond orbitals, and the necessity for synchronization of the covalent phases of the bonds." Burstall and Nyholm[16] suggest that bonding by "higher" and "lower" covalent orbitals is a sounder concept than simply "ionic" or "covalent." Orgel[17] shows that the magnetic moment serves roughly as an indicator, demonstrating whether the covalent character of the bond has passed a certain limiting value. This limiting value is different for each metal ion and depends on its electronic structure.

Orgel[17] has also made a useful contribution in showing the essential similarity of the Pauling and the Penney and Schlapp approaches so far as stereochemical configuration is concerned. The spatial shift of electrons in the crystal field brings about a directed electronegativity which may be equivalent to the stereochemical properties of atomic bond orbitals. It thus seems that the place of magnetic measurements in coordination chemistry is becoming much clearer. But it is no longer possible to say that because a substance has a certain number of unpaired electrons it must have a certain magnetic moment. The observed moment depends in detail on the energy levels of the paramagnetic atom or ion under consideration and on the influence of the crystal field on that atom. Such calculations have been made for only a few substances, but the increasingly valuable information obtainable from paramagnetic resonance studies makes future progress in this direction quite certain.

In the following sections no effort has been made to include all published work in the field. The author has simply selected representative data, illustrations of special problems, and topics of interest to him and, it is hoped, to others. The classification is, in general, according to the Periodic Table position of the central element. This classification is in agreement with the idea expressed above that the magnetic properties of the complex depend more on the electronic structure of the central atom than on the nature of the ligand.

54. Titanium

Magnetic data on the paramagnetic complex compounds of titanium are meagre. The complex fluoride, K_4TiF_6, is said[18] to have a subnormal paramagnetism. Reference has already been made to the normal moment of titanium alum. The complex fluoride, K_3TiF_6, seems also to have a

[16] F. H. Burstall and R. S. Nyholm, *J. Chem. Soc.*, **1952**, 3570.
[17] L. E. Orgel, *ibid.*, **1952**, 4756.
[18] D. P. Raychaudhuri and P. N. Sengupta, *Ind. J. Physics*, **10**, 253 (1936).

normal moment (1.70) for titanium(III), at least at low temperatures.[19] The (4+) oxidation state is diamagnetic[20] as, for instance, in the ion TiF_6^{2+}, and in biscyclopentadienyltitanium(IV) dibromide.[21]

55. Vanadium

Magnetic data are available on a considerable number of vanadium compounds, but some of these are perhaps not properly classed as coordination complexes. In the 3+ oxidation state the alum and the oxychloride, VOCl, have approximately normal moments.[22,23] In the 4+ state the hydrates of vanadyl sulfate[22] and vanadyl dichloride[23] have normal moments for one unpaired electron,[24] as does vanadyl phthalocyanine.[25] Compounds formed by the reactions between vanadium dichloride and nitric oxide appear to have susceptibilities which are in part at least due to the nitric oxide.[26] Nyholm[20] gives vanadium(III) in K_3VF_6 as having a moment of 2.79. The biscyclopentadienyl dichloride[21] has a moment corresponding to one unpaired electron. A series of salicylaldehyde-imine complexes investigated by Bayer[27] et al. give moments in general consistent with the number of unpaired electrons expected in vanadium(III to V). Vanadates and other compounds in which the vanadium has a 5+ oxidation state are diamagnetic or have a small temperature-independent paramagnetism, although a fractional magnetic moment has sometimes been reported for these substances.

56. Chromium

From the astonishing wealth of available data on chromium complexes, a selection will be made to illustrate various points.

The chromous, Cr^{2+}, ion has four $3d$ electrons, all unpaired, giving a theoretical moment of 4.9 Bohr magnetons. In chromous chloride the observed moment is actually 5.0. Octahedral covalent bond formation (d^2sp^3) results in the pairing of two electrons, leaving $\mu = 2.8$.

There are not many data available on divalent chromium complexes. Hume and Stone[28] find moments ranging from 4.4 to 4.9 for chromous

[19] P. Ehrlich and G. Pietzka, *Naturwissenschaften*, **40**, 509 (1953).
[20] R. S. Nyholm and A. G. Sharpe, *J. Chem. Soc.*, **1952**, 3579.
[21] G. Wilkinson, P. L. Pauson, J. M. Birmingham, and F. A. Cotton, *J. Am. Chem. Soc.*, **75**, 1011 (1953).
[22] D. M. Bose and H. G. Bhar, *Z. Physik*, **48**, 716 (1928).
[23] E. Wedekind and C. Horst, *Ber.*, **45**, 262 (1912).
[24] N. Perakis, *J. Phys. radium.*, **8**, 473 (1927).
[25] H. Senff and W. Klemm, *J. prakt. Chem.*, **143**, 82 (1935).
[26] A. G. Whittaker and D. M. Yost, *J. Am. Chem. Soc.*, **71**, 3135 (1949).
[27] E. Bayer, N. J. Bielig, and K. H. Hausser, *Ann.*, **584**, 116 (1953).
[28] D. N. Hume and H. W. Stone, *J. Am. Chem. Soc.*, **63**, 1200 (1941).

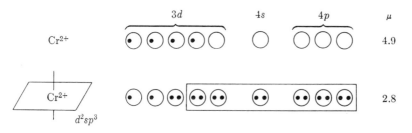

complexes with thiocyanate, with ethylenediamine, and with an ammonia complex of uncertain composition. The chromocyanide gives a low moment of about 3.15, which had previously been noted by Bose[29] and others.[30] Chromous acetate, on the other hand, has virtually zero moment,[31] which may make this compound an example of d^3s hybridization. More probably it is another case like cupric acetate in which, as described in Chapter VIII, the small distance between adjacent cupric ions results in partial quenching of the moment.[32] The chromium in the true organometallic, biscyclopentadienylchromium, is reported by Engelmann[33] as having a moment of 3.20 magneton. This high value for two unpaired electrons is attributed to incomplete orbital quenching, but Wilkinson[34] finds a moment in closer agreement with the spin-only value. The only other complex derived from divalent chromium which has received attention seems to be the dinitrosyldiethyldithiocarbamate,[35] $(ON)_2CrSCSN-(C_2H_5)_2$. Such compounds are called chromonitrosyl salts, but it is not certain what oxidation state is reached by the chromium. The substance is diamagnetic, which is unusual among derivatives of chromium having a valence less than six. The distribution of electrons in this complex is uncertain.

Trivalent chromium complexes have been the object of much investiga-

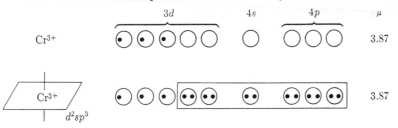

[29] D. M. Bose, Z. Physik, 65, 677 (1930).
[30] P. Råy and H. Bhar, J. Indian Chem. Soc., 11, 899 (1934).
[31] W. R. King, Jr., and C. S. Garner, J. Chem. Phys., 18, 689 (1950).
[32] J. N. Van Niekirk and F. R. L. Schoening, Nature, 171, 36 (1953).
[33] F. Engelmann, Z. Naturforsch., 8b, 775 (1953).
[34] G. Wilkinson, J. Am. Chem. Soc., 76, 209 (1954).
[35] L. Malatesta, Gazz. chim. ital., 70, 729 (1940).

tion. Unfortunately, not much can be learned from magnetic measurements on such compounds because the structures of the extreme types of electrovalence and covalence have the same number of unpaired electrons.

A very large group of trivalent chromium complexes has been studied by Rosenbohm,[36] Bose,[37,42,43] Berkman and Zocher,[38] Jackson,[39] Welo,[40] Biltz,[41] and others.[44-49] These consist of polyammines, cyanides, organo-acid derivatives, polynuclear compounds, and many others. Without exception they all have an effective moment of very close to 3.8 Bohr magnetons. It is true that Bhatnagar[45] finds the green modification of [Cr-$(NH_3)_3(OH_2)Cl_2]Cl$ to have a susceptibility only one-half that of the red and grey modifications, but this lone case probably does not constitute an exception to the rule. For relatively simple complexes, the Weiss law is obeyed with values of Δ equivalent to only a few Centigrade degrees, positive or negative.   Leiterer[44] suggests a possible relationship between Δ and the absorption spectra. The polynuclear compounds are a marked exception. Welo has shown that in compounds of the type $[Cr_3(CH_3COO)_6$-$(OH)_2]Cl\cdot 8H_2O$ the temperature coefficient is very peculiar, with Δ often reaching 500° or even larger. Reasons for this are discussed by Wucher and Gijsman.[49a] The polynuclear complexes of iron are similar in this respect.

Very few studies have been made on the magnetic anisotropy of coordination compounds. Those containing chromium(III) seem to have only a small anisotropy.[50] Chromium in the oxidation state of 4+ is known in the oxide, to be discussed later. Complexes containing this oxidation state are few in number and somewhat difficult to characterize.

[36] E. Rosenbohm, Z. phys. Chem., **93**, 693 (1919). The old value for water, -0.75×10^{-6}, was used by Rosenbohm for calibration purposes. Consequently his very extensive and useful data should all be corrected by the factor 72/75.

[37] D. M. Bose, Z. Physik, **35**, 219 (1926).

[38] S. Berkman and H. Zocher, Z. phys. Chem., **124**, 318 (1926).

[39] L. C. Jackson, Phil. Mag., **4**, 1070 (1927).

[40] L. A. Welo, ibid., **6**, 481 (1928).

[41] W. Biltz, Z. anorg. u. allgem. Chem., **170**, 161 (1928).

[42] D. M. Bose, Phil. Mag., **5**, 1048 (1928).

[43] D. M. Bose, Z. Physik, **65**, 677 (1930).

[44] L. Leiterer, Z. physik. Chem., **B36**, 325 (1937).

[45] S. S. Bhatnagar, B. Prakash, and A. Hamid, J. Chem. Soc., **1938**, 1428.

[46] D. S. Datar and S. K. K. Jatkar, J. Indian Inst. Sci., **22A**, 225 (1939).

[47] P. C. R. Chaudhury, J. Indian Chem. Soc., **16**, 652 (1939).

[48] L. Malatesta, Gazz. chim. ital., **69**, 752 (1939).

[49] L. A. Welo, Phys. Rev., **32**, 320 (1928).

[49a] J. Wucher and H. M. Gijsman, Physica, **20**, 361 (1954).

[50] K. S. Krishnan, A. Mookherji, and A. Bose, Phil. Trans. Roy. Soc. (London), **A238**, 125 (1939).

The peculiar triamminochromium tetroxide, $(NH_3)_3CrO_4$, has a susceptibility corresponding to two unpaired electrons.[45] Chromium(IV) as in the compound K_2CrF_6 has a moment[51] of 2.8. The oxyfluoride, $KCrOF_4$, in which one unpaired electron would appear to be present, has a normal moment of 1.76 according to Nyholm and Sharpe.

The familiar red and blue perchromates are sometimes supposed to contain chromium with a valence of seven. The red potassium perchromate, K_3CrO_8, has a moment of 1.80 Bohr magnetons at room temperature, as have several related compounds.[52-54] This clearly indicates a single unpaired electron. The valence of seven is not excluded by these measurements, but the electronic configuration renders such a valence improbable. The oxidation state of five is compatible with the magnetic results. On the other hand, the blue perchromate has a very small positive susceptibility which is probably not greatly dependent on temperature. This strongly suggests an oxidation state of six, as is found in the chromates. The pyridine salt of perchromic acid is shown by Bhatnagar, Prakash, and Hamid[45] to have a small positive susceptibility, probably because the chromium here also has an oxidation state of six.

Chromic acid anhydride, CrO_3, and many chromates have a small temperature-independent paramagnetism. There is no unpaired electron in such compounds. Thus sodium chromate[55] has a susceptibility of about 0.04×10^{-6}, and the polychromates show corresponding values. Silver chromate in both green and red modifications is diamagnetic, with a susceptibility of about -0.12×10^{-6}. Pyridinium tetrachlorohydroxychromate is slightly paramagnetic, and the corresponding quinolinium compound is diamagnetic.

The substances called chromium chromates, prepared by thermal decomposition of chromates or by action of $AgCrO_4$ on $CrCl_3$, have been studied by Datar and Jatkar,[56] and by Chaudhury.[57] The magnetic susceptibility corresponds to about 2.2 Bohr magnetons per atom of chromium. This is a little difficult to reconcile with the chemical evidence that the ratio Cr^{3+}/CrO_4^{2-} in chromium chromate is 2/3. The magnetic data would support a ratio of 3/2.

Chromium carbonyl, $Cr(CO)_6$, is diamagnetic,[43,58] as appears to be the case for all transition group metal carbonyls.

[51] W. Klemm, Angew. Chem., 66, 468 (1954).
[52] B. T. Tjabbes, Proc. Acad. Sci. Amsterdam, 35, 693 (1932).
[53] B. T. Tjabbes, Z. anorg. u. allgem. Chem., 210, 385 (1935).
[54] W. Klemm and H. Werth, ibid., 216, 127 (1933).
[55] F. W. Gray and J. Dakers, Phil. Mag., 11, 297 (1931).
[56] D. S. Datar and S. K. K. Jatkar, J. Indian Inst. Sci., 22A, 309 (1939).
[57] P. C. R. Chaudhury, J. Indian Chem. Soc., 16, 652 (1939).
[58] W. Klemm, H. Jacobi, and W. Tilk, Z. anorg. u. allgem. Chem., 201, 1 (1931).

Magnetic properties of the peculiar polyphenylchromium compounds have been studied by Klemm and Neuber.[59] All these substances, whether containing three, four, or five phenyl groups on one chromium atom, have a moment of about 1.7 Bohr magnetons. For instance, tetraphenylchromium iodide, measured over the range 90°K. to 293°K., has a moment of 1.67. This apparently means that there is one unpaired electron, contrary to Hein's original proposal that the pentaphenyl series contains chromium with a valence of six. It may be that the tri- and tetraphenylchromiums contain phenylene groups, such as, for instance

$$\left[\begin{array}{c} C_6H_5-C_6H_4 \qquad H \\ \diagdown \qquad \diagup \\ Cr \\ \diagup \qquad \diagdown \\ C_6H_5 \qquad H \end{array} \right] OH$$

which would account for the magnetic data. This problem must be regarded as unsettled. In fact, the writer has heard some doubts expressed concerning the actual characterization of these compounds.[59a]

57. Manganese

The complex compounds of manganese have been reviewed by Goldenberg.[60] Before presenting detailed discussion of the magnetic properties of manganese complexes, it is necessary to repeat two often neglected observations. First, many of the compounds for which data are available were investigated at one temperature only, and the Curie law then used to calculate the magnetic moment. This procedure is equivalent to assuming that the Weiss constant Δ is zero, or at least very small. There is abundant evidence that Δ may be far from small. Manganic phosphate offers a good example. The susceptibility suggests a moment of only 4.49, provided that the Curie law is followed. This is much lower than the theoretical $\mu = 4.90$ for the Mn^{3+} ion. It has, however, been shown that manganic phosphate follows the Curie-Weiss law with $\Delta = 53°$. On recalculation of μ on this basis, an effective moment of 4.89 is obtained, in excellent agreement with theory. A second observation worth making is that too many magnetic measurements on complex compounds have not been accompanied by accurate analyses proving the identity of the compound. Failure to establish purity may readily explain deviations in susceptibilities reported by various authors.

The experimental data on manganese compounds generally show large effective moments. Exceptions are the cyanides, which give good evidence of strong covalent bonding.

[59] W. Klemm and A. Neuber, *ibid.*, **227**, 261 (1936).

[59a] E. O. Fischer, however, reported (at the December meeting of the Chemical Society (London), 1955) the preparation of dibenzenechromium, analogous to the biscyclopentadienyl compounds.

[60] N. Goldenberg, *Trans. Faraday Soc.*, **36**, 847 (1940).

Univalent manganese is not common.   It is said to occur in the cyanide, $K_5Mn(CN)_6$, which is reported by Goldenberg to have a moment of 1.04, and by Bhatnagar, Prakash, and Maheshwari[61] to have $\mu = 1.76$.   The difference is not critical because the Mn^+ ion could have a moment as high as 6.93 Bohr magnetons, corresponding to six unpaired electrons.   The mag-

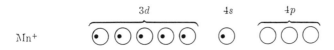

netic data suggest that not more than one electron is left unpaired in this cyanide, but it is not clear why the compound should not be diamagnetic. The slight paramagnetism may be due to partial oxidation, perhaps combined with some temperature-independent paramagnetism.

Divalent ions of manganese have an effective moment of about 5.92. This is approximately the case for $Mn(o\text{-phenanthroline})Cl_2$,[62] $Mn(NH_3)_6$-Br_2,[63] $NH_4MnPO_4 \cdot H_2O$, $K_2Mn(C_2O_4)_2 \cdot 2H_2O$, $(C_5H_6N)_2MnCl_2$,[64] and the pyromeconate.[65]   The pyridinium salts, $(C_5H_6N)MnCl_3 \cdot H_2O$ and $(C_5H_6N)_2$-$MnCl_4$, are also reported as having moments of 5.86 and 5.95, respectively.[61] Manganese phthalocyanine has been studied by Senff and Klemm.[66]   It may contain partly covalent bonds.   The various phthalocyanines are more conveniently discussed together in the next section.   It sometimes occurs that a change of crystal structure causes an abrupt change of the Weiss constant, without any change of the magnetic moment.   Such a change, occurring for Cs_3MnCl_5 at 570°K., is described by Asmussen.[66a]

In connection with the manganous dipyridine dichloride, it should be pointed out that a tetrahedral sp^3 bonded atom would have a moment of

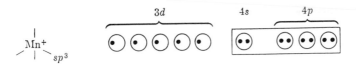

5.92, but that a tetrahedral configuration is not compatible with the small dimensions of the c-axis.   Mellor and Coryell[64] suggest that each metal ion shares four coplanar chloride ions in pairs and holds two pyridine molecules

[61] S. S. Bhatnagar, B. Prakash, and J. C. Maheshwari, *Proc. Indian Acad. Sci.*, 10A, 150 (1939).

[62] L. Cambi and A. Cagnasso, *Atti. acad. nazl. Lincei*, 19, 458 (1934).

[63] B Cabrera, *Inst. int. chim. Solvay, Conseil chim.*, 1929.

[64] D. P. Mellor and C. D. Coryell, *J. Am. Chem. Soc.*, 60, 1786 (1938).

[65] L. Sacconi, *Gazz. chim. ital.*, 80, 372 (1950).

[66] H. Senff and W. Klemm, *J. prakt. Chem.*, 154, 73 (1939).

[66a] R. W. Asmussen, *Proc. Symposium on Coordination Chem.*, Copenhagen 1953, 27–30 (Pub. 1954).

at right angles to the plane of the chloride ions.   The structure then consists of an octahedral ionic complex with two shared edges.

Some complex kojates of the transition group elements have been studied by Wiley, Tyson, and Steller.[67]   The manganese kojate complex has a moment of 6.2, corresponding to a tetrahedral structure, as shown:

Several cyanide complexes of divalent manganese have been studied.[68-70] One is $K_4Mn(CN)_6 \cdot 3H_2O$, the moment for which is given as 2.04 to 2.78. It can scarcely be decided, therefore, whether the manganese contains one or two unpaired electrons in this compound.   Another cyanide, $KMn(CN)_3$, is reported by Goldenberg[60] to have a moment of 4.22, roughly corresponding to three unpaired electrons.   It may contain the ion, $Mn(CN)_6^{4-}$, and should perhaps be written $K_2MnMn(CN)_6$.   On this basis the $Mn(CN)_6^{4-}$ group would have one unpaired electron and the entire compound would have six unpaired electrons per double molecule, in fair agreement with the experimental result.

Engelmann[33] reports that biscyclopentadienylmanganese has a moment of 2.1 which is only a little larger than that for one unpaired electron spin. In this connection it should be mentioned that paramagnetic resonance absorption of the manganous ion shows a fine structure which disappears when complex formation occurs.[71]   It is probable that this method for studying coordination compounds will rapidly increase in popularity.

Trivalent manganese has a moment of 3.32 in the fluoride hydrate,[20] $K_2MnF_5 \cdot H_2O$; and of about 4.90 in the complexes, $NH_4[Mn(C_6H_4OCO_2)_2-$ $(H_2O)] \cdot 2H_2O$, $K_3[Mn(C_2O_4)_3] \cdot 3H_2O$,[72] $Mn(CH_3COO)_3 \cdot 2H_2O$,[73] $Mn(CH_3-COCH_2COCH_3)_3$,[74] $Mn(C_5H_7O_2)_3$, $Mn(C_{14}H_{14}NCS_2)_3$, $Mn(C_8H_{18}NCS_2)_3$,

[67] J. W. Wiley, G. N. Tyson, Jr., and J. S. Steller, *J. Am. Chem. Soc.*, **64**, 963 (1942).

[68] L. Szegö and P. Ostinelli, *Gazz. chim. ital.*, **60**, 946 (1930).

[69] P. Rây and H. Bhar, *J. Indian Chem. Soc.*, **5**, 497 (1928).

[70] S. Freed and C. Kasper, *J. Am. Chem. Soc.*, **52**, 1012 (1930).

[71] M. Cohn and J. Townsend, *Nature*, **173**, 1090 (1954).

[72] C. H. Johnson, *Trans. Faraday Soc.*, **28**, 845 (1932).

[73] W. J. de Haas and B. H. Schultz, *Physica*, **6**, 481 (1939).

[74] L. C. Jackson, *Proc. Phys. Soc. (London)*, **47**, 1029 (1935).

and $Mn(C_5H_{12}NCS_2)_3$.[75] In double salts such as cesium manganese sulfate, the moment of the manganese is also 4.90, as is to be expected.[76]

Moments of from 2.95 to 3.61 have been reported for the cyanide, $K_3Mn(CN)_6$, suggesting a d^3sp^3 octahedral configuration,[41,68,69] but these difficulties have been resolved by the finding that the susceptibility approaches a temperature-independent value at very low temperatures.[76a] Goldenberg[60] gives an almost negligible apparent moment of 0.62 for the compound, $K_3Mn_2(CN)_9 \cdot 4KOH$, which he obtained by adding concentrated potassium permanganate solution to potassium cyanide solution.

Complexes in which manganese has a valence of four are represented by $K_2Mn(IO_3)_6$,[60] $K_2MnF_6 \cdot H_2O$,[60] and K_2MnCl_6.[61] The moment in every case is close to 3.87, as is also the case for the fluoride, $BaMnF_6$, according to Klemm.[51]

The manganates exhibit a normal paramagnetism for one unpaired electron. For $BaMnO_4$ Goldenberg[60] finds a moment of 1.80, which is probably more accurate than the earlier value 2.47 given by Wedekind and Horst.[77] Potassium manganate, K_2MnO_4, has a moment of 1.73 at 295°K. and 1.69 at 90°K.[78]

Potassium permanganate appears to have a small temperature-independent paramagnetism which is exhibited both in the solid and in solution.[77,79,80] The principal susceptibilities on single crystals of potassium permanganate and barium permanganate have been studied by Mookherjee.[81] Silver permanganate is reported by Bhatnagar, Prakash, and Maheshwari[61] to be diamagnetic, as are the basic bismuth permanganates, $Bi_2O_2(OH)MnO_4$ and $Bi_3O_3(OH)_2MnO_4$.[82]

58. Iron

It will be recalled that ferrous ions have a theoretical spin moment of 4.90 Bohr magnetons and that ferric ions, with one more unpaired electron, have a moment of 5.92. For magnetically dilute compounds these values are closely approximated experimentally. Many complex compounds of iron have about the same respective moments. A few representative compounds and their effective moments are: $(NH_4)_2Fe(SO_4)_2 \cdot 6H_2O$,

[75] L. Cambi and L. Szegö, Ber., B64, 2591 (1931).
[76] H. Bommer, Z. anorg. u. allgem. Chem., 246, 275 (1941).
[76a] A. H. Cooke and H. J. Duffus, Proc. Phys. Soc. (London), 68A, 32 (1955).
[77] E. Wedekind and C. Horst, Ber., 48, 105 (1915).
[78] K. A. Jensen and W. Klemm, Z. anorg. u. allgem. Chem., 237, 47 (1938).
[79] P. Collet, Compt. rend., 183, 1031 (1926).
[80] D. P. Raychaudhuri and P. N. Sengupta, Indian J. Phys., 10, 245 (1936).
[81] A. Mookherjee, ibid., 18, 187 (1944).
[82] W. Klemm and J. Oryschkewitsch, Ber., 75B, 1600 (1942).

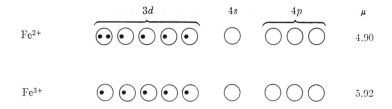

5.25; $Fe(N_2H_4)_2Cl_2$, 4.87; $Fe(OH_2)_4Cl_2$, 5.2; $NH_4Fe(SO_4)_2$, 5.86; K_3Fe-$(C_2O_4)_3\cdot2H_2O$, 5.88; K_3FeF_6, 6.0. The complexes of iron have been the object of almost endless study. We shall first survey the area briefly and then refer to more detailed work on many different substances.

In sharp contrast to the compounds already mentioned, the cyanides of iron have low or diamagnetic susceptibilities. $K_4Fe(CN)_6$ is diamagnetic, and $K_3Fe(CN)_6$ has a moment corresponding to one unpaired electron. The complexes are octahedral, and the reason for the magnetic moments being as they are should be clear from a consideration of the electron distribution.

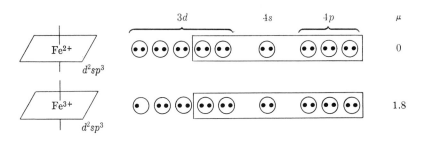

Potassium ferricyanide has, incidentally, a surprisingly large magnetic anisotropy at low temperatures.[83],[84]   The diamagnetic ferrocyanide has a very low anisotropy. When potassium ferrocyanide is added to ferric ion, a soluble blue compound is first formed. This is called soluble Prussian Blue or potassium berlinate, and it has the formula $KFe_2(CN)_6$. The familiar insoluble Prussian Blue is next formed, with the formula sometimes written $Fe_4[Fe(CN)_6]_3$. X-ray data show that both these substances contain octahedral complexes, and the magnetic evidence of Davidson and Welo[85] throws some light on the distribution of iron atoms. The soluble compound gives a susceptibility corresponding to one normal ferric ion for every six cyanide radicals. The insoluble compound gives a moment cor-

[83] L. C. Jackson, *Proc. Roy. Soc.* (*London*), **A140**, 695 (1933).

[84] L. C. Jackson, *Proc. Phys. Soc.* (*London*), **50**, 707 (1938).

[85] D. Davidson and L. A. Welo, *J. Phys. Chem.*, **32**, 1191 (1928).

responding to four-thirds of one normal ferric ion for every six cyanide ions. The magnetic data support the formulas $KFe[Fe(CN)_6]$ and $Fe_4[Fe(CN)_6]_3$ for the soluble and insoluble compounds, respectively. The problem is further discussed by Thompson.[86] There does not seem to be any significant difference in the susceptibilities of Prussian Blue and so-called Turnbull's Blue.[87]

Numerous other cyanides of iron have been studied. The following are diamagnetic: $Na_3Fe(CN)_5NH_3$, $Na_5Fe(CN)_5SO_3$, $Na_4Fe(CN)_5NO_2$, $Na_3Fe(CN)_5OH_2$, $Na_2Fe(CN)_5NO$, $K_3Fe(CN)_5CO$, and many others.[88] Most of these have water of hydration not shown in the formula. It is easy to see why these compounds should be diamagnetic, but Klemm, Jacobi, and Tilk[58] state that $Na_3[Fe(CN)_5NO_2]$ has a moment of about 2.2 Bohr magnetons. This probably means that the iron is ferric. It is not clear whether or not the NO_2 should be put outside the square brackets. Another peculiarity is the diamagnetism quoted by Bose for $K[Fe(NO)_2S_2O_3]$. A rather large group of nitroso complexes of ferrous iron, most of which are paramagnetic, has been investigated, chiefly by Cambi,[89-94] while some triple nitrites of iron have been studied by Rây and Sahu.[95] Among the more interesting of newer complexes are the thionitrosyl derivatives,[95a] of which the compound $Fe(NS)_4$ has a moment of 2.9.

The three carbonyls of iron, $Fe(CO)_5$, $Fe_2(CO)_9$, and $Fe_3(CO)_{12}$, are all diamagnetic. The diamagnetism of the liquid pentacarbonyl is easy to understand, but the other two carbonyls are very peculiar compounds.

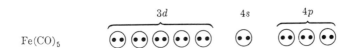

$Fe(CO)_5$

Powell and Ewens[96] have shown the structure to be:

[86] R. C. Thompson, *J. Am. Chem. Soc.*, **70**, 1045 (1948).

[87] A. K. Battacharya, *J. Indian Chem. Soc.*, **18**, 71 (1941).

[88] A. Simon, G. Morgenstern, and W. H. Albrecht, *Z. anorg. u. allgem. Chem.*, **230**, 225 (1937).

[89] L. Cambi and A. Cagnasso, *Gazz. chim. ital.*, **63**, 767 (1933).

[90] L. Cambi, *IX Congr. intern. quim. pura aplicada, Madrid*, **2**, 199 (1934).

[91] L. Cambi, *Z. anorg. u. allgem. Chem.*, **247**, 22 33 (1941).

[92] W. Hieber and R. Nast, *ibid.*, **247**, 31 (1941).

[93] G. Jacini, *Gazz. chim. ital.*, **69**, 714 (1939).

[94] D. P. Mellor and D. P. Craig, *J. Proc. Roy. Soc. N. S. Wales*, **78**, 25 (1944).

[95] P. Rây and H. Sahu, *J. Indian Chem. Soc.*, **23**, 161 (1946).

[95a] M. Goehring, K. W. Daum, and J. Weiss, *Z. Naturforsch.*, **10b**, 298 (1955).

[96] H. M. Powell and R. V. G. Ewens, *J. Chem. Soc.*, **1939**, 286.

$$
\begin{array}{c}
\text{O} \\
\parallel \\
\text{O} \quad\quad \text{C} \quad\quad \text{O} \\
\diagdown \quad\quad \diagup \diagdown \quad\quad \diagup \\
\text{C} \quad\quad\quad \text{C} \\
\text{O}\equiv\text{C}-\text{Fe}-\text{C}-\text{Fe}-\text{C}\equiv\text{O} \\
\diagup \quad \diagdown \quad \parallel \quad \diagup \quad \diagdown \\
\text{C} \quad\quad \text{O} \quad\quad \text{C} \\
\diagup \quad\quad\quad \diagdown \\
\text{O} \quad\quad \text{C} \quad\quad \text{O} \\
\parallel \\
\text{O}
\end{array}
$$

with the Fe-Fe distance only 2.46A. This is, therefore, a situation in which two atoms, each with an odd number of electrons, coexist in the same molecule, and yet the molecule is diamagnetic. There are two possible explanations. Either the electron spins are antiparallel but uncoupled, or else there is some kind of electron pairing taking place. This latter might occur because of the close proximity of the iron atoms to one another, or because of the ring structure present in the molecule. The probable formation of an actual bond between the adjacent iron atoms is considered by Dunitz and Orgel.[97] The diamagnetic dimeric ion, $Fe_2(OH)_2^{4+}$, mentioned in Chapter VIII, is probably another example of complete quenching as in the enneacarbonyl.[98]

Polynuclear structures involving metal atoms are fairly rare. Fe_2Cl_6 is of this type, and certain nonvolatile iron complexes studied by Welo are another example, but these involve a much smaller degree of interaction than in $Fe_2(CO)_9$. At one time it was thought that the brown ferric complex with o-phenanthroline was of the same type,[99] but Michaelis and Granick[100] have shown this to be not so.

Iron tetracarbonyl, which has a molecular weight roughly corresponding to the formula $Fe_3(CO)_{12}$, has a susceptibility which is rather difficult to measure accurately because of slow changes which yield traces of ferromagnetism.[101]

Compounds related to the iron carbonyls are also, like all carbonyls the susceptibilities of which have been measured, diamagnetic. Some of these are $Fe(CO)_3$ (o-phenanthroline), $Fe(CO)_4I_2$, $Fe(CO)_4Br_2$, and $Fe(CO)_2$-(NO_2).[58,10]

A situation somewhat related to that in iron enneacarbonyl occurs in ferric chloride, which has been investigated by Lallemand.[102] The solid follows the Curie-Weiss law with a moment of 5.8 and a Weiss constant of

[97] J. D. Dunitz and L. E. Orgel, *ibid.*, **1953**, 2594.

[98] L. N. Mulay and P. W. Selwood, *J. Am. Chem. Soc.*, **77**, 2693 (1955).

[99] A. Gaines, Jr., L. P. Hammett, and G. H. Walden, Jr., *ibid.*, **58**, 1668 (1936).

[100] L. Michaelis and S. Granick, *ibid.*, **65**, 481 (1943).

[101] H. G. Cutforth and P. W. Selwood, *ibid.*, **65**, 2414 (1943).

[102] A. Lallemand, *Ann. phys.*, **3**, 97 (1935).

12° over the temperature range of 150° to 400°K. Below 150°, anomalies would doubtless begin to intrude. Above 400°K., the susceptibility is difficult to measure because of sublimation, but from 600° to 703°K. the susceptibility is 4.59×10^{-6} and is independent of temperature. Above 703°, the susceptibility decreases once more. The relationship between molar susceptibility and temperature is shown in Fig. 79. These results are scarcely as accurate as desired, but they suggest that Fe_2Cl_6 molecules

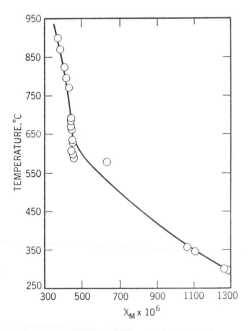

Fig. 79. Molar susceptibility of ferric chloride in the vapor state.

possess a constant and rather low paramagnetism. The molecule has been shown by Hassel and Viervoll[103] to be of the $Cl_2FeCl_2FeCl_2$ type. It seems probable, therefore, that this is another example of diminished paramagnetism caused by adjacent atoms being drawn rather close together, whether these atoms are united in a formal bond or not. Somewhat related results have been obtained by a magnetic study of ferric chloride in nonaqueous solutions.[104]

It has already been mentioned that certain polynuclear complexes are said to show normal moments but extremely large values of the Weiss constant. Thus Welo[40] has shown that iron complexes of the type [Fe₃(CH₃-

[103] O. Hassel and H. Viervoll, *Tids. Kjemi, Bergvesen met.*, **3**, No. 8, 97 (1943).
[104] A. Quartaroli, *Gazz. chim. ital.*, **46**, 371 (1916).

$COO)_6(OH)_2]NO_3 \cdot 6H_2O$ may follow the Curie-Weiss law with Δ often nearly $500°K$. Welo's results have been extended[105] to lower temperatures with the results given in Table XVIII. The explanation for these peculiar results is doubtless related to exchange effects,[106] perhaps of a different kind between one pair of spins and the others in the trinuclear cation.[107]

Reference has already been made to several of the recently discovered compounds formed by various metals and cyclopentadiene. Of these, the first discovered and the one which, at least up to the present, has attracted most interest is biscyclopentadienyliron.[108] This compound is diamagnetic, as is the corresponding bisindenyl derivative.[109] The iodide and the picrate derived from the pentadienyl have, on the other hand, moments corresponding approximately to two unpaired electron spins.

TABLE XVIII

Moments and Weiss Constants for Polynuclear Iron Complexes

Compound	73° to 293°K.		Below 20°K.	
	μ	Δ	μ	Δ
$[Fe_3(CH_3COO)_6(OH)_2]NO_3 \cdot 6H_2O$	5.19	443	1.2	2
$[Fe_3(C_6H_5COO)_6OH](C_6H_5COO)ClO_4 \cdot H_2O$	5.5	572	1.26	6.5

These observations, and other properties, have led to considerable discussion concerning the structure of the compounds.[110,111,111a] Moffitt's very erudite discussion appears to give a satisfactory explanation of the magnetic properties not only of the iron compounds but of others which have been, and will be, mentioned elsewhere. Unfortunately, the theoretical treatment of this matter lies beyond the scope of this book.

We turn now to a large group of complex iron compounds whose stereochemical configuration has been the principal object of study. Of these, the most important are hemin and its derivatives. First, however, we shall mention some less complicated structures.

The complex kojate of ferrous iron has been studied by Wiley, Tyson, and Steller.[67] It has a moment of 5.4, corresponding reasonably well with that expected for four unpaired electrons. The structure is tetrahedral, similar to the kojate of manganese. Other complexes in the same general

[105] B. Tsaï and J. Wucher, *J. phys. radium*, **13**, 485 (1952).
[106] K. Kambe, *J. Phys. Soc. Japan*, **5**, 48 (1950).
[107] A. Abragam, J. Horowitz, and J. Yvon, *Revs. Modern Physics*, **25**, 165 (1953).
[108] G. Wilkinson, M. Rosenblum, M. C. Whiting, and R. B. Woodward, *J. Am. Chem. Soc.*, **74**, 2125 (1952).
[109] E. O. Fischer and D. Seus, *Z. Naturforsch.*, **8b**, 694 (1953).
[110] E. Ruch and E. O. Fischer, *ibid.*, **7b**, 676 (1952).
[111] W. Moffitt, *J. Am. Chem. Soc.*, **76**, 3386 (1954).

category include the glycol complexes,[112] ferric acetylacetonate,[83] the sulfonated pyrocatechol,[113] and some salts of ethylenediaminetetraacetic acid.[114]

The ferrous complex with 3,6-dithia-1,8-bis-(salicylideneamino)-octane is particularly interesting[115] because it has a moment of 3.22. This could possibly be due to two unpaired electrons, but the more probable explanation is that the iron is bound to the sexadentate coordinating group in the same manner as iron(III) is thought to be bound in ferriheme hydroxide, namely by four bonds in six resonating positions.

The α- (yellow), and β- (black) forms of ferrous tetrapyridinedithiocyanates, $[Fe(C_5H_6N)_4(SCN)_2]$, have been shown by Asmussen[116] to have substantially the same susceptibility, with amounts of 5.47 and 5.40 Bohr magnetons, respectively, but two forms of tetraisonitriloferrous halides are diamagnetic.[117]

Ferrous and ferric complexes of dipyridyl and of phenanthroline are quite different from those in which the coordinated molecule has only one functional group. $[Fe^{2+} (dipyridyl)_3]Br_2$,[58] $[Fe^{2+} (dipyridyl)_3]SO_4$,[58] and $[Fe^{2+} (o\text{-phenanthroline})_2]I_2$[41] are diamagnetic. The corresponding ferric salts, such as $[Fe^{3+} (dipyridyl)]Cl_3$ and $[Fe^{3+} (o\text{-phenanthroline})]Cl_3$, are paramagnetic, both with moments of 5.91 Bohr magnetons, corresponding to ionic binding. $[Fe(dipyridyl)_3]_2[[PtCl_6]_3$ and $[Fe(o\text{-phenanthroline})_3]_2 [PtCl_6]$ have moments corresponding to one unpaired electron, which is normal for covalent ferric iron.[88,118] The simple ferric tripyridyl and ferric tri-o-phenanthroline substances are apparently unstable. There is some

TABLE XIX

Magnetic Moments for Phthalocyanine Complexes

Complex	Moment
Cu^{2+}	1.73
Ni^{2+}	0
Co^{2+}	2.16
Fe^{2+}	3.96
Mn^{2+}	4.55
VO^{2+}	1.70

[111a] J. D. Dunitz and L. E. Orgel, *J. Chem. Phys.*, **23**, 954 (1955).
[112] R. Gomer and G. N. Tyson, Jr., *ibid.*, **66**, 1331 (1944).
[113] A. L. Jones and L. B. Yeatts, *ibid.*, **69**, 1277 (1947).
[114] W. Klemm, *Z. anorg. u. Chem.*, **252**, 225 (1944).
[115] F. P. Dwyer, F. Lions, and D. P. Mellor, *J. Am. Chem. Soc.*, **72**, 5037 (1950).
[116] R. W. Asmussen, *Z. anorg. u. allgem. Chem.*, **218**, 425 (1934).
[117] L. Malatesta, A. Sacco, and G. Padoa, *Ann. chim. (Rome)*, **43**, 617 (1953).
[118] A. Simon and H. Knauer, *Z. Elektrochem.*, **45**, 678 (1939).

difference of opinion concerning the magnetic properties of the dipyridyl complex.

The metal phthalocyanines have been studied by Klemm.[66,119]   The moments, which are nearly independent of temperature, are given in Table XIX.   For the sake of convenience, these compounds will all be discussed here.

The structure, which is shown for the copper complex, suggests either a

square planar structure or a tetrahedron.   The magnetic evidence is most striking for the nickel complex, shown by its diamagnetism to have the square dsp^2 structure, which is confirmed by x-ray evidence.   The magnetic evidence is consistent also with square structures for the copper and cobalt complexes, if it is recalled that the orbital contribution to the magnetic moment is appreciable for the latter.   For the iron and manganese complexes, the moments are definitely too high for the dsp^2 configuration. These might be accounted for by tetrahedral structures, but this is improbable, if for no other reason than that of analogy.   The reason is more probably related to the kind and degree of crystal-field splitting of the energy levels, as referred to above.   Senff and Klemm[66] have also studied the complexes formed when iron phthalocyanine is dissolved in pyridine or quinoline.   The structures are probably octahedral.   In both solvents the magnetic moment falls to zero.   Preliminary studies of paramagnetic resonance in the phthalocyanine series (and in hemoglobin) have been reported by Ingram and Bennett.[120]

It will be noted that the diamagnetic anisotropy of the coordinated groups may be quite large in compounds such as the phthalocyanines. This should be taken into consideration in observing and interpreting susceptibility data on such systems.[121]

[119] L. Klemm and W. Klemm, *J. prakt. Chem.*, **143**, 82 (1935).

[120] D. J. E. Ingram and J. E. Bennett, *J. Chem. Phys.*, **22**, 1136 (1954).

[121] G. Berthier, M. Mayot, A. Pullman, and B. Pullman, *J. phys. radium*, **13**, 15 (1952).

Ferric complexes, in addition to those mentioned above, have been no less extensively studied. We shall merely mention the interesting series of compounds given by Nyholm and Sharpe.[20] The following give normal ($\sim$5.9) moments for five unpaired electrons: Li_3FeF_6, Na_3FeF_6, and $(NH_4)_3$-FeF_6; but K_2FeF_5 and $CsFeF_4$ give moments of 4.87 and 4.79, respectively. This difference is doubtless due to the increased magnetic concentration, leading to some exchange interaction between adjacent irons. The series shows that no amount of "ionic" character in the bond can prevent some loss of magnetic moment if the paramagnetic ions are close together. The equally interesting transitions observed on changing the nature of the ligand, rather than the coordination, will be described more fully below in connection with cobalt complexes.

On November 8, 1845, Michael Faraday investigated the magnetic properties of dried blood and noted that he "must try recent fluid blood." Had he done so he might have discovered the difference between arterial and venous blood. The difference between completely oxygenated and deoxygenated blood amounts to 20%. Since that time, there have been several magnetic studies of blood,[122-126] and even of hemoglobin and related compounds, but we are indebted chiefly to Pauling and Coryell and their coworkers for a series of magnetic studies which have led to a notable extension of the knowledge of blood components.

With this better understanding of the structure of hemoglobin and related compounds there has arisen a need for a simpler, more logical nomenclature than the one in use. The system adopted by Pauling and Coryell will therefore be explained first, and its relation to the older names shown, because the latter are still encountered in the biochemical and medical literature.[127]

Hemoglobin. This is a conjugated protein containing native globin and a complex of iron with a porphyrin. From the magnetic standpoint, it is the complex with which we are most concerned. The structure of the porphyrin complex is shown below. The iron may be removed from this complex, and the resulting iron-free pigment is called protoporphyrin. Protoporphyrin is diamagnetic.

Heme. The iron-porphyrin complex; the iron may be ferrous or ferric.

Ferroheme. The ferrous-porphyrin complex, sometimes called reduced hemin.

[122] A. Gamgee, *Proc. Roy. Soc. (London)*, **68**, 503 (1901).

[123] H. Kudo, *Acta Med. Scand.*, **81**, 511 (1934).

[124] F. Haurowitz and H. Kittel, *Ber.*, **66B**, 1046 (1933).

[125] C. Courty, *Thesis*. Faculty of Sciences, University of Paris 1935.

[126] P. Berthier, *Compt. rend.*, **207**, 1254 (1938); **208**, 943, 1435 (1939); **209**, 774 (1939).

[127] D. L. Drabkin, *Ann. Rev. Biochem.*, **11**, 531 (1942).

Ferriheme. The ferric-porphyrin complex ion.

Ferriheme chloride, or hemin. Ferriheme plus chloride.

Ferriheme hydroxide, or hematin. Ferriheme plus hydroxide.

Hemochromogen. A substance with a distinctive absorption spectrum, formed from ferroheme and denatured globin.

Ferrihemochromogen. Hemochromogen containing ferric iron, sometimes called parahematin.

Ferrohemoglobin. Ferroheme plus globin; there are four hemes per globin molecule.

Ferrihemoglobin. Ferriheme plus globin; there are four hemes per globin molecule; ferrihemoglobin is sometimes called acid methemoglobin.

Oxyhemoglobin. Ferrohemoglobin plus oxygen.

Carbonmonoxyhemoglobin. Ferrohemoglobin plus carbon monoxide.

Ferrihemoglobin hydroxide. Alkaline methemoglobin.

The iron in hemin, or ferriheme chloride, has a magnetic moment of about 5.8 Bohr magnetons,[128] although, as we shall see, the precise magnitude depends upon several conditions. The moment obtained from ferrihemoglobin is substantially the same. The iron in ferrohemoglobin and in ferroheme has a moment of about 4.91, or perhaps a little higher. On the other hand, oxyhemoglobin and carbonmonoxyhemoglobin have zero moments.[129] These results are particularly interesting. They show that the complexes probably have d^2sp^3 octahedral bonds. The oxygen in the oxy-complex cannot be molecularly adsorbed or held without dislocation of the two unpaired electrons which give oxygen its paramagnetism. Rather it must be attached in some such fashion as shown, perhaps in resonance with other electron distributions. The structure for carbonmonoxy-

---

[128] L. Pauling and C. D. Coryell, *Proc. Natl. Acad. Sci.*, 22, 159 (1936).

[129] L. Pauling and C. D. Coryell, *ibid.*, 22, 210 (1936).

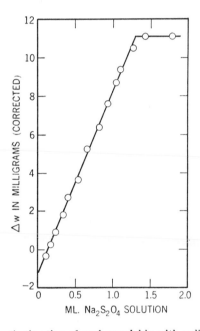

hemoglobin is probably very much the same; at any rate, the great similarity of properties of the two compounds supports this idea. A quantitative study of the reaction between ferrohemoglobin and oxygen has been made by Coryell, Pauling, and Dodson.[130] This involves the interesting technique of magnetic titration; that is, of determining the susceptibility and course of a reaction mixture during addition of a reagent.

Fig. 80. Magnetic titration of oxyhemoglobin with sodium dithionite.

Data obtained from the reaction of oxyhemoglobin with sodium dithionite are shown in Fig. 80. This and similar studies with the carbon monoxide and nitric oxide complexes demonstrate that the susceptibilities of intermediate compounds formed in hemoglobin reactions are linearly related to the number of hemes which have undergone reaction.

[130] C. D. Coryell, L. Pauling, and R. W. Dodson, *J. Phys. Chem.*, **43**, 825 (1939).

The iron in ferrihemoglobin hydroxide (alkaline methemoglobin) has a moment of 4.47, according to Coryell, Stitt, and Pauling.[131]   Hematin in alkaline solution has been shown by Rawlinson[132] to yield a moment of about 3.5.   There is some evidence that this value is modified by the presence of sucrose which is sometimes used to delay settling of the compound.

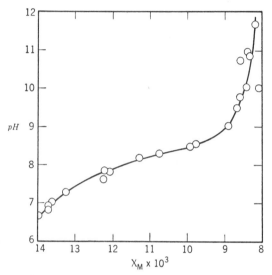

Fig. 81. Magnetic titration of ferrihemoglobin.

Magnetic titration of ferrihemoglobin by Coryell *et al.* yields results of the type shown in Fig. 81 where the molar susceptibility is plotted against pH.   The reaction is first order in hydroxide ion, and it is of course possible to obtain equilibrium constants from these data.   The figure shows only those data obtainable at low ionic concentration.   For higher concentrations the point of inflection is shifted somewhat to higher pH values. The magnetic moment suggests three unpaired electrons, a type which is rare for iron.   The existence of an octahedral covalent complex for ferrihemoglobin hydroxide suggests that in ferrihemoglobin the coordination may still be six, the sixth place being taken by a water molecule.   Perhaps the ion should be written as shown, the transition to the hydroxide involving loss of a proton, with change of bond type, rather than gain of an OH⁻ ion.

Ferrihemoglobin cyanide and ferrihemoglobin hydrosulfide show moments of 2.50 and 2.26, respectively, indicating one unpaired electron and

[131] C. D. Coryell, F. Stitt, and L. Pauling, *J. Am. Chem. Soc.*, **59**, 633 (1937).
[132] W. A. Rawlinson, *Australian J. Exptl. Biol. Med. Sci.*, **18**, 185 (1940).

six octahedral, essentially covalent, bonds.   The structures are therefore
similar to that of the ferricyanide ion.   It is necessary, however, to postulate a rather large orbital contribution in order to explain the relatively

high moments.   Ferrihemoglobin fluoride has, as might be expected, a
moment of 5.92.   Other ferrihemoglobin derivatives which have been
studied are the compounds with azide ion, ammonia, ethanol, and other
alcohols;[133] pyridine;[134] and imidazole.[135]   The iron in these complexes
has moments as shown in Table XX.   Analysis of magnetic and electrode
potential data indicate that ferrihemoglobin may exist in three acid forms,
two of which have susceptibilities slightly different than the third.[126]
It is postulated that one acid group is a histadine imidazolium ion in poor
position for electrostatic coordination of the basic form with the iron atom.
The second acid group is the imino group of a histadine residue, the 3-N
atom of which is strongly coordinated with the iron atom.   The third acid
group of ferrihemoglobin is the iron atom itself which may add a hydroxide
ion or, more probably, coordinate a water molecule which may lose a proton.
   Imidazole ferrihemoglobin is of considerable interest because it may be
that the bond between the heme and the globin involves the imidazole
group of the side chain of a histidine residue.   The moment of the iron
in imidazole ferrihemoglobin can only be approximated; it corresponds
roughly to one unpaired electron or a little higher.   The structure is
probably of the octahedral covalent type.
   Except for the hemochromogens, complexes derived from ferrohemoglobin have been much less thoroughly studied.   The equilibrium between
ferrohemoglobin, cyanide ion, and cyanide ferrohemoglobin has been investigated by Stitt and Coryell.[136]   The stability of the compound is much

[133] C. D. Coryell and F. Stitt, *J. Am. Chem. Soc.*, **62**, 2942 (1940).
[134] C. D. Russell and L. Pauling, *Proc. Natl. Acad. Sci.*, **25**, 517 (1939).
[135] C. D. Coryell and L. Pauling, *J. Biol. Chem.*, **132**, 769 (1940).
[136] F. Stitt and C. D. Coryell, *J. Am. Chem. Soc.*, **61**, 1263 (1939).

TABLE XX

Magnetic Moments of Iron in Some Derivatives of Ferrihemoglobin

Compound	μ_{eff}
Ethanol ferrihemoglobin	5.89
Ferrihemoglobin azide	2.84
Ammonia ferrihemoglobin hydroxide	2.98
Ethanol ferrihemoglobin hydroxide	5.39–5.48
Imidazole ferrihemoglobin	2

less than that of the corresponding ferriheme complex. Cyanide ferro-hemoglobin is diamagnetic with octahedral covalent bonds.

The hemochromogens, compounds of ferroheme and denatured globin, have been studied by Pauling and Coryell and by Rawlinson.[132]   Other organic bases, such as pyridine, form hemochromogen-like substances.   In fact, metals other than iron may also be introduced into the porphyrin complex.   The name hemochromogen is generally used for those characteristically colored compounds derived from ferroheme and an organic base. These substances are all diamagnetic with octahedral d^2sp^3 bonds.   The hemochromogens investigated are those of globin, pyridine, nicotine, and the dicyanide.

The interrelationships between the various derivatives of iron proto-porphyrin may be clarified by the following, taken from Rawlinson's paper:

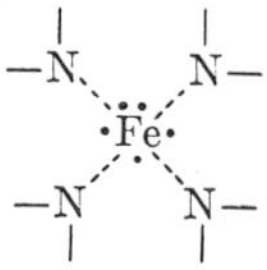

hemin, $\mu = 5.91$

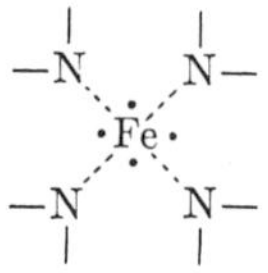

ferroheme, $\mu = 4.90$

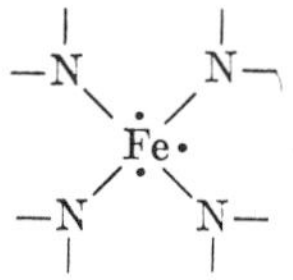

hematin, $\mu = 3.88$

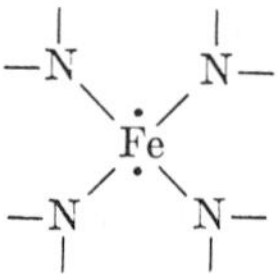

(unknown)

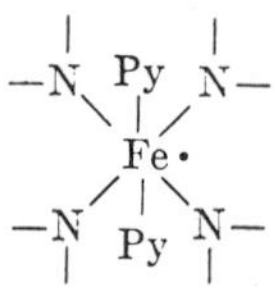

pyridine ferrihemochromogen
(parahematin), $\mu = 1.73$

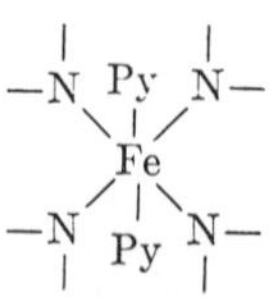

pyridine ferrohemochromogen,
$\mu = 0$

Our chief, and only serious, question in relation to this is the interpretation placed on the observed moment for hematin. It has been shown earlier that ferric salts at moderate and low acidities have a magnetic moment approximately the same as that reported for hematin. The low moment found in, say, ferric perchlorate solutions is due to the presence of a diamagnetic dimeric ion. It may, therefore, be advisable to reserve judgment on the case of hematin until the possibility of similar interactions can definitely be shown to be absent in this substance.

The magnetic state of iron derived from the hemoglobin of different animals has been studied by Taylor and Coryell.[137] The magnetic moments of iron from cow, horse, sheep, and human blood are, respectively, 5.43, 5.43, 5.46, and 5.35. The only one significantly different is the value for human blood, and as it was determined on a single sample from a single individual (C.D.C.) perhaps the difference is not important. An extensive study of bovine hemoglobin indicates that the susceptibility is constant from individual to individual within a species. Hemoglobin content is often measured by the capacity of the blood for oxygen absorption. Taylor and Coryell show, however, that this is not a reliable measure for either the hemoglobin or the total iron. Magnetic measurements reveal, as had previously been established by orthodox chemical tests, a certain fraction of the total iron which is inactive in the absorption of oxygen. For cow blood this amounts to 5.7% of the iron. The results suggest that the "inactive" iron may be a different percentage in human blood. The state of this "inactive" iron is not known with certainty, but it may be in the form of ferrihemoglobin, which has no oxygen-absorbing power.

In this work, Taylor and Coryell used a magnetochemical method for the determination of hemoglobin concentration. This method is more convenient and probably more accurate than the conventional gasometric method. The procedure is as follows:

The hemoglobin solution is reduced to ferrohemoglobin with sodium dithionite, $Na_2S_2O_4$. Then Δw, the apparent change in weight on application of the field in a Gouy balance, is determined. The solution is now saturated with carbon monoxide, and Δw is redetermined. The change in Δw corresponds to a change in molar susceptibility per heme of $12{,}290 \times 10^{-6}$ at 24°C., the effective moment of ferrohemoglobin being taken as 5.46 magnetons. Let Δw for the ferrohemoglobin $= \Delta w_{Hb}$, for the carbon-monoxyhemoglobin $= \Delta w_{HbCO}$, and for the solution being studied $= \Delta w$. Then, the molal susceptibility per heme at 24°C. for the solution under investigation is $\chi_M = (\Delta w - \Delta w_{HbCO})/(\Delta w_{Hb} - \Delta w_{HbCO}) \times 12{,}290 \times 10^{-6}$. The method gives automatic cancellation of the diamagnetic corrections.

Methods such as the above, and the technique of magnetic titration,

[137] D. S. Taylor and C. D. Coryell, *ibid.*, **60**, 1177 (1938).

would appear to have many applications in chemistry. The only difficulty is the time necessary to fill and reset the sample tubes. Perhaps this trouble could be reduced by using one of the newer experimental methods. A substance closely related to hemoglobin is myoglobin, or muscle hemoglobin. The oxygen saturation curve for this substance is a rectangular hyperbola rather than a sigmoid curve. It also has a much higher affinity for oxygen than does hemoglobin. In spite of these differences, the magnetic moment of the iron in myoglobin and in ferrimyoglobin (metamyoglobin) is the same as in the corresponding hemoglobins.[138]

In all this computation of magnetic moments for hemoglobin and related compounds, it has been implied that the Curie law is obeyed. Cambi and Szegö[139] have measured the susceptibility of hemin from 84° to 294°K. and find that it obeys the Curie law.

In this connection it will be recalled that the *ortho-para* hydrogen conversion is catalyzed by paramagnetic substances. Eley[140] has investigated the heterogeneous conversion of *para*-hydrogen from −80° to 120°C. on hemoglobin, hematin, and hemin, as well as on metal-free phthalocyanine and on copper phthalocyanine. As expected, the conversion is catalyzed by the paramagnetic substances but not by the diamagnetic.

There have been a few magnetic studies on other pigments more or less related to hemoglobin. These include verdohemochromogen.[141] The iron in a sample freshly prepared by oxidation of hemin had a moment of 2.16. Similarly, ferrous and ferric cytochrome c and their derivatives have magnetic properties not unlike those of the corresponding hemoglobin compounds.[142] The magnetic behavior of catalase has been studied by Michaelis and Granick,[143] Theorell,[144] and others.[145] The measurements are difficult because of the small iron content. At first it was thought that this compound was another example of iron with three unpaired electrons, as in ferrihemoglobin hydroxide, but later measurements render this uncertain.[146] The magnetic properties of ferritin[147] have also been studied, but all the iron in that substance seems to be in the form of colloidal oxide or hydroxide, which will be discussed in another section. This possibility seems to have been overlooked by Bayer and Hausser.[147a] It is not clear if a

[138] H. T. Theorell and A. Ehrenberg, *Acta Chem. Scand.*, **5**, 823 (1951).
[139] L. Cambi and L. Szegö, *Rend. ist. lombardo sci.*, **67**, 275 (1934).
[140] D. D. Eley, *Trans. Faraday Soc.*, **36**, 500 (1940).
[141] D. P. Craig and D. P. Mellor, *J. Proc. Roy. Soc. N. S. Wales*, **78**, 258 (1946).
[142] H. Theorell, *J. Am. Chem. Soc.*, **63**, 1820 (1941).
[143] L. Michaelis and S. Granick, *J. Gen. Physiol.*, **25**, 325 (1941).
[144] H. Theorell and K. Agner, *Arkiv Kemi*, **A16**, No. 7 (1942).
[145] H. F. Deutsch and A. Ehrenberg, *Acta Chem. Scand.*, **6**, 1522 (1952).
[146] Private communication from Dr. L. Michaelis.
[147] L. Michaelis, C. D. Coryell, and S. Granick, *J. Biol. Chem.*, **148**, 463 (1943).
[147a] E. Bayer and K. H. Hausser, *Experientia* **11**, 254 (1955).

similar interpretation may be placed on the low (3.8) values reported by them for a series of amino acid derivatives of iron(III).

Possible oxidation states of iron higher than (3+) have not received much study. Some reference to susceptibility measurements on (4+) iron is made by Scholder.[147b] Attempts at measurements on such substances in the author's laboratory have always revealed a large ferromagnetism present, presumably as an impurity. Scott[147c] has reported a moment of 3.06 for the iron (6+) in K_2FeO_4, but this involved correction for considerable ferromagnetism. The result should, perhaps, be accepted with reservation, especially as it was obtained by the Gouy method for which the validity of the extrapolation to infinite field is less certain than for the Faraday method.

59. Cobalt

The cobaltous ion has a moment corresponding to three unpaired electrons, with sometimes an unusually large orbital contribution. But complex compounds involving divalent cobalt are less stable than those in which the valence is three. In spite of the relative instability of cobaltous complexes, a surprisingly large amount of work has been done on them. Some of the results are summarized by Mellor and Goldacre.[148]

A few effective moments reported for various cobalt(II) complex compounds are as follows: $[Co(NH_3)_6]Cl_2$, 4.96; $[Co(ethylenediamine)_3]$-Cl_2, 3.82; $[Co(dipyridyl)_3]Cl_2$, 4.85; $[Co(o\text{-phenylenebisdimethylarsine})_3]$-$Cl_2$, 1.92.

Other examples of paramagnetic cobaltous complexes are the quinaldinate,[149] the disalicylaldehyde,[150] the kojate,[67] bis-salicylaldehyde propylenediamine, and bis-(formylcamphor) dihydrate.[151] But the cobaltous biguanidinium complexes, amongst others, have been shown by Rây and Ghosh[152] to have considerably lower moments than those given above. The blue cobaltous bispyridyl compounds[153,154] with a moment of 4.6 undergo a change in a few days with the moment rising to 5.3, parallel with conversion to the violet form. Cobaltocyanides are diamagnetic;[29] but Adamson has found an interesting case in which the diamagnetic $K_3[Co(CN)_5]$ dissolves in excess potassium cyanide to form a paramagnetic

[147b] R. Scholder, Z. Elektrochem., 56, 879 (1952).
[147c] H. J. Hrostowski and A. B. Scott, J. Chem. Phys., 18, 105 (1950).
[148] D. P. Mellor and R. J. Goldacre, J. Proc. Roy. Soc. N. S. Wales, 73, 233 (1940).
[149] N. K. Dutt, J. Indian Chem. Soc., 14, 572 (1937).
[150] G. N. Tyson, Jr., and S. C. Adams, J. Am. Chem. Soc., 62, 1228 (1940).
[151] D. P. Mellor, J. Proc. Roy. Soc. N. S. Wales, 75, 157 (1942).
[152] P. Rây and S. P. Ghosh, J. Indian Chem. Soc., 20, 323 (1943).
[153] E. D. P. Barkworth and S. Sugden, Nature, 139, 374 (1937).
[154] D. P. Mellor and C. D. Coryell, J. Am. Chem. Soc., 60, 1786 (1938).

substance in which the cobalt has an effective moment of 1.72 magnetons.[155] A substantial number of cobalt(II) arylisocyanide complexes have low moments.[156] These anomalies have been considerably clarified by a better understanding of the implications of the Penney and Schlapp treatment of field splitting.[157] The situation may be summarized again as follows: for tetrahedral coordination, if there is no electron pairing between cobalt and ligand, the moment observed will be near the spin-only value (3.8) for three electrons. One may then say that "the orbital contribution is small." For octahedral cobalt(II) complexes with negligible electron pairing, "the orbital contribution may be large." Nyholm has suggested that this distinction may be used as a diagnostic tool in stereochemistry. When electron pairing occurs, it appears that the situation is reversed, with the square planar complexes showing a larger "orbital contribution" and the octahedral complexes a smaller one. What this means is that the observed moment in such cases is generally somewhat larger than 1.8 for the square planar groups. Actually, "strong covalent" octahedral complexes are fairly rare for cobalt(II). The diarsine mentioned above is one example.

The distinction described above for cobalt(II) in tetrahedral, as compared with octahedral, coordination is reflected in the magnetic anisotropy. Tetra-coordinated Co(II) complexes have a low anisotropy while that for octahedral Co(II) complexes is large.[158,159]

Considerable attention has been paid to the magnetic properties of a number of cobaltous chelates including and related to cobalt salicylaldehyde ethylenediimine. These compounds are of interest for the ability shown by many of them to adsorb oxygen reversibly in a manner not unlike that shown by hemoglobin.[160] The results are a little difficult to understand, partly because of the uncertain orbital contribution to the moment of cobalt. But in general it may be said that there is no obvious relation between magnetic properties and oxygen-carrying capacity. All these compounds become diamagnetic on oxygenation. A similar change of susceptibility is shown by the cobalt-histidine complex before and after oxygenation.[161] Most of these substances have normal temperature coefficients of suceptibility.

Biscyclopentadienylcobalt(II) has a magnetic moment corresponding

[155] A. W. Adamson, *ibid.*, **73**, 5710 (1951).
[156] L. Malatesta, A. Sacco, and L. Mattiello, *Gazz. chim. ital.*, **83**, 499 (1953).
[157] B. N. Figgis and R. S. Nyholm, *J. Chem. Soc.*, **1954**, 12.
[158] K. S. Krishnan and A. Mookherji, *Phys. Rev.*, **51**, 528, 774 (1937).
[159] K. S. Krishnan, *Le Magnétisme*, **Vol. III.** Proceedings of the Strasbourg Congress on Magnetism, 1939, p. 247.
[160] M. Calvin and C. H. Barkelew, *J. Am. Chem. Soc.*, **68**, 2267 (1946).
[161] L. Michaelis, *Arch. Biochem.*, **14**, 17 (1947).

to one unpaired spin.[162] The oxidation product $[Co(C_5H_5)_2]^+$ in the form of the bromide or perchlorate is diamagnetic. Similar results have been reported on the bisindenyl compounds.[163]

In most work on cobaltic complexes, it is assumed that the free Co^{3+} ion would have a moment corresponding to four unpaired electrons. Unfortunately, it is difficult to establish this experimentally. Cobaltic fluoride gives a moment which varies with temperature from 1.60 at 90°K. to 2.46 at 293°K.[164] Other efforts to obtain the moment of trivalent cobalt have been made by Bommer,[76] Rây and Sen,[165] and others. $Co_2(SO_4)_3$·18H$_2$O is prepared by electrolytic oxidation, but it seems impossible to obtain the salt free from cobaltous cobalt. The Indian workers obtained a moment of 3.2 Bohr magnetons for the anhydrous salt. Bommer claims that the pure hydrated compound would be diamagnetic and is therefore a covalent aquo-complex. Rubidium cobaltic sulfate is diamagnetic. Cobaltic cyanide, $Co(CN)_3$, is said to exist in a blue form with a moment of 2.7, and a red hydrated form with $\mu = 3.0$. It is clear that all these compounds are complexes and that there are not yet any good experimental data on the simple cobaltic ion. The most nearly clean-cut example of an "ionic" cobalt(III) complex in which exchange effects are not important seems to be $K_3[CoF_6]$ which, according to Klemm,[51] has a moment of 5.3 magnetons.

Aqueous solutions of cobaltic perchlorate are diamagnetic,[166] as mentioned in Chapter VIII. This illustrates the arbitrary nature of the supposed distinction between normal and coordination compounds. The hexaaquocobalt(III) ion is definitely to be classed in the latter group.

The introduction of three ammonia molecules into the fluo-complex, as in $Co(NH_3)_3F_3$, renders the compound diamagnetic.[10] A few other representative amines in which the cobalt has zero moment are $[Co(NH_3)_6]Cl_3$, $[Co(NH_3)_5 \cdot H_2O]_2(C_2O_4)_3$, $[Co(ethylenediamine)_2Cl_2]Cl$, and $[Co(NH_3)_3(NO_2)_2Cl]$. But certain binuclear peroxy ammines[167] which presumably contain trivalent cobalt have a moment of 1.7. There has been some discussion about the supposed diamagnetism of the cobaltinitrites. Cambi[168] has presented some fairly convincing evidence that these substances, of which $Na_3[Co(NO_2)_6]$ is one example, show a fractional ($\sim$0.6) magnetic moment. On the other hand, a few strongly paramagnetic cobalt(III)

[162] E. O. Fischer and R. Jira, Z. Naturforsch., 8b, 327 (1953).

[163] E. O. Fischer, D. Seus, and R. Jira, ibid., 8b, 692 (1953).

[164] P. Henkel and W. Klemm, Z. anorg. u. allgem. Chem., 222, 73 (1935).

[165] P. Rây and D. C. Sen, J. Indian Chem. Soc., 12, 190 (1935).

[166] H. L. Friedman, J. P. Hunt, R. A. Plane, and H. Taube, J. Am. Chem. Soc., 73, 4028 (1951).

[167] L. Malatesta, Gazz. chim. ital., 72, 287 (1942).

[168] L. Cambi, A. Ferrari, and M. Nardelli, ibid., 82, 816 (1952).

complexes are reported by Mukherjee.[169]   These are of quite a complicated nature, involving a Schiff's base as a sexadentate chelate ligand.

Cobalt salts of glyoximes have been studied by Sen and RâAll[170] and by Cambi.[171]   When crystalline cobaltous chloride is added to dimethylglyoxime in acetone solution, a green compound is formed.   This is diamagnetic; Sen and Rây propose the formula

$$
\begin{array}{ccc}
\text{OH} & & \text{O} \\
| & & \| \\
\text{H}_3\text{C--C=N} \quad \text{Cl} \quad \text{N=C--CH}_3 \\
\diagdown \diagup \\
\text{Co} \\
\diagup \diagdown \\
\text{H}_3\text{C--C=N} \quad \text{Cl} \quad \text{N=C--CH}_3 \\
| & & | \\
\text{OH} & & \text{OH}
\end{array}
$$

which contains trivalent cobalt.   A red compound of substantially the same composition is obtained from dimethylglyoxime and anhydrous cobaltous chloride.   This is paramagnetic with a moment of 3.8 Bohr magnetons, corresponding with the expected moment for the cobaltous ion.   The structure is probably $[\text{H}_2\text{D} = \text{Co} = \text{DH}_2]\text{Cl}_2$, where H_2D stands for dimethylglyoxime.   However, further measurements and interpretations are given by Cambi.   The cobaltic ethylenediaminetetraacetic acid complex is diamagnetic.

Cobalticyanides are diamagnetic unless associated with a paramagnetic ion in the positive part of the salt.   Thus the cobalt has zero moment in $\text{K}_3[\text{Co(CN)}_6]$ and in $\text{K}_4[\text{Co(CN)}_5\text{S}_2\text{O}_3]$; but approximately normal moments for the positive ion are found in the cobalticyanides of copper,[172] of the rare earth elements,[173] of nickel, and of cobalt itself.[174]

$\text{Co(CO)}_3\text{NO}$ is diamagnetic although some other nitrosyl derivatives have some rather peculiar properties.   For instance, hydrated CoCl_2 or $\text{Co(NO}_3)_2$, an ammoniacal solution, when treated with nitric oxide give, respectively, black $[\text{Co(NH}_3)_5\text{NO}]\text{Cl}_2(\text{H}_2\text{O})_{0.5}$ and red $[\text{Co(NH}_3)_5\text{NO}]$-$(\text{NO}_3)_2(\text{H}_2\text{O})_{0.5}$.   The first is paramagnetic with $\mu = 1.7$, but the second is diamagnetic.[175]   A somewhat higher susceptibility is reported by Frazer and Long[176] for the first compound, but this is not supported by Mellor and Craig.[177]   Since all other known ammines of trivalent cobalt are

[169] A. K. Mukherjee, Science and Culture, 19, 107 (1953).
[170] D. C. Sen and P. Rây, J. Indian Chem. Soc., 11, 899 (1934).
[171] L. Cambi, Rend. ist. lombardo sci., 71, 85 (1938).
[172] M. A. Rollier and E. Arreghini, Gazz. chim. ital., 69, 499 (1939).
[173] T. Karantassis, C. Vassiliadis, and N. Perakis, Compt. rend., 208, 1720 (1939).
[174] J. Richardson and N. Elliott, J. Am. Chem. Soc., 62, 3182 (1940).
[175] J. L. Milward, W. Wardlaw, and W. J. R. Way, J. Chem. Soc., 1938, 233.
[176] J. H. Frazer and N. O. Long, J. Chem. Phys., 6, 462 (1938).
[177] D. P. Mellor and D. P. Craig, J. Proc. Roy. Soc. N. S. Wales, 78, 25 (1944).

diamagnetic, it is assumed that the red compound is a true nitroso derivative of trivalent cobalt.   The structure of the black compound cannot be given with certainty.

Several investigators have studied the magnetic susceptibility of vitamin B_{12}, which contains cobalt.[178]   The consensus is that the cobalt in this compound is diamagnetic and hence either probably trivalent or possibly divalent with attached oxygen, as in the oxygenated cobaltous chelates.   The trivalence is, apparently, now established by x-ray methods.[178a]

Several binuclear complexes of trivalent cobalt have been studied. These compounds, of which

$$\left[Co\left\{ \begin{matrix} OH \\ \\ OH \end{matrix} \diagdown \diagup Co(NH_3)_4 \right\}_3 \right] Cl_6$$

is an example, are almost all diamagnetic.[37]   There have, however, been a few binuclear peroxy complexes reported by Mathieu[179] as having moments corresponding to one unpaired electron.

Not very much work has been done on the magnetic anisotropy of cobalt(III) complexes.   Strock[180] has investigated the anisotropy of a few amines.

60. Nickel

Application of magnetic moments to complex configuration has been illustrated with reference to certain nickel compounds earlier in this chapter.   The tetrahedral "ionic" type is found in such compounds as Ni$(N_2H_4)_2SO_3$, $Ni(N_2H_4)_2(NO_2)_2$, $Ni(NH_3)_4SO_4$, $[Ni\{C_2H_4(NH_2)_2\}_2]$ $(SCN)_2$·H_2O, and nickel acetylacetonate, all of which have magnetic moments of from about 2.6 to 3.2.   Most of the data are from Rosenbohm.[36]   Nickel bisacetylacetone[181] is a good example of a paramagnetic complex with coordination number four.   Other examples of this type are nickel bisnicotinylacetone, nickel bis-salicylaldehyde, potassium nickel oxalate, and ammonium nickel malonate.   Hexa-coordinated ammines such as Ni$(NH_3)_6SO_4$ are also paramagnetic,[182] as are the nickel complexes of nitriloacetic acid and of ethylenediaminetetraacetic acid.[183]

[178] See, for instance, E. Grun and R. Menasse, *Experientia*, **6**, 263 (1950).

[178a] G. Boehm, A. Faessler, and G. Rittmayer, *Naturwissenschaften*, **41**, 187 (1954).

[179] J.-P. Mathieu, *Compt. rend.*, **218**, 907 (1944).

[180] L. W. Strock, *Z. physik. Chem.*, **B23**, 235 (1935); *Z. Krist.*, **88**, 238 (1934).

[181] L. Cambi and L. Szegö, *Ber.*, **64**, 2591 (1931).

[182] D. P. Mellor and D. P. Craig, *J. Proc. Roy. Soc. N. S. Wales*, **74**, 475 (1941). This paper contains an extensive summary on nickel complexes.

[183] W. Klemm and K.-H. Raddatz, *Z. anorg. u. allgem. Chem.*, **250**, 204 (1942).

$$\begin{array}{c}
\text{H}_3\text{C} \qquad\qquad\qquad \text{CH}_3 \\
\text{C}{=}\text{O} \quad\quad \text{O}{-}\text{C} \\
\text{HC} \qquad \text{Ni} \qquad \text{CH} \\
\text{C}{-}\text{O} \quad\quad \text{O}{=}\text{C} \\
\text{CH}_3 \qquad\qquad\qquad \text{CH}_3
\end{array}$$

nickel bis-acetylacetone

On the other hand, the cyanides, $K_2Ni(CN)_4$ and $K_2Ni(CN)_4{\cdot}H_2O$, are diamagnetic and hence contain planar $Ni(CN)_4{}^{2-}$ groups, a result which is supported by studies of isomorphism. There are many examples of this type, including the nickel glyoximes, potassium nickel dithiooxalate, nickel diacetyldioxime, nickel ethylxanthogenate, nickel ethyldithio-carbamate, bisphenylethylenediamine nickel nitrate, potassium nickel succinimide, and bisxanthic acid nickel. Mellor and Craig list many others, to some of which reference will be made below. The nickel mercaptides apparently belong to this group.[184]

Nickel cyanide heptahydrate, $Ni(CN)_2{\cdot}7H_2O$, has a normal moment for the Ni^{2+} ion, but on dehydration the paramagnetism undergoes a diminution. $Ni(CN)_2$ containing between two and four molecules of water has a moment of only about one-half that for ionic nickel compounds. This suggests that these hydrates contain approximately equal numbers of planar covalent $Ni(CN)_4{}^{2-}$ complexes and ionic $Ni(OH_2)_4{}^{2+}$ or $Ni(OH_2)_6{}^{2+}$ groups. Still further dehydration yields a substance with an apparent moment of about 0.5 Bohr magneton or even less.[185,186] Bose concludes that completely dehydrated nickel cyanide would be diamagnetic. It is not yet possible to predict whether a given coordinating group will form a square or a tetrahedral complex with nickel. Some progress has, however, been made in this direction and will be referred to below.

The nitrosyl and hydroxylamino derivatives of $Ni(CN)_2$ are likewise diamagnetic, or nearly so.[187] Mellor and Craig[182] have shown that solutions of $K_2Ni(CN)_3$ with apparently univalent nickel, are diamagnetic. This is remarkable because of the odd number of electrons in the formula. It is suggested that the structure involves a metal-metal bond such as has been shown to exist in mercurous chloride and in iron enneacarbonyl. The (red) compound $K_3[Ni(CN)_4]$ is, on the other hand, paramagnetic, with a moment of 1.73.[187a]

[184] K. A. Jensen, Z. anorg. Chem., **252**, 227 (1944).

[185] D. M. Bose, Nature, **125**, 708 (1930).

[186] L. Cambi, A. Cagnasso, and E. Tremolada, Gazz. chim. ital., **64**, 758 (1934).

[187] L. Malatesta and R. Pizzotti, ibid., **72**, 174 (1942).

[187a] R. Nast and T. v. Krakkay, Z. Naturforsch., **9b**, 798 (1954).

A few other nickel compounds which have been studied are the di-thiocarbamates which are diamagnetic,[188,189] and the disalicylaldehyde[150,190] and the kojate,[67] in which the nickel atoms have moments of 3.1 and 3.2, respectively. The structures are probably tetrahedral. Nickel disalicyl-aldehyde in solution is a light green color. On hydrogenation it turns to a yellow liquid with a brownish cast, but magnetic measurements indicate the same moment for the nickel in each form. The nickel salicylaldehyde-imines are mostly, but not all, diamagnetic according to Klemm and Raddatz,[183] as are many planar ammino complexes formed from acyl-hydrazones.[191]

Nickel complexes with o-phenanthroline and dipyridyl are diamag-netic,[192] as are the related compounds, nickel dimethylmesoporphyrin[193] and nickel protoporphyrin.[194] All these presumably have the dsp^2 co-valent square structure. Nickel phthalocyanine also belongs to this group.

Nickel glyoximes have been studied by Cambi and Szegö[181] and by Sugden.[195,196] Without exception they are diamagnetic and have the planar structure. The triazene complexes of nickel have been investigated by Dwyer and Mellor.[197] Bisdiazoaminobenzene nickel and bis-4,4-di-methyldiazoaminobenzene nickel are both diamagnetic. Molecular weight determinations indicate dimerization. The structures probably contain

square covalent nickel atoms as shown. Dissolving the compounds in pyridine produces octahedral complexes, the moment for bis-pyridine-bis-4,4-dimethyldiazoaminobenzene nickel being 3.38 Bohr magnetons, sug-gesting two unpaired electrons. The biscyclopentadienyl compound has a moment of 2.8 magnetons.[21]

There have been several efforts to find the factors which determine

[188] L. Cambi and L. Szegö, Ber., 64, 2594 (1931).
[189] L. Malatesta and A. A. Mella, Gazz. chim. ital., 67, 738 (1937).
[190] M. A. Fobes and G. N. Tyson, Jr., J. Am. Chem. Soc., 63, 3530 (1941).
[191] L. Sacconi, Gazz. chim. ital., 83, 884 (1953).
[192] L. Cambi and A. Cagnasso, Atti accad. nazl. Lincei, 19, 458 (1934).
[193] F. Haurowitz and W. Klemm, Ber., 68, 2312 (1935).
[194] L. Pauling and C. D. Coryell, Proc. Natl. Acad. Sci., 22, 159 (1936).
[195] S. Sugden, J. Chem. Soc., 1932, 246.
[196] H. J. Cavell and S. Sugden, ibid., 1935, 621.
[197] F. P. Dwyer and D. P. Mellor, J. Am. Chem. Soc., 63, 81 (1941).

whether nickel complexes will assume the diamagnetic square or the paramagnetic tetrahedral configuration. Sulfur atoms in the coordinating groups often form diamagnetic complexes; for instance, the oxalo complexes are paramagnetic but the thiooxalo complexes are not. For nitrogen and oxygen atoms in the coordinating group, there may be some relationship between the number and arrangement of the double bonds in the group and the tendency to form diamagnetic or paramagnetic complexes. This problem is related, as previously mentioned, to the precise meaning to be attached to structural bond type derived from magnetic measurements. It would appear to be desirable to have exchange reactions, susceptibility measurements, and classical stereochemical studies all made on a series of complexes. One of the few cases in which this has been done is the study by Johnson and Hall[198] on a group of nickel compounds. This useful study showed that, in general, exchange of the central coordinated atoms, using Ni^{63} tracer, proceeds when magnetic and other criteria indicate "ionic" bonding, but not when the bonding is indicated to be strongly covalent. Under certain circumstances, contrary results were obtained with substituted nickel dithiocarbamate complexes, and the bis-salicylaldoxime and bis-salicylaldimine complexes showed exchange even though these compounds are diamagnetic. It is not clear whether a change of bond type may sometimes be produced under the conditions of the exchange experiment.

At one time it was thought that a relation had been discovered between the color and the configuration of nickel complexes. Phenylated ethylenediamines, such as nickel distilbenediamine chloride and nickel diphenylethylenediamine nitrate, form two series of complexes, a blue paramagnetic form and a yellow diamagnetic form. These colored salts readily undergo reversible transformation from blue to yellow.[199,200] Two types of nickel acyloin oximes[201] have also been prepared, a green paramagnetic form and a red diamagnetic form. Another example is found in the red diamagnetic and green paramagnetic nickel alkylphosphines of the type $[Ni(PR_3)_2X_2]$.[201a] But while it is true that many paramagnetic nickel complexes are some shade of green or blue, and the diamagnetic complexes often range from bright red through red-brown to yellow, yet little reliance can be placed on this rule. For instance, vermillion bis-1-hydroxyacridine nickel has a moment of 3.2, and green bis(formylcamphor)-ethylenediamine nickel is

[198] J. E. Johnson and N. F. Hall, *ibid.*, **70**, 2344 (1948).
[199] I. Lifschitz, J. G. Bos, and K. M. Dijkema, *Z. anorg. u. allgem. Chem.*, **242**, 97 (1939).
[200] I. Lifschitz and K. M. Dijkema, *Rec. trav. chim.*, **60**, 581 (1941).
[201] L. Malatesta, *Gazz. chim. ital.*, **68**, 319 (1938).
[201a] R. W. Asmussen, A. Jensen, and H. Soling, *Acta Chem. Scand.*, **9**, 1391 (1955).

diamagnetic,[202] at least in the solid state. Some further observations on color and magnetic state have been made by Russell, Cooper, and Vosburgh.[203]

Another idea is that the electronegativities of the attached groups may determine the configuration of the complex.[204] An exhaustive study of the available data leads Mellor and Craig to the conclusion that while electronegativity may be important, other factors, such as the nature of the functional group in which the atom bonded to nickel occurs, are also significant.

The explanation which seems most promising at present is the effect of bond-angle distortion on the configuration of the complex.[205-210] All complexes in which nickel is bonded to four nitrogen atoms, irrespective of whether these nitrogen atoms belong to pyrrole rings, oxime, or triazene groups, have proved to be diamagnetic. But if, for some reason, the chelate groups are prevented from assuming a coplanar configuration, it is to be expected that the resulting distortion will be reflected in the magnetic moment of the metal ion. Such is the case in the nickel derivative of

3,3',5,5'-tetramethyl-4,4'-dicarbethoxydipyrromethene in which the methyl groups indicated * mutually prevent assumption of a coplanar structure. Owing to the large van der Waals radius of the methyl groups, no amount of distortion of the C—CH₃ bonds could accommodate chelating pyrromethene groups in square coordinated positions. This compound has been shown by

[202] J. E. Mills, and D. P. Mellor, *J. Am. Chem. Soc.*, **64**, 181 (1942).
[203] C. D. Russell, G. R. Cooper, and W. C. Vosburgh, *ibid.*, **65**, 1301 (1943).
[204] D. P. Mellor and D. P. Craig, *J. Proc. Roy. Soc. N. S. Wales*, **74**, 479 (1941).
[205] C. R. Porter, *J. Chem. Soc.* **1938**, 368.
[206] D. P. Mellor and W. H. Lockwood, *Nature*, **145**, 862 (1940).
[207] D. P. Mellor, *J. Proc. Roy. Soc. N. S. Wales*, **74**, 129 (1940).
[208] D. P. Mellor and W. H. Lockwood, *ibid.*, **74**, 141 (1940).
[209] D. P. Mellor, *ibid.*, **75**, 157 (1942).
[210] H. S. French, N. Z. Magee, and E. Sheffield, *J. Am. Chem. Soc.*, **64**, 1924 (1942).

Mellor and Lockwood to be paramagnetic. The nickel has a moment of 3.2 Bohr magnetons corresponding to two unpaired electrons. From this it may be inferred that the nickel-nitrogen bonds have been forced out of their normal square configuration into a tetrahedral structure.

A curious case which may be due to the same effect is found for bis-(formylcamphor)-ethylenediamine nickel. This compound is stated by French, Magee, and Sheffield[210] to be diamagnetic in the solid (which is confirmed by Mellor), but paramagnetic with an apparent moment of 1.9 in methyl alcohol solution. Lifschitz[211] has shown that solutions of this compound are diamagnetic in some solvents, paramagnetic in others. The phenomenon described has been shown by Willis and Mellor[212] to be more general than heretofore suspected. When pyridine is used as a solvent, interaction between solvent and solute sometimes occurs, presumably with formation of octahedral complexes. The moment in such cases rises to that expected for d^2sp^3 bonds, namely about 3 Bohr magnetons. In other cases, the moment observed in solution is less than that expected for two unpaired electrons. It is rather difficult to know what explanation to offer for this peculiar effect. Perhaps under the influence of the solvent there is set up an equilibrium between planar diamagnetic groups and tetrahedral paramagnetic groups. Equilibrium seems to be reached instantaneously, according to Willis and Mellor. An attempt to verify the idea of a tetrahedral $\rightleftharpoons$ planar equilibrium by making measurements over a range of temperature seems to have been successful, at least for the one case of the bis-N-methylsalicylaldimine. When dissolved in chloroform and certain other solvents, this compound shows a decrease of apparent moment as the temperature is raised.[213] Further support for this view is presented by Basolo and Matoush.[214] Very convincing evidence of this kind for a group of oximes and diimines is given by Clark and Odell.[214a] The application of magnetic measurements in determining bond types in distorted complexes is reviewed by Mellor.[207]

Complexes in which nickel has a valence other than two have not received so much attention. Nickel carbonyl, $Ni(CO)_4$, and related compounds, such as $Ni(CO)_2$-o-phenanthroline, have been shown by Oxley,[215] Klemm,[58] and others to be diamagnetic. At first glance this would suggest that $Ni(CO)_4$ should be a square complex. That it is not does not constitute

[211] I. Lifschitz, Rec. trav. chim., 66, 401 (1947).

[212] J. B. Willis and D. P. Mellor, J. Am. Chem. Soc., 69, 1237 (1947).

[213] S. Fujii and M. Sumitani, Science Repts. Tôhoku Imp. Univ., First Series, 37, 49 (1953).

[214] F. Basolo and W. R. Matoush, J. Am. Chem. Soc., 75, 5663 (1953).

[214a] H. C. Clark and A. L. Odell, J. Chem. Soc., 1955, 3431.

[215] A. E. Oxley, Proc. Cambridge Phil. Soc., 16, 102 (1911).

a contradiction for the magnetic criterion because the neutral nickel atom has two more electrons than the Ni^{2+} ion.   As a consequence, the $3d$ orbitals are all filled with electron pairs and the compound has four sp^3

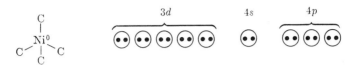

covalent bonds.   Other examples of supposed zero-valent nickel include $Ni[PCl_3]_4$ and $Ni[P(NCO)_3]_4$.   These are both diamagnetic.[216,217]

A supposed complex compound of trivalent nickel and benzamide oxime has been shown by Malatesta and Monti[218] to be of doubtful composition.   Klemm[51] states that the fluoride, K_3NiF_6, has a moment of 2.5 which is, however, dependent on temperature.   A case of trivalent nickel which seems well established is that of the complex with a di-*tert*-arsine, *o*-phenylene-bisdimethylarsine.   Nyholm[219] has shown that the compound, $[NiCl_2(diarsine)_2]Cl$, contains trivalent nickel.   The magnetic moment of the nickel is 1.89.   This moment is clearly a result of the odd number of electrons in the Ni^{+3} ion, and it is not yet clear what bond orbitals may be involved in this complex, but the matter is discussed by Burstall and Nyholm.[16]

Tetrapositive nickel in the alkali nickel periodates of approximate formula, $NaK[Ni(IO_6)]$, have been shown by Rây and Sarma[220] to have approximately zero magnetic moment.   This result has been confirmed in the author's laboratory.   The fluoride, K_2NiF_6, is similarly diamagnetic.[51]

61. Copper

Copper with a valence of one has no unpaired electrons.   As a consequence of this all cuprous compounds are diamagnetic.   Although cupric copper has one unpaired electron with a moment close to 1.73, yet the magnetic criterion is not of much service in determining the structure of cupric complexes.   The reason for this is that covalent copper still has one unpaired electron regardless of the configuration of the bonds.   Thus ammines of the type $[Cu(NH_3)_4](NO_3)_2$ and $[Cu(NH_3)_4(OH_2)_2]SO_4$ were shown by Rosenbohm[36] to have a moment of almost exactly 1.73 Bohr magnetons.   The same is true of cuprichlorides such as $K_2CuCl_4·2H_2O$.

[216] J. W. Irvine, Jr., and G. Wilkinson, *Science*, 113, 742 (1951).

[217] J. Wilkinson, *Z. Naturforsch.*, 9b, 446 (1954).

[218] L. Malatesta and F. Monti, *Gazz. chim. ital.*, 70, 842 (1940).

[219] R. S. Nyholm, *J. Chem. Soc.*, 1950, 2061.

[220] P. Rây and B. Sarma, *J. Indian Chem. Soc.*, 25, 205 (1948).

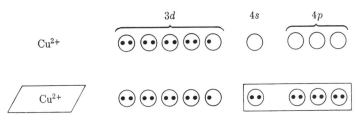

Similarly, the cupric hexammine iodide, bromide, and chloride all show the same moment.

In spite of this drawback, there has been a substantial number of magnetochemical studies of copper complexes. Sometimes it is possible to postulate a structure by analogy with the corresponding nickel complex, but there seems little justification for this. Tyson and Adams[221] give the moment of cupric disalicylaldehyde as 1.9. When the green cupric disalicylaldehyde is dissolved in pyridine, a solution of the same color results. After hydrogenation the solution becomes a deep ruby-red. This change apparently involves a reduction of the copper(II) to copper(I), although not all workers in the field are agreed on this.[222,223]

Like the disalicylaldehyde, the cupric disalicylaldehyde-propylene-diamine and the disalicylaldimine have moments corresponding to one unpaired electron and are probably planar. The same is true of bis-(formylcamphor)-copper dioxanate.[224] Cupric kojate[67] has a moment of 1.9, but here the structure, at least by analogy, may be tetrahedral. Large groups of related compounds have been investigated by Calvin and Barkelew,[225] Rây and Sen,[226] Sacconi,[227] and Ploquin.[228] It will be recalled that cupric acetate crystals show a subnormal moment due to exchange effects between adjacent copper ions, and that a substantial number of other organic derivatives of copper(II) show somewhat similar effects. Even such relatively simple systems as cupric bromide in solution apparently show some susceptibility dependence on hydrogen bromide concentration.[229] Copper cobalticyanide is another copper(II) compound showing an anomalous temperature coefficient of susceptibility.[230] Studies on the dithiocarbamates[231] and on the sulfamates and disulfamates[232] of copper show that here, too, the moment of the copper is normal. The same is probably true of the nitrosyl chloride complex, $CuCl\cdot ClNO$.[233] As pointed out by Baudisch,[234] studies such as these and on complexes involving nitric oxide derivatives are potentially important in the study of trace metal atoms in enzymes and related substances of biochemical interest.

[221] G. N. Tyson, Jr., and S. C. Adams, *J. Am. Chem. Soc.*, **62**, 1228 (1940).
[222] W. K. Wilmarth, M. K. Barsh, and S. S. Dharmatti, *ibid.*, **74**, 5035 (1952).
[223] G. N. Tyson, Jr., and R. E. Vivian, *ibid.*, **63**, 1403 (1941).
[224] D. P. Mellor, *J. Proc. Roy. Soc. N. S. Wales*, **75**, 157 (1942).

While simple cupric salts have been the subject of exhaustive magnetic anisotropy studies, the cupric complexes have received less attention. Rogers[235] has reported the principal susceptibilities of copper imidazole and copper phenylpropiolate. These compounds show a large anisotropy which is ascribed to the anisotropy of the crystal field in which the cupric ions are located.

Compounds of supposed trivalent copper have received little attention. According to Klemm,[51] the fluoride, K_3CuF_6, has a moment of 2.8, which is that expected for two unpaired electron spins. Malatesta[236] has shown that the complex iodate, $K_7Cu(IO_6)_2 \cdot 7H_2O$, is diamagnetic. A corresponding tellurate, $Na_5H_4Cu(TeO_6)_2 \cdot 18H_2O$, appears to have a positive molar susceptibility of 25×10^{-6} at 18°C. This paramagnetism is so small as to suggest nothing more than a trace of Cu^{2+} impurity in the compound. There seems little doubt concerning the existence of copper(III) in these compounds. They are, perhaps, worthy of further investigation. The cuprate described by Klemm, $KCuO_2$, is apparently also free from appreciable paramagnetism.[237]

62. Elements of the 4d and 5d Transition Series

For a long time the magnetic properties of the second and third main transition series have been obscure. Many compounds which seemed to be analogous to those of, say, iron or chromium proved to be diamagnetic. This was thought to be due to covalent bonding on a much larger scale than is found in the 3d series. That this idea is correct is now rapidly emerging, together with a better understanding of how exchange effects may diminish or abolish any paramagnetism an element might be expected to possess. Most of the progress in this direction is due to paramagnetic resonance studies which have proved unusually powerful in revealing crystal fields, splitting of energy levels, spin-orbital, and spin-spin coupling. The dis-

[225] M. Calvin and C. H. Barkelew, J. Am. Chem. Soc., 68, 2267 (1946).

[226] P. Rây and D. N. Sen, J. Indian Chem. Soc., 25, 473 (1948).

[227] L. Sacconi and R. Cini, Ann. chim. (Rome), 42, 723 (1952).

[228] J. Ploquin and C. Vergneau, Bull. soc. chim. France, 1951, 757.

[229] J. A. Dixmier and M. Nortz, Compt. rend., 237, 994 (1953).

[230] N. Perakis, J. Wucher, and H. M. Gijsman, ibid., 239, 243 (1954).

[231] L. Malatesta and A. A. Mella, Gazz. chim. ital., 67, 738 (1937).

[232] L. Lecuir, Ann. chim., 15, 33 (1941).

[233] R. W. Asmussen, Z. anorg. u. allgem. Chem., 243, 127 (1939).

[234] O. Baudisch, Arch. Biochem., 5, 401 (1944).

[235] M. T. Rogers, J. Am. Chem. Soc., 69, 1506 (1947).

[236] L. Malatesta, Gazz. chim. ital., 71, 467, 580 (1941).

[237] K. Wahl and W. Klemm, Z. anorg. u. allgem. Chem., 270, 69 (1952).

cussions of the Oxford University[238],[239] group have clarified this area to an unusual degree. Unfortunately, the explanations lie well beyond the background and experience of the average inorganic chemist interested in coordination chemistry. It must suffice to say that the magnetic properties of these complexes have in general a satisfactory explanation and that this explanation is in terms of field-splitting and exchange effects. Some reference to examples will be made below.

The common silver, Ag^+, ion is, of course, diamagnetic. The possible divalence of silver and of gold in $Cs_2AgAuCl_6$ and in $Cs_2Au_2Cl_6$ has been examined by Elliott.[240] Both compounds are diamagnetic. Paramagnetism is found in the silver compound produced by action of ozone on strongly acidified silver nitrate solution.[241] The moment found corresponds most closely to that expected for Ag^{2+}, which should have one unpaired electron. The possibility of Ag^{3+} is not completely excluded because it is not entirely certain whether this ion would be diamagnetic, like Pd^{2+}, or paramagnetic, like Ni^{2+}. The former seems more probable. Divalent paramagnetic silver in such complexes as $[Ag_xCd_y(C_5H_5N)_4]S_2O_8$ has been studied by Perakis and Capatos,[242] and Sugden[243] gives a list of paramagnetic argentic compounds of which the tris-α,α'-dipyridyl chlorate is one. Capatos and Perakis[244] report an approximately normal value of 1.74 Bohr magnetons for the Ag^{2+} ion in the compound $AgS_2O_4\cdot 4C_5H_5N$. These authors[245] have also studied solid solutions of argentic and cupric compounds.

Paramagnetic resonance studies on the o-phenanthroline persulfate complex, $[Ag(o\text{-phn})_2]S_2O_8$, have given some evidence that the electron hole in the $4d$ subshell is not localized on the silver(II) ion but migrates to the surrounding atoms.[246] The higher oxide is apparently diamagnetic.[247]

Complexes such as $M_7Ag(IO_6)_2\cdot nH_2O$, in which silver appears to have an oxidation state of three, are diamagnetic,[248],[249] as is the fluoride, $KAgF_4$, according to Klemm.[51]

If gold formed an ion with a charge of two plus it would probably be

[238] J. H. E. Griffiths, J. Owen, and I. M. Ward, *Proc. Roy. Soc. (London)*, **A219**, 526 (1953).

[239] K. W. H. Stevens, *ibid.*, **A219**, 542 (1953).

[240] N. Elliott, *J. Chem. Phys.*, **2**, 419 (1934).

[241] A. A. Noyes, K. S. Pitzer, and C. L. Dunn, *J. Am. Chem. Soc.*, **57**, 1229 (1935).

[242] N. Perakis and L. Capatos, *J. phys. radium*, **9**, 27 (1938).

[243] S. Sugden, *J. Chem. Soc.*, **1932**, 161.

[244] L. Capatos and N. Perakis, *Compt. rend.*, **202**, 1773 (1936).

[245] N. Perakis and L. Capatos, *J. phys. radium*, **10**, 234 (1939).

[246] K. D. Bowers, *Proc. Phys. Soc. (London)*, **66A**, 666 (1953).

[247] A. B. Neiding and I. A. Kazarnovskii, *Doklady Akad. Nauk S. S. S. R.*, **78**, 713 (1951). The original of this paper was not available to the author.

[248] L. Malatesta, *Gazz. chim. ital.*, **71**, 467 (1941).

[249] P. Rây and N. C. Chakravarty, *J. Indian Chem. Soc.*, **21**, 47 (1944).

paramagnetic. No measurements appear to have been made on the unstable oxide, AuO, or sulfide, AuS. In its normal valences of one and three, gold is diamagnetic.

The mercurous ion is diamagnetic because it always forms a double ion, Hg_2^{2+}. The mercuric ion has no unpaired electrons. A group of mercuriiodides in several solvents investigated by Gallais[250] are without exception diamagnetic.

Ammonium hexabromohypoantimonate, with the empirical formula $(NH_4)_2SbBr_6$, suggests antimony with the unusual valence of four. This compound might be expected to be paramagnetic, but measurements by Elliott[251] show that it is diamagnetic. Elliott suggests that the compound, which is highly colored, may contain antimony in two different valence states, or alternatively, that there is a covalent bond between two quadrivalent antimony ions. The crystal structure of several such compounds of the general type, M_2SbX_6, has been studied by Jensen[252,253] who suggests that the bromine atom forms a channel through which the antimony ions may enter into an oscillating relation in which their electrons are paired. All such compounds appear to be diamagnetic, as is $BiCl_4$,[254,255] although it is claimed that tetravalent bismuth in the oxide, BiO_2, is paramagnetic.[256]

The electronic configuration of molybdenum, $4s^2$, $4p^6$, $4d^5$, $5s$, parallels that of chromium, and the magnetic properties of molybdenum atoms in complex compounds are similar to those of chromium, with a significant exception. The molybdenum atom is larger and as a consequence often has a coordination number of eight rather than six. For essentially covalent complexes this often results in diamagnetism, where the corresponding chromium compound may be paramagnetic.

Compounds in which molydenum has a valence of three have been studied by Bose,[257] Tjabbes,[258,258a] and Klemm and Steinberg.[259] K_3MoCl_6, $K_3MoCl_6 \cdot 2H_2O$, and $(NH_4)_3[Mo(SCN)_6] \cdot 4H_2O$ all have effective moments of about 3.7 Bohr magnetons, corresponding to three unpaired electrons.

Two complexes containing tetravalent molybdenum have been

[250] F. Gallais, *Compt. rend.*, **205**, 1052 (1937).
[251] N. Elliott, *J. Chem. Phys.*, **2**, 298 (1934).
[252] K. A. Jensen, *Z. anorg. u. allgem. Chem.*, **232**, 193 (1937).
[253] K. A. Jensen, *Z. anorg. Chem.*, **252**, 317 (1944).
[254] R. W. Asmussen, *Z. Elektrochem.*, **45**, 698 (1939).
[255] R. W. Asmussen, *Kemiska*, **Nr. 6**, (1941), p. 81.
[256] S. S. Bhatnagar and K. N. Mathur, *Physical Principles and Applications of Magnetochemistry*. MacMillan and Company, Ltd., London, 1935, p. 214.
[257] D. M. Bose, *Z. physik. Chem.*, **B36**, 325 (1937).
[258] B. T. Tjabbes, *Proc. Acad. Sci. Amsterdam*, **35**, 693 (1932).
[258a] B. T. Tjabbes, *Z. anorg. u. allgem. Chem.*, **216**, 127 (1933).
[259] W. Klemm and H. Steinberg, *Z. anorg. u. allgem. Chem.*, **227**, 193 (1936).

reported by Klemm and Steinberg as having moments corresponding to one unpaired electron. These are $(C_5H_6N)_2[MoOBr_4]$ and $(C_9H_8N)_2[MoOBr]$. The structures are not clear because exactly the same moment is given for the compounds $Rb_2[MoOCl_5]$, $(C_5H_6N)_2[MoOCl_5]$, $(C_5H_6N)_2[MoOBr_5]$, $(C_9H_8N)_2[MoOBr_5]$, and $(C_5H_6N)_2[MoO(SCN)_5]$ in which the molybdenum would appear to have an oxidation state of five. The complex cyanides of tetravalent molydenum, $K_4Mo(CN)_8$ and $K_4Mo(CN)_8 \cdot 2H_2O$, are all diamagnetic. These have been studied by Klemm and Steinberg,[259] Rawlinson,[260] Biltz,[41] and Bose.[257]

Rawlinson has also studied potassium molybdicyanide, $K_3Mo(CN)_8$, in which the molybdenum has a valence of five. The effective moment of this compound is 1.66 Bohr magnetons, but this value is uncorrected for diamagnetism. In this case the moment is clearly not far from the theoretical value for one unpaired electron.

Resonance absorption has been reported by Griffiths et al. for several of the paramagnetic molybdenum complexes. The peculiar "molybdenum blue" substances appear to be diamagnetic, although they are difficult to characterize owing to the range of composition over which they are stable.[261]

Sacconi[262] has also presented evidence that molybdenum(V) chloride, which is paramagnetic in solution at high acidities, becomes diamagnetic as the acidity is lowered to $2N$. This is apparently another example of dimerization in solution.

The binuclear cyclopentadienyl molybdenum(V) derivative, $(C_5H_5)_2$-$(CO)_5Mo_2$, is diamagnetic, as is the corresponding tungsten compound.[34] Molybdenum carbonyl, $Mo(CO)_6$, has been shown by Klemm, Jacobi, and Tilk[58] to be diamagnetic. Molybdic acid anhydride, MoO_3, and the molybdates are diamagnetic, or perhaps have a small temperature-independent paramagnetism. Tjabbes[258] shows that zinc ammonia peroxymolybdate, $Zn(NH_3)_4MoO_8$, is diamagnetic. Polymolybdates[263] are likewise diamagnetic, or perhaps have very small positive susceptibilities. There seem to be small differences in diamagnetism between different isopolymolybdates.[264]

Not very many tungsten complexes have been studied. $K_3W_2Cl_9$, in which tungsten has a valence of three, is stated by Bose[257] to be diamagnetic, although Klemm and Steinberg[259] give it fractional moment of 0.47. The complex cyanide of tetravalent tungsten, $K_4[W(CN)_8]$, and its hydrate, $K_4[W(CN)_8] \cdot 2H_2O$,[265] have zero moment, but $K_2[WCl_5(OH)]$[260] has a

[260] W. A. Rawlinson, Australian Chem. Inst. J. and Proc., 8, 42 (1941).

[261] L. Sacconi and R. Cini, Ann. chim. (Rome), 42, 706 (1952).

[262] L. Sacconi and R. Cini J. Am. Chem. Soc., 76, 4239 (1954).

[263] L. Malatesta, Gazz. chim. ital., 69, 408, 752 (1939).

[264] S. C. Das and P. Rây, J. Indian Chem. Soc., 21, 159 (1944).

[265] L. Welo, Phil. Mag., 6, 481 (1928).

moment corresponding to one unpaired electron. The only pentavalent tungsten complex on which magnetic measurements seem to have been made is $Rb_2[WOCl_5]$. This has a moment of 1.5 Bohr magnetons. $(C_5H_6N)_2$-$[WOCl_4]$ has exactly the same moment, a situation which is paralleled for the corresponding molybdenum compounds. It is not certain, however, that the tungsten necessarily has a valence of five in this pyridinium salt.

Rhenium complexes have not been studied very thoroughly and they give rather anomalous results.[259,266] For instance, the supposedly trivalent rhenium in $[Re(NH_3)_6]Cl_3$, $[Re(NH_5)_6]Br_3$, and $RbReCl_4$ yields diamagnetic compounds. Na_2ReO_3 is also diamagnetic or perhaps very slightly paramagnetic, even though the compound apparently has an odd number of electrons. Perhaps this is due to Re—Re bonds or to a Re^{3+}—Re^{5+} combination. Other compounds of tetravalent rhenium, such $K_2[ReCl_6]$, $Ag_2[ReCl_6]$, and $K_2[ReBr_6]$ are paramagnetic and have moments of about 3.2, but the moments are dependent on the temperature. Jensen[253] finds that the strongly colored K_2ReI_6 has a moment of 3.57 with a Weiss constant of 70°. Pentavalent rhenium may exist in the compounds K_2ReOCl_5, $Re(NH_3)_6Cl_5$, $K_3[ReO_2(CN)_4]$, and $Tl[ReO_2(CN)_4]$, but with the possible exception of the first these are all diamagnetic. An interesting case of a binuclear diamagnetic ion apparently occurs in $[Re_2OCl_{10}]^{4-}$ which is in equilibrium with the paramagnetic monomeric ion as follows: $2[ReOHCl_5]^{2-} \rightleftharpoons [Re_2OCl_{10}]^{4-} + H_2O$. This is reminiscent of the case of partially hydrolyzed ferric ions which also yield a diamagnetic dimer. The structure of the rhenium dimer is not clear. The possibility of an oxygen bridge, as occurs for the ruthenium complex mentioned below, has been criticized.[267]

It will be recalled that the ions of the palladium-platinum groups generally exhibit, with the exception of ruthenium, very small or zero moments. This is even true of substances like palladous nitrate in solution, palladous chloride, and of platinum di- and tetrachlorides. At first glance the magnetic method would not appear to be of much service in determining the structure of substances such as these, but the situation has been clarified by additional data and by an excellent review (of the "pre-resonance" status) on this subject by Mellor.[268]

It will be worthwhile to consider the predicted magnetic moments for the several elements in several configurations,[269] as shown in Table XXI. The available experimental data indicate that the elements of these

[266] W. Klemm and G. Frischmuth, Z. anorg. u. allgem. Chem., 230, 220 (1937).

[267] B. Jezowska-Trzebiatowska and S. Wajda, Bull. acad. polonaise sciences, 2, 219 (1954).

[268] D. P. Mellor, J. Proc. Roy. Soc. N. S. Wales, 77, 145 (1944).

[269] L. Pauling and M. L. Huggins, Z. Krist., 87, 214 (1934).

TABLE XXI

Predicted Moments for Complexes of Pd-Pt Groups

		d electrons	For ionic or sp^3 tetrahedral bonds	For 4 dsp^2 square bonds	For 6 d^2sp^3 octahedral bonds
Ru^{6+}		2	2.83	2.83	2.83
Ru^{4+}	Os^{4+}	4	4.90	4.90	2.83
Ru^{3+}	Os^{3+}, Ir^{4+}	5	5.91	3.88	1.73
$Ru^{2+}, Rh^{3+}, Pd^{4+}$	Ir^{3+}, Pt^{4+}	6	4.90	2.83	0.00
Rh^{2+}	Ir^{2+}	7	3.88	1.73	—
Rh^+, Pd^{2+}	Pt^{2+}	8	2.83	0.00	—

TABLE XXII

Moments for Some Paramagnetic Pd-Pt Group Complexes

Complex	Moment
$KRuF_6$[51]	3.5–4.1
$BaRuF_6$	2.8
Na_3RhF_7	1.74
K_2RhF_6	1.7
$[Ru(NH_3)_4Br_2] Br \cdot H_2O$[270]	~2
$[Ru(NH_3)_4C_2O_4] S_2O_6$	~2
$[Ru(NH_3)_4Cl_2] Cl(H_2O)_{3/4}$	~2
$K_2[RuCl_6]$	3.07
$K_2[RuCl_5H_2O]$	2.04
$K_2[RuCl_5]$	1.8
$K_2[OsCl_6]$	1.44
$(NH_4)_2(OsCl_6)$	1.44
$(NH_4)_2(OsBr_6)$	1.49
$(NH_4)_3(IrCl_6)$	1.67
$K_2(IrCl_6)$	1.65

groups do not in general form ionic complexes. This fact is responsible for the low susceptibilities often found for the compounds of these elements. Nevertheless, paramagnetism has been reported for several ruthenium complexes and for a few complexes of other elements of the groups. Some of the paramagnetic compounds and the approximate moment reported for each are given in Table XXII. In certain cases predicted by Kotani,[270a] of which ammonium hexabromoösmate(IV) is one and $K_3Mn(CN)_6$ as previously mentioned is another, the substance is definitely paramagnetic but the magnetic moment approaches zero at low temperature.[270b]

Diamagnetism appears to be found in nearly all other complexes of

[270] K. Gleu and W. Breuel, *Z. anorg. u. allgem. Chem.*, **237**, 326 (1938).

[270a] M. Kotani, *J. Phys. Soc. Japan*, **4**, 293 (1949).

[270b] R. B. Johannesen and A. R. Lindberg, *J. Am. Chem. Soc.*, **76**, 5349 (1954).

the palladium-platinum groups which have been studied. Amongst these may be mentioned $K_2[RuCl_5OH]$; the nitrosoruthenium dialkyldithio-carbamates,[271] a large series of rhodium complexes;[272] the palladium compounds, $PdCl_2NH_3$, K_2PdCl_4, $K_2Pd(CN)_4$, $K_2Pd(SCN)_2$, K_2PdCl;[273] and the palladium derivative of 3,3',5,5'-tetramethyl-4,4'-dicarbethoxydipyrromethene.[274] Similar results have been reported on a palladium complex, $Pd(NH_3)_2Cl_2 \cdot Pd(NH_3)_2Cl_4$.[275]

Except as noted above, complexes of osmium and iridium appear to be diamagnetic, although Bose and Bhar[276] state that iridium tetrachloride is paramagnetic. Amongst the platinum complexes which have been shown to be diamagnetic are $[Pt(NH_3)_4Cl_2]Cl_2$, $[Pt(NH_3)_3Cl_3]Cl$, $[Pt(NH_3)_2Cl_4]$, K_2PtCl_4, K_2PtCl_6, $Pt(NH_3)_4SO_4$, $PtCl_2 \cdot 2CO$, $PtCl_2 \cdot CO$, and others.

The diamagnetism in at least one case has been shown to be due to an oxygen-bridged dimeric ion. Dunitz and Orgel[97] find that the ion $(Ru_2-Cl_{10}O)^{4-}$ probably has the structure $[(Cl_5)Ru{=}O{=}Ru(Cl_5)]^{4-}$. This type of structure may possibly apply to other examples of dimerization.

Examination of these results shows that the failure of the original Pauling theory relating magnetic moment to structure for these series of elements is considerably less complete than had been believed. Actually, once it is granted that ionic complexes are rare for these elements, then there remain only relatively few instances in which the theory seems inadequate.

63. Heteropolynuclear Complexes

Comparatively few magnetic studies have been made on complexes containing two different transition elements. Such measurements as have been reported suggest that these substances resemble polynuclear complexes in which only one transition element is involved. Thus, the compound $[Cr_3(CH_3COO)_6(OH)_2]$ $Cl \cdot 8H_2O$, to which reference has already been made, resembles $[Cr_2Fe(CH_3OO)_6(OH)_2]Cl \cdot 6H_2O$ in that the moment obtained seems not unreasonable but the Weiss constant may approach $500°$. Welo[277] has shown that $[Cr_2Fe(CH_3COO)_6(OH)_2]NO_3 \cdot 6H_2O$ and $[Fe_2Cr-(CH_3COO)_6(OH)_2]NO_3 \cdot H_2O$ have Weiss constants of 458 and 342°,

[271] L. Cambi and L. Malatesta, *Rend. ist. lombardo sci.*, **71**, 118 (1938).

[272] J. A. Christiansen and R. W. Asmussen, *Kgl. Danske Videnskab. Selskab. Math.-fys. Medd.*, **12**, No. 10, (1934).

[273] R. B. Janes, *J. Am. Chem. Soc.*, **57**, 471 (1935).

[274] D. P. Mellor and W. H. Lockwood, *J. Proc. Roy. Soc. N. S. Wales*, **74**, 141 (1940).

[275] A. J. Cohen and N. Davidson, *J. Am. Chem. Soc.*, **73**, 1955 (1951).

[276] D. M. Bose and H. G. Bhar, *Z. Physik*, **48**, 716 (1928).

[277] L. A. Welo, *Phil. Mag.*, **6**, 481 (1928).

respectively. The relationship of the metal atoms to each other in these compounds is not thoroughly understood but appears to involve three interacting electron spins.[277a]

Another type of heteropoly complex is found in certain ferrocyanides such as $K_2MnFe(CN)_6$, $K_2CoFe(CN)_6$, $K_2CuFe(CN)_6$, and $Cu_2Fe(CN)_6$. These have been studied by Rollier and Arreghini[278] and by Richardson and Elliott.[279] In each case the observed moment agrees with that calculated on the assumption that the substance contains an octahedral covalent complex with d^2sp^3 bonds from the iron to the cyanide groups. The other heavy metal seems to exist as a simple ion in each case. Thus, for $K_2MnFe(CN)_6$ the observed moment of 6.05 Bohr magnetons is about normal for a diamagnetic ferrocyanide complex plus an ionic Mn^{2+} ion.

[277a] H. M. Gijsman, T. Karantassis, and J. Wucher, *Physica*, **20**, 367 (1954).

[278] M. A. Rollier and E. Arreghini, *Gazz. chim. ital.*, **69**, 499 (1939).

[279] J. Richardson and N. Elliott, *J. Am. Chem. Soc.*, **62**, 3182 (1940).

CHAPTER ELEVEN

MOLECULAR PARAMAGNETISM

64. "Odd" Molecules

The great majority of molecular substances is made up of molecules which possess an even number of electrons. It was first pointed out by Lewis[1,2] that those comparatively few molecules with an odd number of electrons should have a permanent magnetic moment and hence be paramagnetic. This view was supported by the experiments of Soné[3] who showed that paramagnetism is a property of nitric oxide and of nitrogen dioxide, but that other oxides of nitrogen, having an even number of electrons, are diamagnetic. Proof of Lewis's theory was established by the experiments of Taylor,[4] who studied chlorine dioxide and an organic free radical, α-naphthyldiphenylmethyl, both of which were found to be paramagnetic. Thallium amalgam and sodium dissolved in liquid ammonia also showed definite, though slight, paramagnetism.

In such compounds there seems to be little or no contribution from the orbital moment so that the susceptibilities are represented by

$$\chi_M = \frac{N\beta^2 4S(S + 1)}{3kT}$$

or for a single unpaired electron, for which $S = \frac{1}{2}$, the molar susceptibility at 20°C. is about 1270×10^{-6}. Except for rather minor deviations, the susceptibilities generally follow the Curie law, although, as for nitric oxide, there are some notable exceptions.

65. Oxygen and Ozone

It may seem peculiar, after the foregoing, that our detailed discussion of molecular paramagnetism should start with a molecule having an even number of electrons. But oxygen is almost unique in that its normal state

---

[1] G. N. Lewis, *Valence and the Structure of Atoms and Molecules*. Chemical Catalog Co., New York, 1923, p. 148.

[2] G. N. Lewis, *Chem. Rev.*, **1**, 231 (1924).

[3] T. Soné, *Science Repts. Tôhoku Imp. Univ.*, **11**, 139 (1922).

[4] N. W. Taylor, *J. Am. Chem. Soc.*, **48**, 854 (1926).

is $^3\Sigma$ so that, although it has an even number of electrons, two of these remain unpaired, and the oxygen molecule is as a consequence strongly paramagnetic. The number of molecules which are similar to that of oxygen in this respect is small, being virtually limited to a few organic biradicals and to some forms of sulfur.

Van Vleck[5] considers limiting cases for diatomic paramagnetic molecules in a manner similar to that which he develops for paramagnetic atoms. These may have multiplet intervals small compared to kT, or large compared to kT. For molecular Σ states the multiplet intervals are negligibly small, and the Σ state of molecular oxygen is established both from the magnetic measurements and from spectroscopic studies. The molar susceptibility is given by

$$\chi_M = \frac{8N\beta^2}{3kT} = \frac{0.993}{T}$$

At $20\,°C$. the theoretical molar susceptibility is 3390×10^{-6}.

The paramagnetism of molecular oxygen has been the subject of much experimental work. Magnetic deflection of a molecular beam of oxygen, gives a moment equal to two Bohr magnetons.[6] Susceptibility measurements are reviewed by Van Vleck[5] and Stoner.[7] Various results on the gas

TABLE XXIV

Molar Curie Constants of Oxygen Gas as Determined by Various Investigators

Experimenter	$\chi_M T$
Curie[8]	0.983^a
Onnes and Oosterhuis[9]	0.970
Soné[10]	0.975
Bauer and Piccard[11]	1.011
Wills and Hector[12]	1.021
Woltjer, Coppoolse, and Wiersma[13]	1.002
Lehrer[14]	0.979

^{a} Corrected for calibration.

[5] J. H. Van Vleck, *Theory of Electric and Magnetic Susceptibilities*. Oxford University Press, Oxford, 1932, p. 264.

[6] R. Schnurmann, *Z. Physik*, **85**, 212 (1933).

[7] E. C. Stoner, *Magnetism and Matter*. Methuen and Company, Ltd., London, 1934, p. 342.

[8] P. Curie, *Ann. chim. et phys.*, **5**, 289 (1895).

[9] H. K. Onnes and E. Oosterhuis, *Leiden Communications*, **134d**.

[10] T. Soné, *Phil. Mag.*, **39**, 305 (1920).

[11] E. Bauer and A. Piccard, *J. phys. radium*, **1**, 97 (1920).

[12] A. P. Wills and L. G. Hector, *Phys. Rev.*, **23**, 209 (1924).

[13] H. R. Woltjer, C. W. Coppoolse, and E. C. Wiersma, *Proc. Acad. Sci. Amsterdam*, **32**, 1329 (1929).

[14] E. Lehrer, *Ann. Physik*, **81**, 229 (1926).

measured near room temperature give $\chi_M T$ ranging from 0.970 to 1.021 with an average of 0.991, which is very close to the theoretical value, 0.993. Results of some of the more important individual determinations are given in Table XXIV. The susceptibility of oxygen (and of nitric oxide) is apparently independent of field strength, down at least to 15 oersteds.[15] The Curie law describes very closely the susceptibility of oxygen. This has been determined by several of the above workers, and by Stössel.[16] However, Woltjer, Coppoolse, and Wiersma[13] believe that there is a small deviation from the Curie law amounting to about 2%, even after their data are extrapolated to zero density to avoid interference from molecular interactions. At higher pressures, the deviations may become appreciable. Goldstein and Rocard[17] find that the susceptibility of oxygen, gaseous, liquid or dissolved in nitrogen, follows the Weiss law $\chi(T + \Delta) = C$, where Δ is numerically 40 times the density. This is probably only a rough approximation, but the belief that the susceptibility of oxygen is affected by the density is supported by Kanzler[18] who finds strict observance of the Curie law between 290° and 625°K. for all densities below 0.12 g. per cc. (corrected to 20°C.). But at $d_{20} = 0.2$ g. per cc., the Weiss law is followed with $\Delta = 5.6°$, and for $d_{20} = 0.4$ g. per cc., $\Delta = 25.8°$.

Liquid oxygen follows the Weiss law. Perrier and Onnes[19] discovered that for solutions of oxygen in liquid nitrogen, the term Δ varies with the concentration of oxygen, from 2.2° for 8.1% O_2, to 29.5° for 74.6% O_2. Analysis of such data led Lewis[20] to postulate the presence of O_4 molecules. This view is supported by the discovery of O_4 in the atmosphere.[21] Its properties are discussed by Pauling.[22]

Solid oxygen has recently been studied fairly thoroughly.[22a,23] There appear to be three modifications of solid oxygen. Gamma-oxygen, stable from 43.8°K. to the triple point, obeys the Curie-Weiss law. For beta-oxygen, stable from 23.8° to 43.8°K., the susceptibility decreases with decreasing temperature. A further decrease occurs on formation of the

[15] A. Burris and C. D. Hause, *J. Chem. Phys.*, 11, 442 (1943).

[16] R. Stössel, *Ann. Physik*, 10, 393 (1931).

[17] L. Goldstein and Y. Rocard, *Compt. rend.*, 196, 1722 (1933).

[18] M. Kanzler, *Ann. Physik*, 36, 38 (1939).

[19] A. Perrier and H. K. Onnes, *Leiden Communications*, 139d, 48.

[20] G. N. Lewis, *J. Am. Chem. Soc.*, 46, 2027 (1924).

[21] O. R. Wulf, *Proc. Nat. Acad. Sci.*, 14, 609 (1938).

[22] L. Pauling, *The Nature of the Chemical Bond.* Cornell University Press, Ithaca, 1939, p. 253.

[22a] A. S. Borovik-Romanov, M. P. Orlova, and P. G. Strelkov, *Doklady Akad. Nauk S.S.S.R.*, 99, 699 (1954). This article was not read in the original.

[23] E. Kanda, T. Haseda, and A. Otsubo, *Science Repts., Research Insts., Tôhoku Univ. Ser. A*, 7, 1 (1955).

alpha-oxygen below 23.8°K. It has sometimes been claimed that the decrease of susceptibility shown by solid oxygen is related to the formation of diamagnetic O_4 molecules. It should be pointed out, however, that the magnetic behavior is that of an antiferromagnetic substance. The oxygen molecules in a clathrate compound are, presumably, unable to rearrange to form the diamagnetic O_4. Down to about 20°K., oxygen enclosed in a *beta*-quinol (hydroquinone) clathrate shows the normal theoretical susceptibility.[24,25] Oxygen dissolved in benzene or in heptane appears to have its normal paramagnetism.[26] The magnetic properties of adsorbed oxygen will be discussed later in this chapter.

Ozone has been the subject of some very conflicting reports in the literature. The molecule has an even number of electrons, and there is no particular reason for expecting it to be like O_2. Furthermore, experimental work on ozone, especially the pure gas and liquid, becomes very difficult, if not hazardous. The most impressive work so far on this substance has been done by Lainé.[27] He finds the susceptibility of pure liquid O_3 to be 0.14 (± 0.02) $\times$ 10^{-6}. This small paramagnetism seems to be independent of temperature. Gaseous ozone appears to be diamagnetic.

66. Magnetic Analysis of Oxygen

The large paramagnetic susceptibility of molecular oxygen makes it possible to develop analytical methods based on this and related properties. The susceptibility of oxygen, at 20°C. and standard pressure, is 142×10^{-9} per cubic centimeter. The only other common gas which has a comparable susceptibility is nitric oxide for which, under the same conditions, $\kappa = 61 \times 10^{-9}$. Virtually all other gases are diamagnetic. There is no doubt that magnetic methods for oxygen analysis have a substantial sensitivity advantage over other physical methods, and that they are simpler and lend themselves to continuous recording more readily than chemical methods of analysis.

At the time of writing, there appear to be at least five different ways in which magnetic analysis of oxygen has been achieved. Instruments based on two different principles are available commercially. The several principles involved are as follows:

(1) The volume susceptibility of the gas mixture is measured directly

[24] D. F. Evans and R. E. Richards, *J. Chem. Soc.*, 1952, 3295.

[25] A. H. Cooke, H. Meyer, W. P. Wolf, D. F. Evans, and R. E. Richards, *Proc. Roy. Soc. (London)*, **A225**, 112 (1954).

[26] B. C. Eggleston, D. F. Evans, and R. E. Richards, *J. Chem. Soc.*, **1954**, 941.

[27] P. Lainé, *Ann. phys.*, **3**, 461 (1935). This paper includes a good review of the literature, to that date.

by a suspension system in an inhomogeneous field. This will be referred to below as the Pauling meter.

(2) The viscosity of oxygen changes somewhat in a magnetic field. This will be referred to below as the Sack-Rein method.

(3) In a homogeneous magnetic field, the thermal conductivity of oxygen is somewhat decreased. This is called the Senftleben method.

(4) In an inhomogeneous magnetic field, oxygen suffers an apparent increase of thermal conductivity due to thermal convection currents. This is sometimes referred to as the Turowski method, or the "magnetic wind."

(5) In a rotating magnetic field, oxygen suffers pressure fluctuations. This is mentioned below as the Luft method.

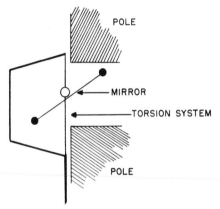

Fig. 82. Principle of the Pauling oxygen meter.

The Pauling meter[28] consists of a glass system in the form of a dumbbell suspended in an inhomogeneous magnetic field produced by an Alnico permanent magnet. The glass assembly is supported on a silica fiber and carries a small mirror. A diagrammatic representation showing one of several proposed systems is given in Fig. 82. The force acting to rotate the system about the axis of suspension is proportional to the magnetic field strength, the gradient of the field, and the difference in volume susceptibility of the glass test body and the atmosphere surrounding it. As the susceptibility of the surrounding atmosphere changes with changing oxygen content, the moving system rotates through an angle which is roughly proportional to the oxygen content. Readings are conveniently reflected on to a scale from the suspended mirror. Various methods may be used for compensation of temperature changes and, with some complica-

[28] L. Pauling, R. E. Wood, and J. H. Sturdivant, *J. Am. Chem. Soc.*, **68**, 795 (1946).

tion, it is possible to adapt the method to continuous recording. Models of this instrument are sold commercially in a variety of designs and sensitivities. The apparatus is fairly widely used. Its principal drawback is the instability associated with a delicate moving system.

The Sack-Rein method for oxygen analysis is based on a principle discovered by Sack and his co-workers.[29] The gas stream to be analyzed is diverted into two capillaries arranged in the same sense as the wires in a Wheatstone bridge. A sensitive-differential manometer is placed in a position corresponding to the galvanometer. Opposite arms of the bridge are now placed between the poles of a magnet. Changes of viscosity produced by the action of the field on the oxygen are reflected as a change of manometer reading. An apparatus using this principle has been described by Rein.[30]

The Senftleben[31] principle, which was apparently based on earlier observations of Lehrer,[32] has also been used by Rein.[33] The apparatus consists of two Pirani hot-wire gauges arranged in a bridge system so that the gas stream moves over both wires. The bridge is balanced, then one of the hot-wire gauges is placed in a magnetic field. The thermal conductivity of oxygen is decreased somewhat in a magnetic field; hence, on application of the field, the bridge is unbalanced to the extent that the gas stream contains oxygen. The effect on which this method relies is not a large one. For instance, at a field of 2000 oersteds, the thermal conductivity of air is reduced by only about 1%; nevertheless, the method appears to have given considerable satisfaction.

The method which appears to have attracted most attention is based on a principle described by Klauer, Turowski, and Wolff.[34] Practical applications of the method have been described by several authors.[35-37] A hot wire is suspended in the gas stream and between the poles of a permanent magnet. As the gas stream is heated by the wire, any oxygen present loses part of its paramagnetism, according to the Curie law. In an inhomogeneous magnetic field, this heated oxygen will then be attracted to the field less strongly than will fresh, unheated oxygen entering in the gas stream. The result of this effect will be a convection current away from

[29] H. Engelhardt and H. Sack, *Physik. Z.*, **33**, 724 (1932).

[30] H. Rein, *Arch. ges. Physiol.*, **247**, 576 (1944).

[31] H. Senftleben, *Ann. Physik*, **6**, 105 (1930); *Physik. Z.*, **31**, 822, 961 (1930).

[32] E. Lehrer, *Ann. Physik*, **81**, 229 (1926).

[33] H. Rein, *Schr. dtsch. Akad. Luftfahrtforsch.*, 1939, pp. 1–7.

[34] F. Klauer, E. Turowski, and T. v. Wolff, *Angew. Chem.*, **54**, 494 (1941); *Z. techn. Physik*, **22**, 223 (1941).

[35] C. A. Dyer, *Rev. Sci. Instr.*, **18**, 696 (1947).

[36] R. D. Richardson, *Trans. Am. Soc. Mech. Engrs.*, **70**, 211 (1948).

[37] E. Lehrer and E. Ebbinghaus, *Z. angew. Physik*, **2**, 21 (1950).

the magnetic field. Proper arrangement of the apparatus will use this convection current to cool the wire. One form of apparatus is shown diagrammatically in Fig. 83. In general, two hot wires may be used in a balanced bridge system. The apparatus apparently has good sensitivity and dependability. It obviously lends itself readily to automatic recording.

A fifth, and final, magnetic method for oxygen analysis has been described by Luft.[38] The sample is placed in a modulated magnetic field produced by rotating one pole of a permanent magnet. This induces fluctuations of pressure which are analyzed by means of a flexible membrane and a condenser.

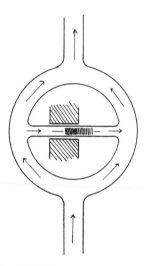

Fig. 83. Principle used in the "magnetic wind" oxygen meter.

The use of magnetic analysis for oxygen has been reviewed by several authors, some of whom have described commercial equipment.[39-43]

The large difference in susceptibility between molecular oxygen and ozone has been used in attempts to analyze liquid mixtures of these substances.[43a]

[38] K. M. Luft, *Compt. rend.*, **230**, 1460 (1950).
[39] R. H. Griffith, *Gas World*, **134**, 522, 583 (1951).
[40] H. Engelhardt, *Dechema Monograph*, 16, 164 (1951).
[41] A. Naumann, *Arch. tech. Messen Lfg.*, **197**, 123 (1952).
[42] E. Ebbinghaus, *Z. angew. Phys.*, **5**, 294 (1953).
[43] A. Linford, *Coke and Gas*, **14**, 195 (1952).
[43a] C. Brown, C. K. Hersh, and A. W. Berger, *J. Chem. Phys.*, **23**, 103 (1955).

67. Sulfur

Because of its similarity to oxygen, the molecule S_2 might be expected to be paramagnetic. Spectroscopic studies show that the ground state of the molecule is $^3\Sigma$, the same as that of oxygen. That sulfur vapor is paramagnetic has been shown by the molecular-beam experiments of Shaw and Phipps.[44] The moment is approximately 2 Bohr magnetons. Direct measurement of the susceptibility of sulfur vapor is more difficult. It has been attempted by Néel[45] and Scott.[46]

The vapor is definitely paramagnetic. Scott shows that the average value of $\chi_M T$ is 0.91 ± 0.09 in the temperature range of 650 to 850°C. This compares with the theoretical value 0.993 as indicated above for oxygen. The calculations are based on the equilibrium data of Preuner and Schupp[47] and seem to confirm those data in the indicated range.

A very interesting development is found in the allotropic modifications of sulfur obtained by chilling the vapor rapidly by allowing it to come in contact with a glass tube containing liquid nitrogen. A purple sulfur, which probably consists of S_2 molecules, is definitely paramagnetic, while a green form appears to be weakly paramagnetic.[48,49] The ordinary yellow forms of sulfur are diamagnetic, with apparently no trace of paramagnetism, provided that the sample is pure. But paramagnetic resonance studies by Gardner and Fraenkel[50] show a reversible absorption above about 190°C. The concentration of unpaired electron spins, that is to say, of free radicals, is estimated at roughly 10^{-5} mole per liter at 200°.

Solutions of sulfur seem to have escaped magnetochemical investigation. Selenium vapor has been shown to be paramagnetic.[51] The monoxides, such as sulfur monoxide, have apparently not been studied magnetically.

68. Oxides of Nitrogen and Related Compounds

Nitric oxide is paramagnetic, but the effective moment is dependent on the temperature. This dependence is due to an unusual combination of spin and orbital contributions to the moment.[52] The doublet width in

[44] E. J. Shaw and T. E. Phipps, *Phys. Rev.*, **38**, 174 (1931).

[45] L. Néel, *Compt. rend.*, **194**, 2035 (1932).

[46] A. B. Scott, *J. Am. Chem. Soc.*, **71**, 3145 (1949).

[47] G. Preuner and W. Schupp, *Z. physik. Chem.*, **68**, 129 (1909).

[48] T. Freund, S. Adler, and C. Sparrow, *J. Chem. Phys.*, **21**, 180 (1953).

[49] F. O. Rice and J. Ditter, *J. Am. Chem. Soc.*, **75**, 6066 (1953).

[50] D. M. Gardner and G. K. Fraenkel, *ibid.*, **76**, 5891 (1954).

[51] S. S. Bhatnagar, H. Lessheim, and M. L. Khanna, *Proc. Indian Acad. Sci.*, 6A, 155 (1937).

[52] J. H. Van Vleck, *op. cit.*, p. 269.

NO is comparable to kT. The situation is then not unlike those encountered in samarium and europium, both of which show marked deviations from the Curie law. Theoretical effective magneton numbers plotted against temperature are shown in Fig. 84.[53-56] The theoretical temperature coefficient is in good agreement with the experimental results. At 20°C., the theoretical effective Bohr magneton number is 1.836. Bauer and Piccard[11] and Soné,[10] found 1.86. Although the boiling point of nitric oxide is 123°K., the data of Wiersma, de Haas, and Capel[56] extend down to 112.8°K. Below that temperature it is scarcely to be expected that the

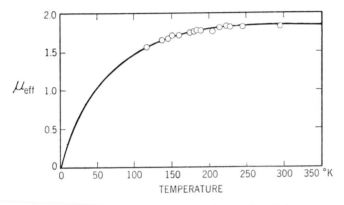

Fig. 84. Theoretical and experimental effective Bohr magneton members for nitric oxide. The experimental data shown here are all relative, hence agreement may be less accurate than shown.

theory for the gas phase would hold. Furthermore, NO dimerizes at low temperatures[57] to N_2O_2 which is diamagnetic. Bizette[58] finds the susceptibility of the liquid at 100°K. to be only 3.52×10^{-6} and shows that this could be interpreted as proving 97% association to N_2O_2. Lips[59] finds that solid NO has a very feeble paramagnetism.

Susceptibility measurements have been used to find the heat of dissociation of the liquid dimer.[60] The value found, 3710 ± 150 cal. per mole is in satisfactory agreement with that found by a nonmagnetic method.

[53] F. Bitter, *Proc. Natl. Acad. Sci.*, 15, 632 (1929).

[54] J. Aharoni and P. Scherrer, *Z. Physik*, 58, 749 (1929).

[55] R. Stössel, *Ann. Physik*, 10, 393 (1931).

[56] E. C. Wiersma, W. J. de Haas, and W. H. Capel, *Leiden Communications*, 212 b.

[57] O. K. Rice, *J. Chem. Phys.*, 4, 367 (1936).

[58] H. Bizette, *Ann. phys.*, 1, 233 (1946).

[59] E. Lips, *Helv. Phys. Acta*, 7, 663 (1934); 8, 247 (1935).

[60] A. L. Smith and H. L. Johnston, *J. Am. Chem. Soc.*, 74, 4696 (1952).

Evans and Richards[24] have determined the susceptibility of nitric oxide in the form of the clathrate complex with *beta*-quinol. Extension of these data[61] to lower temperatures are of interest in the comparison of nitric oxide in this environment with solutions of nitric oxide in krypton. Paramagnetic resonance studies on nitric oxide have been made by Beringer and Castle.[62] Like NO, NO_2 has an odd number of electrons. The susceptibility has been measured by Havens.[63] After allowance has been made for association to N_2O_4, the moment for nitrogen dioxide corresponds to one unpaired electron spin. The Curie law seems to be followed. Other oxides of nitrogen have an even number of electrons.

There is a large number of complex compounds containing nitric oxide. To some of these reference was made in the preceding chapter. Other compounds of this nature more properly belong here. Fremy's salt, $(KSO_3)_2NO$, is an example. This compound, prepared by the oxidation of potassium hydroxylamine sulfonate, forms yellow diamagnetic crystals which dissolve in water to form a rather reactive, violet-blue paramagnetic solution.[64,65] Asmussen points out that the process of solution is probably a reversible chemical change represented by the following equation:

$$[K_2(SO_3)_2NO]_2 \rightleftharpoons 2K_2(SO_3)_2NO$$
$$\text{yellow, diamagnetic} \qquad \text{violet, paramagnetic}$$

The paramagnetism is, of course, due to the peroxylaminedisulfonate ion, $(SO_3)_2NO^{2-}$. This ion has been further investigated in the form of the tetraphenylstibonium salt by paramagnetic resonance.[66] This is a good example of the extraordinary sensitivity of the resonance methods. It is easily possible in this way to demonstrate interaction of the unpaired electron spin with the magnetic moment of the N^{14} nuclear spin.

Other interesting derivatives of nitric oxide studied by Asmussen[66a] include the following: LiNO, NaNO, and KNO. These substances, formed by the action of nitric oxide on the appropriate metal in liquid ammonia, differ somewhat from the hyponitrites, $M_2N_2O_2$, and it might have been thought that as they apparently contain the NO^- ion, which is isosteric with molecular oxygen, the compounds would be paramagnetic. But NaNO, like $Na_2N_2O_2$, is diamagnetic. On the other hand, Asmussen

[61] A. H. Cooke and H. J. Duffus, *Proc. Phys. Soc. (London)*, **A67**, 525 (1954).

[62] R. Beringer and J. G. Castle, Jr., *Phys. Rev.*, **78**, 581 (1950).

[63] G. G. Havens, *ibid.*, **41**, 337(1932).

[64] R. W. Asmussen, *Z. anorg. u. allgem. Chem.*, **212**, 317 (1933).

[65] H. Katz, *Z. Physik*, **87**, 238 (1933).

[66] G. E. Pake, S. I. Weissman, and J. Townsend, *Phys. Rev.*, **85**, 682 (1952); **89**, 606 (1953).

[66a] R. W. Asmussen, *Kemisk*, **Nr.6**, 1941, p. 81.

has shown that the extraordinarily reactive dialkali nitrogen dioxides, such as Na_2NO_2, are at least in part paramagnetic. These substances, which are formed by the action of alkali metal on the corresponding alkali nitrite in liquid ammonia, may perhaps be thought of as a species of inorganic metal ketyl and may possibly exist in equilibrium between the ketyl form and a hypothetical tetraoxyhydrazine form.

$$\begin{matrix} Na-O \\ Na-O \end{matrix} N-N \begin{matrix} O-Na \\ O-Na \end{matrix} \rightleftharpoons 2 \begin{matrix} Na-O \\ Na-O \end{matrix} N$$

Further work by Klemm and Pauli[67] on this substance shows that the increasing susceptibility with increasing temperature probably involves the reaction $N_2O_4^{4-} \rightleftharpoons 2NO_2^{2-}$.

Reference has been made to the compounds formed by the reaction of nitric oxide with vanadium tetrachloride.[68] In at least some of these, the vanadium seems to maintain its paramagnetism. A somewhat similar situation is said to exist in certain iron complexes.[69]

The diaryl nitric oxides form another class of paramagnetic compounds. The simplest of these is diphenyl nitric oxide, $(C_6H_5)_2NO$, studied by Cambi.[70] At 18°C., this compound has an effective moment of 1.71 Bohr magnetons, corresponding closely to one unpaired spin. Several other similar compounds have been studied. Di-p-anisyl nitric oxide, (p-CH$_3$-OC$_6$H$_4)_2$NO, is reported by Cambi, Galavics,[71] Katz,[65] and by Müller, Müller-Rodloff, and Bunge[72] to have a moment corresponding to one unpaired electron spin. Katz states that it follows the Weiss law, $\chi(T + 13) = C$. Müller gives $\Delta = 3°$. Cambi has measured di-p-nitrophenylene nitric oxide, (p-O$_2$NC$_6$H$_4)_2$NO, over the range of 84° to 343°K. This compound also follows the Curie law with $\mu_{eff} = 1.74$ Bohr magnetons. A somewhat more complicated compound

$$\begin{matrix} & & H_3C & & \\ & & | & & \\ H_3C-C & \rule{1cm}{0.4pt} & CH_2 & \rule{1cm}{0.4pt} & C-CH_3 \\ & | & & & || \\ & H_5C_6-N=O & & H_5C_6-N=O & \end{matrix}$$

has been studied by Kenyon and Sugden[73] and by Müller.[72] It also follows the Curie law with a normal molar susceptibility at 20° of about

[67] W. Klemm and R. Pauli, Z. anorg. u. allgem. Chem., 266, 30 (1951).

[68] A. G. Whittaker and D. M. Yost, J. Am. Chem. Soc., 71, 3135 (1949).

[69] O. Baudisch, Science, 108, 443 (1948).

[70] L. Cambi, Gazz. chim. ital., 63, 579 (1933).

[71] F. Galavics, Helv. Phys. Acta, 6, 555 (1933).

[72] E. Müller, I. Müller-Rodloff, and W. Bunge, Ann., 520, 235 (1935).

[73] J. Kenyon and S. Sugden, J. Chem. Soc., 1932, 170.

1300 × 10⁻⁶. According to Müller $\Delta = 2°$, which is scarcely distinguishable from zero. Di-p-anisyl nitric oxide, together with many other organic free radicals, has been investigated by paramagnetic resonance.[74] In at least some cases, it is possible to gain evidence concerning the localization of the odd electron in these compounds.

In all these compounds, there seems to be no tendency toward association, at least over the temperature ranges investigated. There is also no sign of the peculiar temperature coefficient shown by nitric oxide itself. The question might be raised as to whether or not these nitric oxide derivatives should be called "free radicals." Their magnetic behavior is analogous to that of the triarylmethyls to be discussed below. Most workers in the field feel inclined to call a "free radical" any molecule possessing an odd number of electrons. Oxygen is, strictly speaking, a "biradical."

At one time it was thought that nitrosyl chloride, NOCl, and other nitroso compounds might be in Σ states like molecular oxygen. Wilson,[75] however, reports that liquid nitrosyl chloride as well as solid and dissolved p-nitrosodimethylaniline are all diamagnetic. Beeson and Coryell[76] find gaseous nitrosyl chloride to be diamagnetic. The compound is clearly not in a triplet state.

If nitrosyl chloride is diamagnetic, there is no particular reason why its addition compounds with salts should be paramagnetic. Asmussen[77] finds such compounds as $ZnCl_2 \cdot NOCl$ to be diamagnetic unless, as previously pointed out, the salt itself contains a paramagnetic ion.

69. Oxides of Chlorine

The paramagnetism of chlorine dioxide has already been mentioned. As expected, it exhibits paramagnetic resonance absorption.[78] Another paramagnetic oxide of chlorine of interest is the hexoxide, Cl_2O_6. This has been studied in the solid and liquid phases by Farquharson, Goodeve, and Richardson.[79] Between $-40°$ and $10°C$. the susceptibility varies with temperature in a manner which may be explained by the existence of the equilibrium:

$$Cl_2O_6 \rightleftharpoons 2ClO_3$$

The monomolecular form has an odd number of electrons and would, of

[74] A. N. Holden, W. A. Yager, and F. R. Merritt, *J. Chem. Phys.*, 19, 1319 (1951).
[75] E. B. Wilson, *J. Am. Chem. Soc.*, 56, 747 (1934).
[76] C. M. Beeson and C. D. Coryell, *J. Chem. Phys.*, 6, 656 (1938).
[77] R. W. Asmussen, *Z. anorg. u. allgem. Chem.*, 243, 127 (1939).
[78] T. L. Chu, G. E. Pake, D. E. Paul, J. Townsend, and S. I. Weissman, *J. Phys. Chem.*, 57, 504 (1953).
[79] J. Farquharson, C. F. Goodeve, and F. D. Richardson, *Trans. Faraday Soc.*, 32, 790 (1936).

course, be paramagnetic. In the gas phase, the compound is known to exist as ClO_3. Analysis of the magnetic data permits calculation of the equilibrium constant which varies from 2.54×10^{-3} at $-40°$ to 4.91×10^{-3} at $10°C$. The logarithm of the equilibrium constant plotted against reciprocal temperature gives a straight line from which the heat of dissociation is found to be 1730 ± 500 cal. per mole. Such calculations are based on the assumptions that the paramagnetism of ClO_3 is due to one unpaired electron spin and that the Curie law is obeyed. Such assumptions are probably justified because compounds, such as nitric oxide, in which they are not obeyed are quite rare.

70. Alkali Metal Polyoxides and Related Compounds

Oxidation of alkali metals yields compounds to which the formula R_2O_4 and the name alkali "tetroxides" were formerly assigned. But magnetic measurements by Neuman[80] and by Klemm and Sodomann[81] have shown potassium "tetroxide" to be paramagnetic with a moment corresponding to only slightly more than one unpaired electron spin. At one time, it was pointed out that another interpretation of the paramagnetism was formation of an addition complex with molecular oxygen, $O_2 \cdot O_2{}^{2-}$. This, however, has been disproved by x-ray investigation. Helms and Klemm[82] have shown that rubidium and cesium superoxides are also paramagnetic, as is calcium tetroxide.[82a] More recently, sodium superoxide has been prepared and shown to be paramagnetic.[83] Effective magnetic moments reported for these several superoxides at room temperature are shown in Table XXV. Most of these interesting substances have been prepared in pure, or almost pure, form. But the calcium compound was obtained in concentrations of only 2.2 to 4.5%, the remainder being the peroxide. Some of the results reported by Klemm et al. suggest that the Weiss constant may be fairly large for these substances. This suggests less exchange interaction rather than some chemical change or perhaps even some spin-orbital complexity. The moments found at room temperature are in good agreement with that expected for one unpaired spin.

On the other hand it has been reported that sodium superoxide[84] shows a maximum susceptibility at $-80°C$. It is not clear what this effect could mean. Substances showing antiferromagnetism behave in this way,

[80] E. W. Neuman, J. Chem. Phys., 2, 31 (1934).

[81] W. Klemm and H. Sodomann, Z. anorg. u. allgem. Chem., 225, 273 (1935).

[82] A. Helms and W. Klemm, ibid., 241, 97 (1939).

[82a] P. Ehrlich, ibid., 252, 370 (1944).

[83] S. E. Stephanou, W. H. Schechter, W. J. Argersinger, Jr., and J. Kleinberg, J. Am. Chem. Soc., 71, 1819 (1949).

[84] A. B. Neiding and I. A. Kazarnovskii, Zhur. Fiz. Khim, 24, 1407 (1950).

TABLE XXV

Effective Moments for Some Superoxides

NaO_2	KO_2	RbO_2	CsO_2	CaO_4
2.0₇	1.84	1.89	1.89	2.1

but no other cases are known for antiferromagnetism due to polyatomic paramagnetic ions, such as the superoxide ion. The maximum occurs at a phase transition, together with a change of symmetry in the superoxide ion.[85]

It will be clear from these magnetic results that there is no justification for retaining the name "tetroxide" for the alkali metal compounds. The name "superoxide" seems to be satisfactory. It is difficult to believe that compounds could be obtained having even more oxygen than the superoxides.[86] Nevertheless, it has been reported that treatment of dry, powdered potassium hydroxide with oxygen containing 6 to 8% ozone at −10 to −15°C. yields potassium ozonide, KO_3, which may be purified by extraction with liquid ammonia. The effective magnetic moment of this compound is 1.67. The ozonide ion, O_3^-, is thought to be linear. There is some evidence that the proposed ozonide may actually be a mixture, but there is little doubt that it contains a paramagnetic species other than superoxide.[87]

It might be thought that alkali metal chalcogenides, such as the compound K_2S_4, would also be paramagnetic. But Klemm, Sodomann, and Langmesser[88] have found that such is not the case. Of a large number of alkali metal sulfides, selenides, and tellurides studied, all were found to be diamagnetic. Cesium tetraiodide is also diamagnetic[89] and should perhaps be written Cs_2I_8, rather than CsI_4.

71. Hexaarylethanes

Application of magnetic methods has greatly changed the study of organic free radicals. Several standard procedures, such as the colorimetry and ebulliometry of these compounds, have been shown to be subject to errors. Susceptibility measurements have also been of service in testing the various theories of free radical stability.

[85] G. S. Zhdanov and Z. V. Zvonkova, *Doklady Akad. Nauk S.S.S.R.*, **82**, 743 (1952). This article was not available in the original.

[86] I. A. Kazarnovskii, G. P. Nikolskii, and T. A. Abletsova, *ibid.*, **64**, 69 (1949).

[87] T. P. Whaley and J. Kleinberg, *J. Am. Chem. Soc.*, **73**, 79 (1951).

[88] W. Klemm, H. Sodomann, and P. Langmesser, *Z. anorg. u. allgem. Chem.* **241**, 281 (1939).

[89] S. S. Hubard, *J. Phys. Chem.*, **46**, 227 (1942).

A method for calculating the degree of dissociation for the reaction:

$$Ar_3C\text{---}CAr_3 \rightleftharpoons 2Ar_3C$$

has been given by Müller,[90,91] and Roy and Marvel.[92]   This method will be explained with the aid of an example taken from the paper of Roy and Marvel, although it will be pointed out below that some doubts have arisen concerning this procedure.

The degree of dissociation of hexaphenylethane in benzene solution at 20°C. may be calculated from the magnetic susceptibility of the solution as follows:

(1) The percentage of ethane in solution (5.49%) may be calculated from the weights of benzene and chloromethane used to make the chloromethane solution.   It is assumed that conversion of chloromethane to ethane is complete with no loss of solvent.

(2) The susceptibility of the ethane may be calculated from the observed susceptibility of the solution ($\chi = -0.700 \times 10^{-6}$) by an application of the Wiedemann additivity law.   The susceptibility of benzene is taken as -0.708×10^{-6}.   This gives the susceptibility of the ethane as -0.56×10^{-6}.

(3) The molar susceptibility of the partly dissociated ethane is obtained by multiplying its susceptibility by its molecular weight; thus, $\chi_M = -272 \times 10^{-6}$.

(4) From this must be subtracted the diamagnetism of the ethane. This may be calculated from Pascal's empirical constants and is equal to -325×10^{-6}.

(5) The molar paramagnetism of that part of the ethane which is existing as free radicals is then $-272 - (-325) \times 10^{-6} = 53 \times 10^{-6}$.

(6) The degree of dissociation (α) is obtained from the fraction $53/2540 = 2.1\%$.   The quantity 2540×10^{-6} is the molar paramagnetism produced at 20°C. by one mole of ethane completely dissociated into two moles of free radicals.

There are several assumptions in the above calculation.   It is, for instance, never certain that the concentration of ethane is accurately obtained from the analytical data unless elaborate corrections are made for unconverted chloromethane.   A method for doing this is described by Selwood and Dobres.[93]   Another possible source of error may lie in the diamagnetic correction mentioned in step (4) above.   The nature of this correction and its shortcomings will be described below.   A third doubtful

[90] E. Müller, I. Müller-Rodloff, and W. Bunge, *Ann.*, **520**, 235 (1935).

[91] E. Müller and I. Müller-Rodloff, *ibid.*, **521**, 89 (1935).

[92] M. F. Roy and C. S. Marvel, *J. Am. Chem. Soc.*, **59**, 2622 (1937).

[93] P. W. Selwood and R. M. Dobres, *ibid.*, **72**, 3860 (1950).

point is the implicit assumption that the Weiss constant for triarylmethyls is zero. Experiments by Müller and others seem to indicate that while the Weiss constant is never large in these systems, yet it is often far from negligible. It is hard to believe that any appreciable exchange interaction could contribute to the Weiss constant in systems so magnetically dilute as these.

In spite of these doubtful points, the magnetic method has been widely used and has yielded unsuspected information concerning a large variety of ethanes. One of the principal problems in this field has been to determine the effect of substituents on the degree of dissociation. This question is important because it may be expected to throw light on the puzzling stabilization of trivalent carbon in these substances. A large number of hexaarylethanes has been studied by Marvel and by Müller and their respective co-workers. A few of these papers will be referred to as being representative. In general it may be said that magnetic measurements have seemed to place on a quantitative basis discussion of degrees of dissociation and have made it possible to draw certain conclusions concerning the resonance theory and other theories of free-radical stability. Reviews of the field are given by Müller,[94] and Wheland.[95]

Marvel and co-workers[96-100] have shown that in general *ortho* substituents are more effective in promoting dissociation than *meta* substituents, and that *para* substituents are least effective. Their work on substituents tends to show that the effect of resonance energy is minor as compared with the effect of steric factors in determining degree of dissociation. Marvel and Himel[101] have shown that unsymmetrical ethanes may be less dissociated than either of the corresponding symmetrical ethanes. By an unsymmetrical ethane is meant one such as may be prepared by treating with molecular silver equimolecular portions of tri-*p-tert*-butylphenylmethylchloride and *p-tert*-butylphenyldiphenylmethyl chloride. The two symmetrical ethanes are respectively 20 and 7.5% dissociated. The mixture containing the unsymmetrical ethane appears to be only about 3.5% dissociated.

[94] E. Müller, *Z. Elektrochem.*, **45**, 593 (1939).

[95] G. W. Wheland, *Advanced Organic Chemistry*, John Wiley and Sons, Inc., New York, 1949, p. 685*f*.

[96] C. S. Marvel, E. Ginsberg, and M. B. Mueller, *J. Am. Chem. Soc.*, **61**, 77 (1939).

[97] C. S. Marvel and C. M. Himel, *ibid.*, **62**, 1550 (1940).

[98] C. S. Marvel, J. F. Kaplan, and C. M. Himel, *ibid.*, **63**, 1892 (1941).

[99] C. S. Marvel, J. W. Shackleton, C. M. Himel, and J. Whitson, *ibid.*, **64**, 1824 (1942).

[100] C. S. Marvel, F. C. Dietz, and C. M. Himel, *J. Org. Chem.*, **7**, 392 (1942).

[101] C. S. Marvel and C. M. Himel, *J. Am. Chem. Soc.*, **64**, 2227 (1942).

Marvel and his co-workers[102] in several publications have also drawn attention to the fact that hexaarylethanes disproportionate to form substituted methanes and olefinic compounds with constant gradual disappearance of the free radical. The reaction is evidenced as a gradual decrease of magnetic susceptibility with time when a solution containing a free radical is warmed or, in some cases, simply held at room temperature or even lower. For many ethanes, when the temperature is held near 100°C. for several hours, the concentration of free radical, as measured by its susceptibility, may fall to near zero. Different ethanes disproportionate at different rates. Marvel *et al.*[103] have determined that *ortho-* and *para-* substituted phenylethanes disproportionate far more rapidly than those with *meta* substituents, but that unless the *alpha* carbon atom of the substituent has a hydrogen attached to it, disproportionation is extremely slow. The order of this reaction and its activation energy have also been determined, as have the kinetics of reaction of tri-*p*-biphenylmethyl and of tri-*p-tert*-butylphenylmethyl with toluene.[104]

The importance of the disproportionation reaction is that it raises doubts about the use of ebulliometric determination of free-radical concentration.[105] In many cases disproportionation takes place at the boiling point of benzene, and rapid disproportionation takes place at the boiling point of toluene. One of the most interesting observations made during magnetic studies of free radicals has to do with the color of the solutions before and after disproportionation. For a long time colorimetric measurements have been used in the study of free radicals, and it has often been assumed that color in a solution is evidence of the presence of free radicals. But Marvel has shown that colorimetric measurements cannot be relied upon for accurate determination of free-radical concentration. The solution often remains richly colored after disproportionation has completely destroyed all trace of free radicals.

If degrees of dissociation may be calculated from magnetic measurements, then it is obvious that measurements over a range of concentration and of temperature will give means of calculating equilibrium constants, and the heats, entropies, and free energies of dissociation. This has been done for the following ethanes: hexaphenylethane, di-*o*-tolyltetraphenylethane, di-*α*-naphthyltetraphenylethane, tetra-*o*-tolyldiphenylethane, di-*o*-chlorophenyltetraphenylethane, and di-*β*-naphthyltetraphenylethane.[106,107]

[102] C. S. Marvel, W. H. Rieger, and M. B. Mueller, *ibid.*, **61**, 2769 (1939) *et seq.*
[103] C. S. Marvel, M. B. Mueller, C. M. Himel, and J. F. Kaplan, *ibid.*, **61**, 2771 (1939).
[104] R. M. Dobres and P. W. Selwood, *ibid.*, **72**, 5731 (1950).
[105] P. W. Selwood and R. F. Preckel, *ibid.*, **65**, 895 (1943).
[106] R. F. Preckel and P. W. Selwood, *ibid.*, **63**, 3397 (1941).
[107] W. Byerly, H. G. Cutforth, and P. W. Selwood, *ibid.*, **70**, 1142 (1948).

The results show that the heat of dissociation (about 11 kcal. per mole) are all about the same, but that the entropies may vary somewhat from one ethane to another.

The magnetic method has yielded so much interesting information that it is disconcerting to find that the method may be subject to a large systematic error. There are in the literature some indications that the method may give anomalous results. Solutions of the Chichibabin hydrocarbon, to which further reference will be made below, although highly reactive and strongly colored, have been reported on the basis of susceptibility measurements[108] as being not over 2% dissociated. But the *ortho-para* hydrogen conversion on solutions of this substance suggest about 10% dissociation.[109-111] There is also the anomaly that solutions of hexa-*p*-biphenylethane seem to be considerably less dissociated than the pure crystalline solid.

These difficulties are emphasized by the findings of Selwood and Dobres[93] who attempted to measure the heat of dissociation of hexa-*p*-biphenyl-ethane and hexa-*p*-*tert*-butylphenylethane. These substances were found to be only about 70% dissociated, and the apparent degree of dissociation was found to be independent of temperature. These results were obtained by the methods of calculation described above.

A possible explanation of these results is to be found in the diamagnetic correction which must be made as previously described. In large ethanes, this correction may be comparable in magnitude with the paramagnetic contribution, although opposite in sign. The current theory of resonance stabilization implies that additional resonance in the radical stabilizes it with respect to the ethane. The additional resonance is brought about by an increase of electronic currents from those normally produced in isolated aromatic rings. But this is precisely the condition which leads to enhanced diamagnetism perpendicular to the plane of the rings. An explanation for the anomalous magnetic results on these ethanes is that resonance stabilization of the free radicals is accompanied by a large increase of molecular anisotropy. The susceptibility data could be made to yield reasonable results if the diamagnetic correction were to be increased by 80%. This means an increase of 240% in the principal molecular susceptibility normal to the plane of the rings. As yet there is no theoretical justification for assuming that such a large increase of diamagnetism could occur. Unfortunately for this explanation, the only published effort to find some theoretical basis for an increased diamagnetism has led to results in the

[108] E. Müller and I. Müller-Rodloff, *Ann.*, **517,** 134 (1935).
[109] G. M. Schwab and E. Agallidis, *Z. physik. Chem.*, **B41,** 59 (1938).
[110] G. M. Schwab and N. Agliardi, *Ber.*, **73B,** 95 (1940).
[111] G. M. Schwab and E. Schwab-Agallidis, *Z. physik. Chem.*, **B49,** 196 (1941).

opposite direction.[112]   The conclusion that tri-*p*-biphenylmethyl is not associated in toluene solution is supported by absorption spectra studies reported by Chu and Weissman.[113]

Müller[114] dismisses the difficulty with hexa-*p*-biphenylethane as being due to impurities.   But even granting that this is true, the general problem is not solved.   This problem is simply stated: does the molar diamagnetism of a free radical stabilized by resonance differ from half that of the corresponding diamagnetic dimer?   It seems probable that paramagnetic resonance studies will, in due course, solve this problem.   It is now, in principle, possible to measure paramagnetism independent of underlying diamagnetism.   Some results have been reported on a variety of ethanes, such as tri-*p*-nitrophenylmethyl.[115]   Even more important, probably, is the prospect of gaining detailed information concerning electron distribution in free radicals.   Weissman and Sowden[116] have, for instance, been able to find the average distance between the unpaired electron and the methyl carbon in triphenylmethyl.   This is done by observing the hyperfine structure in paramagnetic resonance absorption for the free radical in which the ordinary methyl carbon atom has been replaced by the isotope C^{13}.   The observed line separation is then dependent on the interaction between electronic and nuclear (C^{13}) magnetic moments.

72. Organo-Metallic Free Radicals

In Group IV of the Periodic Table there are several elements which form compounds analogous to ethanes.   Compounds such as hexaphenylditin are well known.   On the basis of boiling point elevation and freezing point depression, several such compounds were formerly thought to be dissociated to free radicals in a manner comparable to hexaphenylethane.   Certain reactions undergone by these compounds also suggest dissociation, but on the other hand the solutions are colorless, whereas all triarylmethyls are colored.   In an effort to settle this question, magnetic measurements[117] have been made on various organo-metallic compounds, such as hexaphenyldigermanium, hexaphenyldilead, hexamethylditin, hexacyclohexyldilead, and hexa-*o*-tolylditin.[118−121]   In every case the compound is shown to be

[112] M. Mayot, G. Berthier, and B. Pullman, *J. chim. phys.*, **50**, 176 (1953).

[113] T.-L. Chu and S. I. Weissman, *J. Am. Chem. Soc.*, **73**, 4462 (1951).

[114] E. Müller, *Fortschr. chem. Forsch.*, **1**, 325 (1949).

[115] L. S. Singer and E. G. Spencer, *J. Chem. Phys.*, **21**, 939 (1953).

[116] S. I. Weissmann and J. C. Sowden, *J. Am. Chem. Soc.*, **75**, 503 (1953).

[117] P. W. Selwood, *ibid.*, **61**, 3168 (1939).

[118] R. Preckel and P. W. Selwood, *ibid.*, **62**, 2765 (1940).

[119] H. Morris and P. W. Selwood, *ibid.*, **63**, 2509(1941).

[120] H. Morris, W. Byerly, and P. W. Selwood, *ibid.*, **64**, 1727 (1942).

[121] K. A. Jensen and N. Clauson-Kaas, *Z. anorg. u. allgem. Chem.*, **250**, 277 (1943).

diamagnetic and hence not dissociated. Later work suggests that the author may have been mistaken concerning the identity of the hexa-*o*-tolylditin, but accurately characterized samples prove to be likewise diamagnetic in solution. In certain cases, the measurements were extended over a considerable range of temperature and of concentration. More recent work on the freezing point of solutions containing hexacyclohexyldilead and hexaphenyldilead in naphthalene and in biphenyl show that the molecules are dimeric and that earlier cryoscopic measurements on these substances were in error.[122] This work makes it probable that no such stable organo-metallic free radical has yet been prepared, although the literature contains many references to such compounds.

More fruitful sources of organo-metallic free radicals are to be found in the alkali metal-hydrocarbon complexes and in the metal ketyls. The alkali metals react with many aromatic hydrocarbons in a variety of solvents. The highly colored compounds so formed are paramagnetic when the hydrocarbon anion is the result of a single electron transfer. A magnetic moment corresponding to one unpaired electron spin is found for the anions [naphthalene]⁻, [anthracene]⁻, [biphenyl]⁻, [phenanthrene]⁻, and [*m*-terphenyl]⁻ in the form of the sodium salts in tetrahydrofuran solution.[123] Studies on the solid salts have also been made.[124] Chu *et al.*[78] have made paramagnetic resonance studies on these systems. The divalent ions are diamagnetic.

Certain aromatic ketones on treatment with alkali metals give metal ketyls of the general formula:

$$\begin{array}{c} R \\ \diagdown \\ \diagup \\ R' \end{array} C\!-\!OM$$

and which have, for a long time, been suspected of being free radicals. The paramagnetism of such compounds was first demonstrated by Sugden[125] who studied *p*-biphenylphenyl ketone potassium and benzophenone potassium. Almost simultaneously, Doescher and Wheland[126] showed that the corresponding sodium ketyls are paramagnetic. The results of the two investigations are in qualitative but not quantitative agreement. This is, perhaps, not surprising in view of later observations that the degree of dissociation is dependent on the particular metal used. Doescher and Wheland measured the dissociation of the *p*-biphenylphenyl metal ketyl

[122] L. Malatesta, *Gazz. chim ital.*, **73**, 176 (1943).

[123] T. L. Chu and S. C. Yu, *J. Am. Chem. Soc.*, **76**, 3367 (1954).

[124] W. A. Holmes-Walker and A. R. Ubbelohde, *J. Chem. Soc.*, **1954**, 720.

[125] S. Sugden, *Trans. Faraday Soc.*, **30**, 18 (1934).

[126] R. N. Doescher and G. W. Wheland, *J. Am. Chem. Soc.*, **56**, 2011 (1934).

in different solvents. They found the degree of dissociation in benzene to be 1.7% and in dioxane 41%. This is a very large difference which does not seem to be paralleled in the dissociation of hexaarylethanes in different solvents, but the effect of solvent on the stability of free radicals is a field which deserves further investigation. Presumably the association of metal ketyls proceeds according to the reaction

$$2 \quad \overset{R \quad R'}{\underset{OM}{\underset{|}{\overset{\diagdown \diagup}{C}}}} \quad \rightleftarrows \quad R - \overset{R'}{\underset{OM}{\underset{|}{\overset{|}{C}}}} - \overset{R}{\underset{OM}{\underset{|}{\overset{|}{C}}}} - R'$$

Magnetic properties of the metal ketyls have been investigated with great thoroughness by Müller and his co-workers.[127,128] The work is summarized and chemical and magnetic data on the large number of metal ketyls and related compounds are presented and compared by Müller and Janke.[129] The free-radical concentration is very different for different compounds, ranging from negligibly small for 2,3,6,7-dibenzoxanthone potassium to about 96% for Michler's ketone potassium, $[(CH_3)_2NC_6H_4]_2$-COK. The degree of dissociation is shown by Müller to be dependent on the nature of the aryl groups, on the presence of oxygen or sulfur attached to the metal, and also on the alkali metal. It is rather surprising that the molecular-field constant seems to show very wide variations of from $-2°$ for Michler's ketone potassium to $-125°$ for fluorenone potassium. This variation cannot be due to the usual crystalline-field or exchange effects but may be due to some reversible chemical change taking place with changing temperature. In fact, the whole question of the free-radical concentration in these substances is made uncertain by the observations of Bent and Harrison[130] who, on the basis of spectrophotometric studies find benzophenone potassium to be quite largely associated to the pinacolate, and fluorenone potassium to show no evidence of association. The magnetic data of Müller and his co-workers indicate a high degree of dissociation for the benzophenone ketyl and a considerably smaller degree for the fluorenone ketyl. Paramagnetic resonance absorption in ketyls has been detected.[131]

A substance which may be related structurally to the ketyls is potassium carbon monoxide.[132] This substance, which is made by treating

[127] E. Müller and F. Teschner, *Ann.*, **525**, 1 (1936).

[128] E. Müller and W. Wiesemann, *ibid.*, **532**, 116 (1938); **537**, 86 (1939).

[129] E. Müller and W. Janke, *Z. Elektrochem.*, **45**, 380 (1939).

[130] H. E. Bent and A. J. Harrison, *J. Am. Chem. Soc.*, **66**, 969 (1944).

[131] C. A. Hutchison, Jr., R. C. Pastor, and A. Kowalsky, *J. Chem. Phys.*, **20**, 534 (1952).

[132] R. W. Asmussen, *Kemiska*, **Nr. 6**, 91 (1941).

potassium with a mixture of carbon monoxide and carbon dioxide, is paramagnetic with a moment of about one-third Bohr magneton. The presence of paramagnetism in a metal carbonyl seems to be very unlikely. Asmussen has, therefore, suggested that the potassium compound exists in an equilibrium represented as follows:

$$\cdot \overset{C-OK}{\underset{\cdot C-OK}{\|}} \quad \rightleftharpoons \quad \overset{C-OK}{\underset{C-OK}{\|}}$$

It must be indicated that this formula is quite speculative.

Some of the biscyclopentadienyl complexes described in the preceding chapter may, perhaps, be considered as organo-metallic free radicals.

73. Hydrazyls

Substituted hydrazines of the type

may readily be oxidized to yield hydrazyls such as α,α-diphenyl-β-picryl-hydrazyl:

Such compounds containing divalent nitrogen are highly dissociated even in the solid state. The magnetic properties of the above have been studied by Katz,[65] Müller, Müller-Rodloff, and Bunge,[90] and Turkevich and Selwood.[133] Katz reports an effective Bohr magneton number of about 0.9, but this is probably a mistake because the other workers report $\mu_{eff} = 1.73$ and 1.66. The Weiss field constant is positive but of uncertain magnitude, being reported as $10°, 20°$, and $37°$. This compound, a stable, solid free radical with a high degree of magnetic dilution, has become so popular with the paramagnetic resonance specialists that there is some question as to what they would do without it.[66,74,78,131,134,135] Several related paramagnetic substances are known. Among them are some

[133] J. Turkevich and P. W. Selwood, *J. Am. Chem. Soc.*, **63**, 1077 (1941).
[134] J. van den Handel, *Physica*, **18**, 921 (1952).
[135] C Kikuchi and V. W. Cohen, *Phys. Rev.*, **93**, 394 (1954).

substituted hydrazines, of which one is tetra-(p-fluorophenyl) hydrazine.[136] This dissociates to the free radical $(p\text{-}FC_6H_4)_2N$. The *ortho-para* hydrogen catalysis by a hydrazyl will be discussed in Chapter XV.

Attempts to prepare a solid paramagnetic hydrazino radical by thermal decomposition of hydrazine have so far failed. This is presumably due to formation of the diamagnetic tetrazane.[136a]

74. Semiquinones and Related Substances

Reduction of a quinone to the corresponding hydroquinone goes through an intermediate unstable stage of reduction called a semiquinone. The semiquinone has an odd number of electrons and it may be stabilized in alkaline solution, forming the paramagnetic semiquinone ion. The investigation of such substances is due chiefly to Michaelis and his co-

quinone   semiquinone   hydroquinone   semiquinone ion

workers.[137] Michaelis, Boeker, and Reber have proved the existence of a paramagnetic intermediate during alkaline reduction of phenanthrene-quinone-3-sulfonate. They used the manometric balance of Wills and Boeker, as modified by Woodbridge. Three different solutions all showed a fall of diamagnetism followed by a rise as the semiquinone ion was formed and then destroyed. The free-radical ion is believed to have the formula

semiquinone ion

which is in equilibrium with the reduced form and with the oxidized form, as well as possibly with the dimerized form, the formation of which is, however, prevented by pyridine or alcohol.[138]

The method used to observe the susceptibilities while the reaction

---

[136] F. Benington, E. V. Shoop, and R. H. Poirier, *J. Org. Chem.*, **18**, 1506 (1953).

[136a] F. O. Rice and F. Scherber, *J. Am. Chem. Soc.*, **77**, 291 (1955).

[137] L. Michaelis, G. F. Boeker, and R. K. Reber, *J. Am. Chem. Soc.*, **60**, 202 (1938).

[138] L. Michaelis and S. Granick, *ibid.*, **70**, 624 (1948).

is taking place eliminates the difficult problem of diamagnetic corrections. At least this is true unless some change of diamagnetism occurs during formation of the free radical. Measurements made on an acid solution of potassium phenanthrenequinonesulfonate during reduction showed changes in the diamagnetism of the same order of magnitude as the experimental error. Hence, as expected, during acid reduction any appearance of the free-radical ion is negligible.[139] The semiquinone ion of p-benzoquinone, which is the simplest of the semiquinones, is unusually unstable in alkaline solution. It has not been studied by susceptibility methods. But Fraenkel and Halford[140] have found paramagnetic resonance absorption in a flowing system in which a solution of hydroquinone is mixed with alcoholic potassium hydroxide just prior to entering the resonance chamber. A similar observation has been reported by Blois.[140a] Such relatively unstable free radicals may apparently be stabilized to some degree by adsorption on a surface of barium hydroxide hydrate.[140b]

Quinhydrone, normally the first product of reduction of quinone, is diamagnetic.[141]

Duroquinone[142]

in a strongly alkaline solution forms a paramagnetic semiquinone free radical of brown color as an intermediate step of the reduction. This free radical has no dimeric form.

Fraenkel[143] has also found paramagnetic resonance absorption for a variety of ketones and other substances in the presence of Lewis acids. For instance, bianthrone shows no resonance absorption when dissolved in an inert solvent at room temperature (although it does so at higher temperatures), but in concentrated sulfuric acid about 10% of the dissolved material becomes paramagnetic. Similar results are found for a variety of organic peroxides, thiols, and disulfides.

There is some chemical evidence that organic disulfides involving

[139] L. Michaelis, R. K. Reber, and J. A. Kuck, *ibid.*, **60**, 214, (1938).

[140] G. K. Fraenkel and R. S. Halford, forthcoming publication.

[140a] S. Blois, *J. Chem. Phys.*, **23**, 1351 (1955).

[140b] D. Bijl, H. Kainer, and A. C. Rose-Innes, *Nature*, **174**, 830 (1954).

[141] Measurements by C. D. Coryell referred to by L. Pauling, *op. cit.*, p. 258.

[142] L. Michaelis, M. P. Schubert, R. K. Reber, J. A. Kuck, and S. Granick, *J. Am. Chem. Soc.*, **60**, 1678 (1938).

[143] J. M. Hirshon, D. M. Gardner, and G. K. Fraenkel, *ibid.*, **75**, 4115 (1953).

an —S—S— bond may dissociate in a manner similar to the hexaarylethanes. Magnetic studies in the author's laboratory[144] have tended to confirm this for 2,2-benzothiazyl disulfide, but further work has cast some doubt on the reality of the effects observed. No paramagnetic resonance absorption has been detected in this substance.[145] It seems probable, therefore, that the author was mistaken in thinking that free radicals could be found here, although Wertz and Vivo have obtained paramagnetic resonance evident for free radicals in diphenyl disulfide.[145a]

Similar types of compounds are formed by many compounds containing nitrogen. For instance, radicals derived from aromatic p-diamines, of the type of Wurster's salts, have been studied by Michaelis, Schubert, and Granick,[146] and by Hughes and Hush.[147] Paramagnetic resonance absorption has been observed in these systems.[148]

Magnetic evidence for the free radical form of the tetramethyl-p-phenylenediaminium ion

$$\left[(CH_3)_2N-\!\!\left\langle\!\!\bigcirc\!\!\right\rangle\!\!-N(CH_3)_2\right]^+$$

as the perchlorate has been given by Katz.[65] Wurster's red has also been studied by Rumpf and Trombe.[149] Still more related paramagnetic compounds as reported by Katz[65] are hydro-p-naphthophenazinium perchlorate

dihydropyocyaninium perchlorate

[144] H. G. Cutforth and P. W. Selwood, ibid., **70**, 278 (1948).

[145] G. K. Fraenkel, forthcoming publication.

[145a] J. E. Wertz and J. L. Vivo, J. Chem. Phys., **23**, 2193 (1955).

[146] L. Michaelis, M. P. Schubert, and S. Granick, J. Am. Chem. Soc., **61**, 1981 (1939).

[147] G. K. Hughes and N. S. Hush, J. Proc. Roy. Soc. N. S. Wales, **81**, 48 (1947).

[148] S. I. Weissman, J. Chem. Phys., **22**, 1135 (1954).

[149] P. Rumpf and F. Trombe, J. chim. phys., **35**, 110 (1938).

and tetra-*p*-tolylhydrazinium perchlorate.

$$CH_3 \underset{CH_3}{\overset{}{\bigcirc}} \quad \overset{ClO_4^-}{\underset{N-N^+}{}} \quad \overset{}{\bigcirc} CH_3$$

Some of these have rather lower susceptibilities than might be expected. It is not clear whether this is due to faulty experimentation or dimerization, or possibly decomposition. The paramagnetism of the semiquinone ion of pyocyanine has also been shown by Kuhn and Schön.[150] Experiments by Pauling and Sturdivant[151] have demonstrated that the two following ions are paramagnetic:

$$CH_3 - \overset{+}{N} - CH_3$$

$$CH_3 - N - H$$

Tri-*p*-tolylaminium perchlorate $[(C_6H_4CH_3)_3N]^+$ ClO_4^- has been demonstrated by Katz[65] and Rumpf and Trombe[152] to have a molar paramagnetism corresponding closely to one unpaired electron spin.

Still more complicated paramagnetic substances are formed by certain dyestuffs, such as the semiquinone ions prepared by reduction of dipyridyl bases. An example of one of these is N,N′-dimethyl-γ,γ′-dipyridinium chloride (methyl viologen), reported by Michaelis.[153]

$$H_3C - \bigcirc - \bigcirc \rangle N - CH_3$$

Michaelis has also prepared semiquinone ions from thiazine dyestuffs, thionine, aminothiazine, and oxonine. An arsenic-containing analog of the pyocyaninium radical mentioned above is found in the reported paramagnetism of the product formed by the reduction of dihydrophenarsazine by formic acid. The structure of the reduced formate may be as shown below:[154]

[150] R. Kuhn and K. Schön, *Ber.*, **68B**, 1537 (1935).

[151] L. Pauling and J. H. Sturdivant, Pauling, *op. cit.*, p. 259.

[152] P. Rumpf and F. Trombe, *Compt. rend.*, **206**, 671 (1938).

[153] L. Michaelis, *J. Am. Chem. Soc.*, **63**, 2446 (1941).

[154] M. B. Neiman, A. Ya. Plotnikov, G. A. Razuvaev, and A. V. Ryabov, *Doklady Akad. Nauk S. S. S. R.*, **64**, 365 (1949).

$$\left[\begin{array}{c} \text{structure} \end{array} \right]^{+} \quad O_2CH^-$$

Somewhat distantly related to the semiquinones is a stable oxygen compound, 2,4,6-tri-*tert*-butyl-1-phenoxyl. This is a dark blue, paramagnetic solid.[154a] Some even more distantly related are some peculiar salts, of which one is 4,4'-dimethoxydiphenylaminium tetrachloroantimonate, $[p\text{-MeOC}_6H_4NH]SbCl_4$. This substance is fairly strongly paramagnetic but has a susceptibility which varies little with temperature down, at least, to 77°K.[154b] On the other hand, the barium salts of alloxantin and its derivatives, formerly thought to form free radicals of the type

$$\text{structure}$$

have been shown by Asmussen[154c] to be diamagnetic.

75. Highly Conjugated Systems, Biradicals

The existence of organic molecules possessing an unpaired electron at once suggests the possibility of two such unpaired electrons being present simultaneously in the same molecule. This situation is found in oxygen as already described and, of course, many of the transition group ions have more than one unpaired electron. But organic biradicals are less common. Most progress in this field is due to Müller, who has pursued the elusive biradicals with great persistence and success.

The best chance of finding such compounds would appear to be in highly conjugated systems.[155] For instance, pentaphenylcyclopentadienyl

$$\text{structure}$$

[154a] E. Müller and K. Ley, *Chem. Ber.*, **87**, 922 (1954).

[154b] H. Kainer and K. H. Hausser, *Chem. Ber.*, **86**, 1563 (1953); *Z. Naturforsch.*, **9a**, 783 (1954).

[154c] R. W. Asmussen and H. Soling, *Acta Chem. Scand.*, **8**, 558 (1954).

[155] E. Müller and I. Müller-Rodloff, *Ber.*, **69B**, 665 (1936).

is completely dissociated, even in the solid state, although it is not a biradical. On the other hand, substances such as 9-(1-naphthyl) xanthyl,[156] tetraphenylrubrene,[157] diphenyldiazomethane,[158] 2,3,6,7-dibenzanthracene, tetra- and triaryl-α-naphthyl derivatives of quinodimethane,[159] p,p'-tetramethyldiaminothiobenzophenone, and numerous ω,ω'-phenylpolyenes are all diamagnetic and quite free from free-radical form within the limits of experimental error.[160]

It should, however, be pointed out that, with increasing complexity, aromatic molecules show an increasing deviation from Pascal's additivity rules. Enderlin[161] has collected the data on several such compounds, as shown in Table XXVI. It might be thought that these deviations indicate

TABLE XXVI

Deviations from Pascal's Rules with Increasing Molecular Complexity

Hydrocarbon	$[\chi_M(\text{Pascal}) - \chi_M(\text{obs.})] \times 10^{-6}$
Benzene	0
Naphthalene	+48
Anthracene	+106
Naphthacene	+142
Tetraphenylnaphthacene	+140 (Müller) +125 (Enderlin)
Dibenzoanthracene	+289

[156] S. Allard, *Compt. rend.*, **199**, 1125 (1934).
[157] L. Enderlin, *ibid.*, **200**, 912 (1935).
[158] E. Müller, *Z. Elektrochem.*, **40**, 542 (1934).
[159] E. Müller and I. Müller-Rodloff, *Ber.*, **68B**, 1276 (1935).
[160] E. Müller and I. Dammerau, *ibid.*, **70B**, 2561 (1937).
[161] L. Enderlin, *Ann. chim.*, **10**, 5 (1938).

some small concentration of unpaired electrons, but Müller has shown that the magnitude of the deviations is independent of temperature. They are more probably related to the effects described by Pacault (p. 119).

Many nitrogen compounds have been studied for possible biradical form but, as pointed out by Müller and Wiesemann,[162] whenever valency tautomerism with formation of the quinoid structure is possible, the magnetic behavior is in accord with such quinoid structure, even though the chemical behavior of the substance may point to the existence of free radicals.

The first true organic biradical discovered was porphyrindine[163] which has been shown by Kuhn, Katz, and Franke,[164] and Müller and Müller-Rodloff[165] to exist in biradical form with a susceptibility corresponding to two unpaired electron spins. The effective Bohr magneton number is dependent on temperature and apparently would approach zero at very low temperatures. A possible explanation for this phenomenon is the existence of an equilibrium of the paramagnetic form with a diamagnetic

paramagnetic high temperature
porphyrindine

diamagnetic low temperature porphyrindine

form. Müller gives the heat of reaction as about 0.56 kcal. per mole. Proof of the biradical form of this compound suggested the definition (Kuhn, Katz, and Franke) of a free radical as a compound containing an uncompensated electron but not necessarily an odd number of electrons.

A rather obvious approach to the biradical problem is to be found in the Chichibabin hydrocarbon, *bis*-(1,4-phenylenediphenylmethyl), but this compound seems to be diamagnetic, presumably owing to its equilibrium with the quinoid form in which the two unpaired electrons become paired off.[166] If the diphenylmethyl groups are attached at the *meta* rather

[162] E. Müller and W. Wiesemann, *Ber.*, **69B**, 2157 (1936).
[163] O. Piloty and W. Vogel, *ibid.*, **36**, 1283 (1903).
[164] R. Kuhn, H. Katz, and W. Franke, *Naturwissenschaften*, **22**, 808 (1934).
[165] E. Müller and I. Müller-Rodloff, *Ann.*, **521**, 81 (1935).
[166] E. Müller and I. Müller-Rodloff, *ibid.*, **517**, 134 (1935).

$(C_6H_5)_2C$—⟨ ⟩—⟨ ⟩—$C(C_6H_5)_2 \rightleftarrows (C_6H_5)_2C$=⟨ ⟩=⟨ ⟩=$C(C_6H_5)_2$

than the *para* positions, then the quinoid form cannot be assumed, and Müller has shown that *bis*-(1,3-phenylenediphenylmethyl) exists about

$(C_6H_5)_2C$ $C(C_6H_5)_2$

6% as free radical at 74°C. in 8% benzene solution.

The compound

$(C_6H_5)_2C$—⟨ ⟩—$\underset{\underset{C_6H_5}{|}}{\overset{\overset{C_6H_5}{|}}{C}}$——$\underset{\underset{C_6H_5}{|}}{\overset{\overset{C_6H_5}{|}}{C}}$—⟨ ⟩—$C(C_6H_5)_2$

is also paramagnetic, at least in part.

The theory of such compounds has been discussed by Hückel.[167]

As soon as it was realized that valency tautomerism to form the quinoid structure must be prevented if biradicals are to be formed, Müller proceeded to restrict rotation about the biphenyl group by the introduction of chlorine atoms to form, for instance, *bis*-[(3,5-dichloro-1,4-phenylene) diphenylmethyl].

This compound in 4% benzene solution at 18°C. is 10% dissociated; and at 70°C., 19%.[168] If two of the phenyl groups are substituted by xenyl or other groups, the dissociation rises to 14% at room temperature and 37% at 80°C.[169,170] The heat of dissociation is 7 ± 2 kilocal. per mole. Further solution of the "biradical" problem came by substituting xenyl groups for all four phenyl groups, as in *bis*-[(3,5 dichloro-1,4 phenylene)-dixenyl-methyl].[170a] This compound is at least 80% in the free-radical form at

[167] E. Hückel, *Z. physik. Chem.*, **B34**, 339 (1936).
[168] E. Müller and H. Neuhoff, *Ber.*, **72B**, 2063 (1939).
[169] E. Müller and E. Tietz, *Naturwissenschaften*, **28**, 189 (1940).
[170] E. Müller, *Angew. Chem.*, **54**, 192 (1941).
[170a] E Müller and E. Tietz, *Ber.*, **74B**, 807 (1941).

80°C. in a 2% benzene solution.[171,172]   Still more biradicals have been reported by Müller.

It will be observed that such compounds as that above raise some interesting questions as to possible modes of association, whether linear or possibly cyclic. They also suggest the question of whether two unpaired electrons at considerable distance from one another produce the same resultant moment as two such electrons in a transition group ion.

This area has been thoroughly reviewed by Müller.[173,174]   It will be noted that porphyrindine differs from the stable hydrocarbon biradicals shown above in a rather fundamental way.   The porphyrindine may exist in a diamagnetic, singlet ground state.   But because the energy of excitation to a paramagnetic triplet state is comparable to kT, it may also exist as a biradical.   The susceptibility of such a substance shows a marked dependence on temperature, and the *apparent* moment is a function of temperature.   The moment of the triplet state is $\mu = 2.84$.   Molecular oxygen is similar to porphyrindine in this respect, but here the paramagnetic triplet state is lower than the diamagnetic singlet state.

The biradical hydrocarbons which are incapable, through steric or other reasons, of assuming a quinoid form are true biradicals in the sense that they are similar to two monoradicals acting independently.   For these biradicals, the magnetic moment is $\mu = 2.4$ and is independent of temperature except, of course, so far as association may alter the concentration of the compound.

For the porphyrindine type of biradical, Müller prefers the term biradicalette, although biradicaloid has also been used.   These are distinguished from the true biradicals, but not very many workers in the field seem to have adopted the first term.

The Chichibabin hydrocarbon is highly colored and quite reactive. It is, therefore, surprising that it has been found to be diamagnetic.   The measurements by Müller could scarcely have detected less than 2% of the compound in the paramagnetic form.   In view of this, Schwab has studied the *ortho-para* hydrogen conversion in the presence of the hydrocarbon and, in spite of criticism by Müller, has maintained his position that a measurable

[171] E. Müller and H. Pfanz, *ibid.*, **74B**, 1051, 1075 (1941).
[172] E. Müller and E. Hertel, *Ann.*, **157** (1944).
[173] E. Müller, *Fortschr. chem. Forsch.*, **1**, 325 (1949).
[174] E. Müller, *Chem.-Ztg.*, **77**, 203 (1953).

concentration of free radicals is present.[175] This difficulty has been resolved by paramagnetic resonance studies which show that in a $0.005M$ solution, about 4% of the compound is in the biradical form. This also illustrates the great power and elegance of paramagnetic resonance methods as compared with classical susceptibility determinations for this kind of problem.[176]

Biradicals of a rather different type have been reported by Lewis, Calvin, and Kasha.[177,178] Acid fluorescein dye, as is well known from the earlier work of Lewis and his co-workers, may be excited to a $^3\Sigma$ phosphorescent state in a boric acid glass. The susceptibility of the molecules in this state is equal to that of molecular oxygen, within the rather large experimental error.

The photoexcitation of a molecule to a paramagnetic state has been called "photomagnetism." Earlier attempts to observe a change of susceptibility on exposure to light gave no definite conclusions with various paramagnetic salt solutions.[179-182] In this connection the case of tetraphenylrubrene is interesting.[183] This compound in solution and on exposure to light and air readily forms peroxides in a manner reminiscent of the behavior of hexaarylethanes. Attempts to detect transient biradicals produced by photoexcitation of the rubrene have been unsuccessful, but it is probable that resonance methods would be more rewarding.

The thermochromic compound, bianthrone, gives paramagnetic resonance absorption after heat treatment, although the susceptibility seems to be independent of temperature. It is scarcely possible to say yet whether this is a triplet state or a true biradical.[184,185]

76. Reacting Systems

The *in situ* study of reacting systems by magnetic methods has considerable attractiveness, although the number of systems so far examined in this way is not large. Several such studies, including the disproportiona-

[175] G. M. Schwab and J. Voitlander, *Naturwissenschaften*, **40**, 439 (1953).

[176] C. A. Hutchison, Jr., A. Kowalsky, R. C. Pastor, and G. W. Wheland, *J. Chem. Phys.*, **20**, 1485 (1952).

[177] G. N. Lewis and M. Calvin, *J. Am. Chem. Soc.*, **67**, 1232 (1945).

[178] G. N. Lewis, M. Calvin, and M. Kasha, *J. Chem. Phys.*, **17**, 804 (1949).

[179] D. M. Bose and P. K. Raha, *Z. Physik*, **80**, 361 (1933).

[180] O. Specchia, *Nature*, **130**, 697 (1932).

[181] G. J. Gorter, *ibid.*, **130**, 60 (1932).

[182] P. W. Selwood, *ibid.*, **131**, 761 (1933).

[183] M. Born and A. Schonberg, *ibid.*, **166**, 307 (1950).

[184] W. G. Nielsen and G. K. Fraenkel, *J. Chem. Phys.*, **21**, 1619 (1953).

[185] W. Theilacker, G. Kortüm, and H. Elliehausen, *Z. Naturforsch.*, **9b**, 167 (1954).

tion of certain hexaarylethanes, have been referred to earlier in this chapter. Part of Michaelis's work on semiquinones is of this nature, and other examples on inorganic systems will be described later. Most of the work in this field has been concerned with polymerization and the effect of oxygen on polymerization rates. The polymerization of thiocyanogen has been studied by Bhatnagar, Kapur, and Khosla.[186] Fresh $0.5N$ solutions in carbon disulfide and in bromoform are diamagnetic, indicating dimerization, but solutions in carbon disulfide and in cyclohexane are said to become paramagnetic, suggesting the existence of SCN molecules, or of $(SCN)_n$ groups where n is an odd number.

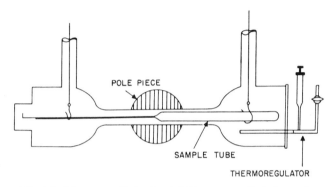

POLE PIECE

SAMPLE TUBE

THERMOREGULATOR

Fig. 85. Diagrammatic horizontal Gouy magnetic balance for studying reaction processes *in situ*.

It is well known that uncatalyzed polymerizations are often preceded by an induction period, and it has been suggested that the polymerization nuclei are free radicals. As free radicals are paramagnetic, they should be detectible, provided the concentration is high enough. Farquharson and Ady[187] have studied polymerizing 2,3-dimethylbutadiene both in the presence and absence of benzoyl peroxide as an accelerator. In the complete absence of an accelerator, there is an induction period of about 3 hours during which the diamagnetic susceptibility falls about 13.6%. The susceptibility then slowly rises in the normal fashion. In the presence of sufficient accelerator, the susceptibility curve rises smoothly throughout the experiment. These data have been used by Farquharson and Ady to calculate a free-radical concentration of about 0.5%. But from more recent studies of polymerization by the rotating sector method, it seems probable that this result is many orders of magnitude too high. Free

[186] S. S. Bhatnagar, P. L. Kapur, and B. O. Khosla, *J. Indian Chem. Soc.*, **17**, 529 (1940).

[187] J. Farquharson and P. Ady, *Nature*, **143**, 1067 (1939).

radicals in a polymerizing system have been detected by paramagnetic resonance.[188]   In polymerizing glycol dimethyl methacrylate, the concentration of free radicals is estimated as 10^{-3} to 10^{-4} molar.

Magnetic studies on the polymerization of styrene have been made by Bhatnagar et al.[189] and by Boardman and Selwood.[190]   The work of the American authors illustrates several points and will be described in some detail.   Measurements were made by the horizontal Gouy method in which a sample tube is suspended from two long threads in such a manner that

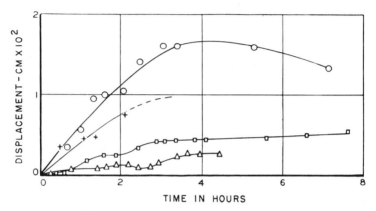

Fig. 86. Changes of diamagnetic susceptibility during thermal polymerization of styrene. O, stockroom styrene vacuum distilled; +, same degassed; □, styrene prepared from cinnamic acid; △, same degassed.

one end of the tube was in a field of about 8000 oersteds supplied by a permanent Alnico magnet.   Changes of magnetic susceptibility of the sample were observed with a micrometer microscope (Fig. 85).   This apparatus was calibrated in several ways, one of which was by observing displacements of the sample tube when it was filled with a dilute solution of dichromate slowly reducing under the influence of sucrose.   The magnetic change is from diamagnetic $Cr_2O_7{}^{2-}$ to paramagnetic Cr^{3+}.   It may be pointed out that the use of a permanent magnet greatly increases the sensitivity and convenience of studies such as these.

The type of experimental results obtained for the oxidation of styrene is shown in Fig. 86.   A measured volume of oxygen was added to styrene. The disappearance of molecular oxygen from the solution was then followed

[188] G. K. Fraenkel, J. M. Hirshon, and C. Walling, J. Am. Chem. Soc., **76**, 3606 (1954).

[189] S. S. Bhatnagar, P. L. Kapur, and G. Kaur, J. Indian Chem. Soc., **17**, 177 (1940).

[190] H. Boardman and P. W. Selwood, J. Am. Chem. Soc., **72**, 1372 (1950).

magnetically.   From these results and similar studies in the presence of inhibitors, it is possible to draw conclusions concerning the initiation process and related aspects of the kinetics of polymerization. Further work by Ihrig and Alyea[190a] gives what appears to be definite susceptibility evidence for free radicals in measurable concentrations in polymerizing methyl methacrylate.   But it is not likely that classical susceptibility methods can any longer compete with paramagnetic resonance absorption in this area.   It has, for instance, been shown by paramagnetic resonance that free radicals are occluded in the polymerization of acrylonitrile and that the concentration of unpaired electrons is about 10^{17} per cubic centimeter.[190b]

77. Adsorbed Paramagnetic Gases

The magnetic properties of adsorbed gases and of the adsorbent appear to be a promising field for research.   The adsorption of diamagnetic gases on substances of interest as catalysts, such as hydrogen on palladium, will be described later.   This section will be reserved for studies of paramagnetic gases as adsorbates.

Oxygen adsorbed on chabasite, on charcoal, on silica, and on platinum has been studied by Aharoni and Simon,[191] Juza and co-workers,[192−196] and Courty.[197]   A simplified diagram of apparatus used is shown in Fig. 87. In this apparatus the force of attraction on the sample is balanced by the field applied to a counterpoise roughly similar in form to the sample itself. The fields are applied momentarily.   The method is based upon the Gouy balance, specially adapted to the problem of adsorption.

Results obtained clearly indicate that the susceptibilities are not additive. This is to be expected if chemical adsorption takes place because, although molecular oxygen is paramagnetic, combined oxygen is diamagnetic.   The measurements therefore afford a means of finding relative proportions of molecularly adsorbed and of combined oxygen.   The results show that at room temperature the proportion of molecularly adsorbed oxygen

[190a] J. L. Ihrig and H. N. Alyea, *ibid.*, **75**, 2917 (1953).

[190b] C. H. Bamford, A. D. Jenkins, D. J. E. Ingram, and M. C. R. Symons, *Nature,* **175**, 894 (1955).

[191] J. Aharoni and F. Simon, *Z. physik. Chem.*, **B4**, 175 (1929).

[192] R. Juza and R. Langheim, *Naturwissenschaften*, **25**, 522 (1937); *Z. Elektrochem.*, **45**, 689 (1939).

[193] R. Juza, R. Langheim, and H. Hahn, *Angew. Chem.*, **51**, 354 (1938); **60A**, 254 (1948).

[194] R. Juza, H. Lübbe, and L. Heinlein, *Z. anorg. Chem.*, **258**, 105 (1949).

[195] R. Juza and F. Grasenick, *Z. Elektrochem.*, **54**, 145 (1950).

[196] R. Juza, *Chem.-Ztg.*, **74**, 55 (1950).

[197] C. Courty, *Compt. rend.*, **216**, 769 (1943); **218**, 832 (1944); **230**, 1588 (1950).

decreases with increasing temperature and time. Fig. 88 shows the percentage of molecularly bound oxygen in dependence on time and temperature. From the temperature coefficient of reaction velocity, it is found that the activation energy of surface-oxide formation is about 5 kcal. per mole.

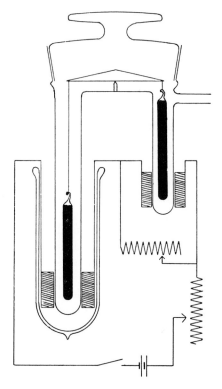

Fig. 87. Magnetic balance for the study of sorbed gases (simplified).

The percentage of oxygen molecularly adsorbed also depends on the outgassing temperature, as shown in Fig. 89. In this connection, Courty emphasizes the possible effects of traces of impurities, such as iron compounds, on the accuracy of such measurements. At $-183°$C., the susceptibility of adsorbed oxygen depends on the thickness of the adsorbed layer, becoming less paramagnetic as the thickness increases. Thus, for a monolayer, the susceptibility is about equal to that of molecular oxygen, but additional layers tend to have the susceptibility of liquid oxygen. This is attributed by Juza to association of the O_2 molecules to diamagnetic O_4.

Apparently the only other adsorbed paramagnetic gas which has received investigation by the magnetic method is nitrogen dioxide, which

is the subject of a report by Reyerson and Wertz,[198,199] and which has also
been studied by Juza.[200]   On silica, the magnetic measurements support

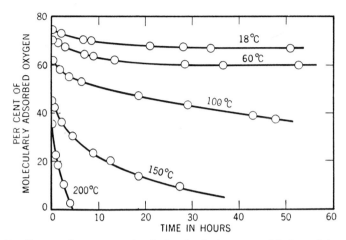

Fig. 88.   Change of per cent molecularly adsorbed oxygen with time, determined
from susceptibility measurements of oxygen adsorbed on charcoal.

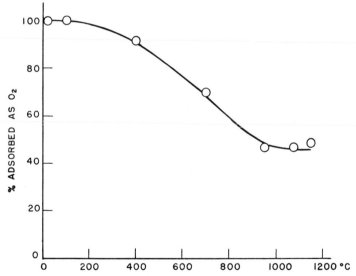

Fig. 89.   Dependence of per cent molecularly adsorbed oxygen on outgassing
temperature, determined from susceptibility measurements.

[198] L. H. Reyerson and J. E. Wertz, *J. Phys. & Colloid Chem.*, **53**, 234 (1949).
[199] L. H. Reyerson and J. M. Honig, *J. Am. Chem. Soc.*, **75**, 3917 (1953).
[200] R. Juza and H. Tentschert, *Z. anorg. chem.*, **262**, 165 (1950).

the view that the adsorbed phase is chiefly dinitrogen tetroxide, while on charcoal and alumina gel the NO_2 seems to be chemisorbed. On graphitized carbon black, the diamagnetism decreases to such a degree as to suggest intercalation of the molecules between the graphite lattice layers, in a manner similar to that in the graphite-bromine system. The work of Reyerson and Honig[199] on nitrogen dioxide adsorbed on high-area rutile suggests some influence of the adsorbed gas on the defect structure, which is known to be produced in titania on evacuation at moderately elevated temperatures.

The adsorption of oxygen on cobalt monoxide has been studied by Bhatnager, Prakash, and Qayyum,[201] but the observed changes of susceptibility are probably in this case due largely to a change of oxidation state of the cobalt. In most of the above studies attention has been directed to changes in the magnetic properties of the adsorbate. In later chapters it will be shown that there is a rapidly broadening area of interest, particularly in connection with catalytically active solids, where the magnetic properties of the adsorbent are shown to change during chemisorption. This may be true whether the adsorbate is paramagnetic or not.

78. Miscellaneous Structural Problems

The structure of boron hydride, B_2H_6, has been the subject of much discussion, because there are insufficient electrons in the compound to give a full quota of electron pair bonds. At one time it was argued that perhaps two of the hydrogen atoms are held to the borons by single electron bonds, as shown.

$$
\begin{array}{c}
\text{H H} \\
\text{H:B:B:H} \\
\text{H H}
\end{array}
$$

This suggestion implies that the compound is paramagnetic. Farkas and Sachsse[202] have studied the para-hydrogen conversion in the presence of boron hydride. They reached the conclusion that this compound is diamagnetic. This result was taken to mean that the structure is a resonance hybrid wherein each bond partakes both of electron pair and single electron character, but it is now realized that this and related compounds may involve a unique protonated type of valence bond. Aluminum trimethyl and aluminum triethyl are also diamagnetic,[203] as are basic beryllium

[201] S. S. Bhatnagar, B. Prakash, and M. A. Qayyum, J. Indian Chem. Soc., 18, 540 (1941).

[202] L. Farkas and H. Sachsse, Trans. Faraday Soc., 30, 331 (1934).

[203] K. S. Pitzer and H. S. Gutowsky, J. Am. Chem. Soc., 68, 2204 (1946).

acetate and beryllium acetylacetonate, in which the presence of single electron bonds was at one time suspected.[204]

A somewhat related problem is the structure of the salt-like compounds, diborane patassium, $K_2(B_2H_6)$, and dioxydiborane potassium, $K_2(B_2H_4)(OH)_2$. The ions, BH_3^- and BOH_3^-, each have an odd number of electrons and should therefore be paramagnetic. But Klemm[205] has shown that the potassium salts of these ions are diamagnetic. The ions are, therefore, probably $(B_2H_6)^{2-}$ and $(B_2O_2H_6)^{2-}$. For the diborane potassium, there is a slight temperature coefficient of susceptibility, with the higher diamagnetism at the lower temperatures. This effect cannot be due to impurities or to temperature-independent paramagnetism. It may result from slight dissociation $(B_2H_6)^{2-} \rightleftharpoons 2(BH_3)^-$ with about 1% of the compound existing as an ionic free radical at 350°K. It appears that triphenylboron sodium, $(C_6H_5)_3BNa$, is diamagnetic.[206]

Hyposulfurous (dithionous) acid, $H_2S_2O_4$, is commonly assumed to exist in the dimeric form, as written. If the acid and its salts contained the ion, SO_2^-, they would be paramagnetic. L. Klemm[207] shows that the salts are diamagnetic. The magnetic evidence, therefore, confirms the view that the doubled formula is correct, as appears also to be true of the dithionates.[208]

The same is true of the hypophosphates, which have been studied by Bell and Sugden.[209] They find that sodium hypophosphate, $Na_2H_2P_2O_6$; its hydrate, $Na_2H_2P_2O_6 \cdot 6H_2O$; silver hypophosphate, $Ag_4P_2O_6$; and guanidine hypophosphate, $(CN_3H_5)_4H_4P_2O_6$, are all diamagnetic and hence correctly written as shown. The same is true of solutions containing the methyl and ethyl esters of hypophosphoric acid. The supposed compounds, arsenic diiodide, AsI_2, and arsenic tetrabromide, $AsBr_4$, are also diamagnetic. Related diamagnetic compounds of antimony and bismuth have been mentioned in the previous chapter. On the other hand, Whittaker and Yost[210] have shown that vanadium tetrachloride is paramagnetic and has a moment near that for one unpaired electron spin, both in the pure compound and in carbon tetrachloride solution. Rice[211] has reported that the imine radical, frozen out as a blue solid, appears to be paramagnetic.

Strontium pernitride, Sr_3N_4, apparently contains N^{3-} ions. These are definitely paramagnetic, but with a rather low moment. This may be due

[204] W. R. Angus and J. Farquharson, *Proc. Roy. Soc. (London)*, **A136**, 579 (1932).
[205] L. Klemm, and W. Klemm, *Z. anorg. u. allgem. Chem.*, **225**, 258 (1935).
[206] T. L. Chu, *J. Am. Chem. Soc.*, **75**, 1730 (1953).
[207] L. Klemm, *Z. anorg. u. allgem. Chem.*, **231**, 136 (1937).
[208] R. W. Asmussen, *Kemiska*, No. 6, 81 (1941).
[209] F. Bell and S. Sugden, *J. Chem. Soc.*, **1933**, 48.
[210] A. G. Whittaker and D. M. Yost, *J. Chem. Phys.*, **17**, 188 (1949).
[211] F. O. Rice and M. Freamo, *J. Am. Chem. Soc.*, **73**, 5529 (1951).

to dimerization to $N_2,^{6-}$ to strong exchange interaction, or possibly to some spin-orbit relationship. The problem, like that of the superoxides, is obviously an interesting one which warrants further study.[212]

Another problem which has been solved by magnetic measurements is the structure of calomel, and the old question of whether the formula should be written HgCl or Hg_2Cl_2. Magnetic measurements on the solid and on the liquid have shown it to be diamagnetic.[213,214] The vapor phase of calomel has also been shown to be diamagnetic.[215] The monomeric formula is, therefore, excluded in all three phases.

Farquharson and Heymann[214] have also shown that solutions of metallic cadmium in molten cadmium chloride are diamagnetic. This rules out the possibility of CdCl molecules or of univalent Cd^+ ions existing as such in these solutions. Similar studies have been made on the supposed dichlorides of gallium and of indium. These are diamagnetic and probably exist in the dimeric form.[216] So-called calcium monochloride, CaCl, is diamagnetic.[217] Both $TlCl_2$ and Tl_2Cl_3 are likewise diamagnetic,[218] as is iodine dioxide.[219] These observations apparently exclude the simple ion, Tl^{2+}, and the monomeric IO_2 molecule.

In Chapter VII it was shown that the magnetic susceptibility of graphite depends on particle size. It appears that soft graphite shows paramagnetic resonance absorption. The width of the absorption changes with changing heat treatment of the graphite and is attributed to spin resonance of the electrons free in two dimensions.[220] A rather more startling development[221] is the evidence that progressive carbonization of several carbonaceous materials, such as cellulose and coal, develops appreciable concentrations of free radicals at various stages of heating. These experiments were done by heating the samples to various temperatures, then measuring the susceptibilities at room temperature. Further exploration of this area, preferably by paramagnetic resonance, is certainly in order. A start in this direction has been made.[221a,221b]

[212] P. Ehrlich and H. J. Hein, *Z. Elektrochem.*, **57**, 710 (1953).

[213] *International Critical Tables*, Vol. VI, p. 357.

[214] J. Farquharson and E. Heymann, *Trans. Faraday Soc.*, **31**, 1004 (1935).

[215] P. W. Selwood and R. Preckel, *J. Am. Chem. Soc.*, **62**, 3055 (1940).

[216] W. Klemm and W. Tilk, *Z. anorg. u. allgem. Chem.*, **207**, 175 (1932).

[217] P. Ehrlich and L. Gentsch, *Naturwissenschaften*, **40**, 460 (1953).

[218] D. J. Meier and C. S. Garner, *J. Chem. Phys.*, **18**, 237 (1950).

[219] W. K. Wilmarth and S. S. Dharmatti, *J. Am. Chem. Soc.*, **72**, 5789 (1950).

[220] J. G. Castle, Jr., *Phys. Rev.*, **95**, 846 (1954).

[221] H. Honda and K. Ouchi, *Science Repts. Tôhoku Imp. Univ.*, *F. Ishikawa Anniversary Vol.* **37**, 55 (1953).

[221a] F. H. Winslow, W. O. Baker, and W. A. Yager, *J. Am. Chem. Soc.*, **77**, 4751 (1955).

[221b] D. J. E. Ingram and J. G. Tapley, *Chemistry & Industry*, **1955**, 568.

Another interesting field is the demonstration by paramagnetic resonance of free radicals in irradiated (x rays or gamma rays) high polymers and, in fact, in many organic substances, such as amino acids and sugars.[222,223] These results are of obvious interest in connection with the mechanical, electrical, and thermal properties of high polymers and with the physiological activity associated with irradiation.

In Chapter VI, p. 102, it was mentioned that there is some susceptibility evidence for a change of free-radical concentration in living cells. Paramagnetic resonance has been applied to this problem and, in a preliminary report, resonance absorption has been shown for a large group of biological substances, such as leaves, roots, rabbit tissue, carrots, frog egg, etc.[224] The estimated free-radical content ranges from 2 to 200 ($\times 10^{-8}$) moles per gram of dried material. This would appear to be a most promising area for intensive study, and new results will doubtless appear before this book is printed.

[222] E. E. Schneider, M. J. Day, and G. Stein, *Nature*, **168**, 644 (1951).
[223] J. Cambrisson and J. Uebersfeld, *Compt. rend.*, **238**, 1397 (1954).
[224] B. Commoner, J. Townsend, and G. E. Pake, *Nature*, **174**, 689 (1954).

CHAPTER TWELVE

FERROMAGNETISM

79. Introduction to Ferromagnetism

This topic is of great technological importance and it is assuming increasing importance in structural inorganic chemistry. Ferromagnetism is not as rare in nature as was once believed; the identity and structure

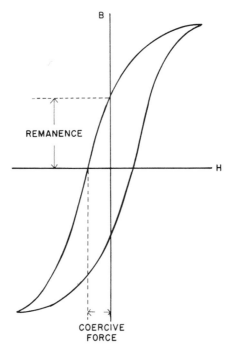

Fig. 90. Hysteresis curve, B/H, showing remanence and coercive force

of many chemical substances may be revealed by examination of their ferromagnetic properties. For our present purposes, ferromagnetism is of three-fold interest. First, thermomagnetic analysis, as described in

286

Chapter III, is useful in the qualitative and quantitative estimation of certain chemical species and in following changes in these species during chemical reaction. Second, the magnetic behavior of the ferrites and related compounds is closely connected with structural inorganic chemistry. And third, there is increasing evidence that much may be learned about the structure of catalytically active solids by study of the ferromagnetism often associated with these substances and mixtures.

Ferromagnetism is difficult to define simply and precisely. With Bitter[1] we shall be content for the moment to say that a ferromagnetic substance is one whose magnetic properties are like those of iron. How, in general, this differs from diamagnetism and paramagnetism should be sufficiently clear from the following discussion to serve the purposes of most readers. A major difference between ferromagnetism and paramagnetism is that the former is a group effect, the latter an atomic or molecular effect.

Ferromagnetic substances are chiefly distinguished by the facts that the susceptibility at low fields may be enormous, and that the specific magnetization is a function of field up to the field at which the substance is said to be saturated. This field is generally readily attainable. Many ferromagnetic substances shows the phenomena of hysteresis and of residual magnetism. A typical hysteresis curve is shown in Fig. 90 on which are also shown the interrelationships among the various quantities involved. There are many excellent texts and reviews on ferromagnetism.[2-9]

If the specific magnetization of a ferromagnetic substance is determined as a function of temperature, it will be found that above a certain fairly well-defined temperature, the induction drops nearly to zero. This, is to say, the substance loses its ferromagnetism and becomes merely paramagnetic. The temperature at which this occurs is known as the Curie point. The Curie point is a critical temperature, not unlike the melting point of an organic compound. Most applications of ferromagnetism to chemical problems involve study of the Curie point.

The changes which occur at the Curie point are not complete at this

[1] F. Bitter, *Introduction to Ferromagnetism*. McGraw-Hill Book Co., Inc., New York, 1937.

[2] R. Becker and W. Doring, *Ferromagnetismus*. Julius Springer, Berlin, 1939.

[3] L. Néel, Le Magnétisme, Vol. II. Proceedings of the Strasbourg Congress on Magnetism, 1939.

[4] L. Néel, *J. phys. radium*, 1, 242 (1940).

[5] E. C. Stoner, *Repts. on Progress in Physics*, 11, 43 (1946–47); 13, 83 (1950).

[6] W. Sucksmith, *J. Iron Steel Inst. (London)*, 163, 51 (1949).

[7] L. F. Bates, *Modern Magnetism*. The University Press, Cambridge, 1951.

[8] R. M. Bozorth, *Ferromagnetism*. D. Van Nostrand Co., Inc., New York, 1951.

[9] K. Hoselitz, *Ferromagnetic Properties of Metals and Alloys*. Oxford University Press, London, 1952.

temperature but continue over a temperature interval.[10]   Experimentally, the Curie point is generally taken as that point, indicated in Fig. 91, where the steepest slope of the specific magnetization is found.   This is generally reproducible within a degree or two.   Somewhat more precise methods for locating the Curie point are described by Stoner.[11]

Above the Curie point most substances follow the Curie-Weiss law, $\chi(T + \Delta) = C$.   The Weiss constant is not always numerically equal to the Curie point.[12,13]   There has, therefore, come into use the term "ferromagnetic Curie point" as distinguished from the Weiss constant.   There is

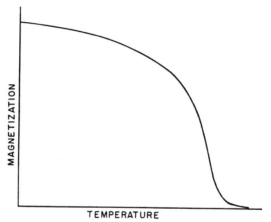

Fig. 91. Intensity of magnetization *versus* temperature for a
typical ferromagnetic substance.

often a difference of 10° or 15° between the two temperatures.   The reason for this difference is probably that long-distance order and short-distance order do not disappear simultaneously as the temperature is raised through the region of the Curie point.   Above the Curie point ferromagnetic substances become normal paramagnetics, although the temperature plotted against reciprocal of susceptibility may not approach a straight line until the Curie point has been greatly exceeded.   Paramagnetic magneton numbers of the common ferromagnetic metals may thus be determined, as shown by Sucksmith and Pearce.[14,15]   Their results are given in Table XXVII.

[10] W. Gerlach, *Z. Elektrochem.*, **45**, 151 (1939).
[11] E. C. Stoner, *Magnetism and Matter*.   Methuen and Company, Ltd., London, 1934, p. 382.
[12] R. Forrer, *J. phys. radium*, **1**, 49 (1930).
[13] L. F. Bates, *Proc. Phys. Soc. (London)*, **43**, 87 (1931).
[14] W. Sucksmith and R. R. Pearce, *Proc. Roy. Soc. (London)*, **A167**, 189 (1938).
[15] See also M. Fallot, *J. phys. radium*, **5**, 153 (1944).

TABLE XXVII

Paramagnetic Magneton Numbers of Iron, Cobalt, and Nickel

Element	Temperature range	$-\Delta$	$C = \chi(T+\Delta)$	μ
Ni	500 to 850°C.	377°C.	0.00548	1.61
Ni	925 to 1200°C.	265	0.00685	1.78
Co	1230 to 1450°C.	1130–1155	0.02080	3.15
Fe from Fe-V alloys	—	—	0.02270	3.20
Fe from δ-phase	—	820	0.02200	3.15

Magneton numbers for ferromagnetic substances[16] may also be obtained from specific magnetizations, σ (e.g., the magnetic moment per unit mass) at a series of temperatures and field strengths T_1, T_2, etc., and H_1, H_2, etc. Extrapolation of σ_{T_1, H_1}, σ_{T_2, H_2} .., to $T = 0$, will give a series of values σ_0, H_1, σ_0, H_2..., which when plotted against reciprocal field and extrapolated to $1/H = 0$ will yield $\sigma_{0,\infty}$. From this, the magnetic moment per gram-atom is readily found. This "saturation" moment is not quite the same as the moment $\mu = g\beta\sqrt{J(J+1)}$ derived from susceptibility measurements on paramagnetic substances. For instance, the saturation-specific magnetization of nickel extrapolated to absolute zero ($\sigma_{0,\infty}$) is 57.50. Then, the number of Bohr magnetons per atom of nickel is obtained by multiplying $\sigma_{0,\infty}$ by the atomic weight and dividing by the Bohr magneton and Avogadro's number. Hence

$$\mu = \frac{57.50 \times 58.49}{9.27 \times 10^{-21} \times 6.025 \times 10^{23}} = 0.604$$

Saturation moments found in this way for iron and cobalt are 2.22 and 1.71, respectively.

The saturation moment is the maximum component of the magnetic moment in the direction of the applied field, namely $\mu = g\beta J$. For our purposes, the principal difference will be that application of the spin-only formula gives a susceptibility moment $\mu = \sqrt{n(n+2)}$ Bohr magnetons whereas the saturation moment is simply $\mu = n$, where n is the number of unpaired electrons.

In general, the moments in ferromagnetic substances are only a fraction of those found in magnetically dilute compounds. (The rare earths are notable exceptions.) This peculiarity has been the subject of considerable discussion. It has been referred by Mott[17] and Slater[18]

[16] E. C. Stoner, *Proc. Leeds Phil. Lit. Sci. Soc.*, **Sect. 3**, 457 (1938).

[17] N. F. Mott and H. Jones, *Properties of Metals and Alloys*. Oxford University Press, Oxford, 1936, p. 222.

[18] J. C. Slater, *J. Applied Physics*, **8**, 385 (1937).

to the fractional number of electrons present in the $3d$ band in metals.
Pauling[19] has used the effect to calculate supposed valency bonds between
atoms in metals. But the theory of ferromagnetism is still far from being
satisfactory, and it is perhaps best not to put too much confidence in these
explanations pending further developments.[20]

In Fig. 92 there are shown typical curves for intensity of magnetization
plotted against field strength. The general form of these curves is the
same for different substances, or for one substance under differing conditions such as particle size, but the curves are not parallel. These differences reflect the fact that some ferromagnetic materials are more

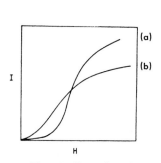

Fig. 92. Intensity of magnetization *versus* field strength
for two different substances.

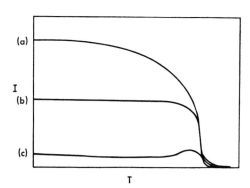

Fig. 93. Intensity of magnetization *versus*
temperature for one substance at three different
fields.

difficult to magnetize than are others. If the purpose of an experiment is
to compare the specific magnetizations of two substances, then it is clear
that quite misleading results may be obtained unless the field is sufficiently
high as to be saturating for both substances.

In Fig. 93 there are shown curves of intensity of magnetization versus
temperature for one substance at several fields. One of the fields is saturating, the others not. It will be noted that the position of the Curie point is
unaffected by change of field, and that accurate determination of the Curie
point is somewhat easier at low fields. This effect and the one described in
the preceding paragraph are found for most ferromagnetic substances.
They suggest that some consideration of and flexibility in field strength is
essential in the magnetochemical study of ferromagnetics.

The origin and nature of ferromagnetism have been the object of much
theoretical study. Most modern theories are based on the classical de-

[19] L. Pauling, *Phys. Rev.*, **54**, 899 (1938) and later papers.

[20] W. Hume-Rothery, *Chemical Society (London) Annual Reports*, p. 42 (1949).

velopment of Weiss,[21] who introduced the concept of the "molecular field." The modern approach to this problem is due in large part to Heisenberg.[22] The existence of ferromagnetism necessitates the presence of a permanent atomic magnetic moment. In all ferromagnetic substances, this moment is supplied solely by the electron spins, the orbital contribution being completely quenched. Ferromagnetism is found only for elements possessing an incomplete lower energy level, such as the $3d$ level in iron, cobalt, and nickel, and the $4f$ level in gadolinium and other rare earth elements.

This is not to say that all elements containing incomplete electron levels are ferromagnetic. Thermal agitation prevents alignment of the spin moments in an applied field to all but a very modest degree, and that only in quite powerful fields. Ferromagnetism arises only when interaction between adjacent atoms or ions is strong enough to hold the electronic moments parallel to each other in spite of thermal agitation. This interaction is found in the Heisenberg exchange interaction, so that the effects producing ferromagnetism are similar in some respects to those producing ordinary covalent bonds between similar atoms, as in molecular hydrogen.

The exchange forces acting in ferromagnetics to align the electronic moments are formally equivalent to a magnetic field of several million oersteds, acting over molecular dimensions. This is the so-called "molecular field" of Weiss. A current theory is that the Heisenberg exchange integral may change sign depending, in part, on the distance between adjacent atoms containing resultant electron spins. In one case, the electronic moments align in opposition to each other and the resultant magnetic moment is actually or near zero. This effect is referred to as "antiferromagnetism" (the subject of the next chapter). In support of this view Slater[23] has shown that ferromagnetism occurs only when the ratio of distance (D) between neighboring atoms in a metal crystal to the radius (r) of the unfilled electron level is an optimum value of 3.0 or slightly greater. For iron $D/r = 3.26$. Thus a substance such as manganese $(D/r = 2.94)$ which is normally antiferromagnetic may become ferromagnetic when the manganese atoms are forced slightly farther apart by the introduction of hydrogen, nitrogen, or other atoms into the manganese lattice. At still greater manganese-manganese distances, the substance becomes merely paramagnetic, as do most similar transition elements and ions with increasing magnetic dilution.

Zener[24] has recently advanced an alternative theory regarding the origin

[21] P. Weiss, *J. phys.*, **6**, 661 (1907).
[22] W. Heisenberg, *Z. Physik*, **49**, 619 (1928).
[23] J. C. Slater, *Phys. Rev.*, **36**, 57 (1930).
[24] C. Zener, *ibid.*, **81**, 440 (1951).

of ferromagnetism. In brief, his theory assumes that normal interaction between d electrons always leads to antiferromagnetism, but that sometimes this is overshadowed by spin coupling, leading to ferromagnetism, between the conduction electrons and the d electrons. This view eliminates the necessity for a change of sign in the exchange integral with changing interatomic distance.

The molecular field acts over rather small distances only, and this assures parallel spin-moment alignment over rather modest volumes,[25] called a "domain." It will be clear that a ferromagnetic substance below

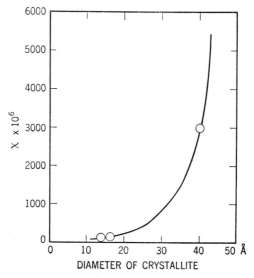

Fig. 94. Ferromagnetism (plotted as apparent susceptibility) as a function of particle size for γ-Fe_2O_3, at room temperature.

the Curie temperature is always "magnetized." This is to say that within a domain all the atomic moments are similarly orientated; but in the absence of an applied field, adjacent domains may be orientated more or less at random to each other unless there is some residual preferred orientation, making the substance a permanent magnet. Methods have been developed for direct observation of the domains which may in certain cases range up to visible sizes.

Ferromagnetism is not an atomic property, but it is difficult to determine the minimum particle size in which this property will develop. Beischer and Winkel[26] attacked the problem through the preparation of

[25] R. M. Bozorth, *Physica*, **15**, 207 (1949).

[26] D. Beischer and A. Winkel, *Naturwissenschaften*, **25**, 420 (1937).

aerosols of nickel and of iron obtained by thermal decomposition of the carbonyls in a nitrogen atmosphere. The particles of nickel, for instance, obtained in this way were about 35 × 60 × 210A. as determined by x-ray methods. These particles were definitely ferromagnetic. More recent work by König[27] puts the minimum ferromagnetic particle size for iron at about 10 to 12A. on a side. Controlled particle size may be achieved to some degree by oxidation of iron carbonyl at several temperatures to yield the ferromagnetic γ-Fe_2O_3. In this substance, the development of ferromagnetism seems to start above a grain size of 30 to 40A., as shown in Fig. 94.[28-31]

Similarly, the ferromagnetic properties of thin metal films differ somewhat from those of matter in the bulk. More recent work seems to show that decreasing particle size leads to a lowering of the Curie temperature. But the problem is complicated by the effect of thermal agitation on very small particles, which begin progressively to act magnetically like paramagnetics rather than like ferromagnetics, as their dimensions go down. This area is of more than ordinary interest in connection with catalytically active solids. It will be discussed more fully in Chapter 15. Some further references to techniques and results on five powders and thin films are given below.[32-38] In this connection, it may be pointed out that the microwave ferromagnetic resonance phenomena may be expected to yield some information concerning the nature of thin metal films of ferromagnetic substances.[39]

It is possible to describe the temperature dependence of magnetization by the law of corresponding states. This is to say that for all ferromagnetic substances, the relative intensity of magnetization ϑ/ϑ_s is related to the reduced temperature T/T_c, by

$$\vartheta/\vartheta_s = \tanh \frac{\vartheta/\vartheta_s}{T/T_c}$$

[27] H. König, ibid., 33, 71 (1946).

[28] A. Winkel and R. Haul, Z. Elektrochem., 44, 823 (1938).

[29] R. Haul and T. Schoon, ibid., 45, 663 (1939).

[30] W. Klemm, ibid., 46, 296 (1940).

[31] L. J. E. Hofer, Colloid Chemistry, ed. Alexander. 7th edition, Reinhold Publ. Corp., New York, 1950, p. 113.

[32] S. Procopiu and G. d'Albon, Compt. rend., 205, 1373 (1937).

[33] A. Aron, Cahiers phys., 4, 19 (1941).

[34] N. Felici, ibid., 21, 19 (1944).

[35] A. Drigo and M. Pizzo, Nuovo cimento, 5, 196 (1948).

[36] M. J. Klein and R. S. Smith, Phys. Rev., 81, 378 (1951).

[37] H. H. Jensen and A. Nielsen, Trans. Danish Acad. Tech. Sci., No. 2, 3 (1953).

[38] E. C. Crittenden, Jr. and R. W. Hoffman, Rev. Mod. Phys., 25, 310 (1953).

[39] K. J. Standley, Science Progress, 38, 231 (1950).

where ϑ_s is the intensity of magnetization at saturation and T_c is the Curie temperature. This law is developed on a simple derivation based on the Weiss molecular field. How well it agrees with experiment is shown in Fig. 95.

The phenomenon of the Curie point is understandable on the basis of the Heisenberg exchange interaction. The relation found is that already presented in Chapter VIII, namely,

$$T_c = \frac{2JzS(S + 1)}{3k}$$

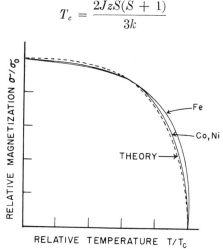

Fig. 95. Relative (reduced) magnetization *versus* reduced temperature, T/T_c, for iron, cobalt, nickel, and theory. This illustrates the so-called law of corresponding states.

where T_c is the Curie point, J the exchange integral, z the number of nearest paramagnetic neighbors to each paramagnetic ion, S is the spin vector sum, and k is the Boltzmann constant. It will be noted that as a ferromagnetic substance becomes diluted with a diamagnetic substance, either J or z or both may diminish, with a resultant lowering of the Curie point. The practical implications of this will be discussed below.

Theortiecal treatment of magnetic hysteresis has not reached quite such a satisfactory stage. The modern theory is based on the crystal anisotropy and magnetostriction. Although ferromagnetic substances exist in cubic crystals, these exhibit ferromagnetic anisotropy owing, presumably, to interaction between electron spins and lattice, as a result of which certain preferred directions are found for spontaneous magnetization. The magnetostriction may be regarded as an induced anisotropy brought about by deformation of the crystal by its own magnetic forces.

It will be noted that a proper sign for the exchange integral is a necessary, although not sufficient, requirement for the appearance of spontaneous magnetization, i.e., ferromagnetism. In compounds the magnetic atoms are in general screened from each other by intervening nonmagnetic atoms, such as oxygen in a metal oxide. Gisolf[40] has pointed out that ferromagnetism can arise in such compounds only when the open lines of interaction between metal atoms are able to form a three-dimensional network as they are in cubic γ-ferric oxide which is ferromagnetic, but not in hexagonal α-ferric oxide which is not ferromagnetic. Some further references to recent work on the theory of ferromagnetism will be found in the reports of the Grenoble and Washington conferences in 1950 and 1952, respectively.[41,42]

80. Iron and Iron Alloys

The magnetic properties of ferromagnetic substances depend on impurities and other factors to such a degree that their study is often hampered by the difficulty of obtaining pure specimens. The preparation of pure iron is no exception. Very pure iron may be obtained by thermal decomposition of iron pentacarbonyl.[43] If this substance is decomposed in a heated chamber so that it does not touch the walls before decomposition occurs, the product will be very pure. A trace of carbon may be removed by heating the iron with a measured quantity of iron oxide, also prepared from iron carbonyl. The purity of such iron is better than 99.9%. There is some question as to whether or not the best electrolytic iron may not be even purer than carbonyl iron.

The magnetic properties of iron are often greatly changed by annealing. In many cases this is essentially a diffusion process leading to elimination of gaseous impurities. In impure iron, the solubility and distribution of impurities may be modified by heat treatment. Magnetic properties, particularly hysteresis, are also influenced by grain size and lattice orientation, which depend in turn on the presence of impurities and on the previous heat treatment. The magnetism also depends on time. The reason for this "aging" process seems to lie in the presence of impurities and to their alteration or diffusion with time. The effect seems definitely to be absent in pure iron.[44]

The purer that iron can be obtained, the higher becomes its permea-

[40] J. H. Gisolf, *Physica*, **15**, 677 (1949).

[41] *Colloques Internationaux, Ferromagnetism and Antiferromagnetism.* Grenoble 1950.

[42] *Rev. Mod. Phys.*, **25**, 1–351 (1953).

[43] T. C. Yensen in Bitter's *Introduction to Ferromagnetism* (*op. cit.*, p. 67). In this work it is erroneously stated that the enneacarbonyl is used.

[44] J. L. Snoek, *Physica*, **6**, 161 (1939).

bility and the lower becomes its hysteresis loss. A *B-H* curve for nearly pure iron is shown in Fig. 96, together with curves for several common commercial irons and steels. A few general references to this field are given below.[2,45,46]

There have been some differences of opinion expressed on the effect of dissolved hydrogen on the magnetic properties of iron. Some authors regard the changes occurring on heat treatment in the presence of hydrogen as being due solely to the elimination of impurities. Reber[47] has shown

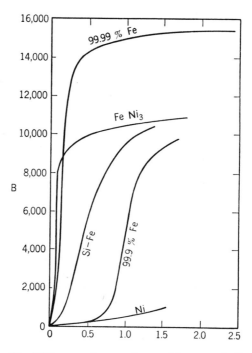

Fig. 96. *B/H* curves for pure iron and for several alloys.

that a rather definite magnetic hardening takes place when hydrogen is electrolyzed into iron.

There is a wealth of data on ferromagnetic alloys of iron.[9] Most of the work in this field has been done with a view to producing new and

[45] O. v. Auwers, "Magnetische und Elektrische Eigenschaften des Eisens und seiner Legierungen" in Gmelin's *Handbuch der anorganischen Chemie*. Verlag Chemie. Berlin, 1937.

[46] R. Becker, *Probleme der technischen Magnetisierungskurve*. J. Springer, Berlin, 1938.

[47] R. K. Reber, *Physics*, 5, 297 (1934).

improved alloys for specific purposes. The use of thermomagnetic methods for structural studies is receiving increasing attention, and some of these methods will be reviewed later. Such studies furnish a sensitive means for quantitative evaluation of heterogeneity in ferromagnetic solid solution. Efforts have been made to place the study of such substances on a sound theoretical basis, and some success in this direction has been achieved.[48-50] When pure, the transition elements generally show ferromagnetism or at least paramagnetism independent of temperature. But in dilute solution in diamagnetic noble metals, transition group metals often exhibit almost free moments. Whether or not the Curie law is obeyed under such circumstances seems to depend partly on electron density. A good introduction to magnetization of ferrous alloys as a function of chemical composition is given by Messkin and Kussmann.[51]

In all work on iron and iron alloys, it should be remembered that oxygen in amounts less than 0.1%, and carbon in amounts less than 0.01% can alter the magnetic characteristics of the metal. The large effect of carbon traces may be due to lattice distortions brought about by carbon atoms or to cementite in the lattice of the iron. The ferromagnetic Curie point for pure iron is about 770°C. The change which occurs on raising the temperature to this point is referred to as a transition from α- to β-iron, although both forms have the same crystal structure. At 900°C. a true transition occurs from the body-centered to the face-centered cubic or γ-form. Addition of carbon lowers the β to γ transition temperature to 710°C. Austenite is generally paramagnetic, but a ferromagnetic form is said to have been obtained by Tarasov and Parker.[52] The room temperature characteristics of iron are dependent not only on the percentage of carbon present but also on the rate of cooling which determines the relative proportions of carbon remaining in solid solution or precipitating as cementite, Fe_3C.

Iron-silicon alloys are much used commercially. Silicon up to a few per cent has a markedly beneficial effect on the hysteresis and eddy losses of transformer steel. This element is very soluble in iron and its promotes the precipitation of carbon as graphite and at the same time combines vigorously with dissolved oxygen. Silicon therefore owes its beneficial effects at least in part to its scavenging action. Alloys of iron high in silicon are paramagnetic.[53] Single crystals of such alloys have been studied by

[48] E. Vogt, *Ann. Physik*, **18**, 771 (1933).

[49] A. Kussmann, *Chem. Ztg.*, **59**, 285 (1935).

[50] W. Messkin and J. M. Margolin, *Z. Physik*, **101**, 456 (1936).

[51] W. Messkin and A. Kussmann, *Die Ferromagnetischen Legierungen*. J. Springer, Berlin, 1932.

[52] L. P. Tarasov and E. R. Parker, *Phys. Rev.*, **56**, 379 (1939).

[53] C. Bedel, *Compt. rend.*, **196**, 262 (1933).

Williams.[54]　The definite compound, Fe_3Si_2, appears to be ferromagnetic,[55] with a Curie point at 91°C. Various other elements such as aluminum, arsenic, tin, and vanadium, alone or in combination, produce effects similar to those of silicon.

Alloys of iron with the other common ferromagnetic metals, cobalt and nickel, have also been very throughly studied.[56,57] Some of these, such as hypernik, FeNi, and permalloy, $FeNi_3$, have remarkably useful magnetic properties. These alloys have exceedingly high permeabilities. Others containing iron, cobalt, and nickel, such as perminvar, have a constant permeability for low magnetizing fields. Still others containing principally iron and cobalt are useful for permanent magnets. In some such alloys, the Curie point exhibits a sort of thermal hysteresis; that is, on rising temperature the ferromagnetism may be lost at, say, 600°C., but on falling temperature the ferromagnetism is not regained until far below 600°. In general, the alloying of one ferromagnetic metal with another yields a ferromagnetic alloy. But the permeability, saturation, hysteresis, and other magnetic properties may be very greatly modified. Still further modification is possible by heat treatment and working. In iron-nickel alloys,[58-60] both the saturation magnetization and the ferromagnetic anisotropy are affected, the order-disorder transformation involving $FeNi_3$. Related considerations apply to these and to many other alloy systems.

Iron, when present as a minor constituent with nonferromagnetic metals, generally imparts ferromagnetism to the whole mass. In very dilute solution, this must be due to precipitation of the iron. But there is some evidence that complexes or "cumuli" rich in iron may sometimes be formed as, for instance, in the copper-iron system.[61] The ferromagnetism of such alloys may sometimes be destroyed by quenching from a temperature high enough to dissolve all the iron. This, however, is not always possible. Bates and Illsley[62] find that iron amalgams retain their ferromagnetism even at very low iron concentrations. This is perhaps due to the presence of iron in these systems as a suspension of colloidal particles rather than as dissolved iron.[63] On the other hand, tempered solid solutions of iron in

[54] H. J. Williams, Phys. Rev., 52, 747 (1937).
[55] C. Guillaud, Compt. rend., 219, 122 (1944).
[56] G. W. Elmen, Bell. System Tech. J., 8, 435 (1929).
[57] A. J. Corson, Gen. Elec. Rev., 45, 573 (1942).
[58] E. M. Grabbe, Phys. Rev., 57, 728 (1940).
[59] P. Taglang, Compt. rend., 229, 704 (1949).
[60] J. J. Went, Physica, 15, 703 (1949).
[61] A. Knappwost and G. E. Bockstiegel, Z. Elektrochem., 57, 700 (1953).
[62] L. F. Bates and P. F. Illsley, Proc. Phys. Soc. (London), 49, 611 (1937).
[63] F. Pawlek, Z. Metallkunde, 41, 451 (1950).

aluminum show no evidence of ferromagnetism and, up to 3% concentration, the influence of the iron is almost negligible.[64]

Iron alloys with the platinum-group metals and with gold yield complex magnetic phase diagrams,[65-70] as do iron-cerium alloys.

81. Cobalt and Cobalt Alloys

The intensity of magnetization of cobalt at saturation lies between that of iron and of nickel. The ferromagnetic Curie point is probably about 1180° ± 20°C., although several authors give a somewhat lower value. The magnetic properties of cobalt are dependent on the previous history of the specimen. The metal in polycrystalline and in single-crystal form has received considerable study.[71-76]

Some publications on cobalt alloys are given below.[77-79] Many more are listed by Bozorth[8] and by Hoselitz.[9] Addition of chromium, aluminum, tungsten, or molybdenum results in all cases in progressive lowering of the apparent magnetic moment of the cobalt. According to Farcas, alloys of cobalt with molybdenum and tungsten are not ferromagnetic. Cobalt amalgams, like those of iron, are ferromagnetic. The cobalt in this system may be concentrated into a single small globule with the aid of a magnet.

There is, of course, a major technological interest in cobalt alloys of the Alnico type, widely used for permanent magnets. For our present purposes, the chief magnetochemical interest in cobalt is in relation to its catalytic activity.

[64] P. Weiss and W. Klemm, Z. anorg. u. allgem. Chem., 245, 288 (1940).

[65] M. Fallot, Compt. rend., 199, 128 (1934). (Fe-Pt)

[66] L. Graf and A. Kussmann, Physik Z., 36, 544 (1935). (Fe-Pt)

[67] M. Fallot, Compt. rend., 205, 227 (Fe-Ru, Fe-Os), 517 (Fe-Ir), 558 (Fe-Rh) (1937).

[68] S. T. Pan, A. R. Kaufmann, and F. Bitter, J. Chem. Phys., 10, 318 (1942). (Fe-Au)

[69] A. R. Kaufmann, S. T. Pan, and J. R. Clark, Revs. Mod. Phys., 17, 87 (1945). (Fe-Au)

[70] J. R. Clark, S. T. Pan, and A. R. Kaufmann, Phys. Rev., 63, 139 (1943).

[71] S. Kaya, Science Rept. Tôhoku Imp. Univ., First Ser., 17, 1157 (1928).

[72] K. Honda and H. Masumoto, Science Repts. Tôhoku Imp. Univ., First Ser., 20, 323 (1931).

[73] T. Farcas, Ann. phys., 8, 146 (1937). (Also Cr, Al, W, and Mo alloys)

[74] T. Farcas, Ann. sci. univ. Jassy, 23, I, 125 (1937).

[75] C. Guillaud and M. Roux, Compt. rend., 229, 1062 (1949).

[76] W. Sucksmith and J. E. Thompson, Proc. Roy. Soc. (London), A225, 362 (1954).

[77] L. F. Bates and C. J. W. Baker, Proc. Phys. Soc. (London), 52, 443 (1940). (Hg)

[78] F. W. Constant, Phys. Rev., 34, 1217 (1929); 35, 116 (1930); 36, 1654 (1930). (Pd, Pt)

[79] G. Grube and O. Winkler, Z. Elektrochem., 41, 52 (1935). (Pd)

82. Nickel and Nickel Alloys

Pure nickel may be prepared by electrolytic deposition or by thermal decomposition of the carbonyl. The specific magnetization of nickel is lower than that of iron, but the pure metal, its single crystals, and its alloys have received almost as much attention. Some references to general papers in this field are given below.[80-85] Very extensive surveys of this area are given by Hoselitz[9] and by Bozorth.[8]

Alloys of nickel with other ferromagnetic metals are themselves ferromagnetic. Addition of a nonferromagnetic metal to nickel generally results in a diminution of ferromagnetism of the alloy, although the alloy does not as a rule lose all its ferromagnetism until the nickel concentration becomes quite low. Various attempts have been made to relate the magnetic properties of nickel alloys to their composition.[86] Dorfman, for instance, has pointed out the relation between atomic moments in solid solution and the number of valence electrons. In general, the valence electrons of a diamagnetic metal such as copper or aluminum are thought to go into the d-band of the nickel, thereby lowering the magnetic moment. The problem is of interest in connection with current theories of catalytic activity and will be mentioned again in Chapter XV. Extensive theoretical studies on this subject are also reported by Néel,[87] Wohlfarth,[88] and Hirone.[80] References to the work of Taglang[59] and of others in this area were given in the previous sections. Relationships between the composition and the Curie temperature of nickel alloys are reported by Marian[89] and Niessen.[90] The Curie point and the saturation moment are roughly linear functions of the valence multiplied by the mole fraction of nickel.

Alloys of nickel and cobalt show no particular magnetic anomalies, except possibly in regard to the anisotropy of single crystals.[91,92] Shih[93]

[80] T. Hirone, *Science Repts. Tôhoku Imp. Univ.*, First Ser., **27**, 101 (1938).

[81] W. Gerlach, H. Bittel, and S. Velayos, *Sitzber. math.-naturw. Abt. bayer Akad. Munchen*, 1936, 81.

[82] S. Kaya, *Science Repts. Tôhoku Imp. Univ.*, First Ser., **17**, 639 (1928).

[83] E. C. Stoner, *Magnetism and Matter*. Methuen and Company, Ltd., London, 1934, p. 435.

[84] G. Gerloff, *Z. Physik*, **99**, 585 (1936).

[85] N. L. Brukhatov and L. V. Kirenskii, *Physik Z. Sowjetunion*, **12**, 602 (1937).

[86] Ya. Dorfman, *ibid.*, **3**, 399 (1933).

[87] L. Néel, *Compt. rend.*, **198**, 1311 (1934); **201**, 135 (1935).

[88] E. P. Wohlfarth, *Phil. Mag.*, **40**, 1095 (1949).

[89] V. Marian, *J. phys. radium*, **8**, 313 (1937); *Ann. phys.*, **7**, 459 (1937).

[90] K. F. Niessen, *Physica*, **6**, 1011 (1939).

[91] C. Sadron, *Ann. phys.*, **17**, 371 (1932).

[92] W. Broniewski and W. Pietrek, *Compt. rend.*, **201**, 206 (1935).

[93] J. W. Shih, *Phys. Rev.*, **50**, 376 (1936).

shows that these crystals have a reversal of the direction of easiest magnetization between about 10 and 20% of cobalt.

Nickel-manganese alloy is unusual.[94] The saturation magnetization passes through two peaks as the percentage of manganese is increased. The hysteresis curves are also unusual, and are markedly dependent on heat treatment.[95] Thompson[96] has shown that the magnetization, electrical resistance, and specific heat of the alloy all indicate that at 510°C. an order-disorder transformation takes place involving Ni_3Mn. The

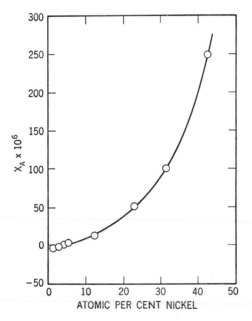

Fig. 97. Atomic susceptibility of nickel as a function of nickel concentration in nickel-copper alloys.

ordered structure is ferromagnetic, with the Curie point at 460°C. Further work on this interesting system is reported by Vol'kenshtein and Komar[97] and by Jaffee.[98]

Some of the many publications on alloys of nickel with nonferromag-

[94] S. Kaya and A. Kussmann, *Z. Physik*, **72**, 293 (1931).

[95] S. Valentiner and C. Becker, *ibid.*, **93**, 795 (1935).

[96] N. Thompson, *Proc. Phys. Soc. (London)*, **52**, 217 (1940).

[97] N. Vol'kenshtein and A. Komar, *J. Exptl. Theoret. Phys. (U.S.S.R.)*, **11**, 723 (1941).

[98] R. I. Jaffee, *J. Applied Phys.*, **19**, 867 (1948).

netic metals are listed below.[99-113]   A few of the main results achieved will
be discussed briefly.

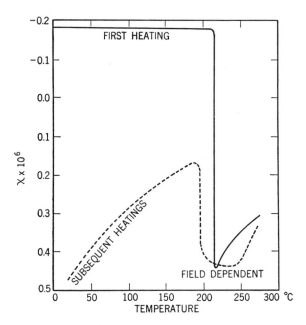

Fig. 98. Nickel amalgam.

For many nickel alloys, the susceptibilities are reasonably well represented by the equation $\chi = a + C/(T + \Delta)$.   In the copper alloys, for

[99] C. Manders, *Ann. Phys.*, **5**, 167 (1936).   (Ag, Zr, Pb, Au, Al, Ti, Si, An, Sb
V, As, Cr, Mo, W, Mn, Ru, Pd, Pt)

[100] E. Vogt and H. Krueger, *Ann. Physik*, **18**, 755 (1933).   (Au)

[101] R. Gans and A. Fonseca, *ibid.*, **61**, 742 (1920).   (Cu)

[102] E. H. Williams, *Phys. Rev.*, **38**, 828 (1931).   (Cu)

[103] K. E. Grew, *Proc. Roy. Soc. (London)*, **A145**, 509 (1934).   (Cu)

[104] W. H. Ross, *Phys. Rev.*, **46**, 46 (1934).   (Cu)

[105] G. Gustafsson, *Ann. Physik*, **28**, 121 (1937).   (Cu)

[106] W. Gerlach, *Z. Metallkunde*, **28**, 80, 183 (1936).   (Be)

[107] J. Schramm, *ibid.*, **30**, 327 (1938).   (Zn)

[108] Y. G. Dorfman and S. Sidorov, *Compt. rend. acad. sci. U.R.S.S.*, **19**, 381 (1938).
(Zn)

[109] L. F. Bates and J. H. Prentice, *Proc. Phys. Soc. (London)*, **51**, 419 (1939).   (Hg)

[110] L. F. Bates and C. J. W. Baker, *Proc. Phys. Soc. (London)*, **52**, 436, 443 (1940).
(Hg)

[111] A. Foster, *Proc. Leeds Phil. Lit. Soc., Sci. Sect.*, **2**, 401 (1933).   (Cr)

[112] G. Grube and O. Winkler, *Z. Elektrochem.*, **44**, 423 (1938).   (Mo)

[113] A. Kussmann and H. Nitka, *Physik Z.*, **39**, 373 (1938).   (Pt)

instance, the results indicate that there exists for nickel a strong para-magnetism independent of temperature. The atomic susceptibility of nickel as a function of nickel concentration in nickel-copper alloys is shown in Fig. 97.

In nickel-zinc alloys, the γ-phase has an abnormally high diamagnetism, suggesting zero moment for nickel. Extremely high diamagnetism is found in other γ-phases, for instance in brass.[114]

Nickel amalgams are interesting. When first prepared the amalgams are diamagnetic, in sharp contrast to those of iron and of cobalt which are invariably ferromagnetic. But when the nickel amalgam is heated to 225°C., it changes irreversibly to ferromagnetism. This transition is shown in Fig. 98.

Nickel-molybdenum alloys show rather complicated magnetic characteristics. The Curie temperatures of the ferromagnetic solid solutions decrease linearly with molybdenum content and reach 0°C. when the proportion of molybdenum reaches 10.5%. A substantial number of nickel alloys containing relatively small concentrations of copper, aluminum, tin, titanium, antimony, vanadium, molybdenum, and tungsten have been re-examined by Dorfman,[115] with results bearing on the general theory of alloy structure. Nickel-carbon systems have been studied by Gerlach.[116]

83. Oxides of Iron

Ferromagnetism is by no means limited to metals and alloys. Various oxides and other compounds of the ferromagnetic elements exhibit this property, as do a few compounds of elements near iron in the periodic table. From the chemist's standpoint, these substances are often of as much or more interest than the metals and alloys. Apart from its scientific interest, the study[117,118] of such ferromagnetic compounds is important in the magnetic concentration of minerals and in the construction of permanent oxide magnets and magnet cores. The magnetic properties of natural and artificial iron-oxygen compounds,[119,120] and the relationships among the hy-

---

[114] H. Endo, Sci. Repts. Tôhoku Imp. Univ., First Ser., 14, 479 (1925).

[115] Ya. Dorfman, J. Exptl. Theoret. Phys. U.S.S.R., 16, 349 (1946).

[116] W. Gerlach and J. von Rennenkampff, Z. Elektrochem., 49, 200 (1943).

[117] C. W. Davis, U. S. Bur. Mines, Rept. Investigations Tech. Papers, No. 3268, 91 (1935).

[118] E. T. Hayes, ibid., No. 3570 (1941).

[119] Y. Kato and T. Takai, J. Inst. Elec. Engrs. Japan, 53, 408 (1933).

[120] Y. Kato, T. Takai, N. Kawai, and H. Aikawa, J. Chem. Soc. Japan, 55, 584 1934).

drates and oxides of iron, are reviewed by Luyken and Kraeber[121] and by Welo and Baudisch.[122]

The ferromagnetism of magnetite, Fe_3O_4, has been known since the earliest times. Socrates refers to it in one of the Platonic dialogues, and, even earlier, Thales of Miletus, in the sixth century before Christ, is supposed to have had knowledge of the mineral. It occurs widely distributed in nature. The name is perhaps derived from Magnesia, the region in Asia Minor where the mineral was found in abundance.

Artificial magnetite may be prepared as follows:[123] a solution containing 1 mole of $FeSO_4$ and 2 moles of $Fe_2(SO_4)_3$ is poured into excess boiling solution of NaOH. The precipitate of Fe_3O_4 is washed free from alkali and dried in a desiccator. An alternative preparation yielding very near the stoichiometric Fe_3O_4 ratio is obtained by burning $Fe(CO)_5$ in a limited supply of air.

Magnetite prepared in different ways seems to have rather different magnetic characteristics and may differ quite sharply from natural magnetite. The ferromagnetic Curie point is about 572°C. The intensity of magnetization at saturation is about the same as that of nickel, or less than one-third that of electrolytic iron. The hysteresis of precipitated magnetite has been studied by Welo and Baudisch.[124,125] Lattice discontinuities affect the magnetic properties, including the hysteresis. Age-hardening[126] produces an increase in the hysteresis constants, as do the temperature and the nature of the reducing agent if the magnetite is prepared by reduction of hematite. Somewhat different magnetic properties are found in natural magnetite from different localities.[127–129] There is no doubt that magnetite has a peculiar second-order transition in the neighborhood of −160°C. Domenicali[130] and others have shown that the change, which is attended with a large drop in magnetization below that temperature, is dependent on crystallographic direction and also, to some extent, on the thermal and magnetic pretreatment of the sample. It is probable that

[121] W. Luyken and L. Kraeber, *Mitt. Kaiser-Wilhelm Inst. Eisenforsch. Dusseldorf,* 16, 169 (1934); 17, 149 (1936).

[122] L. A. Welo and O. Baudisch, *Am. J. Sci.,* 28, 139 (1934); *Chem. Rev.,* 15, 45 (1934).

[123] L. A. Welo and O. Baudisch, *Phil. Mag.,* 50, 399 (1925).

[124] O. Baudisch and L. S. Welo, *Naturwissenschaften,* 14, 1005 (1926).

[125] L. A. Welo and O. Baudisch, *Phil. Mag.,* 3, 396 (1927).

[126] D. J. Doan, *U. S. Bur. Mines Rept. Investigations Tech. Papers,* No. 3400, 65 (1938).

[127] F. Y. Levinson-Lessing, *Centr. Minerat. Geol.,* A1932, 369.

[128] O. N. Al'Thauzen, *Compt. rend. acad. sci. U.R.S.S.,* 31, 566 (1941).

[129] F. Rettig, *Beitr. angew. Geophys.,* 10, 225 (1943).

[130] C. A. Domenicali, *Phys. Rev.,* 78, 458 (1950).

magnetite suffers a phase change at $-160°C.$, losing its cubic structure, and becoming orthorhombic and essentially antiferromagnetic.[131-134]

At temperatures above $-160°C.$, the saturation moment obtained in magnetite is 4 Bohr magnetons. Recalling the difference between saturation moments and paramagnetic moments as previously described, one will see that this corresponds to four unpaired electron spins. An explanation of this has been given by Néel[135] in a comprehensive theory which applies to ferrites in general. Magnetite is properly considered a ferrite because it may be represented by the formula $MO \cdot Fe_2O_3$, in this case $M = Fe^{2+}$. Magnetite happens to have the "inverse spinel" structure. It is well known that in the spinels, the oxide ions form a face-centered cubic lattice and that the positive ions fill interstices between the oxygens. Examination of a model will show that there are two kinds of interstices, one of which has tetrahedral symmetry with four oxygen neighbors, the other octahedral with six oxygen neighbors. In normal spinels, the tetrahedral interstices are occupied by the divalent ions (M^{2+}), the octahedral by Fe^{3+}; but in inverse spinels the Fe^{3+} ions occupy the tetrahedral holes and the divalent ions some of the octahedral. Many variations are of course possible.

Néel's theory, in brief, is that the magnetic ions in tetrahedral holes always have a negative-spin interaction with neighboring ions in octahedral holes, but that interaction of either type with neighboring ions in the same type of holes will be positive. As an example, magnetite, which may be written $FeO \cdot Fe_2O_3$, has for each Fe^{3+} in a tetrahedral hole, one Fe^{3+} and one Fe^{2+} in an octahedral hole. The saturation moments are 5 for Fe^{3+} and 4 for Fe^{2+}. Hence, in each Fe_3O_4 group there are five electron spins in a tetrahedral setting directed antiparallel to five spins in an octahedral setting, with four spins remaining in the octahedral setting and thus capable of being directed parallel to other spins in the same setting. This leads to the conclusion that magnetite has an underlying antiferromagnetism, but that there will be an overlying ferromagnetism of four magnetons per Fe_3O_4 group. The experimental saturation moment is 4.2 magnetons. The theory of Néel has had considerable success and will be discussed further below. The theory serves also to interpret results[136] on magnetite in which Fe^{3+} is progressively substituted by nonmagnetic Al^{3+}.

[131] J. L. Snoek, *Colloques Internationaux, Ferromagnetism and Antiferromagnetism.* Grenoble, 1950, p. 80.

[132] C. Guillaud, *ibid.*, p. 91.

[133] H. J. Williams, R. M. Bozorth, and M. Goertz, *Phys. Rev.*, **91**, 1107 (1953).

[134] B. A. Calhoun, *ibid.*, **94**, 1577 (1954).

[135] L. Néel, *Ann. phys.*, **3**, 137 (1948).

[136] C. Guillaud and A. Michel, *J. phys. radium*, **12**, 65 (1951).

The almost unique position of magnetite amongst minerals and its possible uses are discussed by Dean and Davis.[137]   Colloidal magnetite has been examined by Elmore.[138]

Ferric oxide, Fe_2O_3, has been studied extensively.   It has some interesting and complicated magnetic properties.   There is a strongly ferromagnetic cubic form, γ-Fe_2O_3, or maghemite, and a paramagnetic form, α-Fe_2O_3, which is the mineral hematite.   Possibly still other forms exist.

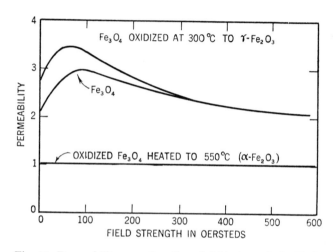

Fig. 99. Permeability as a function of field strength for Fe_3O_4, γ-Fe_2O_3, and α-Fe_2O_3.

If Fe_3O_4 is oxidized in oxygen at 220°C., there is a change of color from black to red accompanied by no important change of magnetic properties. If the temperature is now raised, at about 400°C. an irreversible change begins to take place with the loss of almost all of the ferromagnetism and the formation of α-Fe_2O_3.   But if Fe_3O_4 is heated in the absence of oxygen, it retains its color and ferromagnetism up to its Curie point and it may even be heated above 800°C. without destroying the reversibility of its thermomagnetic characteristics.   The permeabilities of the several phases are shown in Fig. 99.   The magnetic properties of γ-Fe_2O_3 appear to be almost identical with those of Fe_3O_4, and the Fe_2O_3 derived by oxidation of Fe_3O_4 at low temperature retains the magnetite structure. Fe_3O_4 and γ-Fe_2O_3 differ therefore only in color and in the presence of extra oxygen atoms which seem to be without influence on the magnetic properties.   There is

[137] R. S. Dean and C. W. Davis, *Am. Inst. Mining Met. Engrs.*, *Tech. Pub.*, **No. 795** (1937).

[138] W. C. Elmore, *Phys. Rev.*, **54**, 1092 (1938).

no ferrous iron in γ-Fe_2O_3. This fact seems to dispose of the suggestion that its magnetic properties are due to solid solution of magnetite in rhombohedral α-Fe_2O_3.[139] Haul and Schoon[140] show that the unit cell of γ-Fe_2O_3 is $Fe_{24}O_{36}$. The oxidation reaction is therefore

$$Fe_{24}O_{32} + 2O_2 \longrightarrow Fe_{24}O_{36}$$
$$\text{(magnetite)} \qquad\qquad \text{(maghemite)}$$

No essential difference was found in lattice constants or intensity distribution for γ-Fe_2O_3 prepared in several different ways.

Various magnetic characteristics of γ-Fe_2O_3 are given by Koenigsberger.[141] There is some doubt as to the Curie point. Welo and Baudisch[122] give 620°C. Other estimates range down to 500°C. The difficulty is that in the neighborhood of 400°C. the transition of ferromagnetic γ-Fe_2O_3 to nonferromagnetic α-Fe_2O_3 proceeds with considerable speed.

Other magnetic properties apparently vary in different samples in somewhat the same way as that found for magnetite.[142] The precise transition point for the change from cubic γ-Fe_2O_3 to rhombohedral α-Fe_2O_3 is also indefinite and depends on the method of purification. The ferromagnetic oxide may be stabilized[143] by introduction of sodium hydroxide, alumina, or silica, but the ferromagnetism of this substance is slowly diminished on standing. γ-Fe_2O_3 is a spinel type of compound in which the places normally occupied by the M^{2+} ions are vacant. To some degree this deficiency, and the instability which it produces, may be compensated by the addition of foreign ions. A method for finding the Curie point of γ-Fe_2O_3 is to find the Curie points of a series of oxides stabilized with alumina, then to extrapolate to a composition representing pure γ-Fe_2O_3. The transition itself is an interesting one which has received considerable study.[144,145] It is a very peculiar fact that the oxide stabilized by alkali may be treated to remove the alkali without much loss of stability. The activation energy for the transition has been determined by thermomagnetic analysis.[146] The magnetic properties of γ-Fe_2O_3 are further discussed by Herrmann.[146a]

Magnetite and maghemite are by no means the only ferromagnetic

[139] A. Michel and A. Girard, *Compt. rend.*, **201**, 64 (1935).

[140] R. Haul and T. Schoon, *Z. physik. Chem.*, **B44**, 216 (1939).

[141] J. G. Koenigsberger, *Naturwissenschaften*, **22**, 90 (1934).

[142] F. Wagenknecht, *Kolloid-Z.*, **112**, 35; **113**, 65 (1949).

[143] J. Huggett, *Ann. chim.*, [10], **11**, 447 (1929).

[144] A. Michel, G. Chaudron, and J. Bénard, *Colloques Internationaux, Ferromagnetism and Antiferromagnetism.* Grenoble, 1950, p. 51.

[145] V. Cirilli, *Gazz. chim. ital.*, **80**, 347 (1950).

[146] F. E. DeBoer and P. W. Selwood, *J. Am. Chem. Soc.*, **76**, 3365 (1954).

[146a] E. Herrmann, *Arhiv. Khem.*, **22**, 85 (1950); **23**, 22 (1951).

oxides of iron which have been reported. There is a group of oxide hydrates which will be discussed below, and there are also several oxides of rather doubtful status. Michel and Gallissot[147] suggest that the variable Curie points found for some of these substances may be due to a dependence of Curie point on the size of the crystallites. Bhargava and Prakash[148] state that the oxide resulting from heating ferrous oxalate in air is strongly paramagnetic, but that the oxides prepared from ferric oxalate or ferric benzoate are ferromagnetic. Hilpert, Maier, and Hoffmann[149] claim that hydrolysis of basic iron chloride, FeOCl, followed by dehydration at 250°C., yields a new ferromagnetic iron oxide. This view is supported by Forrer[150] who shows, however, that rapid dehydration at 275°C. yields an oxide of only slight ferromagnetism, but slow dehydration yields a strongly ferromagnetic oxide whose Curie point is 350°C. If this is heated more strongly, another ferromagnetic state results with Curie point 520°C. Finally, on heating at 600°C., a nonferromagnetic product results. The first strongly ferromagnetic form is the only one with the cubic lattice of γ-Fe_2O_3, all the others being rhombohedral. Glemser and Gwinner[151] claim the preparation of a new ferromagnetic hexagonal ferric oxide by oxidation of a ferrous salt after addition of excess sodium hydroxide. Whether or not these various products represent distinct chemical substances is uncertain. Chaudron and Michel[152] insist that there are only two varieties of Fe_2O_3: a rhombohedral, stable, feebly ferromagnetic form with Curie point 675°C.; and a cubic, unstable, strongly ferromagnetic form, transformable into the rhombohedral form at about 500°C., and readily dissociated in a vacuum into Fe_3O_4 and oxygen.

Ferric oxide forms two hydrates, α-$Fe_2O_3 \cdot H_2O$ or α-FeOOH, which is the mineral goethite, and γ-$Fe_2O_3 \cdot H_2O$ or γ-FeOOH, which is lepidocrocite.[153-157] Both these substances are paramagnetic with the same susceptibility of 42×10^{-6}; both obey the Curie law. The dehydration of hydrated γ-ferric oxide at moderate temperatures yields ferromagnetic γ-Fe_2O_3, a fact first observed long ago by von Kobell.[158] Further heating

[147] A. Michel and M. Gallissot, *Compt. rend.*, **207**, 140 (1938).

[148] L. N. Bhargava and S. Prakash, *Z. anorg. u. allgem. Chem.*, **217**, 27 (1934).

[149] R. S. Hilpert, K.-H. Maier, and A. Hoffmann, *Ber,*, **71B**, 2676 (1938).

[150] R. Forrer, *Compt. rend.*, **207**, 670 (1938).

[151] O. Glemser and E. Gwinner, *Z. anorg. u. allgem. Chem.*, **240**, 161 (1939).

[152] G. Chaudron and A. Michel, *Compt. rend.*, **208**, 90 (1939).

[153] O. Baudisch and L. A. Welo, *Naturwissenschaften*, **21**, 659 (1933).

[154] L. A. Welo and O. Baudisch, *Phil. Mag.*, **17**, 753 (1934).

[155] W. H. Albrecht, *Ber.*, **B62**, 1475 (1929).

[156] W. H. Albrecht and E. Wedekind, *Z. anorg. u. allgem. Chem.*, **202**, 205, 209 (1931).

[157] R. Chevallier and S. Mathieu, *Compt. rend.*, **207**, 58 (1938).

[158] F. von Kobell, *Grundzuge der Mineralogie.* Nürmberg 1838, p. 304.

above about $500°C$. will, of course, yield $\alpha\text{-Fe}_2\text{O}_3$. The transition of lepido-crocite to maghemite has been carefully investigated by Welo and Baudisch.[159] It appears that the compounds γ- and $\alpha\text{-FeOOH}$ may be intermediates in the transition $\gamma\text{-Fe}_2\text{O}_3 \rightarrow \alpha\text{-Fe}_2\text{O}_3$. Maghemite is very readily converted to $\alpha\text{-Fe}_2\text{O}_3$ if heated with water in a sealed tube. Further studies on the preparation and magnetic properties of lepidocrocite are reported by Michel and Gallissot.[160] Colloidal $\gamma\text{-Fe}_2\text{O}_3$ has been studied by Elmore[138] and by Boutaric and Bonneviale.[161]

It was mentioned above that $\alpha\text{-Fe}_2\text{O}_3$ has been thought to be feebly ferromagnetic. This conclusion was definitely reached by Hayes,[162] but further work suggests that the ferromagnetism often encountered in hematite is due to a small magnetite or maghemite impurity. In the writer's laboratory, little difficulty has been experienced in preparing $\alpha\text{-Fe}_2\text{O}_3$ apparently free from field-strength dependence of susceptibility. But there is a substantial amount of evidence of several kinds that there is present a weak, anisotropic ferromagnetism which disappears below $15°C$.[163,164]

A number of studies has been made on the hydrous oxides of uncertain composition which sometimes exhibit ferromagnetism, sometimes not. Quartaroli[165] finds that a compound with exceptionally large susceptibility may be obtained by precipitation from ferrous ammonium sulfate, followed by hydrogen peroxide oxidation. Similarly, ferromagnetic gels are sometimes produced by the addition of base to mixtures of ferrous and ferric ions in solution.[166−169]

It was pointed out above that substances of the general formula $MO \cdot Fe_2O_3$, of which magnetite is one, are known as ferrites. If the ion M^{2+} has approximately the same radius as Fe^{2+}, the resulting ferrite[170] will have the cubic spinel structure and will, in many cases, be ferromagnetic. These substances, sometimes referred to as "ferroxcubes," have received extensive theoretical and technological study. An application stems from

[159] L. A. Welo and O. Baudisch, *Phil. Mag.*, **24**, 80 (1937); **31**, 103 (1941).

[160] A. Michel and M. Gallissot, *Compt. rend.*, **206**, 1252 (1938).

[161] A. Boutaric and R. Bonneviale, *Bull. soc. chim. France, Mém.*, **2**, 1998 (1935).

[162] E. T. Hayes, *U. S. Bur. Mines, Repts. Investigations Tech. Papers*, **No. 3570** (1941).

[163] L. Néel, *Revs. Mod. Phys.*, **25**, 58 (1953).

[164] P. W. Anderson, F. R. Merritt, J. P. Remeika, and W. A. Yager, *Phys. Rev.*, **93**, 717 (1954).

[165] A. Quartaroli, *Gazz. chim. ital.*, **63**, 279 (1933).

[166] R. Chevallier and S. Mathieu, *Compt. rend.*, **206**, 1469, 1955 (1938).

[167] T. Katourai and K. Yamasaki, *Kolloid-Z.*, **84**, 311 (1938).

[168] T. Kita, *Sci. Papers Inst. Phys. Chem. Research (Tokyo)*, **40**, 123 (1942).

[169] T. Katusurai, *Bull. Inst. Phys. Chem. Research (Tokyo) Chem. Ed.*, **23**, 216 (1944).

[170] H. Forestier, *Compt. rend.*, **192**, 842 (1931).

the high permeability together with low electrical conductivity; they are discussed by Snoek[171] and others.[172,173]

Some of the ferrites, such as $ZnO \cdot Fe_2O_3$, are not ferromagnetic. It has been found that a mixed crystal formed from zinc ferrite, together with a ferromagnetic spinel such as copper or manganese ferrite, has a much higher permeability than do either the copper ferrite or the manganese ferrite alone. This useful effect is related to the lowering of the Curie point produced when a ferromagnetic substance is diluted with a nonferromagnetic.

An outline of Néel's theory of ferromagnetism in ferrites was presented above, in connection with magnetite. It remains to give a few examples of the theory in its applications to other ferrites. The reviews of Snoek[131] and Guillaud[132] should be consulted for further examples. For a ferrite of the composition $MnO \cdot Fe_2O_3$, the theory calls for a saturation moment of 5 magnetons (obs. 5.0) because the Mn^{2+} ion has five unpaired electrons and these are free to align parallel with five spins from the iron in sites of the same kind, but are counterbalanced by five spins from the iron in sites of the other kind. On the other hand, the ferrite $ZnO \cdot Fe_2O_3$ will have zero moment because the Zn^{2+} is diamagnetic, the 10 spins in the two iron ions merely opposing each other.

It will be clear also that in a spinel the eight positive valences (necessary to balance the four oxygen ions) need not be made up of $(1 \times 2) + (2 \times 3)$ positive charges, as in those examples mentioned above. Thus, in γ-Fe_2O_3 there are $(\frac{1}{3} \times 0) + (\frac{8}{3} \times 3) = 8$; or in lithium ferrite, $Li_{0.5}$-$Fe_{2.5}O_4$, probably $(1 \times 3) + (0.5 \times 1) + (1.5 \times 3) = 8$. The saturation moment in lithium ferrite is made up of five spins opposed to 7.5 spins, with the lithium contributing nothing. This leaves a moment of 2.5 (obs. 2.5) magnetons. For substances in which the ferromagnetism arises from atoms in two kinds of sites, Néel suggests the term "ferrimagnetism." A review of ferrimagnetism is given by Smart.[173a] It may aid the reader if the several kinds of magnetism are summarized in terms of the interactions which give rise to them.

A. If no permanent magnetic dipoles are present, the substance will be diamagnetic.

[171] J. L. Snoek, *New Developments in Ferromagnetic Materials*. Elsevier Publ. Co., New York, 1947.

[172] A. Fairweather, E. F. Roberts, and A. J. E. Welch, *Reports on Progress in Physics*, **15**, 142 (1952).

[173] E. W. Gorter, *Saturation Magnetization and Crystal Chemistry of Ferrimagnetic Oxides* Thesis, University of Leiden, 1954. Also, *Philips Research Repts.*, **9**, 295, 321, 403 (1954).

[173a] J. S. Smart, *Am. J. Phys.*, **23**, 356 (1955).

B. If permanent magnetic dipoles are present, there arise four different possibilities. These are:

1. No interaction between the dipoles yields paramagnetism.
2. Positive interaction yields ferromagnetism.
3. Negative interaction yields antiferromagnetism.
4. Simultaneous unequal positive and negative interaction yields ferrimagnetism.

It should be mentioned that methods alternative or supplementary to Néel's have been suggested for the theoretical treatment of ferrimagnetism.[173b,c]

Among the astonishing variety of ferrites and related oxides which have been studied, the following few will be mentioned: nickel (ferrite, aluminates); and nickel (ferrite, gallates); various combinations of lithium, iron, aluminum, chromium, titanium, and copper; and ferric oxides and rare earth oxides (some of these, such as $Fe_2O_3 \cdot Sm_2O_3$, have two Curie points.[174-177] The magnetic properties of the rare earth ferrites (if they may be so called) are quite difficult to understand, although an attempt to interpret them has been made by Néel.[177a] Ferrimagnetism is also shown by a variety of chromites, such as $FeCr_2O_4$, and by similar compounds in which the oxygen is replaced by sulfur.[177b] In a few cases it appears that there may be some negative interaction between the electrons in atoms occupying similar sites. At any rate, the observed moments are occasionally lower than might be predicted. In all examples of ferrimagnetism, as in many examples of antiferromagnetism to be discussed in the next chapter, the distances between adjacent transition ions are so great as effectively to prohibit any exchange interaction between them directly. There has, therefore, grown up the belief that exchange in such systems proceeds through a negative-ion bridge. In the ferrites, this is simply an oxide ion. Exchange interaction taking place in this fashion is known as "superexchange."

84. Other Ferromagnetic Substances

In this section there will be brief reference to ferromagnetic substances

[173b] Y. Yafet and C. Kittel, *Phys. Rev.*, **87**, 290 (1952).

[173c] S. V. Vonsovskii, *Izvest. Akad. Nauk S.S.S.R., Ser. Fiz.*, **18**, 312 (1954).

[174] L. R. Maxwell and S. J. Pickart, *Phys. Rev.*, **92**, 1120 (1953).

[175] E. Kordes and E. Röttig, *Z. anorg. u. allgem. Chem.*, **264**, 34 (1951).

[176] E. Pouillard, *Ann. chim.*, **5**, 164 (1950).

[177] G. Guiot-Guillain, *Compt. rend.*, **237**, 1654 (1953).

[177a] L. Néel, *Compt. rend.*, **239**, 8 (1954).

[177b] F. K. Lotgering, *The Ferrimagnetism of Some Sulphides and Oxides*, Thesis, University of Utrecht, 1956. (Will appear in *Philips Research Repts.*)

other than those already mentioned. But the chief interest in such substances is often to be found in the reactions which they undergo and in their mutual (phase) relationships. Further reference to some of these substances will be found later in this chapter and also in the following chapter.

Ferrous sulfide[178] is probably weakly ferromagnetic,[144] although it has been claimed that pure FeS is antiferromagnetic.[179,180] The ferromagnetism definitely depends on the amount of dissolved or combined sulfur in the system. Michel *et al.*[144] give the Curie point for pure FeS as 600°C. The saturation intensity is not high. Compounds of the type of pyrrhotite, Fe_7S_8, are also ferromagnetic, although not strongly so.[181] Pyrrhotite is very peculiar in its magnetic properties.[182,183] Its ferromagnetism is practically restricted to the base of the hexagonal plane. It is paramagnetic along other planes. According to Ramaseshan,[184] iron pyrites are paramagnetic, although the susceptibilities of different samples vary rather widely. Ferric sulfide, Fe_2S_3, the existence of which has long been open to question, appears to be strongly ferromagnetic.[185] The disulfide, FeS_2, is virtually diamagnetic.[186]

Hilpert, Maier, and Hoffmann prepared thiomagnetite, $FeS \cdot Fe_2O_3$, by heating equimolar amounts of FeS and Fe_2O_3 in an atmosphere of nitrogen.[187] The compound has a Curie point at 580°C. It also shows an anomaly at $-138°$ to $-118°$C., similar to that shown by one variety of magnetite.

Other ferromagnetic compounds of iron include the carbides, nitrides, and borides. Cementite, Fe_3C, is of considerable interest from the part it plays in influencing the magnetic properties of steel. It has a fairly high saturation intensity, and its Curie point is about 210°C. There are at least two other ferromagnetic iron carbides, to which reference will be made later. The compound, Fe_4N, has been prepared by Guillaud.[188] The Curie point is reported as 488°C. Silicides and other compounds are referred to

[178] P. Weiss and R. Forrer, *Ann. phys.*, **12**, 279 (1929).

[179] S. Miyahara, *Proc. Phys. Math. Soc. Japan*, **22**, 358 (1940).

[180] K. Yosida, *Physica*, **17**, 794 (1951).

[181] A. Michel, *Ann. chim.*, **8**, 317 (1937).

[182] T. Okamura, T. Hirone, and S. Miyahara, *Proc. Phys. Math. Soc. Japan*, **23**, 132 (1941).

[183] H. Haraldsen and W. Klemm, *Z. anorg. u. allgem. Chem.*, **223**, 409 (1935).

[184] S. Ramaseshan, *Proc. Indian Acad. Sci.*, **25A**, 201 (1947).

[185] S. V. Lipin, *J. Applied Chem. (U.S.S.R.)*, **16**, 258 (1943).

[186] L. Néel and R. Benoit, *Compt. rend.*, **237**, 444 (1953).

[187] R. S. Hilpert, K.-H. Maier, and A. Hoffmann, *Ber.*, **71B**, 2682 (1938).

[188] C. Guillaud and H. Creveaux, *Compt. rend.*, **222**, 1170 (1946).

by Michel *et al.*[144] Ferromagnetism is also found in certain carbonitrides of iron.[188a]

Cobaltous oxide is apparently not ferromagnetic, although Bhatnagar[189] reports that the oxide obtained by heating metallic cobalt in nitric acid is so. The oxide, Co_3O_4, sometimes exhibits ferromagnetism but this may be due to partial reduction to the metal. Bose and Raychaudhuri[190] have found both CoO and Co_3O_4 to be paramagnetic. Similarly nickel oxide has often been reported as being ferromagnetic but this seems to be due to metallic nickel,[191] although ferromagnetism in high oxygen NiO has recently been described.[191a,191b] Reference to this will be made in the next chapter. Nickel disulfide, NiS_2, is ferromagnetic, as are the corresponding cobalt and manganese sulfides.[192] The existence of a ferromagnetic nitride of nickel, approaching the formula Ni_4N, is mentioned by Bernier.[193]

The most familiar ferromagnetic substances containing manganese are the Heusler alloys which normally contain manganese, aluminum, and copper.[194,195] The maximum intensity of magnetization at saturation is about the same as that for nickel, and the Curie temperature is about 330°C. In these alloys the aluminum may be replaced by tin, arsenic, antimony, bismuth, boron, gallium, or indium.[196] The copper may be replaced by silver. The intermetallic compounds, $SnMn_4$ and $SnMn_2$, are also ferromagnetic, as is the Mn_2In phase in the manganese-indium system,[197-199] and a substance of approximate composition Mn_2SbO.[199a]

Ferromagnetism has also been reported for a large group of manganese

[188a] R. Bridelle and A. Michel, *Compt. rend.*, **239**, 274 (1954).

[189] S. S. Bhatnagar, B. Prakash, and M. A. Qayyum, *J. Indian Chem. Soc.*, **18**, 540 (1941).

[190] A. K. Bose and D. P. Raychaudhuri, *Science and Culture*, **3**, 246 (1937).

[191] W. Klemm and K. Hass, *Z. anorg. u. allgem. Chem.*, **219**, 82 (1934).

[191a] Y. Shimomura, I. Tsubokawa, and M. Kojima, *J. Phys. Soc. Japan*, **9**, 521 (1954).

[191b] N. Perakis, A. Serres, G. Parravano, and J. Wucher, *Compt. rend.*, **242**, 1275 (1956).

[192] H. Haraldsen and W. Klemm, *Z. anorg. u. allgem. Chem.*, **223**, 409 (1935).

[193] R. Bernier, *Ann. chim.*, **6**, 104 (1951).

[194] S. Valentiner and G. Becker, *Z. Physik*, **83**, 371 (1933).

[195] L. A. Carapella and R. Hultgren, *Trans. Am. Inst. Mining Met. Engrs.*, **No.** 1405 (1941).

[196] F. A. Hames and D. S. Eppelsheimer, *J. Metals*, 1, No. 8, Trans., 495 (1949).

[197] H. H. Potter, *Phil. Mag.*, **12**, 255 (1931).

[198] H. H. Potter, *Proc. Phys. Soc.*, **41**, 135 (1939).

[199] W. V. Goeddel and D. M. Yost, *Phys. Rev.*, **82**, 555 (1951).

[199a] G. D. Adam and K. J. Standley, *Proc. Phys. Soc. (London)*, **67A**, 1022 (1954).

phosphides, arsenides, carbides, nitrides, and so forth.[200-215] One of the most peculiar of these is manganese arsenide. This substance is ferromagnetic at room temperature but loses this property at 45°C. When the substance is cooled the ferromagnetism does not reappear above 34°C. This peculiar effect is apparently related to a phase transition in which there is a contraction perpendicular to the axis of six-fold symmetry without other change. Somewhat related effects are shown by certain other compounds of manganese, although not by the phosphide.[216] One of the most interesting series of ferromagnetic manganese compounds has been reported by Jonker and van Santen.[217] Lanthanum hypomanganite, $LaMnO_3$, in which the manganese has an oxidation state of 3+, forms mixed crystals with various manganites, $Me^{2+}MnO_3$, provided Me^{2+} has a fairly large radius as Ca^{2+}, Ba^{2+}, Pb^{2+}. Some of these mixed crystals have been shown to have the perovskite structure. These are ferromagnetic with a maximum moment for the $LaMnO_3$-$CaMnO_3$ system at 30% $CaMnO_3$. This maximum corresponds to seven unpaired electron spins attributed to one Mn^{3+} ion and one Mn^{4+} ion. The Curie temperature also reaches a maximum at 30% $CaMnO_3$. Interest in this system arises from the nature of the interactions which must be responsible for the ferromagnetism. Interactions between Mn^{3+}-Mn^{3+} and between Mn^{4+}-Mn^{4+} are generally found to be negligible or negative. Interaction between Mn^{3+}-Mn^{4+} may be positive, leading to ferromagnetism, but these pairs of ions are separated by an oxide ion. If this is the source of the ferromagnetism, then it must be considered a case of superexchange, through the oxygen. Reference to this phenomenon has often been made in connection

[200] O. von Auwers, *Z. anorg. u. allgem. Chem.*, **108**, 49 (1919).

[201] L. F. Bates, *Proc. Roy. Soc. (London)*, **A117**, 680 (1928). (As)

[202] L. F. Bates, *Phil. Mag.*, **8**, 714 (1929); **13**, 393 (1932); **16**, 657 (1933). (As)

[203] L. F. Bates, *Proc. Phys. Soc. (London)*, **42**, 441 (1930); **43**, 87 (1931). (As)

[204] A. Kussmann and B. Scharnov, *Z. Physik*, **47**, 770 (1928).

[205] R. Ochsenfeld, *Ann. Physik*, **12**, 353 (1932). (N)

[206] B. G. Whitmore, *Phil. Mag.*, **7**, 125 (1929). (As, P)

[207] E. Persson, *Z. Physik*, **57**, 115 (1929).

[208] K. Thielmann, *Ann., Physik*, **37**, 41 (1940). (Bi)

[209] W. Messkin and A. Kussmann, *Die Ferromagnetischen Legierungen.* J. Springer, Berlin, 1932.

[210] C. Guillaud, *Ann. phys.*, **4**, 671 (1949). (As, Sb)

[211] C. Guillaud, *J. recherches centre natl. recherche sci. (Paris)*, **Hors ser. 1946,** 27. (Sb, Bi)

[212] A. Serres, *J. phys. radium*, **8**, 146 (1947). (S, Sb, Sn, Te)

[213] C. Guillaud, *ibid.*, **12**, 143 (1951). (Bi)

[214] G. Grube and O. Winkler, *Z. Elektrochem.*, **42**, 815 (1936). (Pd)

[215] M. Auwarter and A. Kussmann, *Ann. Physik*, **7**, 169 (1950). (Pt)

[216] K. H. Sweeney and A. B. Scott, *J. Chem. Phys.*, **22**, 917 (1954).

[217] G. H. Jonker and J. H. van Santen, *Physica*, **16**, 337 (1950).

with antiferromagnetism, but this seems to be the first case in which it yields ferromagnetism.

Similar ferromagnetic compositions[218] are found in the system (La, Sr)CoO_3 in which positive superexchange apparently takes place between Co^{3+} and Co^{4+}.

Ferromagnetism is also found in some chromium compounds, such as the telluride, hydride, arsenides, and certain oxides.[144] It has been known for a long time that some substance produced by the oxidation of chromium sesquioxide exhibits ferromagnetism. It has been surmised that this might be the dioxide, and some fairly convincing evidence to this effect is presented by Guillaud, Michel, et al.[144] The Curie temperature is 116°C. On the other hand, the substance was not obtained pure, and Bhatnagar[219] has reported a normal paramagnetic susceptibility corresponding to two unpaired electrons for a compound believed to be CrO_2. This question is of some interest in connection with the use of magnetic measurements in the study of catalytically active solids containing chromium. There has been perhaps too much tendency to look for ferromagnetism in a certain compound. A more realistic approach is to look for ferromagnetism at certain interatomic distances favorable to ferromagnetism. These distances do not, of necessity, correspond to a definite stoichiometric compound. The ferromagnetism of CrO_2 has, however, been recently confirmed by Glemser,[220] and others.[220a]

One of the most surprising cases of ferromagnetism has been reported by Gruner and Klemm[221] for AgF_2. This substance shows a well-defined Curie point at $-110°C$. AgO does not show this effect.

Bates and Taylor[222] find that when powdered chromium, obtained from chromium amalgam, is heated with sulfur in vacuum, ferromagnetic compounds are formed. At least two combinations of uncertain composition occur. Their Curie points are at 30° and 90 to 100°C. Chromium-platinum alloys are generally paramagnetic, but Friederick and Kussmann[223] find that in the concentration range of 7 to 20% chromium, the alloys are ferromagnetic with Curie points ranging from 50°C. on the platinum side to 900°C. on the chromium side.

Ferromagnetism has also been found in the metals of the rare earth

[218] G. H. Jonker and J. H. van Santen, ibid., 19, 120 (1953).

[219] S. S. Bhatnagar, B. Prakash, and A. Hamid, J. Chem. Soc., 1938, 1428.

[220] O. Glemser, U. Hauschild, and F. Trüpel, Z. anorg. u. allgem. Chem., 277, 113 (1954).

[220a] S. M. Ariya, S. A. Shchukarev, and V. B. Glushkova, Zhur. Obscheĭ. Khim., 23, 1241 (1953). (This paper was not available to the author.)

[221] E. Gruner and W. Klemm, Naturwissenschaften., 25, 59 (1937).

[222] L. F. Bates and G. G. Taylor, Proc. Phys. Soc. (London), 51, 33 (1939).

[223] E. Friederick and A. Kussmann, Physik Z., 36, 185 (1935).

elements. Gadolinium was discovered by Urbain, Weiss, and Trombe[224,225] to be ferromagnetic, with a Curie point of about 16°C. The only other rare earth metal which seems to have received extensive study in this way is dysprosium,[226] which has a Curie temperature in the neighborhood of 105°K., but this seems to depend somewhat on the field. It will be clear that most, if not all, paramagnetic rare earth elements will be expected to become ferromagnetic at low temperatures. In fact, some degree of field-strength dependence of susceptibility and of incipient ferromagnetism is quite common among paramagnetic substances at extremely low temperatures. Gadolinium-magnesium alloys also exhibit ferromagnetism.[227] Ferromagnetism in uranium hydride will be referred to in Chapter XIV.

85. Some Chemical Applications of Ferromagnetism

In this section there will be presented a few examples of magnetic methods used in physical metallurgy, in phase studies involving inorganic compounds, in a variety of industrial control problems, and in mineralogy. The examples will be restricted to those in which ferromagnetism is a dominant property; and, even in this group, those studies of primary interest in heterogeneous catalysis will be deferred to Chapter XV.

In the study of metals and alloys, the primary magnetic properties, Curie point and saturation intensity, are of value in connection with composition and phase constitution. The secondary properties, such as permeability and coercive force, are sensitive to grain structure, stress, lattice defects, and the presence of impurities. Some applications of these methods were presented in Chapter III. One further example will be given here. This deals with the use of the thermomagnetic curve in the study of a precipitation process. Many other examples are given by Hoselitz.[9]

The example chosen is the nickel-gold system as studied by Gerlach.[228] An alloy containing 23 atom % gold and heated to homogeneity at 950°C. gives a thermomagnetic curve (I) shown in Fig. 100. The Curie point at 95°C. is in agreement with the expected recession on the addition of a diamagnetic metal. If, now, the alloy is held at 400°C. for progressively longer periods, the thermomagnetic curve changes, as shown in Fig. 100. A phase with Curie point at 325°C. appears. This corresponds roughly to a solution containing 3 atom % gold, and this phase increases in amount as the heating time increases. This is a clear indication of the precipitation

[224] G. Urbain, P. Weiss, and F. Trombe, *Compt. rend.*, **200**, 2132 (1935).

[225] F. Trombe, *J. recherches centre natl. recherche sci. Labs. Bellevue (Paris)*, No. 23, 61 (1953).

[226] F. Trombe, *Compt. rend.*, **221**, 19 (1945).

[227] F. Gaume-Mahn, *Bull. soc. chim. France*, **1954**, 569.

[228] W. Gerlach, *Z. f. Metallkunde*, **28**, 2, 117 (1936); **29**, 102, 124 (1937).

of a nickel-rich phase. It might be expected that the original phase would simultaneously become richer in gold, but the slow rise of the Curie point from 95°C. to about 120° must mean, as pointed out by Hoselitz, that some very gold-rich aggregates must be present during the reaction, thus accounting for the apparent depletion of gold in both "visible" constituents. A more complicated case in the copper-iron system has been given, more recently, by Knappwost.[229]

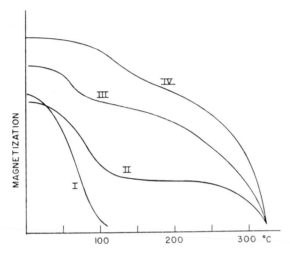

Fig. 100. Specific magnetization *versus* temperature for nickel-gold alloys, showing increasing precipitation.

Turning to nonmetallic systems, the principal applications of magnetic methods in this area are to qualitative and quantitative estimation of ferromagnetic components. An excellent example is the phase relationships of the iron-oxygen system near FeO. This was described earlier on p. 58. It will be recalled that the paramagnetic FeO disproportionates at moderate temperatures into iron and magnetite. Thus, a sample of FeO prepared by quenching from a fairly high temperature will show a strong, irreversible increase of magnetization as the temperature is subsequently slowly raised. A fairly substantial number of similar studies has been made on other systems. One of the most important of these is the iron-carbon system. Most of these studies have, however, been made with a view to elucidating the mechanism of the Fischer-Tropsch and related catalytic syntheses. They will be referred to in Chapter XV. It might be thought that permeability, coercive force, and so forth might also have applica-

[229] A. Knappwost. *Z. Elektrochem.*, 56, 840 (1952).

tions in this area, but so far not much use has been made of them. Considerable use is made, however, in some industrial laboratories of the permeability, coercive force, and Curie point of mineral and metal samples under investigation. Those methods related to the Curie point have been described in Chapter III. Some of these tests are described under Standards of the American Society for Testing Materials, but most have been developed for highly specialized analytical work and are not commonly found

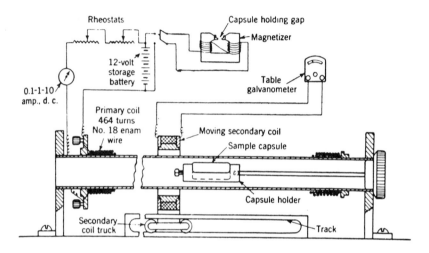

Fig. 101. A form of coercimeter for determining coercive force, principally of powdered specimens. (Reproduced from *U. S. Bur. Mines, Rept. Invest.*, 3400.)

even in well-equipped analytical and testing laboratories. In general, such methods tend to be empirical; that is to say, the methods consist of comparing the magnetic behavior of a sample with that of a standard. This area was summarized by von Auwers[230] and the essentials remain the same, although many refinements of technique have been introduced. The general nature of the field will be indicated by a few examples. Among the results of such tests may be mentioned the development of magnetic separation methods for minerals, and the possible relation between coercive force and geochemical history of lodestones.[231,232] Such studies may, of course, be carried on with instruments of types described in Chapter III, but

[230] O. von Auwers, *Phys. Z.*, **28**, 871 (1927).

[231] C. W. Davis, *U. S. Bur. Mines, Repts. Investigations Tech. Papers*, **No. 3268**, 91 (1935).

[232] D. J. Doan, *ibid.*, **No. 3400**, 65 (1938). This paper contains an excellent review of the magnetic properties of iron oxides, especially of magnetite.

the specialized instruments which have been developed are more convenient for the purpose.[233]

The first instrument to be described is the "Coercimeter." Its use depends on the fact that, between certain limits, there is a linear relationship between coercive force and specific surface of ferromagnetic powders. The instrument may thus be used to determine grain size and to follow

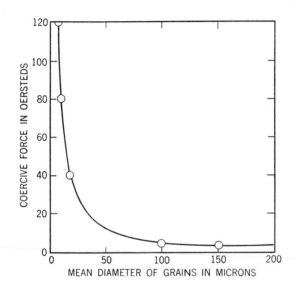

Fig. 102. Relationship between coercive force and particle size. Extremely small sizes are not shown.

the progress and efficiency of grinding operations.[234–237] The sample is magnetized first in a strong field, then removed to a controlled field the strength of which can be balanced against the residual magnetism of the sample. Exact balance is indicated by a movable secondary coil attached to a galvanometer. The primary current producing the controlled field is measured by an ammeter. A diagram of one type of the apparatus is shown in Fig. 101. It should be pointed out that coercive force may be defined in two ways, either as the field of force necessary to reduce ϑ, the intensity

[233] F. S. Wartman, *ibid.*, **3400**, 33 (1938).

[234] H. Neumann, *Archiv. techn. Messen*, **4**, T64 (1933).

[235] V. H. Gottschalk, *U. S. Bur. Mines, Rept. Investigations Tech. Papers*, **3268**, 83 (1935); **3400**, 21 (1938); *Physics*, **6**, 127 (1935).

[236] C. W. Davis and M. Hartenheim, *Rev. Sci. Instr.*, **7**, 147 (1935).

[237] F. D. DeVaney and W. H. Coghill, *Am. Inst. Mining Met. Engrs., Tech. Pub.*, **No. 862** (1938).

of magnetization, to zero in an ϑ-H curve, or as the force necessary to reduce B to zero in a B-H curve. It is the former which is measured by the "Coercimeter" described. A curve showing the dependence of coercive force on grain size is shown in Fig. 102. Probably coercive force depends on other factors as well as specific surface, and extension of the applicability of the "Coercimeter" is to be expected to such properties as strains, lattice discontinuities, and carbon content.

The determination of carbon content in a steel is a common and important analytical problem. Many efforts have been made to solve it without recourse to chemical methods and, for specialized cases, some of these

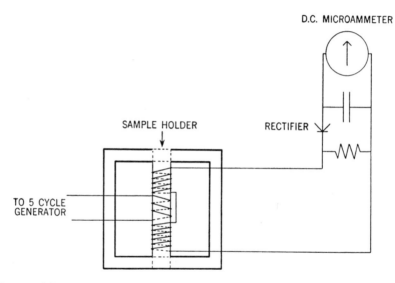

Fig. 103. A low frequency AC permeameter. [After Rogers, Wentzel, and Riott, *Trans. Am. Soc. Metals*, **29**, 969 (1941).]

have been very successful.[238,239] Properties such as magnetic saturation, permeability at low field strength, and coercive force have all been tried. It is generally necessary to give the sample a careful heat treatment before measurement. Sometimes the kind of heat treatment necessary depends on the carbon content. A low frequency A.C. permeameter devised by Rogers, Wentzel, and Riott gives reasonably good results for routine work. A primary and a secondary coil are wound around a sample holder (Fig. 103). The primary is connected to a five-cycle generator, the secon-

[238] P. Klinger and H. Fucke, *Archiv. Eisenhütten.*, **3**, 347 (1929).

[239] B. A. Rogers, K. Wentzel, and J. P. Riott, *Trans. Amer. Soc. Metals*, **29**, 969 (1941).

dary is connected through a copper oxide rectifier and suitable resistances
to a direct current microammeter.   The carbon content of a specimen

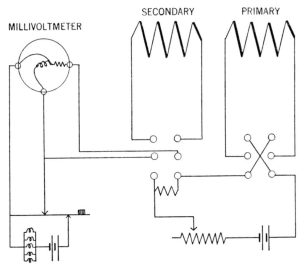

Fig. 104. Electrical circuit of the "Carbanalyzer."   (After Work and Clark, *Trans. Am. Inst. Mining Met. Engrs.*, **1940**, 140.   *Iron Steel Div.*, 475.)

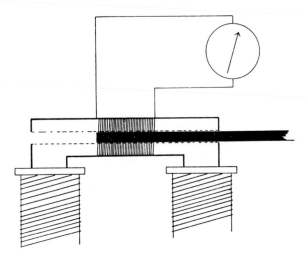

Fig. 105. Isthmus permeameter.

placed in the sample holder may be related by calibration curves to the
readings of the microammeter.

The "Carbanalyzer,"[240] a diagram of which is shown in Fig. 104, is a special form of permeameter. It measures the change in flux in a bar produced by a known change in magnetic force. The instrument requires a specially cast sample, but it is rugged, requires no elaborate training for its use, and gives the carbon content in a steel bath with great rapidity.

The "Carbometer"[241] is a related type of permeameter in which the sample is magnetized under certain standardized conditions. The intensity of magnetization is measured by induction in a coil attached to a ballistic galvanometer. The galvanometer reading is proportional to the difference

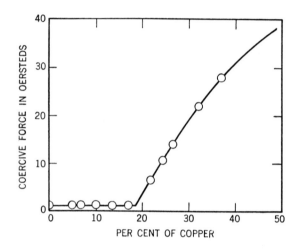

Fig. 106. Coerceive force for an alloy containing a 1:1 ratio of iron and nickel and a varying proportion of copper.

in induction caused by two fields of different strength. As for the "Carbanalyzer" a specially designed test bar is required, but under favorable conditions the carbon content of a steel may be given in units of 0.01% in 2 minutes.

Another type of permeameter[241a] specially designed for saturation and coercive force measurements is shown in Fig. 105. The sample is magnetized, then rapidly withdrawn from a secondary coil mounted as shown. Readings of the galvanometer attached to the secondary indicate the magnetization of the sample. An example of the results obtained for the

[240] H. K. Work and H. T. Clark, *Am. Inst. Mining Met. Engrs., Tech. Publ.*, **No. 1132** (1939).

[241] G. Soler, *Metal Progress*, **31**, 159 (1937).

[241a] A. Kussmann, *Z. Metallkunde*, **26**, 25 (1934).

coercive force of an iron-nickel-copper alloy is shown in Fig. 106. Related data are given by Butts and Reiber.[242]

Still another isthmus permeameter of very flexible design is described by Gottschalk and Davis.[243] Various other instruments such as the Siemens "Ferrometer"[244] (Fig. 107) of similar design and purpose are also in use. The applications of such instruments could probably be extended almost indefinitely. Their use has, for instance, been suggested in controlling the rate of formation of tin-iron alloy during hot-dip tinning.[245]

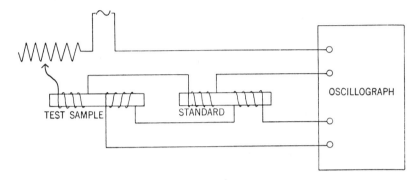

Fig. 107. Siemens ferrometer.

We complete this section with a brief outline of magnetic methods as applied to mineralogy. The magnetic study of natural substances is not often rewarding from the point of view of structural chemistry. Many, if not most, natural substances contain varying proportions of iron, and this iron, or part of it, may be in an unpredictable magnetic state. To report, for instance, that a sample of natural pyrolusite has a magnetic susceptibility of 200×10^{-6} merely betrays the fact that the sample is, magnetically speaking, grossly impure, although the actual weight per cent of impurity may be quite small.

A field in which such measurements have some use is in geochemical mapping and prospecting, and although this lies somewhat apart from the chief purpose of this book, the method will be referred to briefly below.

Occasional references to the magnetic properties of individual mineral specimens has been made throughout this book. To these we may add augite, epidote, tourmaline, and a tektite. The magnetic anisotropy has

[242] A. Butts and P. L. Reiber, Jr., *A.S.T.M. Proc.*, **49**, 857 (1949).

[243] V. H. Gottschalk and C. W. Davis, *U. S. Bur. Mines, Repts. Investigations Tech. Papers*, **3268**, 51 (1935).

[244] W. Thal, *Z. techn. Phys.*, **15**, 469 (1934).

[245] A. V. Seyboldt, *Trans. Am. Soc. Metals*, **29**, 937 (1941).

also been measured.[246] Natural mica has been investigated by Nilakantan,[247] and Kendall and Yeo[248] have studied both natural and synthetic micas. The magnetic susceptibility of coal has been reported by Wooster and Wooster[249] and others. Some coal samples exhibit magnetic anisotropy.

There has been a number of attempts to relate magnetic properties to the geochemical history of minerals.[250–259] Applications of such methods to the history of such minerals as magnetite are obvious. A group of further references in this field is given below.[260–271b] These should be adequate to introduce the reader to the general area.

[246] A. Sigamony, *Proc. Indian Acad. Sci.*, **20A**, 15, 200, 261 (1944).

[247] P. Nilakantan, *ibid.*, **8A**, 39 (1938).

[248] J. T. Kendall and D. Yeo, *Nature*, **161**, 476 (1948).

[249] W. A. Wooster and N. Wooster, *Proc. Conf. Ultra-fine Structures of Coals and Cokes*, Brit. Coal Utilisation Research Assoc., **944**, 322.

[250] J. G. Koenigsberger, *Beitr. angew. Geophys.*, **4**, 385 (1934).

[251] E. Thellier, *Colloques Internationaux. Ferromagnetism and Antiferromagnetism.* Grenoble, 1950, p. 57.

[252] K. G. Bronshtein, *J. Geol. Ukrain. Acad. Sci.*, **7**, Nos. 1–2, 167, 178 (1940).

[253] R. Chevallier and J. Pierre, *Ann. Phys.*, **18**, 385 (1932).

[254] H. Reich, *Beitr. angew. Geophys.*, **9**, 40 (1941).

[255] K. Puzicha, *ibid.*, **9**, 158 (1941).

[256] F. Kutscher, *ibid.*, **9**, 187 (1941).

[257] B. Marsch and H. J. Schoene, *ibid.*, **8**, 195 (1939).

[258] H. Reich, *Z. deut. geol. Ges.*, **93**, 443 (1941).

[259] O. N. Al'Thauzen, *Compt. rend. acad. sci. U.R.S.S.*, **31**, 661 (1941).

[260] J. S. Koehler, *Am. J. Physics*, **10**, 275 (1942). (Changes produced by crystal dislocations.)

[261] G. Ising, *Geol. Fören. Förh.*, **64**, 126 (1942). (Layered clays)

[262] A. M. Gaudin and H. R. Spedden, *Am. Inst. Mining Met. Engrs., Tech. Pub.* **No. 1549** (1943). (sulfide minerals)

[263] L. L. Nettleton and T. A. Elkins, *Geophysics*, **9**, 60 (1944). (rock classification)

[264] E. Niggli, J. Altmann, and H. Vos, *Schweiz. mineralog. petrog. Mitt.*, **26**, 92 (1946). (manganese-iron, data on Mn ores and minerals)

[265] W. E. Seeds and J. H. J. Poole, *Sci. Proc. Roy. Dublin Soc.*, **24**, 135 (1946). (serpentine deposits)

[266] V. I. Karmazin and B. I. Naugolnikov, *Zavodskaya Lab.*, **12**, 712 (1946). (iron ores)

[267] H. R. Joesting, L. O. Bacon, and J. H. Getz, *U. S. Bur. Mines, Rept. Invest.* **No. 4175** (1948). (manganese-iron ore deposits)

[268] W. T. Millar, H. E. Kuehn, G. E. Dent, and R. S. Sanford, *ibid.*, **No. 4338**, (1948). (magnetite)

[269] J. McG. Bruckmaster and B. S. Rao, *Proc. Phys. Soc.*, **63B**, 931 (1950). (igneous rocks)

[270] D. A. Kiskyras, *Neues Jahrb. Mineral., Geol., Abhandl.*, **80A**, 297 (1950). (pyrrhotite)

[271] J. W. Graham, *J. Geophys. Research*, **58**, 243 (1953).

An attempt has been made to relate Néel's theory of ferrimagnetism to certain problems of geomagnetism.[272]

Magnetic prospecting methods have some use in the correlation of strata information obtained from wells situated at various distances from each other. Susceptibilities are plotted as a function of well depth.[273] The sequence of susceptibilities in the different strata is related to similar sequences obtained from other wells in the vicinity. In this way it may be possible to locate tectonic structures favorable to the accumulation of valuable mineral deposits. Other properties such as radioactivity, fossil content, and heavy mineral content, are used for the same purpose.

[271a] J. Roquet, *Ann. Geophys.*, **10**, 226 (1954).

[271b] J. E. Hiller, *Fortschr. Mineral.*, **33**, 155 (1955).

[272] G. Fanselau and F. Frolich, *Forschungen v. Fortschr.*, **28**, 134 (1954).

[273] "A Method of Determining Magnetic Susceptibility of Core Samples" in *Geophysical Prospecting*, published by the American Institute of Mining and Metallurgical Engineers, 1932.

CHAPTER THIRTEEN

ANTIFERROMAGNETISM

86. Introduction to Antiferromagnetism

In Chapter VIII it was pointed out that the theory of atomic paramagnetic susceptibilities applies only to atoms and ions which are free from mutual exchange interaction; that is, to those which are magnetically dilute. In Chapter XII it was indicated how magnetically concentrated substances generally show strong exchange interaction between adjacent magnetic atoms or ions, and that this effect may lead, on the one hand to ferromagnetism, on the other to antiferromagnetism. Ferromagnetism arises from a parallel locking of spin moments. Antiferromagnetism arises from an antiparallel locking of spin moments. The phenomenon of antiferromagnetism is found in more diversified substances than is ferromagnetism and, although it has assumed no comparable technological importance, it is theoretically just as interesting.

The susceptibility of a typical antiferromagnetic substance as a function of temperature is shown in Fig. 108. The critical point is known as the antiferromagnetic Curie temperature, although it is more frequently called the Néel point. It bears considerable resemblance to its more familiar counterpart, the ferromagnetic Curie point.

Above the Curie point, most antiferromagnetics follow the Curie-Weiss law and yield magnetic moments which seem reasonable on the basis of the expected number of unpaired electrons in the magnetic ions. Below the Curie point, the susceptibility drops precipitously and sometimes becomes more or less dependent on field strength. Passage through the critical point is accompanied by a specific heat anomaly. It is a so-called second-order transition.

It will be recalled that the ferromagnetic Curie point often differs by several degrees from the Weiss constant as determined above the Curie point. There is increasing evidence in antiferromagnetics to show that T_c, the temperature at which the susceptibility is a maximum, may be much smaller numerically than Δ in the Curie-Weiss law. For instance, for manganous oxide, the critical point occurs at about 122°K., but the Weiss constant is about five times larger.

326

Suggestions for understanding the phenomenon of antiferromagnetism were first made by Néel.[1,2]   The theory of the effect has been developed by Néel,[3] Kramers,[4] Hulthén,[5] Bitter,[6] Van Vleck,[7] and others.   Extensive discussions will be found in the reports of the Grenoble and Washington Conferences in 1950 and 1952, respectively.   These were published in *J. phys. radium* for March 1951 and *Revs. Mod. Phys.* for January 1953.   The present status of the subject is reviewed by Lidiard.[8]

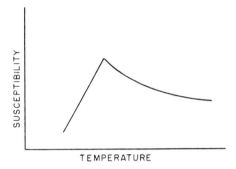

Fig. 108. Temperature dependence of susceptibility for a typical antiferromagnetic.

Early developments in the theory of antiferromagnetism, considering nearest neighbors only, suggested that $\Delta = T_c = 2JzS(S+1)/3k$, where J is the exchange integral, z the number of nearest paramagnetic neighbors possessed by each paramagnetic ion, S the spin-quantum number, and k the Boltzmann constant.   More recent developments have been described by Van Vleck.[9]   These developments are due to the suggestion of Néel that antiferromagnetic substances may be thought of as consisting of two sublattices in one of which the atomic moments all orientate in one direction while in the other sublattice they all orientate in the opposite direction. Consideration of the influence of second nearest neighbors on each other make it less mysterious why Δ is often much larger than T_c.   For relatively simple structures, there is a fair agreement between theory and experiment,

[1] L. Néel, *Ann. Phys.*, **18**, 64 (1932).

[2] L. Néel, *ibid.*, **5**, 256 (1936).

[3] L. Néel, *ibid.*, **3**, 137 (1948).

[4] H. A. Kramers, *Physica*, **1**, 182 (1934).

[5] E. Hulthén, *Proc. Amsterdam Acad. Sci.*, **39**, 190 (1936).

[6] F. Bitter, *Phys. Rev.*, **54**, 79 (1938).

[7] J. H. Van Vleck, *J. Chem. Phys.*, **9**, 85 (1941).

[8] A. B. Lidiard, *Reports on Progress in Physics*, **17**, 201 (1954).

[9] J. H. Van Vleck, *Colloques Internationaux, Ferromagnetism and Antiferro-magnetism.*   Grenoble, 1950, p. 114.

but the results of theory have not yet reached the stage where they may be considered very helpful in the solution of purely chemical problems. The antiferromagnetic Curie point is reasonably satisfactorily given by

$$T_c = {}^2/_3 |J| zk^{-1} S(S+1)$$

while above the Curie point the susceptibility obeys a Curie-Weiss law

$$\chi_A = Ng^2\beta^2 S\,(S+1)/[3k\,(T + \Delta)]$$

where all the terms have their usual significance. The quantities T_c and Δ for a few typical antiferromagnetics are given in Table XXVIII. It should be added that antiferromagnetism, like ferromagnetism, is strongly dependent on crystal structure, and that below the Curie temperature the magnetization is highly anisotropic in single crystals.

TABLE XXVIII

Curie Temperatures and Weiss Constants for Some Typical Antiferromagnetic Substances

Substance	$T_c\,°K.$	$-\Delta\,°K.$
MnF_2	72	113
FeF_2	79	117
MnO_2	84	316
MnO	122	610
FeO	198	570

For antiferromagnetic oxides, such as MnO, it seems probable that exchange interaction is important only between second nearest manganese neighbors along a straight line through an oxide ion. Such a process is referred to as superexchange. The antiferromagnetism of MnO_2 has been related by Bizette to exchange through two oxygens along the line Mn-O-O-Mn. In view of the active interest in antiferromagnetism it may be hoped that developments in theory will soon permit some application of magnetic measurements to structural problems involving colloidal substances to which reference will be made later.

There has been some consideration of the transition metals, other than those showing ferromagnetism, as antiferromagnetics. These will, however, be considered in the following chapter.

87. Antiferromagnetic Substances

In this section there will be reviewed some experimental data on antiferromagnetic substances. Some references will also be given to other substances which, though magnetically concentrated, do not seem to show antiferromagnetism. The order will be that of increasing atomic number, and attention will be paid to more or less definitely characterizable substances. Questions involving phase ratios and stoichiometry will be discussed in a later section.

While antiferromagnetism is generally considered to be found only in elements and compounds of the transition series, it will be recalled (p. 257) that superoxides show some evidence of being antiferromagnetic at low temperatures.

Neutron diffraction has proved to be particularly useful in the study of antiferromagnetism (and of ferromagnetism). This has been especially true in confirming the view of Néel concerning the two interlocking sublattices; but the subject of neutron diffraction lies beyond the scope of this book. Paramagnetic resonance has also been applied to several antiferromagnetics.[10] While the results look promising they are difficult to interpret.

Titanium. Starr, Bitter, and Kaufmann[11] have studied the susceptibilities of solid titanium dichloride and trichloride over a wide range of temperature. The compounds are definitely paramagnetic and the trichloride shows a strong anomaly at low temperatures. This and other titanium halides have also been studied by Klemm and co-workers.[12,13] Unfortunately, the agreement between the two sets of workers is not good. Klemm states that titanium trichloride becomes definitely antiferromagnetic below 60°C. But at somewhat higher temperatures fair agreement is found with the spin-only formula. Titanium triiodide shows quite small susceptibilities at all temperatures.

Measurements in the author's laboratory have shown titanium sesquioxide to be definitely antiferromagnetic, with a critical point near the specific heat anomaly at about 250°K. The susceptibility of the titanium in this compound is quite low owing, presumably, to strong exchange effects.[14] There is a surprising increase of susceptibility in the neighborhood of 473°C.[14a]

Vanadium. The magnetically concentrated compounds of this element have been fairly thoroughly studied. They are reviewed by Bizette.[15] The pentoxide seems to have a small paramagnetism which is independent of temperature. The dioxide[16] shows a strong antiferromagnetic Curie point

[10] L. R. Maxwell and T. R. McGuire, *Revs. Mod. Phys.*, **25**, 279 (1953).

[11] C. Starr, F. Bitter, and A. R. Kaufmann, *Phys. Rev.*, **58**, 977 (1940).

[12] W. Klemm and L. Grimm, *Z. anorg. u. allgem. Chem.*, **249**, 209 (1942).

[13] W. Klemm and E. Krose, *Z. anorg. Chem.*, **253**, 209 (1947).

[14] S. F. Adler and P. W. Selwood, *J. Am. Chem. Soc.*, **76**, 346 (1954).

[14a] M. Foëx and J. Wucher, *Compt. rend.*, **241**, 184 (1955).

[15] H. Bizette, *J. phys. radium*, **12**, 161 (1951).

[16] W. Klemm and E. Hoschek, *Z. anorg. u. allgem. Chem.*, **226**, 359 (1936)

at about 68°C. But this critical point although confirmed by Perakis and Wucher,[18] seems not to be present in all forms of the compound.[16a] Above this temperature, the moment seems to be about normal for one unpaired electron.[17] Measurements on a sample containing 3% of the sesquioxide seem to show some kind of hysteresis in the heating-cooling curves between 115 and 350°K.[18]

Vanadium sesquioxide has been studied by Hoschek and Klemm[19] and by M. Foëx.[20] The susceptibility of this substance is very peculiar. Between −83° and 60°C., the Curie-Weiss law is followed with an approximately normal moment for two unpaired electrons. From 60° to 110°C., the susceptibility is constant, while above 250° the Curie-Weiss law is again followed.

Magnetic measurements on some vanadium spinels and related substances have been reported by Rüdorff and Reuter.[21] Other magnetically concentrated compounds of vanadium which have been studied include the sulfides, halides and arsenides.[22] The susceptibilities of these and related compounds are further discussed by Klemm[16,19] and Foëx.[17]

Chromium. The susceptibility of chromium sesquioxide is reported by several investigators to vary with the mode of preparation,[23,24] but others claim that the differences are due to traces of adsorbed gases.[25] It seems to the writer that the differences found by various workers for the susceptibilities of chromia and similar compounds are related to the strong influence of the state of aggregation on magnetic properties, as will be described in a later section. Chromia shows a very weakly defined antiferromagnetic Curie point in the neighborhood of 45 to 55°C.; the susceptibility at liquid air temperature is definitely lower than at room temperature.[26,27] Above the Curie point, it has an approximately normal moment of about 3.8 Bohr magnetons, but a Weiss constant of well over 300°. The established ferromagnetism of chromium dioxide was mentioned in

[16a] M. S. Archer, D. S. P. Roebuck, and F. J. Whitby, *Nature*, **174**, 754 (1954).

[17] G. Foëx, *Bull. soc. chim. France*, **1949**, Mises au point D157.

[18] N. Perakis and J. Wucher, *Compt. rend.*, **235**, 354 (1952).

[19] E. Hoschek and W. Klemm, *Z. anorg. u. allgem. Chem.*, **242**, 63 (1939).

[20] M. Foëx, S. Goldsztaub, R. Wey, J. Jaffray, R. Lyand, and J. Wucher, *J. recherches centre natl. recherche sci.*, Lab. Bellevue (*Paris*), **21**, 237 (1952).

[21] W. Rüdorff and B. Reuter, *Z. anorg. Chem.*, **253**, 177 (1947).

[22] A. Morette, *Bull. soc. chim.*, **9**, 146 (1942).

[23] W. H. Albrecht and E. Wedekind, *Z. anorg. u. allgem. Chem.*, **210**, 105 (1933).

[24] C. J. Gorter, W. J. de Haas, and J. van den Handel, *Proc. Acad. Sci. Amsterdam*, **36**, 168 (1933).

[25] S. S. Bhatnagar, A. Cameron, E. H. Harbard, P. L. Kapur, A. King, and B. Prakash, *J. Chem. Soc.*, **1939**, 1433.

[26] G. Foëx and M. Graff, *Compt. rend.*, **209**, 160 (1939).

[27] J. Volger, *Nature*, **170**, 1027 (1952).

Chapter XII. Chromium trioxide, CrO_3, has no unpaired electrons, but Tilk and Klemm[28] have shown that it has a small temperature-independent paramagnetism. Other magnetically concentrated chromium compounds which have been studied include the sulfide, selenide, telluride, and antimonide.[29-31] In this connection the work of Rüdorff and Stegemann is instructive.[32] They have compared the lattice constants and magnetic susceptibilities for chromic sulfide, sodium thiochromite, and potassium thiochromite. The sulfide is strongly antiferromagnetic, but the two thiochromites have negative values of the Weiss constant and approximately normal moments for three unpaired electrons. The data and the interpretation put on them by Rüdorff and Stegemann are shown in Table XXIX.

TABLE XXIX

Cr-Cr Distance and Weiss Constant for Cr_2S_3 and the Alkali-Thiochromite

	Cr-Cr distance A.	$\Delta°C.$	Interaction
Cr_2S_3	2.78–3.42	—	Very strong atomic binding with antiparallel spin.
$NaCrS_2$	3.53	− 37	Weak atomic binding with parallel spin.
$KCrS_2$	3.62	−116	Stronger atomic binding with parallel spin.

It should be pointed out that in these compounds, if covalent bonds exist between adjacent chromium ions as suggested by Haraldsen and Klemm,[33] such bonds may be present only in the hexagonal chromium layers and not between the layers. Such model substances as these therefore give a relatively simple means of studying mutual magnetic interaction between paramagnetic ions.

The halides of chromium have also received extensive investigation.[34-37] Chromic fluoride and chromic chloride follow the Curie-Weiss law reasonably well near room temperature, but near liquid hydrogen temperature the susceptibility becomes markedly dependent on field strength. As shown by de Haas, Schultz, and Koolhaus,[38] the susceptibility of anhydrous

28 W. Tilk and W. Klemm, *Z. anorg. u. allgem. Chem.*, **240**, 355 (1939).

29 H. Haraldsen and E. Nygaard, *Z. Elektrochem.*, **45**, 686 (1935).

30 H. Haraldsen and E. Kowalski, *Z. anorg. u. allgem. Chem.*, **224**, 329 (1935).

31 G. Foëx and M. Graff, *Compt. rend.*, **209**, 160 (1939).

32 W. Rüdorff and K. Stegemann, *Z. anorg. u. allgem. Chem.*, **251**, 376 (1943).

33 H. Haraldsen and W. Klemm, *ibid.*, **220**, 183 (1934).

34 H. Bizette and B. Tsaï, *Compt. rend.*, **211**, 252 (1940).

35 W. Klemm and E. Krose, *Z. anorg. Chem.*, **253**, 226 (1947).

36 C. Starr, F. Bitter, and A. R. Kaufmann, *Phys. Rev.*, **58**, 977 (1940).

37 S. S. Shalyt, *J. Exptl. Theoret. Phys. (U.S.S.R)*, **8**, 518 (1938); **9**, 1073 (1939); *Compt. rend. acad. sci. U.R.S.S.*, **24**, 680 (1939).

38 W. J. de Haas, B. H. Schultz, and J. Koolhaas, *Physica*, **7**, 57 (1940).

chromic chloride shows a complete hysteresis loop at 14.8°K. For chromous chloride, the susceptibility is a complicated function of temperature.[39]

Manganese. The oxides of manganese have received intensive study.[40] Manganous oxide, MnO, is one of the classical examples of antiferromagnetism. Among the many series[41-44] of magnetic measurements on this substance, the most reliable seem to be those of Bizette, Squire, and Tsaï. The sharp antiferromagnetic Curie point is at −151°C., which is close to the well-known specific-heat anomaly. Above this temperature, the Curie-Weiss law is followed with a moment of 5.9 Bohr magnetons and a Weiss constant of about 610°. Below the Curie point, there may be some field-strength dependence of susceptibility.

Manganese sesquioxide, Mn_2O_3, probably exists in two forms. Of these the α-Mn_2O_3 is the better established. Its magnetic properties have been studied by Bhatnagar et al.,[25] Honda,[41] and others.[40] No antiferromagnetic Curie point appears down to −189°C. The γ-Mn_2O_3 likewise gives no evidence of antiferromagnetism.[40]

The compound Mn_3O_4 has also been studied by Honda[41] and others.[40] No Curie point has been found down to −185°C.

One of the most interesting of manganese compounds is the oxyhydroxide, MnOOH. This substance has been shown in the author's laboratory[40] and elsewhere[45] to have a susceptibility virtually independent of temperature from −185° to 25°C. This appears to indicate a Curie point above room temperature, but at somewhat elevated temperatures the compound decomposes. The substance is certainly worth further study.

Manganese dioxide has also received extensive investigation. Well-crystallized pyrolusite obtained by thermal decomposition of manganous nitrate has been shown by Bhatnagar et al.,[25] and several others[40] to have a reciprocal susceptibility approximately linear with temperature. The author finds some curvature below room temperature. Bizette and Tsaï[46,47] report the antiferromagnetic Curie point as −189°C. Measurements on a single crystal obtained by oxidation of manganite, MnOOH, show an increasing anisotropy when the temperature is taken below the Curie

[39] E. Lips, *Helv. Phys. Acta*, **7**, 537 (1934).
[40] T. E. Moore, M. Ellis, and P. W. Selwood, *J. Am. Chem. Soc.*, **72**, 856 (1950).
[41] K. Honda and T. Soné, *Science Repts. Tôhoku Imp. Univ., First Ser.*, **3**, 139 (1914).
[42] R. W. Tyler, *Phys. Rev.*, **44**, 776 (1933).
[43] A. Birckel, *Cahiers phys.*, No. **25**, 45 (1944).
[44] H. Bizette, C. F. Squire, and B. Tsaï, *Compt. rend.*, **207**, 449 (1938).
[45] W. H. Albrecht, *Z. anorg. Chem.*, **259**, 291 (1949).
[46] H. Bizette and B. Tsaï, *Proceedings of the Paris Conference on the Polarization of Matter.* April 4–9, 1949.
[47] H. Bizette, *Colloques Internationaux, Ferromagnetism and Antiferromagnetism.* Grenoble, 1950, p. 13.

point. It must be emphasized that in this and similar compounds, the susceptibility is greatly influenced by the perfection of the crystal lattice and by the presence of impurities in modest amounts. The susceptibility of a transition metal oxide is in no sense linear with concentration if the diluent is in solid solution and not merely mechanically mixed.

Manganese trifluoride seems not to exhibit antiferromagnetism, but manganous fluoride, chloride, and bromide[48] at low temperatures show various magnetic anomalies. The fluoride, MnF_2, has a Curie point at about $72°K$. The magnetic anisotropy of a single crystal of this substance has been measured by Griffel and Stout.[49,50] Above about $100°K$., the anisotropy is quite small, but below the Curie point it becomes very large indeed. The susceptibility perpendicular to the c-axis increases slightly from $70°$ to $14°K$. but that parallel to the c-axis approaches zero at $0°K$. This peculiar behavior is somewhat like that found in ferrous carbonate. It is apparently due to a chain-like superstructure with opposed electron spins linking the chains to each other.

Many manganese sulfides, selenides, tellurides, borides, nitrides, and arsenides show antiferromagnetism, at least in certain stoichiometrical proportions.[51-54] These are listed by Bizette[15] and Lidiard.[8]

Iron. Bizette and Tsaï[55] have shown ferrous oxide to have a maximum in the susceptibility curve at $198°K$. Above this temperature, the Curie-Weiss law is followed with a Weiss constant of $570°$. Here again it must be emphasized that the magnitude of the Weiss constant must be quite sensitive to impurities and crystal lattice imperfections. Below the Curie point, the susceptibility of ferrous oxide shows some dependence on field strength. It should be pointed out that stoichiometric FeO is rarely if ever attained, and that the magnetic and crystallographic properties are strongly dependent on the composition.[56]

The *alpha* form of iron sesquioxide has been the subject of much investigation. It is sometimes said to be ferromagnetic, and there is no doubt that most natural specimens and many laboratory-prepared samples show moderate to slight field-strength dependence of susceptibility and other evidence of ferromagnetism. But, as pointed out in Chapter XII, it is not difficult to prepare samples which seem to be free from any indication

[48] W. Klemm and E. Krose, *Z. anorg. Chem.*, **253**, 226 (1947).
[49] M. Griffel and J. W. Stout, *J. Chem. Phys.*, **18**, 1455 (1950).
[50] H. Bizette and B. Tsaï, *Compt. rend.*, **238**, 1575 (1954).
[51] J. W. Stout and M. Griffel, *Phys. Rev.*, **76**, 144 (1949).
[52] H. Bizette and B. Tsaï, *Compt. rend.*, **209**, 205 (1939).
[53] W. J. de Haas, B. H. Schultz, and J. Koolhaas, *Physica*, **7**, 57 (1940).
[54] C. Starr, F. Bitter, and A. R. Kaufmann, *Phys. Rev.*, **58**, 977 (1940).
[55] H. Bizette and B. Tsaï, *Compt. rend.*, **217**, 390 (1943).
[56] B. T. M. Willis and H. P. Rooksby, *Acta Cryst.*, **6**, 827 (1953).

of ferromagnetism, and the evidence is certainly not complete that the pure compound is ferromagnetic. In the author's laboratory, such samples have often been prepared by precipitation from a *fresh* sample of ferric nitrate, made by oxidation of ferrous ammonium sulfate with concentrated nitric acid. This question is carefully reviewed by Néel[57,58] who believes that the apparent ferromagnetism often found in this compound is due to an impurity, although other opinions are often expressed. There seems little doubt that pure α-Fe$_2$O$_3$ has an antiferromagnetic Curie point at 675°C. Above this temperature, the moment seems a little higher than anticipated for five unpaired electrons. Some further references to the supposed ferromagnetism of this substance are indicated below.[59-62] In the neighborhood of 250°K., α-Fe$_2$O$_3$ undergoes a transition with a sharp rise of susceptibility. This transition disappears on the addition of quite small amounts of titanium dioxide.[63]

Ferrous fluoride, according to Bizette and Tsaï,[64] exhibits antiferromagnetism with a Curie point at 79°K. These authors have also examined ferric fluoride.[65] As might be expected, it shows some field-strength dependence of susceptibility at low temperatures.

Anhydrous ferrous chloride has a specific-heat anomaly at 14°K. and another at slightly higher temperature. The magnetic susceptibility shows remanence and hysteresis near these temperatures.[66-68] Ferric chloride in the anhydrous state seems to follow the Curie-Weiss law with a Weiss constant of 12° over the temperature range 150° to 293°K.[69-71]

Among other antiferromagnetic compounds of iron which have been studied, ferrous *o*-silicate is interesting as having considerably greater magnetic dilution than most substances showing this property.[72]

[57] L. Néel, *Compt. rend.*, **228**, 64 (1949).

[58] L. Néel, *Ann. phys.*, **4**, 249 (1949).

[59] R. Chevallier and Z. E. Begui, *Bull. soc. chim.*, **4**, 1735 (1937).

[60] J. L. Snoek, *Physica*, **16**, 333 (1950).

[61] R. Chevallier, *Colloques Internationaux, Ferromagnetism and Antiferromagnetism*. Grenoble, 1950, p. 24.

[62] C. Guillaud, *ibid.*, p. 341; *J. phys. radium*, **12**, 489 (1951).

[63] F. J. Morin, *Phys. Rev.*, **78**, 819 (1950).

[64] H. Bizette and B. Tsaï, *Compt. rend.*, **212**, 119 (1941).

[65] H. Bizette and B. Tsaï, *ibid.*, **209**, 205 (1939).

[66] C. Starr, F. Bitter, and A. R. Kaufmann, *Phys. Rev.*, **58**, 977 (1940).

[67] S. S. Shalyt, *Compt. rend. acad. sci. U.R.S.S.*, **20**, 657 (1938).

[68] S. S. Shalyt, *J. Exptl. Theoret. Phys. (U.S.S.R.)*, **8**, 518 (1938).

[69] G. A. Milyutin and S. S. Shalyt, *Compt. rend. acad. sci. U.R.S.S.*, **24**, 680 (1939).

[70] S. S. Shalyt, *J. Exptl. Theoret. Phys. (U.S.S.R.)*, **15**, 246 (1945).

[71] A. Lallemand, *Ann. phys.*, **3**, 97 (1935).

[72] R. Chevallier, *J. phys. radium*, **12**, 172 (1951).

Cobalt. The situation respecting the oxides of cobalt is somewhat confused by reports of ferromagnetism,[73] which may, however, be due simply to partial reduction to metal. Cobaltous oxide,[74,75] CoO, is antiferromagnetic with a Curie point at one time reported at $-2°C$.; later work gives $19°C$.[76] Cobaltous fluoride and cobaltic fluoride have been studied by Henkel and Klemm.[77] It is not clear that these substances exhibit antiferromagnetism. Both, however, show an increase of effective moment with increasing temperature. Other halides of cobalt, as well as the sulfides, have been studied by Klemm and Schüth.[78] Still other references are given by Lidiard.[8]

Nickel. Nickelous oxide apparently may be said to have an antiferromagnetic Curie point at about $374°C$.[79] The study of this substance is also somewhat confused by the difficulty of obtaining the stoichiometric compound and the intrusion of traces of ferromagnetism. Nickel fluoride, NiF_2, has, like cobaltous fluoride, an effective moment which increases with increasing temperature. The cyanide, $Ni(CN)_2$, is reported by Serres[80] to have a low susceptibility. This result, which is confirmed by Fereday,[81] may possibly be related to exchange effects between adjacent nickel atoms, but are more probably connected with covalent bonds between nickel and cyanide. Numerous other studies of nickel halides, sulfides, and other compounds have been made.[82] Nickel compounds in which the nickel has a valence higher than two seem to yield quite low magnetic moments, regardless of the state of magnetic dilution.[83]

Copper. Cuprous compounds are diamagnetic.[84] Cupric oxide has a very low paramagnetism.[85] There seems little doubt that it exhibits antiferromagnetism, with a Curie point at about $150°C$. Copper fluoride,[86-88]

[73] A. K. Bose and D. P. Raychaudhuri, *Science and Culture*, **3**, 246 (1937).

[74] H. Bizette, *Ann. Phys.*, **1**, 233 (1946).

[75] M. F. Trombe, *Colloques Internationaux, Ferromagnetism and Antiferromagnetism*. Grenoble, 1950, p. 22.

[76] C. Henry LaBlanchetais, *J. phys. radium*, **12**, 765 (1951).

[77] P. Henkel and W. Klemm, *Z. anorg. u. allgem. Chem.*, **222**, 73 (1935).

[78] W. Klemm and W. Schüth, *ibid.*, **210**, 33 (1933).

[79] M. Foëx and C. Henry LaBlanchetais, *Compt. rend.*, **228**, 1579 (1949).

[80] A. Serres, *Ann. phys.*, **20**, 441 (1933).

[81] R. A. Fereday, *Proc. Phys. Soc. (London)*, **46**, 214 (1934).

[82] P. Rây and D. N. Sen, *J. Indian Chem. Soc.*, **25**, 205 (1948).

[83] P. Rây, A. Bhaduri, and B. Sarma, *ibid.*, **25**, 51 (1948).

[84] H. Dressnandt, *Z. Physik*, **115**, 369 (1940).

[85] H. Bizette and B. Tsaï, *Proceedings of the Paris Conference on the Polarization of Matter*. April 4–9, 1949.

[86] P. Henkel and W. Klemm, *Z. anorg. u. allgem. Chem.*, **222**, 73 (1935).

[87] W. J. de Haas, B. H. Schultz, and J. Koolhaas, *Physica*, **7**, 57 (1940).

[88] S. S. Bhatnagar, H. Lessheim, and M. L. Khanna, *J. Indian Chem. Soc.*, **14**, 445 (1937).

CuF_2, has a moment somewhat dependent on temperature and at low temperatures it has a susceptibility somewhat dependent on field strength. At very low temperatures, cupric chloride dihydrate becomes antiferromagnetic.[89] The phosphides, Cu_3P and CuP_2, have been studied by Haraldsen.[90] They are both diamagnetic. Obviously, they do not contain any ordinary form of cupric ion.

Molybdenum. Molybdenum dioxide has almost zero magnetic susceptibility. Experiments in the author's laboratory have shown that no antiferromagnetic Curie point appears up to 1100°C. This peculiar effect is possibly due to a species of covalent bond between adjacent molybdenum ions. The effect is made possible by the closeness of approach of molybdenum atoms to each other in the lattice. In this respect molybdenum is like rhenium in the dioxide, and possibly also like the platinum- and palladium-group oxides. Most molybdates have only a small temperature-independent paramagnetism, but heteropolymolybdates containing transition ions, such as Cr^{3+}, Fe^{3+}, Mn^{4+}, Ni^{2+}, Cu^{2+}, Mn^{2+}, and Co^{2+}, often show normal moments for these ions.[91] Molybdenum in the disulfide, molybdenite, appears to be diamagnetic, although anisotropy measurements reveal some temperature dependence. Molybdenum tellurides[92] seem to be diamagnetic, or at best to have only a very small paramagnetism.[93]

Silver. The few known paramagnetic silver compounds are generally magnetically dilute. An exception[94] seems to be the difluoride, AgF_2, which is reported by Gruner and Klemm to have a molar susceptibility for the argentic ion of only 440×10^{-6}. There can be little doubt that exchange effects occur in this compound. Reference to its ferromagnetism at low temperature has already been made (p. 315).

Rare Earths. The paramagnetic rare earths, such as dysprosium sesquioxide, are probably the most magnetically concentrated compounds known. But, because of the sequestration of the $4f$ electrons and their screening from external influence, no antiferromagnetism is shown by any of these substances.

Tungsten. Tungsten dioxide shows a subnormal susceptibility but not to the extreme degree shown by molybdenum dioxide. Dutta[95] has shown that the sulfide, tungstenite, is paramagnetic, but Morette[93] has shown the ditelluride to be diamagnetic.

[89] J. van den Handel, H. M. Gijsman, and N. J. Poulis, *Physica*, **18**, 862 (1952).

[90] H. Haraldsen, *Z. anorg. u. allgem. Chem.*, **240**, 337 (1939).

[91] P. Rây, A. Bhaduri, and B. Sarma, *J. Indian Chem. Soc.*, **25**, 51 (1948).

[92] A. K. Dutta, *Indian J. Phys.*, **18**, 249 (1944); **19**, 225 (1945).

[93] A. Morette, *Ann. chim.*, **19**, 130 (1944).

[94] E. Gruner and W. Klemm, *Naturwissenschaften*, **25**, 59 (1937).

[95] A. K. Dutta and B. C. R. Chowdhury, *Indian J. Phys.*, **23**, 131 (1949).

Rhenium.   The oxides, sulfides, and halides of this element generally have a small temperature-independent paramagnetism.   The pentachloride may have a normal moment at elevated temperatures.[96]

Uranium.   The two oxides, UO_2 and U_3O_8, follow the Weiss law.   The dioxide has the rather large Weiss constant of $\sim 220°$.   It seems probable that this compound would show an antiferromagnetic Curie point at very low temperatures.   There is little doubt that uranium shows exchange effects, and that this forms a contrast between uranium and the rare earths, but no evidence of a Curie point has been found down to the temperature of liquid hydrogen.[97]

88.   Hydrous Oxides[98]

The addition of a base to a ferric salt solution results in the precipitation of a familiar reddish-brown substance often called ferric hydroxide, or better, hydrous ferric oxide.   This substance may be partially dried to a powder or to a fairly hard mass.   The x-ray or electron-diffraction pattern tends to be diffuse and difficult or impossible of interpretation.   Electron microscope studies yield little information except that the particles are very small or are aggregates of submicroscopic particles.   The specific surface area of the substance is generally very high.   If the substance is strongly heated it undergoes a vigorous exothermal change after which it has become crystalline α-iron sesquioxide.

The above description is characteristic of most oxides and hydroxides of the metals.   Such substances are often called "gels."   These substances are of major importance in several branches of chemistry, especially in catalysis, but knowledge of their structure remains in a rudimentary state. In the following pages there will be described a magnetic method through which the degree of attenuation of such substances may be followed in a semiquantitative way, and which gives some promise of ultimately yielding precise knowledge concerning their structure.   The observation on which this work is based is that the hydrous oxides and hydroxides of the paramagnetic ions are, in general, magnetically dilute substances.[99]   (In some respects their magnetic properties are those of rather dilute solid solutions as of, say, chromia in alumina which, with similar systems, was described in Chapter VIII.)   The significance of this observation will be clear if the magnetic susceptibility of chromium in crystalline chromia is compared

[96] W. Schüth and W. Klemm, *Z. anorg. u. allgem. Chem.*, **220**, 193 (1934).

[97] B. M. W. Trapnell and P. W. Selwood, *Nature*, **169**, 840 (1952).

[98] P. W. Selwood, C. F. Davis, Jr., and M. Ellis, *J. Am. Chem. Soc.*, **72**, 3549 (1950).

[99] P. W. Selwood, R. P. Eischens, M. Ellis, and K. Wethington, *ibid.*, **71**, 3039 (1949).

TABLE XXX

Susceptibilities ($\times 10^6$) for Chromia and for Chromia Gel

	$X_{25}°$	$X_{-170}°$
Cr_2O_3, crystalline oxide	25	23
Cr_2O_3, gel oxide	37	82
Cr^{3+} in crystalline oxide	37	33
Cr^{3+} in gel oxide	78	174

with that in chromia gel, as shown in Table XXX. It will be seen that the susceptibility per gram of chromium in the gel at $-170°C$. is over five times greater than that in the crystalline oxide. This shows that exchange effects

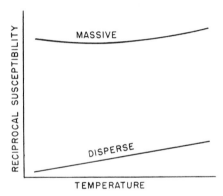

Fig. 109. Reciprocal susceptibility *versus* temperature for chromia gel and for crystalline chromia. The antiferromagnetic Curie point for crystalline Cr_2O_3 is not very sharply defined.

and the phenomena associated with antiferromagnetism are almost or completely absent in the gel. In Fig. 109 there are shown reciprocal susceptibilities plotted against temperature for a typical chromia gel and for the crystalline oxide. For the gel the Curie-Weiss law is followed with a Weiss constant of 104°. The magnetic moment is 4.3 Bohr magnetons, slightly higher than expected. In Fig. 110 there are shown susceptibilities plotted against temperature for a typical disperse (gel) solid and for the corresponding massive (crystalline) solid.

In the present status of the theory of antiferromagnetism, it is scarcely possible to make a quantitative interpretation of the magnetic data in terms of gel structure. But there is evidence from work on solid solutions, as previously described, that the Weiss constant varies linearly, or nearly so, with magnetic dilution, and that this variation is probably linear with the number of nearest paramagnetic neighbors. If this is true we may write

$z' = z\Delta'/\Delta$ where z',Δ' are number of nearest neighbors and Weiss constant, respectively, for the gel, and z,Δ the same for the crystalline oxide. In chromia it is a little difficult to known what value should be taken for z in the crystal. This is because there are actually several neighbors at slightly different distances, but the number *nine* is probably not too much in error. Then the average number of nearest neighbors possessed by each chromium ion in the gel is $z' = 9 \times 100/300 = 3$.

This is an astonishing degree of attenuation for the chromium ions in the gel, but it is not inconsistent with evidence from other sources, such as surface-area studies. Such a degree of attenuation could probably be achieved only by threads no more than a very few atoms thick.

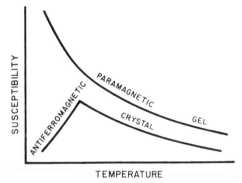

Fig. 110. Comparison of susceptibility-temperature curves for a typical oxide in the disperse (gel) state and the corresponding massive (crystalline) state.

There are several objections to the procedure described, and a more nearly quantitative method must wait for further developments in the theory of the antiferromagnetic Curie point. A few of these objections are as follows: (1) the formula given is based on a body-centered structure only; (2) the Weiss constant does not always equal the Curie point numerically; (3) the minimum distance between nearest neighbors, and hence the exchange integral, may not be the same in gel and crystal; (4) the Weiss constant depends on factors other than exchange effects; (5) in some gels the calculation made would yield less than one nearest neighbor. In spite of these difficulties, it is anticipated that the method will prove a useful tool in the chemistry of paramagnetic gels. There will now be given some further examples of the results obtained on various gels.

In Fig. 111 there are shown susceptibilities per gram of chromium for a chromia gel undergoing progressive dehydration through the temperature at which the exothermic transition occurs. Figure 112 shows Weiss constant

and surface area for the same series of samples.   During this dehydration
the magnetic moment changed only slightly, from 4.0 to 3.5 Bohr magnetons.   It will be noted that aggregation of chromium ions begins at an early

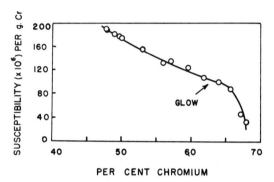

Fig. 111. Susceptibility *versus* chromium concentration during dehydration of a chromia gel.

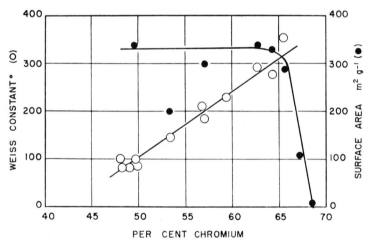

Fig. 112. Weiss constant and specific surface area as a function of the
dehydration shown in Fig. 111.

stage of dehydration before the surface area has started to diminish.   Also
it will be seen that the loss of surface area in going through the glow
effect is accompanied by a precipitous drop of susceptibility.   The work
of Foëx and Wucher[100] seems to indicate that the amorphous form of chromia
may have a magnetic moment somewhat dependent on temperature.

[100] G. Foëx and J. Wucher, *Compt. rend.*, **232**, 2193 (1951)

Ferric oxide gel gives results quite similar to chromia gel, with one notable difference. This difference is that the magnetic moment observed tends to be about 30% lower than the value 6.0 expected for five unpaired electrons. It seems probable that the low moment is due to some kind of covalent bond between adjacent iron ions, in the same way that the moment of molybdenum is even further reduced in molybdenum dioxide. This view is supported by the finding that hydrolyzed ferric ion solutions may contain a large proportion of a diamagnetic dimeric ion (p. 167). It should be noted that the high susceptibility of ferric oxide gels (as compared with crystalline α-Fe_2O_3) has been reported several times.[101-103] The fact that this is associated with a subnormal moment for the iron has also been known for a long time.

Manganese dioxide in its several "active" forms shows a good example of the magnetic dilution which accompanies gel structure.[104] The increased susceptibility and attendant increased catalytic activity have been noted by Amiel, Rodier, and Brenet,[105] who have advanced a somewhat different explanation for the phenomenon. It will be noted that manganese dioxide tends to decompose rather than go through a "glow" transition. The magnetic moment rises during the change from Mn^{4+} to Mn^{3+}. It is found that slow reduction of gel-like manganese dioxide causes a rise followed by a fall of the Weiss constant.[106]

Hydrous copper oxide has not been prepared in a magnetically dilute form. The familiar transition from blue cupric hydroxide to black cupric oxide is accompanied by a very large decrease of susceptibility.[107] This effect is also found for the hydroxide-oxide transition for cobalt, and for nickel. Manganous hydroxide is likewise magnetically dilute even in the crystalline state. Vanadium dioxide gel shows the magnetic dilution effect, although the Weiss constant ($\sim$225°) suggests a less attenuated structure than for several of the other gels studied.[40]

89. Phase Ratios and Stoichiometry

Magnetic studies have been of considerable service in the study of phase relationships. Sometimes hitherto unsuspected phases have been revealed in supposedly pure stoichiometric compounds.

[101] L. Blanc, *Ann. Chim.*, **6**, 18 (1926).

[102] C. Courty, *Thesis.* Faculty of Sciences, University of Paris, 1935.

[103] A. Boutaric and P. Berthier, *J. chim. phys.*, **41**, 170 (1944).

[104] T. E. Moore, M. Ellis, and P. W. Selwood, *J. Am. Chem. Soc.*, **72**, 856 (1950).

[105] J. Amiel, G. Rodier, and J. Brenet, *Proceedings of the Paris Conference on the Polarization of Matter.* April 4–9, 1949.

[106] P. W. Selwood, T. E. Moore, M. Ellis, and K. Wethington, *J. Am. Chem. Soc.*, **71**, 693 (1949).

[107] L. Chaumeton, *Compt. rend.*, **206**, 1104 (1938).

The system titanium-oxygen has been studied over the range $TiO_{2.00}$ to $TiO_{0.58}$ by Ehrlich.[108,109] The susceptibility-composition diagram is shown in Fig. 113. It is claimed by Ehrlich that these results show atomic combinations between Ti^{3+} and Ti^{2+} ions, and that only for quite high Ti^{4+} ion concentrations do the Ti^{3+} ions become independent. It seems to the author, however, that exchange effects between adjacent Ti^{3+} ions would be adequate to explain the results. The situation must resemble in part that found in molybdenum dioxide. Ehrlich's results probably represent a strongly antiferromagnetic Ti_2O_3 diluted with a diamagnetic (though not isomorphous) TiO_2.

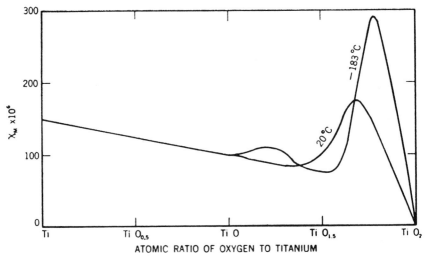

Fig. 113. Susceptibility *versus* composition for the titanium-oxygen system.

It is a curious fact that certain compositions derived from calcining magnesium titanate or barium titanate show fairly strong paramagnetic or even ferromagnetic behavior.[110,111] This has been confirmed in the author's laboratory.

The vanadium-oxygen system has been studied by Klemm[112,113] over the range of $VO_{1.5}$ to $VO_{2.5}$. All compositions appear to be antiferromagnetic to varying degrees, and some rather large susceptibility changes

108 P. Ehrlich, *Z. Elektrochem.*, **45**, 362 (1939).

109 P. Ehrlich, *Z. anorg. u. allgem. Chem.*, **247**, 53 (1941).

110 E. K. Weise and H. Katz, *Phys. Rev.*, **86**, 1046 (1952).

111 G. Hazato and K. Aida, *Rept. Glass Research Inst. Tôhoku Imp. Univ.*, No. **3**, 7 (1949).

112 E. Hoschek and W. Klemm, *Z. anorg. u. allem. Chem.*, **242**, 63 (1939).

113 W. Klemm and L. Grimm, *Naturwissenschaften*, **27**, 787 (1939).

occur over a narrow composition range. There are also some abrupt changes of susceptibility with temperature. For instance, in the composition range of $VO_{1.9}$ to $VO_{2.1}$, the susceptibility rises at $68°C$. from 0.5 to 7.0 ($\times$ 10^{-6}).

The chromium-oxygen system has been studied over the range of Cr_2O_3 to CrO_3. As previously mentioned, there is a ferromagnetic phase (p. 315) near CrO_2.[114]

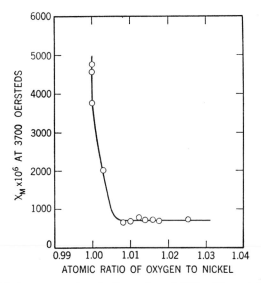

Fig. 114. The nickel-oxygen system in the region of NiO. These data may, however, have to be modified in the light of new information referred to in the text.

The system manganese–oxygen[115] has been studied over the range of MnO to Mn_2O_3, and over the range of Mn_2O_3 to MnO_2.[106] It is well known that MnO takes up oxygen readily with scarcely any change in crystal lattice until the composition approaches Mn_2O_3. Such oxygen is "active" in the sense that its presence imparts strong oxidizing ability to the system. The magnetic measurements show that the oxygen uptake is accompanied by a decrease of magnetic moment, and hence almost certainly of oxidation state, for the manganese. The reaction may be regarded as a random oxidation of Mn^{2+} ions to Mn^{3+} ions. The skeleton MnO lattice structure remains until, through extreme attenuation, it collapses in favor of the Mn_2O_3 lattice. The Mn_2O_3-MnO_2 system is remarkable for the curious rise and fall of Weiss constant which occurs during progressive reduction

[114] O. Glemser, U. Hauschild, and F. Trüpel, *ibid.*, **40**, 317 (1953).

[115] T. E. Moore, M. Ellis, and P. W. Selwood, *J. Am. Chem. Soc.*, **72**, 856 (1950).

of the dioxide. This effect on the Weiss constant was referred to in connection with supported oxides of manganese. It does not seem to be
paralleled in other transition-metal oxide systems.

The iron-oxygen system is greatly complicated by the recurrence of
ferromagnetism, as previously described. Solid-solution formation among
the oxides of iron is discussed by Michel[116] and by Leitgebel and Bocke-
muhl.[117] Attempts have been made to use magnetic measurements for
determination of the proportion of ferrous to ferric iron in complex systems.[118]

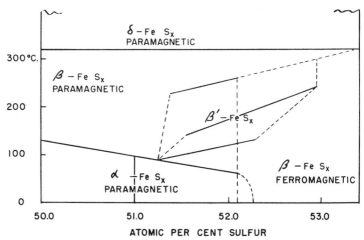

Fig. 115. The iron-sulfur system. The original article should be seen for details.

The nickel-oxygen system[119] has been studied in the region near NiO.
Different samples of this substance often show widely different susceptibilities. This is due, at least in part, to the possible presence of metallic
nickel, the identity of which may be established by its Curie point. Figure
114 shows molar susceptibility as a function of composition over the range
$NiO_{0.99}$ to $NiO_{1.04}$. Klemm doubts if the system becomes stable without a
slight excess of oxygen, but Bhatnagar and Bal[120] claim that NiO has a
definite chemical existence and that when properly prepared it is paramagnetic. Reference to the ferromagnetism of NiO has already been
made on p. 313. The nickel oxide-barium oxide system has been studied
by Lander.[121]

[116] A. Michel, *Ann. chim.*, **8**, 317 (1937).
[117] W. Leitgebel and K. Bockemühl, *Z. anorg. u. allgem. Chem.*, **225**, 209 (1935)
[118] O. Gott and W. Krings, *ibid.*, **239**, 345 (1938).
[119] W. Klemm and K. Haas, *ibid.*, **219**, 82 (1934).
[120] S. S. Bhatnagar and G. S. Bal, *J. Indian Chem. Soc.*, **11**, 603 (1934).
[121] J. J. Lander, *Acta Cryst.*, **4**, 148 (1951).

An interesting series of abnormal valent copper compounds, such as $KCuO_2$, is described by Klemm.   Some of these are paramagnetic.[122]

A phase study on the system niobium–oxygen has been reported by Brauer.[123]   The data, which include measurements on pure niobium metal, seem to parallel those mentioned above for the system titanium-oxygen, but the unexpected appearance of ferromagnetism in several samples makes the results somewhat difficult to interpret.

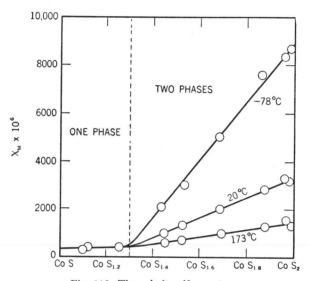

Fig. 116. The cobalt-sulfur system.

The uranium-oxygen system has been studied by Dawson and Lister[124] in the region of UO_2 to $UO_{2.3}$.   The susceptibility of U^{4+} in this system seems to increase with increasing oxygen.   This may be due to dilution with diamagnetic oxide ions and U(VI).   These studies have recently been extended to urania-thoria solid solutions and the change of magnetic susceptibility which occurs with progressive oxidation of the uranium[124a].

The system lead–oxygen has so far yielded no paramagnetic phase.[125,126]

Phase studies on the various transition elements in combination with sulfur have yielded extremely complex results.   The iron-sulfur system

[122] W. Klemm, *Proc. Intern. Symposium Reactivity of Solids.*   Gothenburg, 1952, Pt. I, 173 (Pub. 1954).

[123] G. Brauer, *Z. anorg. Chem.*, **256**, 10 (1948).

[124] J. K. Dawson and M. W. Lister, *J. Chem. Soc.*, 1950 (2181).

[124a] J. K. Dawson and L. E. J. Roberts, *J. Chem. Soc.*, **1956**, 78.

[125] L. Welo and M. Petersen, *Phys. Rev.*, **49**, 864 (1936).

[126] A. Baroni, *Gazz. chim. ital.*, **68**, 387 (1938).

has been investigated by Juza and Biltz,[127] and with exceptional thoroughness by Haraldsen.[128,129]   The susceptibilities are complex functions of composition and of temperature.   In some cases there is an abrupt change from antiferromagnetism to ferromagnetism with changing sulfur content. Haraldsen's results are summarized in the phase diagram shown in Fig. 115.

Similar types of measurements on the system cobalt–sulfur, from CoS to CoS_2, have been made by Haraldsen.[130]   The data are summarized in Fig. 116.   Haraldsen has also studied the systems chromium–sulfur,

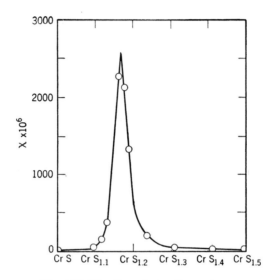

Fig. 117. The chromium-sulfur system.

chromium–selenium, and chromium–tellurium.[131–133]   For the Cr–S system there is a very sharp maximum of susceptibility at $CrS_{1.175}$. Above 165°K. and below 310°K., the substance of this composition is ferromagnetic, as shown in Figs. 117 and 118.

The chalcogenides of vanadium have been studied by Klemm.[134,135] The tellurides are not well defined, but the sulfides and selenides show

[127] R. Juza and W. Biltz, Z. anorg. u. allgem. Chem., **205**, 273 (1932).
[128] H. Haraldsen, ibid., **231**, 78 (1937); **246**, 169, 195 (1941).
[129] R. Benoit, Compt. rend., **234**, 2174 (1952).
[130] H. Haraldsen, Z. anorg. u. allgem. Chem., **224**, 85 (1935).
[131] H. Haraldsen and E. Kowalski, ibid., **224**, 329 (1935).
[132] H. Haraldsen and A. Neuber, ibid., **234**, 337, 353, 372 (1937).
[133] H. Haraldsen and F. Mehmed, ibid., **239**, 369 (1938).
[134] E. Hoschek and W. Klemm, ibid., **242**, 49 (1939).
[135] W. Klemm, Atti X° congr. intern. chim., **2**, 696 (1938).

some interesting properties.   For instance, VSe$_{1.5}$ shows a peak of susceptibility which is very strong at $-183°C$. but just perceptible at room temperature.

Other systems which have been studied include chromium-antimony,[136]
manganese-nitrogen,[137,138] the so-called "molybdenum blues," and the
tungsten bronzes.   The "molybdenum blues" apparently have only a

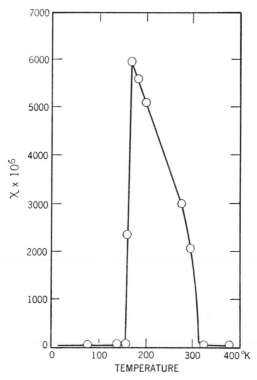

Fig. 118. Susceptibility-temperature relationship for the atomic ratio CrS$_{1.17}$.

very small paramagnetism in spite of the probable presence of pentavalent
molybdenum in these substances.[139]   The tungsten bronzes are often
thought of as containing pentavalent tungsten, or possibly a mixture of
tetra- and hexavalent tungsten.   Magnetic measurements[140,141] yield

[136] H. Haraldsen and T. Rosenquist, *Tids. Kjemi, Bergvesen Met.*, **3**, 81 (1943).
[137] C. Guillaud and J. Wyart, *Compt. rend.*, **222**, 71 (1946).
[138] P. M. Stubbin and D. P. Mellor, *J. Proc. Roy. Soc. N. S. Wales*, **82**, 225 (1948).
[139] L. Sacconi and R. Cini, *J. Chem. Phys.*, **18**, 1124 (1950).
[140] F. Kupka and M. J. Sienko, *ibid.*, **18**, 1296 (1950).
[141] L. E. Conroy and M. J. Sienko, *J. Am. Chem. Soc.*, **74**, 3520 (1952).

susceptibilities which are definitely low in comparison with that of an atom or ion containing one unpaired electron. This has been interpreted as evidence that the bronzes are actually solutions of alkali metal in tungsten trioxide. While the susceptibilities are not inconsistent with this view, it should be pointed out that a low susceptibility could be caused by exchange effects. General problems related to magnetic studies of phase systems are discussed by Klemm[142] and by Haraldsen.[143]

90. Miscellaneous Problems

In this section there will be described two further studies which involve some of the principles presented earlier in this chapter.

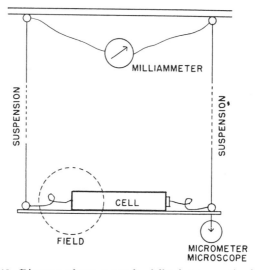

Fig. 119. Diagram of apparatus for following magnetic changes in the manganese dioxide of a dry cell during discharge.

It is often desirable to follow chemical and structural changes which occur *in situ*, so to speak, without the necessity for removal of samples. Several examples of using magnetic methods for this purpose have been described. A further application is to the depolarizer action which occurs during discharge and recovery in the Leclanché dry cell. Manganese is the only paramagnetic constituent in the cell, and natural and commercial samples of pyrolusite used as a depolarizer all have the disperse structure

---

[142] W. Klemm, *Fiat Review of German Science*, 1939–1946, Vol. 9, Pt. II.

[143] H. Haraldsen, *Avhandl. Norske Videnskaps-Akad. Oslo I. Mat.-Naturv. Klasse* 1947, No. 4.

referred to earlier, and hence lend themselves readily to interpretation of the magnetic data. Magnetically dilute manganese oxides have susceptibilities which are virtually linear with oxidation state of the manganese.

This experiment[144] has been done by suspending a small cell horizontally by two fine copper wires which served both as suspension and electrical conductors. One end of the cell was placed in a field of about 9000 oersteds supplied by a large permanent magnet. Motion of the cell during

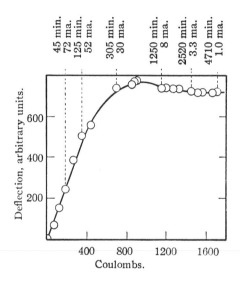

Fig. 120. Deflection *versus* discharge for a dry cell.

discharge and recovery was observed by a micrometer microscope. The arrangement of apparatus is shown in Fig. 119. Results are shown in Fig. 120 where deflection during discharge, and hence change of oxidation state of the manganese, is plotted against coulombs withdrawn. As expected, the cell contents became more paramagnetic during discharge. In this study it was found that all reduction of the manganese occurs during discharge and that none occurs during recovery.

The other study to be described here is the possible use of magnetic anisotropy measurements to determine the oxidation state of elements in compounds where this is not readily found by chemical or other tests. Krishnan and Banerjee[145] have used this method to investigate the structure of the mineral manganite, MnOOH, or manganese oxyhydroxide.

[144] P. W. Selwood, R. P. Eischens, M. Ellis, and K. Wethington, *J. Am. Chem. Soc.*, **71**, 3039 (1949).

[145] K. S. Krishnan and S. Banerjee, *Trans. Faraday Soc.*, **35**, 385 (1939).

The ion Mn^{2+} being in an S state, and since for such ions the spin momenta are little affected by crystalline electric fields, substances containing only Mn^{2+} ions should show only slight magnetic anisotropy even in highly asymmetrical fields. This reasoning is verified by anisotropy measurements on many Mn^{2+} compounds, the maximum observed anisotropy being about 8×10^{-6}. For compounds which unquestionably contain Mn^{4+} ions, there do not appear to be any experimental data, but the ground state is $^4F_{3/2}$ and in its Stark pattern, produced in an electric field, the lowest level is nondegenerate. Owing to this circumstance and to the feebleness of coupling between orbital and spin-angular momenta of electrons in the incomplete shell, this ion should also exhibit very little anisotropy, even in highly asymmetric fields.

On the other hand, the Mn^{3+} ion should have a large anisotropy, and this is verified in such compounds as the Mn^{3+} acetylacetonate, which has an anisotropy of about 75×10^{-6} per gram-ion of Mn^{3+} at 31°C. Hence a measurement on the compound, $MnOOH$, should indicate whether this substance contains Mn^{2+} and Mn^{4+} ions which exhibit slight anisotropy, or Mn^{3+} which exhibits a large anisotropy. Actually, for single crystals of manganite, $\chi_c - \chi_a = 4 \times 10^{-6}$, and $\chi_c - \chi_b = 3.0 \times 10^{-6}$ per gram-mass containing 1 gram-atom of Mn. From this it follows that the substance actually contains equal numbers of Mn^{2+} and Mn^{4+} ions. On the other hand, it will be recalled that $MnOOH$ has a susceptibility virtually independent of temperature. This may be due to exchange effects, but it might possibly be related to the anomalous behavior of Mn^{3+} in $K_3Mn(CN)_6$ described on p. 209, and the explanation offered by Kotani (p. 242). Studies similar to the above could probably be applied to other substances, although it is clear that paramagnetic resonance would be even more helpful.

CHAPTER FOURTEEN

METALLIC DIAMAGNETISM
AND PARAMAGNETISM

91. Introduction

Most metals are either diamagnetic or paramagnetic. The very few which are ferromagnetic at or near room temperature have been discussed in an earlier chapter. Some idea of the distribution of magnetism among the metals and other elements may be gained from Fig. 121, in which there are given the approximate susceptibilities per gram-atom at room temperature. The values given in this figure are illustrative only and should not be used without some consideration of how the susceptibilities may be affected by physical state, temperature, polymorphic transitions, and so forth.

In general, paramagnetism is found in those metals possessing an incomplete electron shell, and hence belonging to a transition series. Paramagnetism is also found in most of the alkali and alkaline earth metals. Most other metals are diamagnetic. The atomic susceptibilities of metals vary quite widely and are not often readily interpreted according to principles presented for isolated atoms and ions in Chapter VIII. The susceptibilities of most paramagnetic metals are quite small and are comparable in magnitude with, although of course opposite in sign from, diamagnetic susceptibilities. Manganese and palladium are the most strongly paramagnetic metals, while bismuth has the highest atomic diamagnetism.

It should be pointed out that the susceptibilities of many metals are so small that the presence of ferromagnetic impurities in extremely small amounts may completely conceal the true susceptibilities. It is essential, in making magnetic susceptibility measurements on solids, to work at two or more field strengths. The method of Honda and of Owen[1,2] for correcting for ferromagnetic impurity consists of measuring the susceptibility at fields larger than those required to saturate the ferromagnetic substance. Then $\chi = \chi_\infty + \vartheta/H$ where ϑ is the saturation intensity of magnetization

[1] K. Honda, *Ann. Physik*, **32**, 1027 (1910).
[2] M. Owen, *ibid.*, **37**, 657 (1912).

351

for the ferromagnetic substance, χ is the measured susceptibility, and χ_∞ will be the susceptibility of the impurity-free specimen.

Furthermore, the susceptibility of a metal seems often to depend on the previous mechanical history of the specimen,[3] although this may be due in part to impurities and to their precipitation on cold working. Some authors have reported a dependence of susceptibility on particle size.

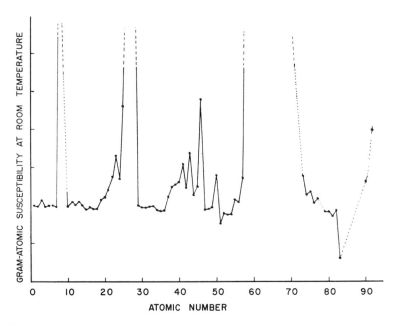

Fig. 121. Atomic susceptibility *versus* atomic number for the chemical elements.

This question has been reviewed by Bhatnagar[4] who finds that in general the magnetic susceptibility of metals is independent of particle size. Of course, oxidation, contamination, or change of microcrystalline structure may affect the susceptibility, and these may be rather difficult to avoid when fine powders are dealt with. Changes in susceptibility generally occur during melting and during allotropic change.[5]

Theories of magnetism in metals have been developed by Pauli,[6]

[3] T. S. Hutchison and J. Reekie, *Phys. Rev.*, **73**, 517 (1948).
[4] S. S. Bhatnagar, M. R. Verma, and M. Anwar-ul-Haq, *Kolloid-Z.*, **78**, 9 (1937).
[5] Y. Shimizu, *Science Repts. Tôhoku Imp. Univ., First Ser.*, **25**, 921 (1937).
[6] W. Pauli, *Z. Physik*, **41**, 81 (1927).

Landau,[7] Peierls,[8] Wilson,[9] Pauling,[10] and others.   The subject is treated by Van Vleck,[13] Seitz,[12] Mott[11] and Pauling.[14]

The diamagnetic metals appear to be so either because all electrons are paired, or because the feeble paramagnetism associated with the conductivity electrons does not compensate for the rather large diamagnetism due to substantial numbers of electrons in orbits of large radius as found in many metals.   In a few cases, this feeble paramagnetism is a little larger than the underlying diamagnetism.   Those elements possessing incomplete d-levels are paramagnetic, occasionally quite strongly so, but more often with the moment strongly reduced by exchange effects or possibly by covalent bonds between adjacent atoms.   It will, of course, be clear that the metallic properties of metals may be quite different from those of isolated atoms.   The rare earth metals, as will be shown, are particularly interesting in this respect, because the sequestration of the $4f$ electrons persists even at such high magnetic concentrations as are found in the metallic state.

Heretofore, the magnetic properties of the nonferromagnetic metals have not assumed very much importance in chemistry.   But with growing interest in the structural chemistry of metals and intermetallic compounds, there is increasing reason to present this area in somewhat more detail than would have been justifiable a few years ago.   Susceptibility measurements on nonferromagnetic alloys are also beginning to be used for the solution of chemical problems.   For true solid solutions of metals miscible in all proportions, the susceptibility generally varies uniformly with concentration, although the variation is seldom linear.   For other types of alloys, markedly irregular susceptibility-composition curves are the rule.   Some references to this field are given below.[15−17]

[7] L. Landau, *ibid.*, **64**, 629 (1930).

[8] R. Peierls, *ibid.*, **81**, 186 (1933).

[9] A. H. Wilson, *Theory of Metals.*   Cambridge University Press, London, 1936, p. 108.

[10] L. Pauling, *Phys. Rev.*, **54**, 899 (1938), and later papers.

[11] N. F. Mott, *Le Magnétisme*, Vol. II.   Proceedings of the Strasbourg Congress on Magnetism, 1939, p. 1.

[12] F. Seitz, *The Modern Theory of Solids.*   McGraw-Hill Book Co., Inc., New York 1940.

[13] J. H. Van Vleck, *Theory of Electric and Magnetic Susceptibilities.*   Oxford University Press, Oxford, 1932, p. 347.

[14] L. Pauling, *Proc. Intern. Congr. Pure and Applied Chem.* (*London*), **11**, 249 (1947).

[15] H. Jones, *Helv. Phys. Acta*, **7 Suppl. II**, 84 (1934).

[16] E. Vogt, *Z. Metallkunde*, **27**, 40 (1935).

[17] W. L. Bragg, C. Sykes, and A. J. Bradley, *Proc. Phys. Soc.* (*London*), **49**, 96 (1937).

The present status of the theories of magnetism in metals will be summarized briefly. In general, the electron-band theory has developed to the point where it gives a satisfactory quantitative prediction of most properties for some metals and alloys. In this theory, the underlying view is that each electron is represented by a wave-function which extends over the whole crystal. Emphasis is therefore placed on the crystal and the assembly as a whole. The feeling is that further development of the band theory is largely a matter of overcoming the mathematical difficulties.

In considerable contrast to the band theory, there has been developed a more "chemical" approach by Pauling.[10] The Pauling theory considers the behavior of electrons in the immediate vicinity of each atom and, just as in consideration of typical chemical compounds, deals especially with the electrons involved in binding an atom to its nearest neighbors. For instance, in going from potassium to vanadium the number of bonding electrons increases from one to five per atom, with a corresponding increase in the number of covalent bonds between which resonance can occur. This leads to much diminished paramagnetism and ferromagnetism than would be expected if all electrons in the d-orbitals were unpaired to the same degree that they are in ions of the corresponding elements. This view, developed by Pauling, gains support from numerous experimental observations, such as crystal structure and cohesive strength. A discussion of the Pauling theory is given by Hume-Rothery.[18, 18a]

There is much in the theory of antiferromagnetism which is common to other cooperative phenomena, such as occur in metals and alloys. Some progress has been made in considering the nonferromagnetic transition metals (Cr, Mn, etc.) as antiferromagnetics. This is reviewed by Lidiard.[19] Some progress is also being made in the application of paramagnetic and nuclear-magnetic resonance techniques to metals and alloys. Spin resonance of the conduction electrons in metallic sodium has been observed, with a g-factor apparently that expected for a free electron.[20] It has been found by Knight[21] that the nuclear-spin resonance frequency is generally higher in metals than in an insulating medium, such as an oxide, even though the spin is associated with the same isotopic nucleus in each case. This shift is caused by the local field produced by the conduction electrons in the metal. This phenomenon and related effects may be expected to give increasing information concerning order-disorder transformations in alloys and about the structure of metals and alloys in general.[22]

[18] W. Hume-Rothery, *Chemical Society Annual Reports*, **1949**, p. 42.

[18a] W. Hume-Rothery, H. M. Irving, and R. J. P. Williams, *Proc. Roy. Soc* (*London*), **A208**, 431 (1951).

[19] A. B. Lidiard, *Reports on Progress in Physics*, **17**, 237 (1954).

[20] T. W. Griswold, A. F. Kip, and C. Kittel, *Phys. Rev.*, **88**, 951 (1952).

[21] W. D. Knight, *ibid.*, **76**, 1259 (1949).

[22] N. Bloembergen and T. J. Rowland, *Acta Met.*, **1**, 731 (1953).

92. Experimental Data on Pure Metals

Some experimental data on polycrystalline pure metals and metalloids are given in alphabetical order in the following pages. The rare earths, together with scandium and yttrium, are considered as a group. Single crystals are considered in a later section. Except as indicated, the values are those given by Owen,[23] which are based on his own and on Honda's original work;[24] on Honda's data in the International Critical Tables; and on Stoner's compilation.[25] Most of Honda's results are considered less reliable now than they were at the time of publication, owing to the probable presence of impurities in many of his samples. This is, of course, an almost inevitable development in view of the great progress made in recent years in all branches of physical metallurgy. Kriessman and Callen[26] have prepared a useful review on the magnetic properties of the nonferromagnetic transition metals.

Aluminum. Weiss and Klemm[27] give $\chi_A = 16.7 \times 10^{-6}$ at room temperature. Auer[28] gives 17.4×10^{-6}. The magnetic properties of aluminum are sensitive to minute traces of ferromagnetism caused by iron.

Antimony. For ordinary polycrystalline antimony $\chi_A = -99 \times 10^{-6}$, although the graphs given by Busch and Vogt[29] seem to indicate a value nearer -81×10^{-6}. The susceptibility is sensitive to traces of impurities.[30] "Explosive" antimony[31] has a susceptibility per gram of about -0.3×10^{-6}.

Arsenic. The atomic susceptibility at room temperature is -5.5×10^{-6}. The several different allotropic modifications all have about the same susceptibility. Stöhr[32] reports that the element is slightly paramagnetic at $-183°C$.

Barium. Lane[33] has shown barium metal to have a susceptibility somewhat dependent on temperature. From $\chi_A = 20.4 \times 10^{-6}$ at $20°C$. it rises to 57.0×10^{-6} at $400°$. There is slight discontinuity at $350°$, which parallels an anomaly in the electrical conductivity of barium at that temperature.

[23] M. Owen, *Ann. Physik*, **37**, 657 (1912).

[24] K. Honda, *ibid.*, **32**, 1027 (1910).

[25] E. C. Stoner, *Magnetism and Matter.* Methuen and Company, Ltd., London, 1934, p. 508.

[26] C. J. Kriessman, Jr., and H. B. Callen, *Phys. Rev.*, **94**, 837 (1954).

[27] P. Weiss and W. Klemm, *Z. anorg. u. allgem. chem.*, **245**, 288 (1940).

[28] H. Auer, *Z. Physik*, **92**, 283 (1934).

[29] G. Busch and O. Vogt, *Helv. Phys. Acta*, **27**, 241 (1954).

[30] H. Stöhr and W. Klemm, *Z. anorg. u. allgem. Chem.*, **244**, 205 (1940).

[31] C. C. Coffin, *Can. J. Research*, **13A**, 120 (1935).

[32] H. Stöhr, *Z. anorg. u. allgem. Chem.*, **242**, 138 (1939).

[33] C. T. Lane, *Phys. Rev.*, **44**, 43 (1933).

Beryllium. The International Critical Tables value of -9×10^{-6} for the atomic susceptibility of this metal is probably considerably in error.

Bismuth. This metal has been the subject of much magnetic study. It is remarkable for its high diamagnetism, for its temperature coefficient of susceptibility, for its structure-sensitivity, and for its curious field-strength dependence of susceptibility at low temperatures. At room temperature, the susceptibility per gram-atom is about -284×10^{-6}. Over a fairly wide temperature range, the susceptibility may be represented by $\chi_t = \chi_{t_0} + \alpha(t - t_0)$ where α is a constant, and t, t_0 are two temperatures. At the melting point (271°C.), the susceptibility drops[34,35] to a small fraction of its original diamagnetism. Very thin films of evaporated bismuth apparently have a slightly smaller diamagnetism than massive bismuth. Lane[36] has shown that below 0.5μ, the susceptibility is somewhat dependent on film thickness. The magnetic properties of bismuth have been reviewed by Gerritsen.[37]

Boron. L. Klemm[38] reports $\chi_A = -6.7 \times 10^{-6}$ at 20°C. and -6.8×10^{-6} at $-183°$.

Cadmium. The atomic susceptibility of the polycrystalline metal is -19.7×10^{-6}. The interesting temperature dependence of susceptibility[39] has been studied in connection with single-crystal studies to be mentioned later.

Calcium. The susceptibility per gram-atom is stated to be 44×10^{-6}, but this must be regarded as approximate only.

Cesium. Contrary to former claims, cesium is paramagnetic, as are all the other alkali metals.[40,41] The susceptibility per gram-atom rises slightly from 26.5×10^{-6} at 100°C. to 34.5×10^{-6} at $-183°$.

Chromium. The susceptibility per gram-atom of polycrystalline chromium metal is uncertain. The value, 160×10^{-6}, obtained by Bates and Baqi[42] compares with 182×10^{-6} obtained by Söchtig.[43] McGuire and Kriessman[44] give 178×10^{-6}. But all these determinations involve various corrections, especially for Cr_2O_3. In view of the large variations found for Cr_2O_3 prepared in different ways (p. 337), we are inclined to

[34] A. Goetz and A. B. Focke, *ibid.*, **45**, 170 (1934).

[35] A. Goetz, O. Stierstadt, and A. B. Focke, *Z. Physik*, **98**, 118 (1935).

[36] C. T. Lane, *Phys. Rev.*, **51**, 863 (1937).

[37] A. N. Gerritsen, *Nederland. Tijdschr. Natuurkunde*, **10**, 160 (1943).

[38] L. Klemm, *Z. Elektrochem.*, **45**, 354 (1939).

[39] S. R. Rao and S. Sriraman, *Proc. Roy. Soc. (London)*, **A166**, 325 (1938).

[40] W. Klemm and B. Hauschulz, *Z. Elektrochem.*, **45**, 346 (1939).

[41] B. Böhm and W. Klemm, *Z. anorg. u. allgem. Chem.*, **243**, 69 (1939).

[42] L. F. Bates and A. Baqi, *Proc. Phys. Soc. (London)*, **48**, 781 (1936).

[43] H. Söchtig, *Ann. Physik*, **38**, 97 (1941).

[44] T. R. McGuire and C. J. Kriessman, *Phys. Rev.*, **85**, 452 (1952).

favor the very low susceptibility 138×10^{-6} per gram-atom of chromium as given by Wangenknecht.[45] The susceptibility is slightly dependent on temperature from 90 to 620°K. The preparation of iron-free samples of chromium is not easy. It may be achieved by electrolytic preparation of chromium amalgam from which the mercury may be distilled in vacuum.

Copper. The atomic susceptibility at room temperature is -5.27×10^{-6} and is virtually independent of temperature.[45a] Ordinary commercial copper has a substantial ferromagnetic impurity. Colloidal copper is stated by Rao[46] to have a somewhat larger diamagnetism than massive copper.

Gallium. From the work of Marchand[46a] on single crystals it may be concluded that the average atomic susceptibility at room temperature is about -21.7×10^{-6}, and for the liquid at 40°C. about -2.5×10^{-6}; but measurements on a powdered sample gave results in rather poor agreement.

Germanium. The diamagnetism of germanium has been reported by Stöhr and Klemm[47] to depend somewhat on temperature, χ_A being -8.9×10^{-6} at 20°C. and -11.0×10^{-6} at -183°C. At slightly lower temperature, 75°K., germanium is said to go through a transition during which the diamagnetism increases about one hundred fold.[48] Rao[49] gives a somewhat larger diamagnetism at room temperature. The susceptibility of n- and p-type semiconductive germanium has been studied by Stevens and Crawford,[50] who do not report the anomaly mentioned by Squire. There is considerable doubt concerning it.

Gold. The metal is diamagnetic, with an atomic susceptibility at room temperature of about -30×10^{-6}.

Hafnium. Kriessman and Callen[26] list $\chi_A = 75 \times 10^{-6}$.

Indium. The metal is diamagnetic, with an atomic susceptibility at room temperature of -12.6×10^{-6}.

Iridium. The metal is slightly paramagnetic, with χ_A at room temperature equal to 35×10^{-6}.

Lead. The metal is diamagnetic, with χ_A at room temperature equal to -25×10^{-6}.

Lithium. Starr and Kaufmann[51] report $\chi_A = 25.9 \times 10^{-6}$ at 20°C.

[45] F. Wangenknecht, Z. anorg. Chem., **275**, 59 (1954).
[45a] R. Bowers, personal communication, forthcoming in Phys. Rev.
[46] S. R. Rao, Proc. Indian Acad. Sci., **2A**, 249 (1935).
[46a] A. Marchand, Compt. rend., **241**, 468 (1955).
[47] H. Stöhr and W. Klemm, Z. anorg. u. allgem. Chem., **244**, 205 (1939).
[48] C. F. Squire, Phys. Rev., **58**, 202 (1940).
[49] S. R. Rao, Current Sci., **14**, 19 (1945).
[50] D. K. Stevens and J. H. Crawford, Jr., Phys. Rev., **92**, 1065 (1953).
[51] C. Starr and A. R. Kaufmann, ibid., **59**, 476 (1941).

They find that between 13.9°K. and 300° K., the susceptibility per cubic centimeter is given by $\kappa \times 10^6 = 1.90 + 7.8/T$. There is some doubt as to whether the major part of the temperature-dependent term may be caused by dissolved iron as an impurity. Earlier atomic susceptibilities for this metal are $18(\times 10^{-6})$ by Rao and Sriraman,[52] and 3.5, considered most probable by Owen.[2]

Magnesium. The best value is apparently still that of Honda,[24] namely 6×10^{-6} at room temperature.

Manganese. This metal is of particular interest because, although it is paramagnetic, its structure lacks very little of that necessary for the establishment of ferromagnetism. The atomic susceptibility at room temperature is about 580×10^{-6} for the crystalline α form, possibly somewhat less for the β form.

Pure manganese metal has been studied by Shimizu,[53] Wheeler,[54] Grube and Winkler,[55] Serres,[56] Bates and Pantulu,[57] and most recently by Arrott, Coles, and Goldman.[57a] There still remains some doubt as to the exact form of the susceptibility-temperature curve. If sufficient pains are taken to insure the absence of impurities, both solid and gaseous, the susceptibility is apparently nearly independent of temperature, at least from $-183°C.$ to $600°C.$ Above $600°$, there appears to be some very erratic temperature dependence, which may not be entirely reversible. The possibility, however, of oxidation or of nitride formation cannot be completely ruled out. Amorphous manganese prepared by Bates and Pantulu by vacuum distillation of the amalgam under most rigid conditions has a susceptibility somewhat higher than is reported for the massive form. Over the range of 90 to $600°C.$, this substance follows the Weiss law $\chi = 2.174 \times 10^{-2}/(T + 1540)$.

Mercury. Bates and Baker[58] report that mercury purified by the Hulett method (distillation under reduced pressure in a current of air) gives an irregular temperature coefficient of susceptibility. But after the mercury has been boiled for 2 hours under reduced pressure, the susceptibilities lie on a smooth curve. At $18.5°C.$ $\chi_A = -33.8 \times 10^{-6}$ and at $287.5°C.$ $\chi_A = -32.8 \times 10^{-6}$. Rao and Aravamuthachari[59] report a susceptibility for mercury of -33.2×10^{-6} at room temperature.

[52] S. R. Rao and S. Sriraman, *Proc. Indian Acad. Sci.*, **5A**, 343 (1937).

[53] Y. Shimizu, *Sci. Repts. Tôhoku Imp. Univ., First Ser.*, **19**, 411 (1930).

[54] M. A. Wheeler, *Phys. Rev.*, **41**, 331 (1932).

[55] G. Grube and O. Winkler, *Z. Elektrochem.*, **42**, 815 (1936).

[56] A. Serres, *J. phys. radium*, **9**, 377 (1938).

[57] L. F. Bates and D. V. R. Pantulu, *Proc. Phys. Soc. (London)*, **47**, 197 (1935).

[57a] A. Arrott, B. R. Coles, and J. E. Goldman, *Phys. Rev.*, **98**, 1864 (1955).

[58] L. F. Bates and C. J. W. Baker, *ibid.*, **50**, 409 (1938).

[59] S. R. Rao and S. Aravamuthachari, *Proc. Indian Acad. Sci.*, **9A**, 181 (1939).

Molybdenum. The metal is paramagnetic, with an atomic susceptibility at room temperature of about 90×10^{-6}.

Niobium. Kriessman[26] gives $\chi_A = 209 \times 10^{-6}$.

Osmium. This metal appears to be the least strongly paramagnetic of the palladium-platinum group. The atomic susceptibility at room temperature is $\sim 9.5 \times 10^{-6}$.

Palladium. Over a limited temperature range, the Curie-Weiss law is followed. The high paramagnetism,[60] $\chi_A = 558 \times 10^{-6}$, seems to indicate much less pairing of electrons through bond formation than in any of the other elements of this group.[61-63]

Platinum. Like palladium, platinum metal shows a relatively large atomic paramagnetism of 189×10^{-6} at room temperature, with adherence to the Curie-Weiss law over a limited temperature range.[61] Takatori[64] reports a diminution in the susceptibility of platinum when the metal is reduced to a fine powder. The effect of small amounts of foreign substances on the magnetic properties of platinum has been studied by Theron.[65]

Plutonium. It is astonishing that the magnetic susceptibility of this element is known with more precision than that of many "common" elements. Dawson[65a] gives $\chi_A = 627 \times 10^{-6}$ at room temperature. This appears to be the α form.

Potassium. According to Klemm and his co-workers,[66,67] the susceptibility per gram-atom of potassium at 20°C. is 21.5×10^{-6}. This appears to be almost independent of temperature.

Rare Earths. The magnetic properties of the rare earth metals are no less interesting than are those of rare earth compounds, as described in Chapter VIII. Scandium, yttrium, and lanthanum metals have been studied by Bommer.[68] The susceptibilities are all positive and dependent on temperature, that for scandium being considerably more so than the others. At 19°C., the susceptibility per gram-atom of scandium is $315 \pm 10 \times 10^{-6}$, and that of lanthanum is about 112×10^{-6}. Lanthanum has also been studied by Trombe,[69] with results not in very good agreement with those of Bommer.

[60] A. N. Guthrie and L. T. Bourland, *Phys. Rev.*, **37**, 303 (1931).

[61] F. E. Hoare and J. C. Walling, *Proc. Phys. Soc. (London)*, **64B**, 337 (1951).

[62] P. Collet and G. Foëx, *J. phys. radium*, **2**, 290 (1931).

[63] E. Vogt, "Magnetismus der Metallischen Elements," *Ergeb. exact. Naturw.*, **11**, 323 (1932).

[64] N. Takatori, *Science Repts. Tôhoku Imp. Univ., First Ser.*, **25**, 489 (1936).

[65] R. Theron, *Compt. rend.*, **208**, 1634 (1939).

[65a] J. K. Dawson, *J. Chem. Soc.*, **1954**, 3393.

[66] W. Klemm and B. Hauschulz, *Z. Elektrochem.*, **45**, 346 (1939).

[67] B. Böhm and W. Klemm, *Z. anorg. u. allgem. Chem.*, **243**, 69 (1939).

[68] H. Bommer, *Z. Elektrochem.*, **45**, 357 (1939).

[69] F. Trombe, *Compt. rend.*, **198**, 1591 (1934).

Susceptibilities per gram-atom of the other rare earth metals are shown in Fig. 122. These are all for room temperature, and it should be emphasized that several of the results given are only rough approximations. In view of the increasing interest in these substances, it would be desirable to have some more reliable data for some of these elements. This is perhaps especially true of samarium, europium, terbium, and ytterbium.

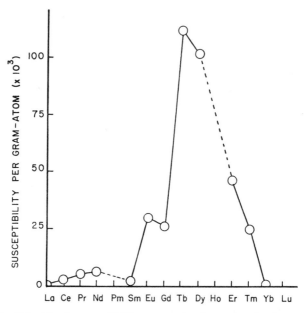

Fig. 122. Atomic susceptibility *versus* atomic number for the rare earth metals. Some of the higher atomic numbers are probably considerably in error. Data are for room temperature, in some cases extrapolated.

Metallic cerium has received much study.[70-75] There are at least three different polymorphic forms, which differ considerably in their magnetic properties. The magnetic properties of metallic cerium seem also to be unusually sensitive to traces of iron. Praseodymium and neodymium have

[70] L. F. Vereshchagin, L. V. Shubnikov, and B. G. Lazarev, *Physik. Z. Sowjetunion, Arb. Gebiete Tiefer Temp.*, **Special No.,** 107 (June, 1936).

[71] R. I. Yams, *Physik Z. Sowjetunion*, **12**, 729 (1937).

[72] F. Trombe, *Ann. phys.*, **7**, 385 (1937).

[73] C. Starr and A. R. Kaufmann, *Phys. Rev.*, **58**, 657 (1940).

[74] F. Trombe and M. Foëx, *Ann. chim.*, **19**, 417 (1944).

[75] F. Trombe and M. Foëx, *Compt. rend. réunion ann. avec comm. thermodynam., union intern. phys.* Paris 1952. Changements de phases 308.

been studied by Klemm and Bommer,[76] Trombe, and others.[77,78] These elements follow the Curie-Weiss law, except at low temperatures. Gadolinium metal has been shown by Urbain, Weiss, and Trombe[79-81] to be ferromagnetic below room temperature. The only other rare earth metals which seems to have received much magnetic study are dysprosium and holmium, although Spedding *et al.* give a preliminary report on erbium.[82] Dysprosium has been extensively investigated.[83,84] It definitely becomes ferromagnetic at low temperatures, with a Curie point at about 85°K. The magnetic moment of over 7 Bohr magnetons is very high, but is not so high as expected on the basis of the presumed electronic structure. Bommer[85] finds that below 195°C. the susceptibility of holmium is somewhat dependent on field strength. At higher temperatures, $\chi = C/(T - 87°)$.

The interest in the susceptibilities of the rare earth metals lies in the fact that the 4f electrons seem to be unaffected by external influences to almost the same degree that they are in the compounds of these elements. This is to say that the moments calculated from measurements on the metals are in most cases equal to the moments found for the trivalent ions. Exceptions are europium, ytterbium, and possibly terbium, which seem, in part at least, to assume the moment associated with the di-, di-, and tetravalent states, respectively. This view is supported by the anomalous atomic volumes shown by europium and ytterbium.

Rhenium. Knowledge of the magnetic properties of metallic rhenium comes from Perakis and Capatos.[86] They give $\chi_A = 68.6 \times 10^{-6}$, virtually independent of temperature from $-79°$ to $20°C$. This value has been confirmed recently,[86a] but Asmussen and Soling[86b] give a lower value, 56×10^{-6}

Rhodium. The atomic susceptibility at room temperature is 101×10^{-6} This follows the Curie-Weiss law over a limited temperature range.

[76] W. Klemm and H. Bommer, *Z. anorg. u. allgem. Chem.*, 231, 138 (1937); 241, 264 (1939).

[77] C. Henry LaBlanchetais, *Compt. rend.*, 234, 1353 (1952).

[78] J. F. Elliott, S. Legvold, and F. H. Spedding, *Phys. Rev.*, 94, 50 (1954).

[79] G. Urbain, P. Weiss, and F. Trombe, *Compt. rend.*, 200, 2132 (1935).

[80] F. Trombe, *ibid.*, 201, 652 (1935).

[81] J. F. Elliott, S. Legvold, and F. H. Spedding, *Phys. Rev.*, 91, 28 (1953).

[82] S. Legvold, F. H. Spedding, F. Barson, and J. F. Elliott, *Revs. Mod. Phys.*, 25, 129 (1953).

[83] F. Trombe, *J. recherches centre natl. recherche sci. Labs. Bellevue (Paris)*, No. 23, 61 (1953).

[84] J. F. Elliott, S. Legvold, and F. H. Spedding, *Phys. Rev.*, 94, 1143 (1954).

[85] H. Bommer, *Z. anorg. u. allgem. Chem.*, 242, 277 (1939).

[86] N. Perakis and L. Capatos, *Compt. rend.*, 196, 611 (1933); 198, 1905 (1934).

[86a] C. M. Nelson, G. E. Boyd, and W. T. Smith, Jr., *J. Am. Chem. Soc.*, 76, 348 (1954).

[86b] R. W. Asmussen and H. Soling, *Acta. Scand.*, 8, 563 (1954).

Rubidium. Klemm[40,41] gives the atomic susceptibility as 19.2×10^{-6}, and as falling slightly with rising temperature.

Ruthenium. It is curious that this element, which is the only member of the palladium-platinum group to show nearly normal paramagnetism in its compounds, has one of the smallest atomic susceptibilities as a metal. At room temperature, $\chi_A = 44 \times 10^{-6}$.

Selenium. The atomic susceptibility is -26.5×10^{-6}. Prasad and Dharmatti[87] have shown that prolonged grinding of selenium results in a change of susceptibility. It is not certain whether or not part of this change may be due to adsorbed impurities, or perhaps to a polymorphic transition.

Silicon. $\chi_A = -5.3 \times 10^{-6}$.

Silver. The metal is diamagnetic, $\chi_A = -22 \times 10^{-6}$. This is almost independent of temperature.

Strontium. Rao and Savithri[88] give $\chi_A = 91.2 \times 10^{-6}$ at room temperature. With increasing temperature the susceptibility rises, then falls slowly.

Tantalum. The atomic susceptibility[88a] at room temperature is said to be 153×10^{-6}.

Technetium. It is implied by Daunt and Cobble[89] that the susceptibility is about four times larger than that of rhenium, and this is confirmed by Nelson[86a] et al. $\chi_A = 270 \times 10^{-6}$ at room temperature.

Tellurium. Prasad and Dharmatti[90] have studied the effect of grinding. At room temperature, $\chi_A = -40.8 \times 10^{-6}$.

Thallium. Nevgi[91] gives $\chi_A = -58 \times 10^{-6}$ for the polycrystalline α (hexagonal) form. For the β (face-centered cubic) form, stable above $235°C$., $\chi_A = 44 \times 10^{-6}$. There is a 10% drop of diamagnetism at the melting point.

Thorium. The atomic susceptibility at room temperature is $(132 \pm 10) \times 10^{-6}$, according to L. Klemm.[38]

Tin. Rao and Subramanian[92] confirm earlier observations that the white variety is slightly paramagnetic, with $\chi_A = 4.5 \times 10^{-6}$ at $30°C.$, but at the melting point, $233°C.$, the metal becomes diamagnetic, with $\chi_A = -5.1 \times 10^{-6}$. The change is reversible. The atomic susceptibility

[87] M. Prasad and S. S. Dharmatti, *Indian J. Phys.*, **11**, 1 (1937).

[88] S. R. Rao and K. Savithri, *Proc. Indian Acad. Sci.*, **14A**, 584 (1941).

[88a] F. E. Hoare, J. S. Kouvelites, J. C. Matthews, and J. Preston, *Proc. Phys. Soc.* (*London*), **67B**, 728 (1954).

[89] J. G. Daunt and J. W. Cobble, *Phys. Rev.*, **92**, 507 (1953).

[90] M. Prasad and S. S. Dharmatti, *Indian J. Physics*, **11**, 393 (1938).

[91] M. B. Nevgi, *J. Univ. Bombay*, **7**, Part 3, 19 (1938).

[92] S. R. Rao and K. C. Subramanian, *Phil. Mag.*, **21**, 609 (1936).

of gray tin,[93] measured at room temperature, is said to be about -37×10^{-6}.

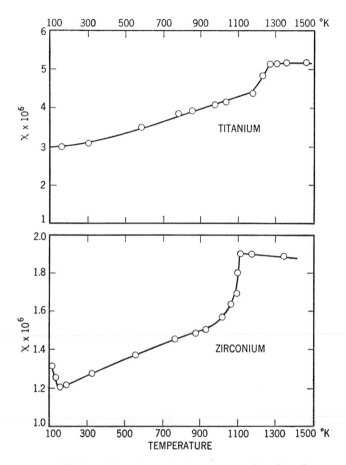

Fig. 123. Susceptibilities of titanium and zirconium as a function of temperature.

Titanium.   The metal has been studied by L. Klemm[38] and by Squire and Kaufmann.[94]   With increasing temperature, as shown in Fig. 123, the susceptibility increases until an anomalous region is reached in the neighborhood of 1200°K.   This anomaly, which parallels one shown by zirconium metal, is reproducible and not subject to hysteresis.   The effect is probably associated with a change of crystal structure.   At room temperature, $\chi_A = 153 \pm 5 \times 10^{-6}$.

[93] G. Busch and E. Mooser, *Z. physik. Chem.*, **198**, 23 (1951).

[94] C. F. Squire and A. R. Kaufmann, *J. Chem. Phys.*, **9**, 673 (1941).

Tungsten. So far as has been reported,[26] the atomic susceptibility is about 55×10^{-6}.

Uranium. Bates and Mallard[95] report a susceptibility of $\chi_A = 414 \times 10^{-6}$ at 20°C. The susceptibility increases slightly with increasing temperature, and this is confirmed by Kriessman and McGuire.[96] There are abrupt increases[97] of susceptibility at 698°C. and 808°C.

Vanadium. L. Klemm[38] reports $\chi_A = 230 \times 10^{-6}$ at 20°C. and at $-183°$, but Kriessman[26] gives the slightly higher value of 255×10^{-6}.

Zinc. For the polycrystalline metal at room temperature, $\chi_A = -11.4 \times 10^{-6}$. The temperature coefficient is complex and will be discussed further in connection with crystal anisotropy.[98,99]

Zirconium. The metal has been studied by L. Klemm[38] and by Squire and Kaufmann.[94] Like titanium, the susceptibility shows an anomaly at high temperature. As shown in Fig. 123, the susceptibility rises almost vertically just below 1100°K. There is a possible rise of susceptibility below 50°K., but this may be due to ferromagnetic impurities. At room temperature, $\chi_A = 122 \times 10^{-6}$.

93. Magnetic Anisotropy of Pure Metal Crystals

This topic has not yet assumed very much importance in the solution of purely chemical problems. Most attention has been directed in recent years toward the deHaas-van Alphen effect[100] shown by certain metals at very low temperatures. If magnetic measurements are made on a crystal of bismuth along its axis of maximum susceptibility at or below liquid air temperature, the susceptibility oscillates about an average value as the field strength is increased. Figure 124 shows the effect at liquid helium temperature. The effect has been studied also by Shoenberg[101,104] Blackman,[102] Peierls,[103] and others. Many other metals, and graphite, show this effect at low temperatures.

Other anisotropy measurements have been taken on single crystals of

[95] L. F. Bates and J. R. Mallard, *Proc. Phys. Soc.* (*London*), **63B**, 520 (1950).

[96] C. J. Kriessman, Jr. and T. R. McGuire, *Phys. Rev.*, **85**, 71 (1952).

[97] L. F. Bates and D. Hughes, *Proc. Phys. Soc.* (*London*), **67B**, 28 (1954).

[98] J. C. McLennan, R. Ruedy, and E. Cohen, *Proc. Roy. Soc.* (*London*), **A121**, 9 (1928).

[99] S. R. Rao and S. Sriraman, *ibid.*, **A166**, 325 (1938).

[100] W. J. deHaas and P. M. van Alphen, *Proc. Acad. Sci. Amsterdam*, **34**, 1249 (1931); **36**, 158 (1933).

[101] D. Shoenberg, *Proc. Roy. Soc.* (*London*), **A170**, 341 (1939).

[102] M. Blackman, *ibid.*, **A166**, 1 (1938).

[103] R. Peierls, *Z. Physik*, **81**, 186 (1933).

[104] D. Shoenberg, *Phil. Trans. Roy. Soc.* (*London*), **A245**, 1 (1952).

various metals, including cadmium, germanium, indium, tellurium, thallium, tin, and zinc, but this list is by no means meant to be complete.[105-116]

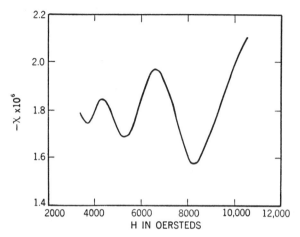

Fig. 124. The de Haas-van Alphen effect in bismuth at very low temperatures.

94. Metal Hydrides

In this section there will be presented some data on compounds or mixtures formed by certain metals and hydrogen. In such cases, it is not always clear what may be the mode of bonding between metal and hydrogen. In some cases, the compound is clearly a salt-like hydride. In others, it may be a covalent bond or, sometimes, merely interstitial molecular hydrogen.

The magnetic susceptibility of hydrogenized palladium is an old

[105] S. R. Rao, *Current Sci.*, **13**, 125 (1944).   (Bi, Cd, Te, Zn)

[106] J. C. McLennan, R. Ruedy, and E. Cohen, *Proc. Roy. Soc. (London)*, **A121**, 9 (1928).   (Cd, Zn)

[107] S. R. Rao, *Proc. Indian Acad. Sci.*, **4A**, 186 (1936).   (Zn)

[108] H. J. Hoge, *Phys. Rev.*, **48**, 615 (1935).   (Sn)

[109] S. R. Rao and S. Sriraman, *Proc. Roy. Soc. (London)*, **A166**, 325 (1938).   (Cd)

[110] S. R. Rao and S. R. Govindarajan, *Proc. Indian Acad. Sci.*, **10A**, 235 (1939). (Te)

[111] S. R. Rao and A. S. Narayanaswamy, *Current Sci.*, **6**, 276 (1937).   (Tl)

[112] S. R. Rao and K. C. Subramanian, *Phil. Mag.*, **21**, 609 (1936).   (Tl)

[113] J. A. Marcus, *Phys. Rev.*, **76**, 621 (1949).   (Cd, Zn)

[114] J. Verhaege, G. Vanderschmeersche, and G. LeCompte, *ibid.*, **80**, 758 (1950). (In)

[115] L. F. Bates, *Modern Magnetism.*   Cambridge University Press, 1950, p. 180.

[116] G. Busch and N. Helfer, *Helv. Phys. Acta*, **27**, 201, (1954).   (Ge)

problem, first studied by Graham.[117]   More recently Svensson[118] has found that the susceptibility of palladium diminishes linearly with increasing hydrogen content and finally reaches a value just below zero for a volume ratio H/Pd of 800/1.   Substantially the same form of change is shown by Sieverts and Danz[119] to occur when deuterium is substituted for hydrogen.   These changes (Fig. 125), which are further discussed by Michel and Gallissot[120] and by Wucher,[121] seem to show that, as it takes 0.64

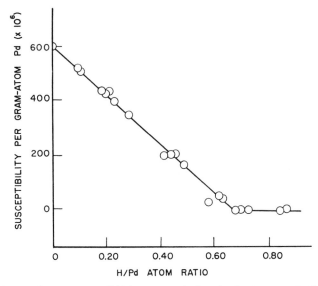

Fig. 125. Susceptibility *versus* H/Pd atom ratio for the hydrogen-palladium system

atom of hydrogen to destroy the paramagnetism of one palladium atom, there must be an average of 0.64 hole in the 4*d* shell of palladium.   This result has significance in the band theory of metals and in its application to heterogeneous catalysis.   A good review of the experimental data is given by Smith,[122] but the idea there expressed, that the hydrogen is present as protons, is not generally accepted.   This topic will be referred to again in the following chapter.

Other hydrides studied, chiefly by Trzebiatowski and his co-

[117] T. Graham, *Ann. chim. et phys.*, **16**, 197 (1869).

[118] B. Svensson, *Ann. Physik*, **18**, 299 (1933).

[119] A. Sieverts and W. Danz, *Z. physik. Chem.*, **B38**, 61 (1937).

[120] A. Michel and M. Gallissot, *Compt. rend.*, **208**, 434 (1939).

[121] J. Wucher, *Ann. phys.*, **7**, 317 (1952).

[122] D. P. Smith, *Hydrogen in Metals*.   University of Chicago Press, Chicago, 1948, p. 214.

workers,[123-125] include those of titanium, niobium, tantalum, and uranium. In addition to these, the zirconium-hydrogen system has been studied by Squire and Kaufmann.[94]   The effect of hydrogen on titanium is first to raise the susceptibility. This is presumably due to the extra electrons supplied by the hydrogen. At higher hydrogen concentrations, the effects are more complicated owing, presumably, to some degree of antiferromagnetism, and other effects. The deuterides are similar. For the zirconium system, the susceptibility at room temperature is reduced by 40% near the ratio ZrH_2. The high temperature anomaly is also altered. The niobium-hydrogen system has a lower susceptibility than the pure metal, as does the tantalum-hydrogen system.

The uranium-hydrogen system is remarkable in that UH_3 and UD_3 exhibit ferromagnetic properties below 174°K. and 172°K., respectively. This result of Trzebiatowski's work has recently been confirmed by Gruen.[125a]   In view of this result, it might be predicted that hydrides of some of the transuranium elements might become ferromagnetic at room temperature.   By contrast, the ferromagnetism of gadolinium is lost in the hydride and deuteride.[126]

One other system which has been studied is manganese-hydrogen.[127]

95. Alloys and Intermetallic Compounds

Some reference was made to ferromagnetic alloys and intermetallic compounds in Chapter XII, and the distinction between these and the merely dia- or paramagnetic alloys and intermetallic compounds mentioned below is somewhat arbitrary.   Until recently there was little chemical interest in the latter group, but two related developments suggest that this situation is changing. One of these is the use of magnetic data, chiefly by Pauling,[128,129] in elucidation of structure; and the other is the application of such considerations and of electron-band theory to problems in heterogeneous catalysis. Pauling's interpretation will be briefly described here; the application to catalysis will be mentioned in the next chapter.

Let us start with krypton of which the 36 electrons in unshared pairs

[123] W. Trzebiatowski and B. Stalinski, *Bull. acad. polonaise, sci.*, **1**, 131, 317 (1953).

[124] B. Stalinski, *ibid.*, **2**, 245 (1954).

[125] W. Trzebiatowski, A. Sliwa, and B. Stalinski, *Roczniki Chem.*, **28**, 12 (1954). Some of these papers were not available to the author.

[125a] D. M. Gruen, *J. Chem. Phys.*, **23**, 1708 (1955).

[126] F. Trombe, *Compt. rend.*, **219**, 182 (1944).

[127] M. A. Wheeler, *Phys. Rev.*, **49**, 642 (1936).

[128] L. Pauling, *J. Chem. Soc.*, **1948**, 1461.

[129] L. Pauling, *Proc. Roy. Soc. (London)*, **A196**, 343 (1949).

fill all stable orbitals in this element. Krypton thus enters into no stable bonding with other atoms. But bromine, with one orbital containing a single electron, can use this orbital to form a single stable electron-pair bond. Selenium, with two less electrons, can form two covalent bonds, which it appears to do both in compounds and in the element itself. Continuing in this way, it might be expected that arsenic and germanium would show covalences of three and four respectively, and that gallium, zinc, and copper would have valencies of five, six, and seven. Tin, like germanium, actually appears to have a covalency of four in gray tin and in a number of intermetallic compounds. In the compound $NaZn_{13}$, one of the zinc atoms, at least, actually seems to have a covalency of six. But in general, as shown by Pauling, the maximum covalency is rarely reached. If two of four valency electrons are paired, the valency, as in some of the atoms in white tin, might be reduced to two, or rather, the tin atoms may be thought of as having a fractional valency. In metallic zinc, resonance between a valency of four and valency of six in the ratio of three to one, respectively, leads to an overall valency of four and one-half. This valency is shown by 12 of the 13 zinc atoms in $NaZn_{13}$. This concept has been quite fruitful in the prediction of magnetic properties as well as other properties for a substantial number of alloys and intermetallic compounds, although there are many aspects of the problem which have not yet been solved.

When a diamagnetic metal is simply dissolved in a paramagnetic metal, the effect is similar to that already described for the dilution of a ferromagnetic metal such as nickel with a diamagnetic metal such as copper. It appears that the valency electrons of the diamagnetic metal tend to fill the d-band of the paramagnetic metal and that, as a consequence, the diamagnetic elements with several valency electrons are more effective than those with only one.

There will be given below some references to experimental data on alloys and intermetallic compounds. These are in addition to the substantial groups referred to in previous chapters. Some especially interesting systems will be selected for comment. An active area which does not greatly concern us is the study of superconducting alloys and their magnetic properties.

Amalgams have received fairly extensive study. The magnetic properties of alkali metal amalgams have been studied by Franke and Katz,[130] Rao and Aravamuthachari,[131] and Klemm and Hauschulz.[132] In most cases the maxima and minima, and the changes in direction of

[130] W. Franke and H. Katz, Z. anorg. u. allgem. Chem., **231**, 63 (1937).

[131] S. R. Rao and S. Aravamuthachari, Proc. Indian Acad. Sci., **9A**, 181 (1939).

[132] W. Klemm and B. Hauschulz, Z. Elektrochem., **45**, 346 (1939).

susceptibility plotted against concentration, correspond to compounds. These compounds are also indicated by thermoanalysis, although there are a few cases in which the two methods disagree. As an example of the work done by Klemm and Hauschulz, it may be mentioned that magnetic measurements clearly indicate the existence of KHg_9, K_2Hg_9, KHg_3, KHg_2 and KHg as compounds in potassium amalgam.

Copper amalgams have been studied by Bhatnagar[133] and by Bates and Tai.[134] The susceptibilities are approximately linear with concentration when first prepared but they are said to decrease with aging and hardening of the amalgam. Silver amalgams have been studied by Bates and Ireland.[135]

Amalgams of chromium and of manganese have been studied by Bates and Tai.[136] The apparent atomic susceptibility of chromium in dilute amalgam is 23×10^{-6}. This is a contrast to manganese, the atomic susceptibility of which is said to reach the very high value of $13{,}700 \times 10^{-6}$ at room temperature. This large value is, however, in substantial agreement with that found for manganese in alloys with copper, silver, or gold, although the susceptibility depends on concentration and on solvent.[137]

Europium and samarium amalgams have been studied by Douglas and Yost.[138] The effective moment for europium is 8.3 Bohr magnetons, which is in good agreement with the Klemm and Bommer value on the pure metal, and with theory for the divalent ion. But samarium in the amalgam yields a moment of about 2.3, which is higher than Klemm's result on the pure metal and which is intermediate between the moments for the Sm^{2+} and Sm^{3+} ions. It may be that samarium amalgam contains a mixture of di- and trivalent ions.

Palladium amalgam has recently been the subject of study by Ubbelohde.[139] While palladium is fairly strongly paramagnetic, the compounds $PdHg_{5.2}$ and $PdH_{0.15}Hg_4$ are diamagnetic.

Some other studies on amalgams are mentioned below.[140-142]

Palladium and platinum have also received fairly extensive investi-

[133] S. S. Bhatnagar, P. L. Kapur, and G. L. Mittal, *Proc. Indian Acad. Sci.*, **10A**, 45 (1939).

[134] L. F. Bates and L. C. Tai, *Proc. Phys. Soc. (London)*, **48**, 795 (1936).

[135] L. F. Bates and A. W. Ireland, *ibid.*, **49**, 642 (1937).

[136] L. F. Bates and L. C. Tai, *ibid.*, **49**, 230 (1937).

[137] G. Gustafsson, *Ann. Physik*, **25**, 545 (1936).

[138] D. L. Douglas and D. M. Yost, *J. Chem. Phys.*, **18**, 1418 (1950).

[139] A. R. Ubbelohde, *J. Chem. Soc.*, **1950**, 1143.

[140] H. S. V. Ramiah, *J. Mysore Univ.*, **1**, 155 (1941).   (Cd)

[141] D. Krishna Iyer, *J. Annamalai Univ.*, **11**, 77 (1941).   (Zn, Cd, Sn, Pb, Se, and Bi)

[142] L. F. Bates and L. C. Tai, *Proc. Phys. Soc. (London)*, **48**, 795 (1936).   (Bi)

gation in connection with other alloy systems, but the other members of the palladium-platinum groups have almost been ignored. A reason for this lies in the comparatively large paramagnetism of these two elements and interest in knowing what happens to this paramagnetism, and presumably to the free d-band electrons which cause it, when metals containing various numbers of valency electrons are introduced as alloying agents. For instance, alloys of palladium and silver show no paramagnetism below 50 atom % of palladium.[143] In some cases the susceptibility is markedly

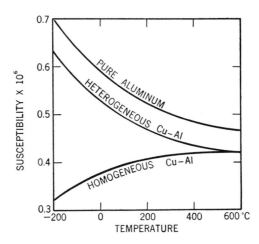

Fig. 126. Aluminum-copper alloy before and after tempering.

dependent on crystalline structure. Thus the copper-platinum system shows substantially different susceptibilities, depending on whether or not the samples are annealed. A few other references are given below.[144−149]

Other alloys containing aluminum include, in particular, the copper-aluminum system. Figure 126 shows the susceptibility plotted against temperature for aluminum and for a copper-aluminum alloy, the latter both in solid solution and in heterogeneous form.[150] The nature of the

[143] B. Svensson, *Ann. Physik*, **14**, 699 (1932). (Pd-Ag, Pd-Cu)

[144] G. Rienäcker and H. Gaubatz, *Naturwissenschaften*, **28**, 534 (1940). (Cu-Pt)

[145] C. H. Johansson and J. O. Linde, *Ann. Physik*, **5**, 762 (1930) (Au-Pt)

[146] H. J. Seemann, *Z. Metallkunde*, **24**, 299 (1932). (Cu-Au, Cu-Pd, Cu-Pt)

[147] E. Vogt and H. Krueger, *Ann. Physik*, **18**, 755, 771 (1933). (Au-Ni, Cu-Pd, Cu₃Pd, Cu₃Pt, etc.)

[148] J. Wucher, *Ann. phys.*, **7**, 317 (1952). (Pd-Ag, Al, An, Cu, Pb, Sn)

[149] F. E. Hoare, J. C. Matthews, and J. C. Walling, *Proc. Roy. Soc.* (*London*), **A216**, 502 (1953). (Pd-Ag)

[150] H. Auer, *Z. Elektrochem.*, **45**, 608 (1939).

reforming action, its velocity, and its activation energy may all be obtained by magnetic measurements. It is a very interesting fact that pure aluminum at room temperature is slightly paramagnetic, yet aluminum in dilute solid solution in copper is diamagnetic. This appears to mean that the aluminum atoms in solution are stripped of three valence electrons and occupy lattice positions in a triply ionized state.[151]

It is found, in general, that alloys in the Hume-Rothery γ-phase show anomalous diamagnetism. These include Cu-Zn, Cu-Cd, Ag-Zn, and many others crystallizing in a complex cubic structure containing 52 atoms in the unit cell.

References to some related systems are given below.[152-155]

Alloys consisting solely of alkali metals have been studied by Böhm and Klemm.[156] The formation of either intermetallic compounds or of mixed crystals generally lowers the susceptibility. The system Na-K shows a susceptibility linear with concentration at 20° and at −78°C. But at −183° there is a slight minimum at the atomic ratio Na$_2$K. Other similar systems such as Na-Cs and K-Cs show fairly large negative deviations from linearity.

Alloys of the coinage metals with each other and with other non-ferromagnetic metals generally have susceptibilities which are linear with concentration or nearly so. Intermetallic compounds, when formed, are often indicated by rather striking maxima or minima, or by change of direction in the susceptibility-concentration curve.

Alloys of lanthanum with metals such as nickel or manganese are interesting because of the possible influence of the $4f$ level on the electron distribution. It appears that such systems maintain a very low paramagnetism up to fairly high concentrations of the more magnetic element. This is presumably due to filling of the $3d$ level by valence electrons from the lanthanum. The $4f$ level of the lanthanum apparently remains empty.[157,158]

Neither in this section nor the last have the effects on the magnetic properties of metals of gases other than hydrogen been mentioned. Some

[151] E. Vogt and B. Harms, *Ann. Physik*, **42**, 501 (1942-3).

[152] E. Vogt, *Appl. Sci. Research*, **4B**, 34 (1954).   (Mn-Al, Pb-Ag)

[153] H. Bittner and H. Nowotny, *Monatsh.*, **83**, 1308 (1952).   (Cu-Al, Cu-In, Ag-Hg, Pd-Hg, Ag-In).

[154] G. Foëx and J. Wucher, *Compt. rend.*, **238**, 1281 (1954).   (NiAl$_3$, CoAl$_4$, FeAl$_3$, MnAl$_6$, CrAl$_7$)

[155] H. Klee and H. Witte, *Z. physik. Chem.*, **202**, 352 (1954).   (MgCu$_2$-MgZn$_2$, MgCu$_2$-MgAl$_2$, MgCu$_2$-MgSi$_2$, MgZn$_2$-MgAl$_2$)

[156] B. Böhm and W. Klemm, *Z. anorg. u. allgem. Chem.*, **243**, 69 (1939).

[157] G. Foëx, *Helv. Phys. Acta*, **26**, 199 (1953), a review.

[158] A. Serres, *J. phys. radium*, **13**, 46 (1952).   (La-Mn)

discussion of this matter will be made in the next chapter. The effect of nitrogen on manganese is described by Bates et al.[159]

A few references to other alloy systems are given below.[160-179]

96. Ammonia Solutions of Metals

It is well known that liquid ammonia will dissolve alkali and alkaline earth metals. At low and moderate concentrations, the solutions are blue; at high concentrations, the solutions take on a coppery, metallic luster. The nature of these solutions has been the subject of much investigation, and some light has been thrown on the problem by magnetic susceptibility measurements. The ammonia solutions which have been investigated in this way are those containing sodium, potassium, and cesium, together with a few observations on calcium and barium.[180-183]

Some results are shown in Fig. 127. These data are qualitatively, although not quantitatively, in agreement with the idea that the solutions are to be considered essentially as metals in which some sort of equilibrium

[159] L. F. Bates, R. E. Gibbs, and D. V. R. Pantulu, *Proc. Phys. Soc. (London)*, **48,** 665 (1936).

[160] R. Gans and A. Fonseca, *Ann. Physik*, **61,** 742 (1920). (Ni-Cu)

[161] J. W. Shih, *Phys. Rev.*, **38,** 2051 (1931). (Fe-Au)

[162] E. H. Williams, *ibid.*, **38,** 828 (1931). (Ni-Cu)

[163] K. E. Grew, *Proc. Leeds Phil. Soc.*, **2,** 217 (1931). (Ni-Cu)

[164] C. G. Montgomery and W. H. Ross, *Phys. Rev.*, **43,** 358 (1933). (Pb-Ag)

[165] H. Auer, E. Riedl, and H. J. Seemann, *Z. Physik*, **92,** 291 (1934). (Au-Ag)

[166] K. E. Grew, *Proc. Roy. Soc. (London)*, **A145,** 509 (1934). (Ni-Cu)

[167] C. S. Smith, *Physics*, **6,** 47 (1935). (γ-brasses, Cu-Zn, Cu-Cd, Ag-An, Ag-Cd)

[168] C. T. Lane, *Applied Phys.*, **8,** 693 (1937). (γ-brasses)

[169] E. Hildebrand, *Ann. Physik*, **30,** 593 (1937). (Au-Co, Cu-Co, Pt-Rh)

[170] D. Shoenberg, *Nature*, **142,** 874 (1938). (Au-Bi)

[171] W. Broniewski, S. Franczak, and R. Witkowski, *Ann. phys.*, **10,** 5 (1938). (Au-Cu, Au-Ag, Ag-Cu, Cu-Ni)

[172] A. R. Kaufmann and C. Starr, *Phys. Rev.*, **59,** 690 (1941). (Cu-Ni)

[173] H. Stöhr and W. Klemm, *Z. anorg. u. allgem. Chem.*, **241,** 305 (1939). (Ge-Al, Ge-Sn)

[174] A. W. David and J. F. Spencer, *Trans. Faraday Soc.*, **32,** 1512 (1936). (Tl-Bi Tl-Cd)

[175] F. Mahn, *Ann. phys.*, **3,** 393 (1948). (Ce-Mg)

[176] J. A. Marcus, *Phys. Rev.*, **76,** 621 (1949). (γ-brass)

[177] A. Morette, *Compt. rend.*, **215,** 86 (1942). (Te-Mo)

[178] F. M. Gal'perin and T. M. Perekalina, *Doklady Akad. Nauk S.S.S.R.*, **69,** 19 (1949). (Cr-Te, Co-Te, Ni-Te, V-Te)

[179] J. W. Stout and L. Guttman, *Phys. Rev.*, **79,** 396 (1950). (In-Tl)

[180] E. Hüster and E. Vogt, *Physik Z.*, **38,** 1004 (1937).

[181] E. Hüster, *Ann. Physik*, **33,** 477 (1938).

[182] S. Freed and H. G. Thode, *J. Chem. Phys.*, **7,** 85 (1939).

[183] S. Freed and N. Sugarman, *ibid.*, **11,** 354 (1943).

exists involving diatomic metal molecules, metal ions, and solvated electrons. The problem is discussed by Yost and Russell[184] and by Birch and MacDonald.[185] Such solutions exhibit paramagnetic resonance absorption, as do solutions of alkali metals in methylamine and in ethylenediamine.[186-188] The absorption lines are characterized by an extreme sharpness and seem

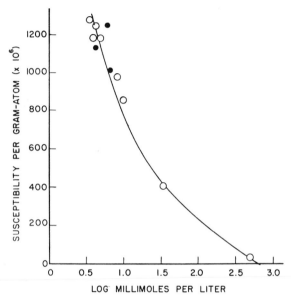

Fig. 127. Susceptibility of alkali metals in liquid ammonia; (O) = K, (●) = Cs.

to indicate that the unpaired electrons in these systems are even freer than they are in organic free radicals. The theory of magnetic properties in metal-ammonia solutions has recently been studied by Deigen[188a].

The susceptibilities of solid solutions of sodium in ammonia at 78°K. are not greatly different from those of the same concentration in the liquid state.[189] This contributes further evidence against the view once expressed that such solutions could be superconducting as high as 180°K.

[184] D. M. Yost and H. Russell, Jr., *Systematic Inorganic Chemistry*. Prentice-Hall, Inc., New York, 1944, pp. 140–4.

[185] A. J. Birch and D. K. C. MacDonald, *Trans. Faraday Soc.*, 44, 735 (1948).

[186] C. A. Hutchison, Jr. and R. C. Pastor, *Phys. Rev.*, 81, 282 (1951).

[187] M. A. Garstens and A. H. Ryan, *ibid.*, 81, 888 (1951).

[188] E. C. Levinthal, E. H. Rogers, and R. A. Ogg, Jr. *ibid.*, 83, 182 (1951).

[188a] M. F. Deigen, *Zhur. Eksptl. i Teoret. Fiz.*, 26, 293 (1954). (This paper was not available to the writer.)

[189] R. B. Gibney and G. L. Pearson, *ibid.*, 72, 76 (1947).

CHAPTER FIFTEEN

MAGNETOCHEMISTRY AND HETEROGENEOUS CATALYSIS

97. Introduction

That branch of magnetochemistry which has yielded the most practical results, and a wealth of unique information virtually unattainable by other methods, is in the field of catalysis and the structure of catalytically active solids. For that reason a whole chapter will be devoted to it.

It has frequently been remarked that many elements and compounds of major importance in catalysis are those, such as nickel, palladium, manganese dioxide, and copper "chromite," which show ferromagnetism or paramagnetism and which are of more than ordinary interest for their magnetic properties. A reason for this is now becoming clear. A current theory of catalysis by metals and semiconductors relates activity to the number of electrons in the d-band. In general, those elements and substances with incomplete electron levels are those in which electronic transitions from catalyst surface to adsorbed molecule, and the reverse, are greatly facilitated. These are, of course, the transition elements and one finds, as a result, that magnetic measurements are often useful in ascertaining the composition and structure of the catalyst. A newer and potentially much more important application is the use of magnetic methods in studying the actual electronic interactions between adsorbent and adsorbate.

Magnetic methods are useful in catalysis primarily as tools for structural investigations in the same way that x rays or electron diffraction are useful. There is also an area, of minor importance at present, in which the magnetic state of the catalyst, or the presence of macromagnetic fields, is thought to influence catalytic activity. This whole area is one which is being vigorously pursued in several laboratories at the present time. Most work in the field is devoted to heterogeneous catalysis, but some activity in the homogeneous field will be referred to. The several branches into which magnetism and catalysis fall may be summarized as follows: (1) qualitative and quantitative analysis of ferromagnetic components such as the iron carbides; (2) the various reaction processes which they undergo; (3) the dispersion and structure of supported oxides such as chromia-alumina; (4) the structure of metals and alloys and, in particular, the particle-size distribution of ferromagnetic metals, such as nickel on kieselguhr; (5) the mechanism of chemisorption; (6) the use of nuclear resonance in the study of catalytically active solids; and (7) magnetic state and reaction velocity.

References to some earlier reviews in this area are given below.[1-3]

98. Identification of Catalyst Components

Catalyst components present in trifling amounts often have a profound effect on catalytic activity. Components present in substantial amounts are sometimes present in obscure forms or in very complicated mixtures. For these reasons it is often necessary in catalytic work to call on every resource of modern analytical chemistry. Thermomagnetic analysis is useful in this respect. Although the method is limited to those elements and compounds which show ferromagnetism, it is, within that area, a tool of quite exceptional power.

Several examples of thermomagnetic analysis, including some applications to catalysis, were given in Chapter III (p. 46) and some other examples were mentioned in Chapter XII (p. 316). These examples were concerned chiefly with the identification and estimation of carbides of iron, such as cementite, and with solution and precipitation processes in metals. In this section some of the principles involved are reviewed and one or two additional examples given.

Ferromagnetic substances are characterized by unique Curie temperatures which may be used for identification purposes in the same way that the melting point of an organic compound may be used. Thus the existence of a Curie point near 358°C. is strong evidence for the presence of metallic nickel. But, like melting points, Curie temperatures may be lowered or obscured by certain complexities. In general, the Curie temperature is not changed by the mere mechanical mixing of a ferromagnetic component with a nonferromagnetic component. But a solid solution generally has a lower Curie temperature. This means that impurities may often depress the Curie point or perhaps make it less sharp than for the pure substance. This is, of course, also true of melting points and most other transitions. Furthermore, the Curie temperature is lowered by decreased particle size.

[1] P. W. Selwood, *Chem. Revs.*, **38**, 41 (1946).

[2] P. W. Selwood, in *Advances in Catalysis*, Vol. III, Academic Press, Inc., New York, p. 27, 1951.

[3] P. W. Selwood, in *Catalysis*, Vol. I.   P. H. Emmett, Editor.   Rheinhold Publ. Corp., New York, 1954, p. 353.

The effects of particle size become observable below about 100A. This is a particle-size region of considerable interest in catalysis. Some attempts to use the effect for particle-size determination will be described below. It is sometimes stated that particles below a certain size do not show ferromagnetism, but this is probably due to a depression of the Curie point below room temperature. It may be noted also that some ferromagnetic substances, such as γ-Fe$_2$O$_3$, decompose or undergo a phase transition below the Curie point, becoming nonmagnetic.

The quantitative estimation of ferromagnetic components depends on the linear relationship between magnetization and mass. It is often possible to estimate the proportion of such components with considerable accuracy. An example is, for instance, the amount of reduced nickel in a nickel-silica catalyst. But here, also, consideration must be given to the fact that the magnetization is linear with mass only at temperatures considerably below the Curie point, that dissolved or chemically-combined impurities may lower the specific magnetization if they donate electrons to the magnetic element, and that particle size has some rather obscure effects, as will be shown below.

It will be clear that a trace of ferromagnetic component, or impurity in a paramagnetic or diamagnetic substance is easily revealed because the observed susceptibility shows some dependence on field strength. The author has often shown the presence of nickel in supposedly pure copper by this method, even though the nickel defied spectroscopic detection. Such methods depend, of course, on having the nickel present essentially as a mechanical mixture or, at least, as a fairly concentrated Cu-Ni solid solution. Dilute solutions of nickel in copper are not ferromagnetic.

It might be thought that paramagnetic components in diamagnetic solids would similarly lend themselves to detection and estimation. The author has used this method to detect very small amounts, say, of praseodymium sesquioxide in lanthana, but it will be clear that the method becomes sensitive only at quite low temperatures. At liquid helium temperatures, susceptibility measurements are quite sensitive in such cases, but it is doubtful, even so, if they can compete with paramagnetic resonance absorption.

99. Reaction Processes

In Chapter III (p. 54) and elsewhere, reference was made to the use of thermomagnetic methods in following the rates of certain reactions. Reactions mentioned were those involving the several iron carbides and their transformations, the decomposition of cobalt carbide and nickel carbide, the disproportionation of ferrous oxide, and the phase transition of γ-ferric oxide. All these are of interest in catalysis and especially so in connection with the Fischer-Tropsch synthesis. Some amplification of our previous remarks will be given here, and the study of so-called active oxides will also be mentioned. It is sometimes surmised that the rate of, say, nickel oxide being reduced by hydrogen to nickel metal may conveniently be followed by magnetic methods. This may be true for pure nickel oxide, but application of the method to mixtures or supported nickel catalysts may, as described in a later section, lead to serious difficulties.

The iron carbides are actually considerably more complicated than heretofore supposed, and we are indebted chiefly to Hofer[4] and his associates for elucidation of this problem. There are certainly three definite carbides. The composition of cementite is well established as Fe_3C, but both Hägg carbide(χ) and "hexagonal close-packed" carbide (ϵ) are apparently richer in iron than the formula Fe_2C would imply. Of course it will be understood that complexities such as deviations from stoichiometry abound in this area of solid-state chemistry. There may also be a carbide approximating FeC, with a Curie point at 380°C. Cohn and Hofer have examined the transitions between h.c.p. and Hägg carbides and have shown that the synthesis of cementite from iron and a higher carbide proceeds through Hägg. They have also been able to calculate activation energies for these and other similar reactions. Other studies on iron carbides and iron-nickel carbides are described by Michel.[5]

Reference was made above to the decomposition of cobalt carbide, which is not ferromagnetic, to metallic cobalt, and it was mentioned (p. 56) that the rate of this reaction is conveniently studied magnetically. Michel[6] has shown, however, that there may be a ferromagnetic solid solution formed between 260 and 310°C. This may complicate the interpretations previously given.

Two other studies will be mentioned. Bernier[7] has shown that supported nickel on thoria will form a paramagnetic hexagonal nitride near Ni_3N in the presence of ammonia at 170°C. He also showed that this nitride goes over to a ferromagnetic face-centered cubic nitride near Ni_4N in vacuum at 190°. This would appear to be an interesting system for further study.

The other study to be mentioned is the finding that alumina in a promoted unreduced iron catalyst apparently does not go into solid solution in the Fe_3O_4 which is present.[8] This is a result of considerable interest in

[4] E. M. Cohn and L. J. E. Hofer, *J. Chem. Phys.*, **21**, 354 (1953).

[5] A. Michel, *Proc. Intern. Symposium Reactivity of Solids*, Gothenburg, 1952, Pt. 2, 929 (1954).

[6] J. Drain and A. Michel, *Bull. soc. chim. France*, **1951**, 517.

[7] R. Bernier, *Ann. chim.*, **6**, 104 (1951).

[8] L. R. Maxwell, J. S. Smart, and S. Brunauer, *J. Chem. Phys.*, **19**, 303 (1951).

the study of synthetic ammonia catalysts. It seems to imply that the iron and aluminum oxides are separately aggregated because the magnetite has a normal Curie temperature, although the specific magnetization is quite low. When the sample is reduced, the thermomagnetic curve seems to be normal for iron. The results on the unreduced sample have been disputed by Westrik.[9] They may be related to particle-size effects.

Two additional references to reviews in this field are given below,[10,11] but the interested reader should not fail to see the papers of Hofer *et al.* to which reference has been made.

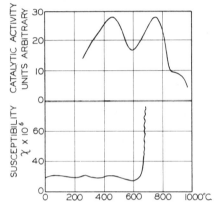

Fig. 128. Change of susceptibility, measured at room temperature, as a function of progressive sintering for the system CaO–Fe$_2$O$_3$.

There is interest in the processes which occur when two or more metal oxides are mixed and sintered. Here the emphasis is on the process itself rather than the final product as previously described for the ferrites and related substances (p. 309). Much of the work in this field is due to Hüttig, who has prepared adequate reviews[12-15] of the several hundred papers in the field, most of them being his own. The procedure has been to prepare various oxide mixtures and then to follow magnetic susceptibility and other properties as the solid state reaction proceeds toward formation of a compound, or in some cases, of a solid solution. For instance, the reaction of zinc oxide plus ferric oxide would be followed through to the formation

[9] R. Westrik, *J. Chem. Phys.*, **21**, 2094 (1953).
[10] H. Merkel, *Chem.-Ing.-Tech.*, **23**, 570 (1951).
[11] A. Michel, *Ind. chim. belge*, **17**, 643 (1952).
[12] G. F. Hüttig, *Kolloid-Z.*, **94**, 137, 258 (1941).
[13] G. F. Hüttig, *ibid.*, **97**, 281 (1941).
[14] G. F. Hüttig, *ibid.*, **98**, 263 (1942).
[15] G. F. Hüttig, *ibid.*, **99**, 262 (1942).

of zinc ferrite spinel.   In many cases, the properties of such reacting mixtures are by no means linear with heating time and temperature.   In a substantial number of such cases, the several phases formed during the

TABLE XXXI
Active Oxides

Oxide	Reference	Oxide	Reference
Al_2O_3-Fe_2O_3	(22)	CuO-Fe_2O_3	(22,26)
BaO-Fe_2O_3	(18)	Fe_2O_3-SiO_2	(22)
BeO-Cr_2O_3	(23)	Fe_2O_3-TiO_2	(22)
BeO-Fe_2O_3	(17,22,24,25)	MgO-Al_2O_3	(17)
CaO-Fe_2O_3	(16,17,18,19)	MgO-Cr_2O_3	(17,19,27)
CdO-Cr_2O_3	(23)	MgO-Fe_2O_3	(22,28,29,30,31,32,33)
CdO-Fe_2O_3	(26)	NiO-Fe_2O_3	(28)
Cr_2O_3-Al_2O_3	(22)	PbO-Cr_2O_3	(23)
Cr_2O_3-Fe_2O_3	(22)	PbO-Fe_2O_3	(26)
Cr_2O_3-SiO_2	(22)	SrO-Fe_2O_3	(18)
Cr_2O_3-TiO_2	(22)	ZnO-Cr_2O_3	(20,21)
CuO-Al_2O_3	(22)	ZnO-Fe_2O_3	(17,22,24,34,35,36,37,38)
CuO-Cr_2O_3	(22,23)		

[16] G. F. Hüttig, J. Funke, and H. Kittel, *J. Am. Chem. Soc.*, **57**, 2470 (1935).

[17] G. F. Hüttig, D. Zinker, and H. Kittel, *Z. Elektrochem.*, **40**, 306 (1934).

[18] H. Kittel and G. F. Hüttig, *Z. anorg. u. allgem. Chem.*, **219**, 256 (1934).

[19] H. Kittel and G. F. Hüttig, *ibid.*, **217**, 193 (1934).

[20] G. F. Hüttig, S. Cassirer, and E. Strotzer, *Z. Elektrochem.*, **42**, 215 (1936).

[21] G. F. Hüttig, H. Radler, and H. Kittel, *ibid.*, **38**, 442 (1932).

[22] G. F. Hüttig, T. Meyer, H. Kittel, and S. Cassirer, *Z. anorg. u. allgem. Chem.*, **224**, 225 (1935).

[23] H. Kittel, *ibid.*, **222**, 1 (1935).

[24] G. F. Hüttig *et al.*, *ibid.*, **337**, 209 (1938).

[25] G. F. Hüttig and H. Kittel, *Gazz. chim. ital.*, **63**, 833 (1933).

[26] H. Kittel, *Z. anorg. u. allgem. Chem.*, **221**, 49 (1934).

[27] T. Meyer and G. F. Hüttig, *Z. Elektrochem.*, **41**, 429 (1935).

[28] H. Forestier and N. Vetter, *Compt. rend.*, **209**, 164 (1939).

[29] G. F. Hüttig, W. Novak-Schreiber, and H. Kittel, *Z. physik. Chem.*, **A171**, 83 (1934).

[30] G. F. Hüttig, E. Rosenkranz, B. Steiner, and H. Kittel, *Z. anorg. u. allgem. Chem.*, **217**, 22 (1934).

[31] G. F. Hüttig and E. Zeidler, *Kolloid-Z.*, **75**, 170 (1936).

[32] H. Kittel, *Z. physik. Chem.*, **A178**, 81 (1936).

[33] H. Kittel, G. F. Hüttig, and Z. Hermann, *Z. anorg. u. allgem. Chem.*, **212**, 209 (1933).

[34] G. F. Hüttig, *Z. Angew. Chem.*, **49**, 882 (1936).

[35] G. F. Hüttig, *Z. Elektrochem.*, **44**, 571 (1938).

[36] G. F. Hüttig, *J. chim. phys.*, **36**, 84 (1939).

[37] G. F. Hüttig, H. Kittel, and H. Herrmann, *Z. anorg. u. allgem. Chem.*, **210**, 26 (1933).

[38] G. F. Hüttig, H. E. Tschakert, and H. Kittel, *ibid.*, **223**, 241 (1935).

reaction process may be of interest as catalysts. One example will be chosen to illustrate the method and the nature of the results.

If calcium oxide and ferric oxide are heated together, there occurs evidence of chemical and structural changes in the neighborhood of 800°C. These changes include the x-ray diffraction, the appearance of ferromagnetism, reduced catalytic activity, and so forth. There are indications of preliminary changes occurring before the temperature of 800°C. is reached. The observed susceptibility changes are shown in Fig. 128. Hüttig interprets these results in terms of an active intermediate oxide, and by holding the temperature just below that at which the ferrite is formed, he has prepared the intermediate compound in substantial amount.

Systems which have been studied in this way by Hüttig and others are listed in Table XXXI. In spite of the wealth of information produced on these systems, it is difficult to think of intermediate compounds being identified by the usual standards by which compounds are characterized. But there is no doubt concerning the "active" state in which oxides and oxide mixtures may be prepared.

100. Supported Oxide Systems

One of the commonest procedures in heterogeneous catalysis is the preparation of an active mass supported on a relatively inactive mass. Thus the catalyst consisting of chromia supported on γ-alumina is widely used in dehydrogenations. Such systems are often amorphous to x rays and do not lend themselves readily to the usual methods of structural study. In this section there will be described how magnetic susceptibility measurements have been used to gain some information concerning these substances.

Applications of this method will first be described for the supported chromia-alumina system.[39] Such catalysts may be made by impregnating high-area γ-alumina with chromic acid solution, followed by drying, ignition, and reduction in hydrogen. Different ratios of chromia to alumina are obtained by changing the concentration of the chromic acid solution used for impregnation. Alternatively, the impregnation step may be carried out with a solution of chromic nitrate. The magnetic susceptibilities of the chromium ions in a series of such catalysts as a function of chromium concentration in the finished catalyst are shown in Fig. 129. Such data, for want of a better name, are referred to as susceptibility isotherms. It will be noted that the susceptibility of the chromium becomes much larger at low concentrations, and that the susceptibility

[39] R. P. Eischens and P. W. Selwood, *J. Am. Chem. Soc.*, 69, 1590, 2698 (1947); 70, 2271 (1948).

isotherm turns upward rather sharply in the neighborhood of 6% chromium. The difference in the susceptibility per gram of chromium becomes greatly magnified as the temperature is lowered.

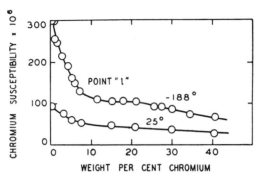

Fig. 129. Susceptibility isotherms for chromia supported on γ-alumina.

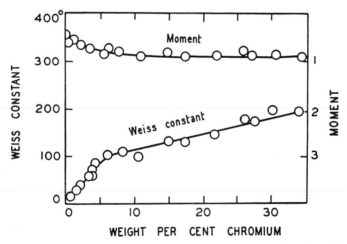

Fig. 130. Magnetic moment and Weiss constant as a function of chromium concentration for supported chromia-alumina.

The susceptibility of the chromium in these systems is found to obey the Curie-Weiss law up to fairly high chromium concentrations. It is, therefore, possible to compute Weiss constants and magnetic moments over the chromium concentration range. These are shown in Fig. 130. It will be noted that the moment is almost constant, but that the Weiss constant varies greatly with changing chromium concentration. The situation is then not unlike that described for chromia-alumina solid solutions in Chapter VIII. It will be recalled that oxide gels, or hydrous oxides, of the transition elements were shown (p. 337) to behave in part like magnetically dilute substances, in sharp contrast to the corresponding crystalline oxides. Following the rather crude interpretation given for the gels, which are also of interest in catalysis, it can be said that the number of nearest chromium ion neighbors in the supported oxides is directly proportional to the Weiss constant. Thus, at the point where the susceptibility isotherm turns up sharply, sometimes called point "l," the chromium ions on the alumina surface cannot be atomically dispersed in a two-dimensional solid solution, but must be aggregated into layers, perhaps about three atom layers thick. On the other hand, estimates of the covering power of chromia show that 6% chromium per gram of catalyst could not possibly exist in a uniform layer three atom layers thick over the whole support surface. This surface may be estimated by the low temperature adsorption of nitrogen and, for the system described, is over 200 square meters per gram. It can, therefore, only be concluded that the chromia on the alumina surface is aggregated into widely separated patches. So far the magnetic method has given no information concerning the shape of these patches, but the method certainly makes it possible to follow relative degrees of dispersion or aggregation of the active component in a supported catalyst. Some success has been achieved in relating this structural information to actual catalytic activity. For instance, the activity for dehydrocyclization of n-heptane to toluene has been shown to bear a close correlation to the magnetic susceptibility of the chromia. This is doubtless a reflection of the increased accessibility of the chromia at low cencentrations. It may be noted also that if chromia is supported on low-area α-alumina, the magnetic susceptibility of the chromia remains quite low.

The general applicability of the susceptibility isotherm method for estimating promoter dispersion has been amply confirmed, as will be pointed out below. Additional magnetic evidence to be presented in the next section virtually proves the existence of clusters in supported nickel catalysts, and independent evidence based on surface areas and activities strongly support the same concept in chromia-alumina.[40] It will be understood that the degree of clustering is dependent on the catalyst preparation procedure, and that catalysts formed by coprecipitation are more effectively dispersed than those made by impregnation.

Supported oxides of manganese show some interesting magnetic characteristics.[41] For instance, impregnation of γ-alumina, followed by ignition at 200°C., yields susceptibility isotherms of the form shown in Fig. 131. These are characterized by the unusual sharpness of point l and by the

[40] J. Varga, G. Rabó, and P. Steingaszner, Acta. Chim. Hung., 1, 94, 146 (1951).

[41] P. W. Selwood, T. E. Moore, M. Ellis, and K. Wethington, J. Am. Chem. Soc., 71, 693 (1949).

fact that, as shown in Fig. 132, both Weiss constant and moment show
large changes which occur as a function of manganese concentration.   The
change in the magnetic moment is related to a change of oxidation state

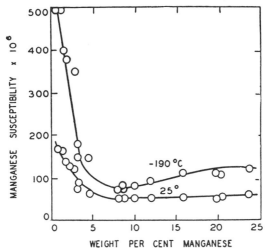

Fig. 131. Susceptibility isotherms for manganese oxide
supported on alumina and not heated over 200°C.

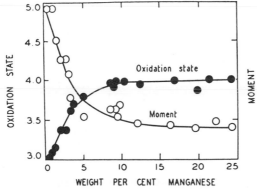

Fig. 132. Magnetic moment and chemical oxidation
state for manganese oxide supported on alumina.

of the manganese.   At low concentrations, the manganese takes a valence of
3+, apparently in imitation of the aluminum ions in the support, while
at higher concentrations the valence of the manganese is 4+ as in manganese dioxide.   This effect of the support structure in modifying the oxidation
state of the supported ions is found for several other systems and is known

as valence inductivity. The reality of this effect has also been established by other workers.[42,43] Perhaps factors other than the purely geometric one are operative in causing "valence inductivity," because Saito finds some influence of cupric oxide as a support on the oxidation state of manganese. Some relations have also been found between structure, as shown by magnetic measurements, and catalytic activity for such reactions as the decomposition of hydrogen peroxide and the oxidation of carbon monoxide.[44]

Other supported oxide systems which have been studied include nickel oxide on alumina and on titania,[45] ferric oxide on alumina and on titania,[46] copper oxide on alumina,[47] vanadia on alumina.[48] Silver, molybdenum, rhenium, cobalt, tungsten, uranium, neodymium,[2] and titanium sesquioxide[49] on a variety of supports have also received some attention. In a substantial number of cases, it is possible to relate the structural information obtained by the susceptibility isotherm method to the actual catalytic activity. A careful study by Milligan and Richardson[49a] on the dual hydrous oxide system $NiO-Al_2O_3$ suggests that part of the anomalous magnetic moment found in the author's laboratory for supported NiO on $\gamma-Al_2O_3$ may be due to the effect of the crystalline field on the Ni^{2+} ion rather than to the presence of Ni^{3+} as previously suggested.[45]

Ferric oxide shows the subnormal magnetic moment previously referred to. This is probably due (p. 169) to exchange interaction between adjacent irons, possibly acting through an oxide ion. The depression of the moment is obviously a measure of the extent to which a bond between iron ions may be operative. Supported silver, molybdenum, and rhenium show no evidence of paramagnetism when supported in the form of their oxides. Cobalt shows the expected abnormal moment; neodymium shows no effect of dispersion. Uranium, and to some degree tungsten, show some effect of dispersion. Some supported systems show quite subtle and elusive examples of ferromagnetism. Supported vanadia is one of these.[48] The influence of various supports in effecting dispersion and modifying oxidation states has also been studied.[50] Some supported metals are of more catalytic interest in the reduced form as metals rather than as the oxides.

[42] J. Amiel, Mme. G. Rodier, and G. Rodier, *J. chim. phys.*, **51**, 719 (1954).

[43] H. Saito, *J. Chem. Soc. Japan* (forthcoming). The writer is indebted to Dr. Saito for letting him see this manuscript, in translation, before publication.

[44] J. Mooi and P. W. Selwood, *J. Am. Chem. Soc.*, **74**, 1750, 2461 (1952).

[45] F. N. Hill and P. W. Selwood, *ibid.*, **71**, 2522 (1949).

[46] P. W. Selwood, M. Ellis, and K. Wethington, *ibid.*, **71**, 2181 (1949).

[47] P. W. Selwood and N. S. Dallas, *ibid.*, **70**, 2145 (1948).

[48] P. W. Selwood and L. Lyon, *Discussions, Faraday Soc.*, **No. 8**, 222 (1950).

[49] S. F. Adler and P. W. Selwood, *J. Am. Chem. Soc.*, **76**, 346 (1954).

[49a] W. O. Milligan and J. T. Richardson, *J. Phys. Chem.*, **59**, 831 (1955).

[50] P. W. Selwood and L. Lyon, *ibid.*, **74**, 1051 (1952).

These will be described more fully in the next section. To summarize: it may be said that this method gives information concerning the oxidation state and the state of aggregation of supported transition group oxides. This information is often of a kind which is difficult or impossible to obtain in any other way.

Direct investigation of magnetic changes occurring during the adsorption of paramagnetic ions from solution, before conversion to an oxide, has received less attention. The method is of obvious applicability to chromatographic processes. Bhatnagar[51] has examined the adsorption of iron, nickel, cobalt, and manganese salts from solution by charcoal and silica. With silica the susceptibilities are not far from additive, but with charcoal he finds that the metal ions apparently become diamagnetic. This suggests a type of binding similar to that found in the diamagnetic cyanide and carbonyl complexes of the transition elements. It is difficult to reconcile these results with the report by Rüdorff and Schulz[52] that the adsorption or intercalation of ferric chloride vapor in charcoal seems to make no change in the magnetic susceptibility of the ferric chloride.

Rogers[53] has obtained results on adsorbed ions of nickel, cobalt, manganese, and iron on charcoal and on silica gel which are in direct disagreement with Bhatnagar's results on charcoal. It seems probable that the bonds between adsorbed ions and charcoal, as on silica, are essentially normal ionic bonds. More difficult to understand is the claim by Kobozev[54] that ions of nickel, cobalt, iron, and other elements show abnormal magnetic moments, rising to tens of Bohr magnetons, when adsorbed at quite low surface coverages on silica gel and other supports. The effect is even said to be observed with reduced silver. Kobozev interprets these effects as being due to "superparamagnetism" in which the normally random electron-spin orientation is strongly oriented in the direction of an applied field. The effect is not to be confused with ferromagnetism. The writer must confess that, after a long experience with such systems, he is suspicious of any such apparent increase of paramagnetism. Traces of ferromagnetic impurities and ferromagnetic phases may be extremely elusive. The supposed effect could and should be investigated by paramagnetic resonance absorption before any conclusion is reached.

Some applications of nuclear magnetic resonance in connection with catalyst structure will be described later.

[51] S. S. Bhatnagar, K. N. Mathur, and P. L. Kapur, *Indian J. Physics*, **3**, 53 (1928).

[52] W. Rüdorff and H. Schulz, *Z. anorg. u. allgem. Chem.*, **245**, 121 (1940).

[53] M. T. Rogers and R. Vander Vennen, *J. Am. Chem. Soc.*, **75**, 1751 (1953).

[54] N. I. Kobozev, V. B. Evdokimov, I. A. Zubovich, and A. N. Mal'tsev, *Zhur. Fiz. Khim.*, **26**, 1349 (1952). This article was not read in the original.

101. The Structure and Activity of Metals and Alloys

In this section some remarks will be presented on a current theory of heterogeneous catalysis as it relates to magnetic properties. The current status of magnetic methods as applied to particle-size distribution and some related effects will also be presented.

The parameters which govern heterogeneous catalysis are not yet adequately defined. One of these parameters is possibly the "geometric" factor which includes the specific surface area and the geometrical arrangement of the atoms which are on the surface. Another factor, as yet less thoroughly studied, is the "electronic" factor, which may be described briefly, and somewhat inadequately, as the number of electrons available for interaction with an adsorbed molecule of reactant, and the energetics associated with those electrons. The magnetic application is chiefly to find the number of such available electrons. While the idea of an electronic factor has been proposed a number of times in the past quarter century, it has only recently received much attention. The discussion given here is based chiefly on a paper by Dowden.[55]

In a substantial number of heterogeneous reactions, there appear to be electron-transfer and exchange reactions between the surface and the adsorbed phase. In order to participate in such reactions, the catalyst crystallite must possess vacant or occupied levels which are capable of accepting or donating electrons to form the activated complex. In particular, if the rate-controlling step involves donation of electrons to the catalyst, the d-band in the catalyst must possess "holes"; or, expressing it in terms more familiar to most chemists, the catalyst atoms must possess available unoccupied orbitals. If the rate-controlling step involves transfer of an electron to the reactant molecule, then there must be at least some available d-band electrons in the catalyst. It has generally been thought that the d-band character of the active center was that of the catalyst crystal as a whole, but there is some evidence that this is not necessarily true.

Thus, many catalysts of great importance have almost-filled or just-filled d-bands, and activity is found to vary in a rapid and fairly predictable way among these elements. The magnetic moment is, of course, a measure of d-band filling; hence, as suggested several years ago,[1] catalytic activity activity and magnetism are actually in part different manifestations of a more fundamental atomic property, namely, the d-band character of the element. Dowden extends this idea to include the covalent bonding features of Pauling's metal valency theory.

These ideas apply also to alloys. If an element with loosely held

[55] D. A. Dowden, *J. Chem. Soc.*, **1950**, 242.

valency electrons, such as copper, is added in solid solution to a transition element possessing holes in the d-band, such as nickel, the change in activity parallels the decline in the number of holes per nickel atom. This change is also reflected in the gradual loss of ferromagnetism of the nickel alloy with increasing copper content. In a number of cases, catalyst poisons operate by a similar process; that is, by filling of all d-band holes with valency electrons supplied by the poison. It will be clear that magnetic susceptibility is not the only measure of d-band character, although it is possibly the most useful one. Electrical conductivity and related phenomena are also important.

Of the several recent papers dealing with these effects, three or four will be selected for mention. Dowden and Reynolds[56] have summarized earlier data and have reported on four reactions: the hydrogenation of styrene, the decomposition of formic acid and of methanol, and the decomposition of hydrogen peroxide, over nickel-iron and nickel-copper. The results are in accord with previous observations that activity for the first three reactions decreases parallel with decreasing ferromagnetism and with decreasing availability of d-band holes. The reverse is true of the hydrogen peroxide decomposition because, according to the Haber-Weiss mechanism, this reaction requires electron transfer from the catalyst to the reacting molecule.

Equally interesting results have been reported by Couper and Eley[57] on the *para*-hydrogen conversion on palladium-gold alloys. The activation energy increases abruptly between 30 and 40 atomic % palladium. Magnetic susceptibility measurements identify this composition as corresponding to complete filling of the d-band in palladium. It will be recalled that the paramagnetism of palladium is destroyed by dissolved hydrogen. Couper and Eley have shown that this also destroys the activity of palladium and point out that this may account for a number of obscure examples of catalyst poisoning by hydrogen. Similar observations have been described in a series of papers by G.-M. Schwab[58] and his co-workers. Schwab has extended the activity studies to a substantial number of metals and alloys, including homogeneous Hume-Rothery alloys, and has determined the activation energy and the "steric factor" (the pre-exponential constant in the Arrhenius equation) for numerous catalyzed reactions. Extension of these ideas to the actual mechanism of chemisorption is expected to develop rather rapidly in the near future as a result of some new observations to be presented in the following section.

Apart from the work mentioned above, there have not been many

[56] D. A. Dowden and P. W. Reynolds, *Discussions Faraday Soc.*, **No. 8,** 184 (1950).
[57] A. Couper and D. D. Eley, *ibid.*, **No. 8,** 172 (1950).
[58] G. M. Schwab, *ibid.*, **No. 8,** 166 (1950).

studies in which an attempt is made to relate catalytic activity of metals and alloys (and semiconductors) directly to magnetic measurements, although indirect correlations are frequently cited. One such study, carried out in the author's laboratory, will be described.[59] A copper catalyst activated with nickel may be prepared by the addition of nickel nitrate solution to precipitated copper hydroxide, followed by drying, ignition, and reduction at a moderately elevated temperature. The specific magnetization for reduced samples containing about 1% nickel is quite small, indicating that only a small fraction of the nickel is present as metal in particles large enough to exhibit ferromagnetism down to room temperature. It is not certain that this small fraction of the nickel is the fraction

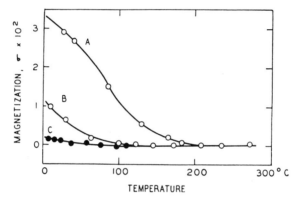

Fig. 133. Thermomagnetic curves for nickel supported on copper for (A) active, (B) partially sintered and thus deactivated, and (C) strongly sintered, inactive, samples.

responsible for catalytic activity in, say, the hydrogenation of benzene, but the evidence suggests that this is the case.

Figure 133 shows thermomagnetic curves for fresh active catalyst, for catalyst partially thermally deactivated, and for catalyst completely thermally deactivated. For the sample represented in Fig. 133, which contained 2% nickel, the active catalyst converted about 50% of benzene under standardized condition; the partially deactivated catalyst converted about 15% of benzene; the deactivated catalyst showed negligible activity.

These data may be interpreted as indicated above. At the temperature of the hydrogenation of benzene, 175°C., the active catalyst was only slightly ferromagnetic, and the partially deactivated catalyst was not ferromagnetic. It is clear that the active mass contained no massive pure nickel. This is obvious because of the disappearance of all ferromagnetism

    [59] H. Morris and P. W. Selwood, *J. Am. Chem. Soc.*, **65**, 2245 (1943).

at a temperature nearly 100° below the Curie point of pure nickel. From the shape of the thermomagnetic curve, it is clear that the bulk of the active mass is not homogeneous, but consists rather of a continuous series of solid solutions, as described on p. 52.   Figure 133 shows that thermal deactivation is attended with a recession of the Curie point.   In this system, thermal deactivation must be accompanied by a diffusion process whereby the nickel gradually forms a homogeneous solid solution in the copper.   The process may be considered as one of dilution by copper of the nickel-rich copper nickel alloys.   The loss of activity with increased sintering may, therefore, be directly related to the filling of the *d*-band of the nickel by the valency

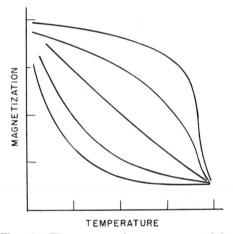

TEMPERATURE

Fig. 134. Thermomagnetic curves reported by
Michel for supported nickel catalysts.

electrons of the copper, although at the time this work was done the concept of the "electronic" factor and its relation to *d*-band was not generally known.   The presence of nonhomogeneous solid solutions in this nickel-copper catalyst system is supported by x-ray studies.[60]   There is some evidence that maximum catalytic activity per gram of nickel in nickel-copper alloys is not necessarily achieved for pure nickel.[61]   It will, of course, be understood that loss of *d*-band vacancies is not the only mechanism by which catalytic activity may be destroyed.

We turn now to a group of studies on supported nickel in which the principal emphasis is on particle size.   For the most part, the nickel in these systems is in electrically insulated particles.   This, as will be seen in the next section, gives rise to some remarkable effects.

[60] N. Kadota and S. Ikeda, *ibid.*, **73**, 4475 (1951).
[61] R. J. Best and W. W. Russell, *ibid.*, **76**, 838 (1954).

Michel[62-64] has shown that slow reduction of nickel-silica catalysts or of certain other catalyst components, may yield supported nickel in a form which is ferromagnetic but which possesses no unique Curie temperature. The thermomagnetic curves for such mixtures, such as shown in Fig. 134, were attributed by Michel to imperfect crystallization of the nickel in particles of various dimensions. He assumed that small particles of nickel would have lower Curie temperatures than large particles, and that a distribution of particle sizes would give the unique thermomagnetic curves shown. Without attempting a quantitative interpretation, Michel has presented data in which the slope of the thermomagnetic curve is plotted

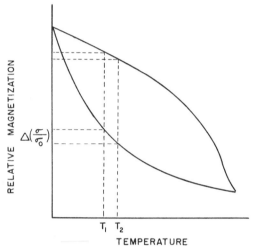

Fig. 135. Illustration of a method for interpreting the Michel type of thermomagnetic curves.

against temperature and has used these curves as a rough, but remarkably illuminating, measure of nickel particle-size distribution in several catalyst systems.

This has also been studied in the writer's laboratory.[65] The principal problem was to attach a scale of particle diameters to Michel's plot of slope versus temperature. Let us say that 50% of the magnetization is found to be in particles with Curie point above T_1 as shown in Fig. 135; and that 40% of the magnetization is found in particles with Curie point above T_2.

[62] A. Michel, *Ann. chim.*, **8**, 317 (1937).

[63] A. Michel and M. Gallissot, *Compt. rend.*, **206**, 1252 (1938).

[64] A. Michel, R. Bernier, and G. LeClerc, *J. chim. phys.*, **47**, 269 (1950).

[65] P. W. Selwood, S. Adler, and T. R. Phillips, *J. Am. Chem. Soc.*, **76**, 2281 (1954); **77**, 1462 (1955).

Then, 10% of the nickel must have a Curie temperature between T_1 and T_2. To find particle diameters, it is recalled that Curie temperature is directly proportional to coordination number. The coordination number in massive nickel may be taken as 12; but in very small particles, those nickel atoms on the surface make an appreciable contribution to the whole, so that the average coordination number, $\bar{z}$, is less than 12. Assuming spherical particles, one may then write $T_c/631° = \bar{z}/12$, where T_c is the

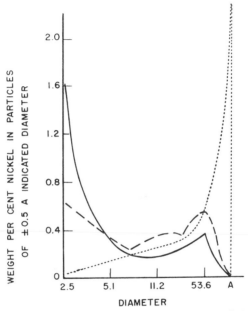

Fig. 136.   Distribution curve of particle sizes in a nickel-silica catalyst. (These curves involve certain assumptions as described in the text.)   Reduced sample———; partially sintered— — —; strongly sintered . . . . .

observed Curie point of a particle in which the average coordination number for each nickel atom is $\bar{z}$. For massive nickel $T_c = 631°$K. and $\bar{z} = 12$. In this way it is possible to set up a scale of particle diameters as shown in Fig. 136. X-ray line-width broadening results are in agreement with this scale for the upper end of the scale, say from 50 to 100 A., but other evidence suggests that the figures at the lower end of the scale may be too low.

Striking results by this method are obtainable by using a coprecipitated nickel silicate as the starting material. The method, as shown in Figs. 137 and 138, permits a distinct study to be made of the reduction process as compared with the sintering process in which the particles of nickel grow. One may, for instance, determine that reduction in such systems is often

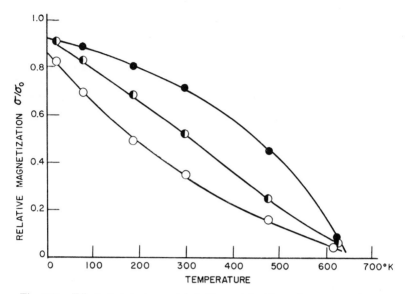

Fig. 137.   Effect of sintering a nickel-silica catalyst in an inert atmosphere.
Reduced O;   partially sintered ◑;   strongly sintered ●.

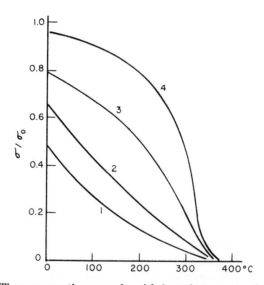

Fig. 138.   Thermomagnetic curves for nickel catalysts prepared under several
conditions: (1) Ni-SiO₂ coprecipitate;   (2) Ni-Al₂O₃ multiple impregnation;
(3) Ni-Al₂O₃ single impregnation;   (4) massive Ni.

complete even though the reduction temperature may be quite moderate and the samples exhibit virtually no ferromagnetism at room temperature.[65a] Similarly, samples prepared by an impregnation technique always show much larger particles than those prepared by coprecipitation. It is also possible to relate catalytic activity to particle-size distribution in a manner that has not heretofore been possible.

The idea that the Curie temperature of a ferromagnetic metal may depend on particle size receives support from work on thin films of nickel.

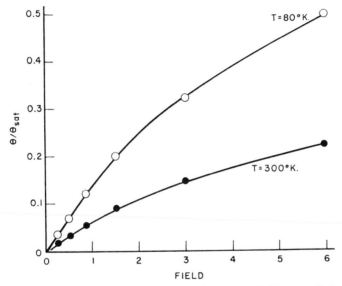

Fig. 139. Specific magnetization plotted as θ/θ_{sat} versus field strength for nickel-silica catalysts, at two temperatures. The abcissa scale is not clear from the paper of Heukelom et al., but presumably reaches a maximum of 2000 oersteds.

This was mentioned previously (p. 293), and the earlier work is reviewed by Allen.[66] Of greatest interest for our present purposes is the demonstration that for films below 100 atom layers (111 plane), the Curie temperature begins to recede appreciably. Film thicknesses and Curie points given by Crittenden and Hoffman[67] are 20A., 250°K.; 39A., 400°K.; 139A., 550°K.

There have recently appeared two other related magnetic methods for studying particle sizes in ferromagnetic powders. Before describing these, some of Néel's ideas[68] concerning ferromagnetism in extremely small parti-

[65a] J. A. Sabatka and P. W. Selwood, J. Am. Chem. Soc., 77, 5802 (1955).
[66] J. A. Allen, Reviews of Pure and Applied Chemistry, 4, 133 (1954).
[67] E. C. Crittenden, Jr., and R. W. Hoffman, Revs. Mod. Phys., 25, 310 (1953).
[68] L. Néel, Compt. rend., 228, 664 (1949).

cles will be presented in outline. In a normal ferromagnetic domain, all the electronic moments orientate as a group in an applied field, and the size of the domain is such that thermal vibrations do not appreciably disturb this orientation until one goes above the Curie point. But as the particle size diminishes, the effect of thermal vibrations becomes increasingly important and the sample begins to resemble a paramagnetic rather than a ferromagnetic substance. Two effects of major importance which appear are that the approach to saturation with increasing field becomes more and more difficult, and that residual magnetism is quickly destroyed at all ordinary temperatures.

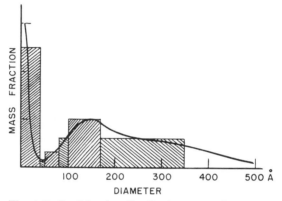

Fig. 140. Particle size distribution curve for Raney nickel as obtained by Weil's method.

A group at the Royal Dutch Shell Laboratories[69] has used the magnetization curves, intensity of magnetization versus field strength (Fig. 139), to find particle diameters in nickel-silica catalysts similar to those described above. Measurements are generally made at room temperature only and involve a very great extrapolation to find the magnetization at saturation. In spite of this, the method seems a good one for finding particle diameter and degree of reduction. Activation energies for the reduction and the sintering processes may be obtained. It will be noted, however, that the method does not provide, in its present state of development, any idea of particle-size distribution, and is to this degree less satisfactory than the Michel method.

It will be worth while to compare the two methods and to show where the next advance will probably be made. Michel's method, as extended to low temperatures by the writer, consists in measuring magnetization at

[69] W. Heukelom, J. J. Broeder, and L. L. Van Reijen, *J. phys. chim.*, **51**, 473 (1954).

constant, fairly high, field strength and of lowering the temperature until, by extrapolation to absolute zero, saturation is achieved. The rate at which saturation is achieved (i.e., the slope of the thermomagnetic curve) is taken as a rough indication of particle-size distribution. Heukelom *et al.* do approximately the same thing by a mathematical extrapolation to saturation, but all at room temperature only. It is clear that a further development will require a precise description of the intensity of magnetization as a function of temperature, field, and particle size. This must then be summed over all possible sizes. It seems that a complete quantitative description of such catalyst systems, at least in terms of particle size and distribution, is not too much to expect in the next few years.

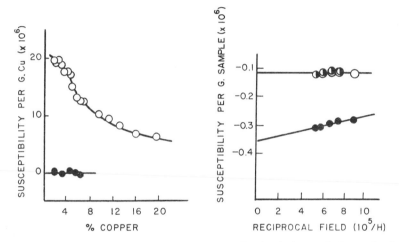

Fig. 141. Magnetic data on supported copper on alumina before and after reduction, sintering, and reoxidation. The variation of susceptibility with field strength is also shown. Oxidized (O), reduced (●), sintered and reoxidized (◑).

Still another approach has been used by Weil.[70,71] He takes advantage of the fact that, as shown theoretically by Néel,[68] while the residual magnetism of a small particle, say of nickel, may relax to zero in a very small time, this time will be increased and become measurable at very low temperatures. Weil, making measurements of coercive force at 1.4°K., is able to set up a particle-size distribution curve for Raney nickel, as shown in Fig. 140. The method is of more than ordinary interest, and it is unfortunate that it was first used on a system so complex as Raney nickel. Néel[71a] has recently investigated this subject further and shows that the time

[70] L. Weil, *Compt. rend.*, **229**, 584 (1949).
[71] L. Weil, *J. chim. phys.*, **51**, 715 (1954).
[71a] L. Néel, *Compt. rend.*, **241**, 470 (1955).

dependence of coercive force is readily observable in several ferromagnetic metals in very small particles.

It would appear that ferromagnetic resonance might have some applications to problems such as this. Griffiths[72] has studied thin nickel films in this way, and Bagguley[72a] has reported on colloidal nickel.

Application of these or similar methods to other metals has apparently not yet been attempted, or at least not published. Kobozev[73] has found no ferromagnetism in supported iron below a certain surface coverage. Such measurements should obviously be carried out over a temperature range.

In the author's laboratory, an attempt has been made to study the sintering of supported copper metal.[74] Copper oxide supported on γ-alumina shows a more or less normal susceptibility isotherm (p. 381), with the interesting feature that infinite magnetic dilution seems to be reached at low concentrations and corresponds, as expected, to one unpaired electron spin. If, now, this system is reduced in hydrogen, the susceptibility falls (Fig. 141) to zero, with no evidence of atomically dispersed copper being present. It was thought that if the reduced phase was strongly sintered in vacuum, the copper particles might grow and, then, on reoxidation the susceptibility per gram of copper would be found to have diminished, corresponding to a lower degree of dispersion. Actually, this never occurs, the reason probably being that the small particles of copper are effectively insulated from each other by the mass of alumina.

102. The Mechanism of Chemisorption

In a previous chapter we discussed the magnetic susceptibility of adsorbed paramagnetic gases, such as oxygen and nitrogen dioxide on silica, titania, and especially on charcoal (p. 279). In this section we present some newly discovered magnetic effects which give promise of making possible substantial gains in the knowledge of chemisorption on metals and of the mechanism of heterogeneous catalysis in general.

It will be recalled (p. 365) that hydrogen adsorbed on palladium causes a reduction of the magnetic susceptibility which is linear with the quantity of hydrogen adsorbed and which becomes zero at a H/Pd ratio of about 0.64. But palladium is unique in the way in which it takes up hydrogen; and the possibility of extending this method to other metals, and especially to iron, cobalt, and nickel, seemed quite remote. The ferromagnetism of

[72] J. H. E. Griffiths, *Physica*, **17**, 253 (1951).

[72a] D. M. S. Bagguley, *Proc. Roy. Soc. (London)*, **A228**, 549 (1955).

[73] V. B. Evdokimov, I. N. Ozerelskovskii, and N. I. Kobozev, *Zhur. Fiz. Khim.*, **26**, 135 (1952).

[74] P. E. Jacobson and P. W. Selwood, *J. Am. Chem. Soc.*, **76**, 2641 (1954).

these metals suggested that even if an effect of adsorbed gases occurred, it would be masked and impossible of detection.   The only successful earlier attempt to apply magnetic measurements directly to a problem involving chemisorption on a metal seems to be that of Dilke, Eley, and Maxted[75] in which it was shown that adsorbed dimethyl sulfide contributes an electron to the d-band of a palladium powder substrate, thus reducing its paramagnetism.

In the author's laboratory,[65] it has been found that chemisorbed gases may produce quite large changes in the specific magnetization of supported nickel catalysts.   The effect will first be described with respect to chemisorbed hydrogen.   If a coprecipitated nickel-silica catalyst is slowly reduced in hydrogen at, say, 350°C., flushed with carefully purified helium, and then cooled to room temperature, the specific magnetization will lie on the anomalous Michel-type of thermomagnetic curve.   If, now, hydrogen is admitted to the sample at room temperature, the specific magnetization will fall almost instantly.   Changes of magnetization of 20% are often observed.   The effect is reversible if the sample is heated moderately in vacuum or in pure helium.   The chemisorbed hydrogen may in part be removed at room temperature by prolonged pumping, or by flushing with helium.   The effect described is dependent on the preparation method and the degree of sintering of the catalyst.   Larger nickel particles, determined by the shape of the thermomagnetic curve as described in the previous section, show a decreasing influence of chemisorbed hydrogen. Massive nickel does not show the effect.

Other chemisorbed gases show similar effects on the magnetization of the nickel, but the sign of the effect may be different.   Oxygen, carbon monoxide, and nitrous oxide produce an increase of magnetization.   Water vapor produces a decrease like that of hydrogen, but benzene has no observable effect.   These experiments have to be performed with care because the reduced catalyst samples are pyrophoric and almost instantly oxidize completely on exposure to air.   The effect of chemisorbed oxygen is demonstrated by passing over the sample a mixture of helium plus 0.2% of oxygen.

These effects are interpreted as follows: chemisorbed gases interact with the metal substrate by donating or accepting electrons.   In the case of chemisorbed hydrogen, the magnetism falls, indicating some filling of the d-band of the nickel which is normally thought to have an average of 0.6 electron hole per nickel atom.   A large particle of nickel has such a small ratio of surface to mass that even a complete monolayer of chemisorbed hydrogen could not contribute enough electrons to make a perceptible

[75] M. H. Dilke, D. D. Eley, and E. B. Maxted, *Nature*, 161, 804 (1948).

change in the d-band electron density. But a small particle, containing only a few nickel atoms, might suffer an observable change of magnetic moment. This is believed to be the effect observed. Oxygen, carbon monoxide, and nitrous oxide must be chemisorbed on nickel by a process of removing electrons from the nickel. An effect was observed with nitrogen also, but there is the possibility that this was due to a residual trace of oxygen in the nitrogen. It may be added that these experiments were done on an apparatus described in Figs. 28 and 29, pp. 42–43.

The mechanism of chemisorption has been discussed by many writers. For the case of hydrogen on metals, the evidence is described by Eley.[76] The metal-hydrogen bond is thought to be a more or less normal covalent bond, but opinion on this point is not unanimous. The magnetic evidence given here seems to prove that the mechanism is certainly one of electron donation from hydrogen to metal, but the magnetic method does not differentiate between covalently bound hydrogen and hydrogen present as protons. The views expressed here also receive strong support from Suhrmann's[77-79] experiments on the change of electrical conductivity of nickel in thin films subject to chemisorbed gases. The addition of an electron to the metal might be expected to raise the electrical conductivity by increasing the concentration of electrons in the conductivity band. Removal of electrons would have the opposite effect. Figure 142 is similar to one given by Suhrmann, but with the addition of the magnetic data. Correspondence between Suhrmann's data and the magnetic data is complete. It may be added that the change of electrical conductivity becomes appreciable at

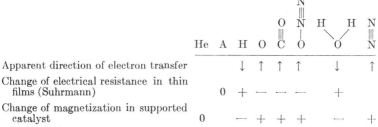

	He	A	H	O	C≡O	N≡N–O	H–O–H	N≡N
Apparent direction of electron transfer			↓	↑	↑	↑	↓	↑
Change of electrical resistance in thin films (Suhrmann)		0	+	—	—	—		+
Change of magnetization in supported catalyst		0	—	+	+	+	—	+

Fig. 142. Direction of electron transfer during chemisorption on nickel.

film thicknesses below about 75 atom layers. These results also agree, as to sign, with changes in work function reported by Suhrmann and others. One further point which may be mentioned here is that when a metal particle accepts an electron as it does in these experiments, it thereupon takes on some of the superficial characteristics of the next higher element

[76] D. D. Eley, *J. Phys. & Colloid Chem.*, **55**, 1017 (1951).
[77] R. Suhrmann, *J. Colloid Sci.*, Suppl. 1, 50 (1954).
[78] R. Suhrmann, *Z. Elektrochem.*, **56**, 351 (1952).
[79] R. Suhrmann and W. Sachtler, *Z. Naturforsch.*, **9a**, 14 (1954).

in the Periodic Table. Thus, nickel may tend to resemble copper by a sort of pseudo-transmutation. The opposite effect, of course, occurs when the adsorbate takes an electron away from the nickel. It might be wondered if hydrogen may ever saturate the d-band of nickel to the extent that the nickel loses all its magnetism. A simple calculation will show that a

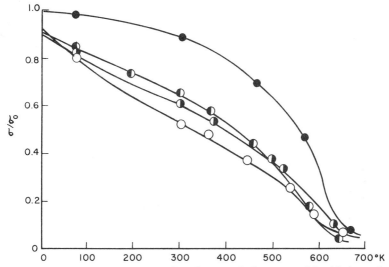

Fig. 143. Thermomagnetic curves for three typical commercial nickel catalysts. U.O.P. Nickel Hydrogenation Catalyst (O), Harshaw Ni-0107 (◐), Girdler G-12 (◐), sintered Harshaw (●).

sphere of nickel about 13 A. in diameter might lose all its magnetism if each surface nickel atom accepted one electron from an adsorbed hydrogen atom. The maximum decrease of magnetism observed to date is about 50%, but perhaps the reason for this will be found in the next paragraph.

When hydrogen is adsorbed on supported nickel at room temperature and the magnetic measurements are then carried down to, say, 20°K., it might be expected that the decreasing particle size which comes in to view, so to speak, at low temperatures would show an increasing influence of adsorbed hydrogen. Actually, the influence of adsorbed hydrogen (put on at room temperature) is found to become greater down to about −190°C., but it then becomes much less at still lower temperatures. The only conclusion so far reached from this evidence is that hydrogen is adsorbed on the smallest nickel particles by a hydride ion mechanism in which electrons are taken from the nickel particle. If this idea is substantiated, it will clarify many obscure phenomena related to catalyst specificity and selective poisoning mechanisms.[79a]

We shall conclude this section with a few remarks on possible future

[79a] L. E. Moore and P. W. Selwood, *J. Am. Chem. Soc.*, **78**, 697 (1956).

applications of the effect described. It is entirely feasible not only to study the mechanism of chemisorption under almost any condition of adsorbate, temperature, and pressure which might be encountered in catalytic practice, but also to make these measurements during the actual course of catalytic action. Some preliminary measurements have already been reported from the writer's laboratory[65] on the effect in nickel which is actually catalyzing

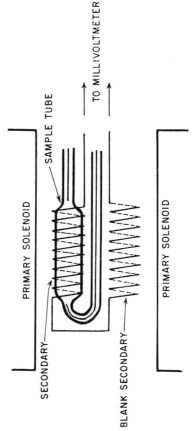

Fig. 144. Assembly for simultaneous measurement of magnetization and gas adsorption on catalytically active nickel.

the hydrogenation of benzene. There is no reason why such measurements should not be extended to any reaction which is catalyzed by supported nickel metal. It is essential that the nickel should be in a high state of dispersion, but this is certainly true of most commercial nickel samples, as shown in Fig. 143. Each of the samples indicated shows a fairly strong effect of adsorbed hydrogen. There seems no reason why the method should not apply equally well to cobalt and iron, provided these metals may be obtained in a similarly dispersed state.

Full exploitation of the effect described requires simultaneous measurement of gas volumes adsorbed and of specific magnetization. This, owing to the large dead-space, is not feasible in apparatus of the Faraday type (Fig. 29, p. 43), but it may be done by an induction method.[79b] A standard volumetric gas adsorption train is modified as follows: the sample, consisting of 5 to 10 g. of pelleted catalyst, is placed in the center of a large solenoid of several thousand turns carrying about 1 ampere stabilized A.C. A secondary coil (shown in Fig. 144) compactly surrounds the sample. The secondary has about 50 turns and is connected in opposition

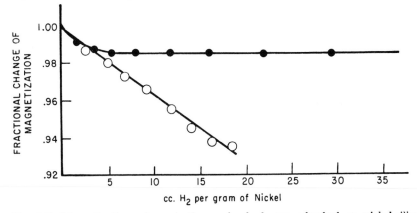

Fig. 145. Magnetization-volume isotherms for hydrogen adsorbed on nickel-silica catalyst. (●), H_2 adsorbed and magnetization measured at $-196°C.$; (O), H_2 adsorbed and magnetization measured at $27°C.$

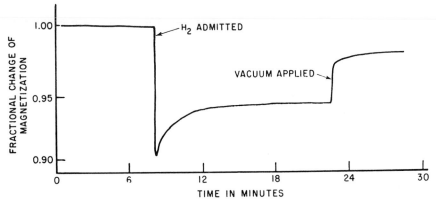

Fig. 146. Automatic recording of magnetization changes on nickel-silica catalyst as hydrogen is adsorbed, and desorbed, at room temperature.

[79b] P. W. Selwood, J. Am. Chem. Soc., **78**, 249 (1956).

to an identical secondary. The difference in emf induced in these coils is observed on a vacuum tube millivoltmeter, which also lends itself to automatic recording. Heating or cooling elements may be introduced in the core of the primary solenoid to surround the sample as may be desired.

Figure 145 shows magnetization-volume isotherms obtained with this apparatus for hydrogen on a coprecipitated nickel-silica catalyst containing 34% nickel. The different effects of physically adsorbed hydrogen *versus* chemisorbed hydrogen are clearly shown. It will be obvious that the temperature of adsorption need not be the same as the temperature at which the magnetic measurements are made in this apparatus.

Figure 146 shows an automatic recording of the magnetic changes which occur when hydrogen is admitted to a previously evacuated sample. This technique is especially useful in the study of transitory phenomena. It will be seen that a large drop of magnetization occurs practically instantaneously when the hydrogen is admitted. Part of this drop is probably due to warming of the sample by the heat of chemisorption. The sample then cools down and soon reaches a steady state. Evacuation of the sample at room temperature quickly removes some of the hydrogen with recovery of part of the magnetization. But much hydrogen remains adsorbed, even after long evacuation. The extension of the method to paramagnetic metals such as platinum is less promising by direct susceptibility methods, but this would appear to be a problem made to order for paramagnetic resonance absorption. Even the extension of the method to diamagnetic metals such as copper seems not impossible, provided that the metal in question has an isotope possessing a permanent nuclear magnetic moment, as does copper. The experiment could then be done by nuclear magnetic resonance, taking advantage of the effect found by Knight[80] in which the conductivity electrons in a metal produce a shift in the nuclear magnetic resonance peak as compared with the same metal in an insulating medium such as an oxide.[81]

103. Applications of Nuclear Resonance to Catalysis

So far there have not been very many direct applications of nuclear or paramagnetic resonance to problems in catalysis. There have, of course, been many studies of substances directly or indirectly of interest as catalyst components. A few exploratory studies of nuclear resonance have been made in the author's laboratory, and they will be described.

---

[80] W. D. Knight, *Phys. Rev.*, **76**, 1259 (1949).

[81] Some of the material presented here has not yet been published but will shortly appear in the Journal of the American Chemical Society.

It was pointed out in Chapter IV that proton relaxation times may be greatly modified by the presence of paramagnetic ions. Thus, the addition of a little ferric nitrate to pure water will reduce the proton relaxation time from several seconds to a few thousandths of a second.[82] It has been thought that the reciprocol relaxation time is proportional to the concentration of the paramagnetic ions multiplied by the square of the effective paramagnetic moment.

An application of proton relaxation times has been found in the study[83,84] of supported oxide catalysts, such as the chromia-alumina system, to which reference was made above (p. 380). The application is an attempt to measure the accessibility of a catalyst surface to reacting molecules. The accessibility of a supported catalyst bears no obvious relation to the total surface area, because the active portion of the catalyst surface may be any fraction of the whole surface. It has been found that supported

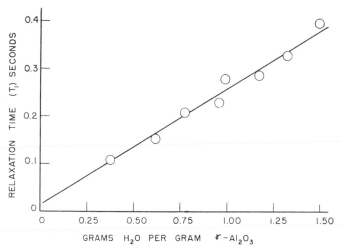

Fig. 147. Variation of proton relaxation time with water
concentration for water adsorbed on γ-alumina.

paramagnetic oxides catalyze the nuclear relaxation process almost as well as do dissolved ions. A given weight of catalyst sample of, say, Cr_2O_3-Al_2O_3 is just covered with water which serves as the proton carrier. The relaxation time of these protons is determined as T_1. Then, a true water solution of, say, chromic sulfate is obtained of such concentration that it also gives a relaxation time, T_1. The moles of chromium in the catalyst sample are divided by the volume of water used to give M_1; the molar concentration of the chromic sulfate solution is M_0. Then, the accessibility

[82] N. Bloembergen, E. M. Purcell, and R. V. Pound, *Phys. Rev.*, **73**, 679 (1948).

[83] R. B. Spooner and P. W. Selwood, *J. Am. Chem. Soc.*, **71**, 2184 (1949).

[84] P. W. Selwood and F. K. Schroyer, *Discussions Faraday Soc.*, No. **8**, 337 (1950).

of the chromia in the catalyst is $a = 2M_0/M_1$, where the factor 2 corrects for 180° shielding. Accessibilities, so defined, often range from a few per cent up to nearly 100%. In several systems, they have been shown to be directly proportional to reaction velocity. The chief feature of the nuclear method as compared with direct determination of susceptibilities is that the former measures surface paramagnetism while the latter measures bulk paramagnetism.

Unfortunately for this approach, further experiments[85] have shown that the reciprocal relaxation time is proportional to the square of the magnetic moment of the dissolved (or supported) paramagnetic ion only when the spin-orbital coupling is weak, or when the ion is in an S spectroscopic state. This makes the method less attractive than it seemed at first.

Another difficulty which has arisen is the discovery that common diamagnetic catalyst supports, such as high-area alumina or silica, may themselves have a substantial effect on the proton relaxation time.[86] Figure 147 shows the proton relaxation time as a function of water-alumina ratio. Similar results are obtained on a variety of supports and on typical silica-alumina cracking catalysts. Various organic liquid, such as alcohols and hydrocarbons, may be used as the proton source. These effects are doubtless related to the changing average environment experienced by a proton in an adsorbed molecule. While these observations make the study of supported paramagnetic oxides even less promising, they suggest a new approach to pore structure and the study of interactions between adsorbed molecules and adsorbent. These observations are quite closely related to studies of the intensity of resonance absorption as a function of water absorbed in hygroscopic materials of biological origin.[87]

104. Magnetism and Reaction Velocity

In this section we shall outline three topics in which the central feature is the direct action of the magnetic state of a catalyst on reaction velocity, or alternatively, the action of the magnetic field itself, either *macro* or *micro*. These topics are (1) the Hedvall effect, (2) certain aspects of the paramagnetic *ortho-para* hydrogen conversion, and (3) the direct action referred to above.

The catalytic activity of ferromagnetic substances in the neighborhood of the Curie temperature has been extensively investigated by Hedvall and his co-workers.[88] The results on a variety of reactions show that at the Curie point there is a sharp increase of the temperature coefficient of

[85] R. L. Conger and P. W. Selwood, *J. Chem. Phys.*, **20**, 383 (1952).

[86] T. W. Hickmott and P. W. Selwood, *J. Phys. Chem.*, **60**, 452 (1956).

[87] T. M. Shaw and R. H. Elsken, *J. Chem. Phys.*, **18**, 1113 (1950).

[88] J. A. Hedvall, R. Hedin, and O. Persson, *Z. physik. Chem.*, **B27**, 196 (1934), and later papers.

reaction velocity. For instance, the rate of decomposition of nitrous oxide shows above the Curie point a substantially more rapid increase with rising temperature than it does below the Curie point. The changes which occur are sharply defined only when the Curie point itself is sharply defined. Figure 148 shows results obtained on several systems. On a homogeneous copper-nickel alloy for which the Curie temperature is 337–340°C., the change of reaction rate occurs at 339°. Hedvall has extended these observations to a sufficient number of reactions and catalyst systems so that there can be little doubt about the reality of the phenomenon, which is generally called the "Hedvall effect." A twofold theoretical explanation for the effect has been given by Dowden.[55] First, it is known that the work function of pure nickel increases a little as the temperature is raised through

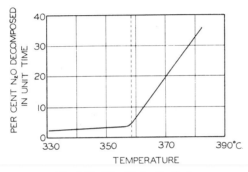

Fig. 148. The Hedvall effect.

the Curie point. This will change the activation energy for reactions proceeding at the surface by acceptance or donation of electrons, but whether the effect is to increase or decrease the velocity (positive or negative Hedvall effect) will depend on the nature of the process. This phase of the explanation is further discussed by Suhrmann and Sachtler.[79] The other part of Dowden's explanation relates the change of velocity to the change of entropy which occurs in the metal at the Curie temperature. The effect of this change is always to increase reaction velocity at the surface.

Examples which are actually negative Hedvall effects have been known for a long time.[89] The rate of oxidation of iron shows a discontinuity at the Curie temperature. Uhlig[90] has shown that the oxidation rate of chromium-iron alloys undergoes a definite increase of activation energy at the Curie temperature. Rates of reactions proceeding at surfaces actually suffer some change of activation energy at any kind of transition. Fores-

[89] G. Tammann and G. Siebel, *Z. anorg. u. allgem. Chem.*, **148**, 297 (1925).

[90] H. H. Uhlig and A. de S. Brasunas, *J. Electrochem. Soc.*, **97**, 448 (1950).

tier[91] reports changes at the antiferromagnetic Curie point of chromia and at an anomaly in the coefficient of expansion of nickel oxide.

Many attempts have been made (and some patents taken out) on methods to change reaction velocity by magnetizing a catalyst such as nickel. So far as the writer is aware, none has been successful and substantiated with the possible exception of one mentioned below.

Reference has already been made in Chapter I to the catalysis of the *ortho-para* hydrogen conversion by paramagnetic substances. This effect, discovered by Farkas and Sachsse,[92] makes it possible to determine magnetic moments by measurement of the velocity of the conversion p-$H_2 \rightarrow$ p-H_2 or the reverse. The conversion may be either homogeneous, as in the presence of molecular oxygen, or heterogeneous, as on a chromic oxide surface. Diamagnetic gases do not catalyze the reaction, but diamagnetic solids, such as charcoal, are often excellent catalysts, for reasons which are discussed below.

The theory of the paramagnetic conversion given by Wigner[93] and by Kalckar and Teller[94] shows that the velocity constant should be proportional to the square of the Bohr magneton number. For several ions of the rare earths, k/μ^2 actually varies from 0.181 for Pr^{3+} to 0.502 for Yb^{3+}. This is said to be explained by the decreasing collision diameter with increasing nuclear charge. The collision efficiency of the process is quite small, being only 10^{-12} to 10^{-14}.

The heterogeneous *ortho-para* hydrogen conversion has been studied by Taylor and Diamond,[95] among others. Contact with the diamagnetic lanthanum oxide produced only 17% conversion in 6 hours, but less than 3 minutes of contact with the strongly paramagnetic gadolinium oxide produced 100% conversion. Turkevich and Selwood[96] showed that while an organic free radical, α,α-diphenyl-β-picrylhydrazyl, gave only a slight conversion, as did zinc oxide alone, yet a mixture of these two substances gave a rapid conversion. This effect seems to show that two factors are necessary for the conversion, namely, a micro-inhomogeneous field produced in this case by the paramagnetic free radical, and long contact, ensured by van der Waals' adsorption of the hydrogen on the zinc oxide. This catalysis

[91] G. Nury and H. Forestier, *Proc. Intern. Symposium Reactivity of Solids.* Gothenberg, 1952, p. 189.

[92] A. Farkas and H. Sachsse, *Sitsb. Preuss. Akad. Wiss.*, **1933**, 268; *Z. phys. Chem.*, **B23**, 1, 19 (1933).

[93] E. Wigner, *Z. phys. Chem.*, **B19**, 203 (1932); **B23**, 28 (1933).

[94] F. Kalckar and E. Teller, *Proc. Roy. Soc. (London)*, **A150**, 520 (1935).

[95] H. S. Taylor and H. Diamond, *J. Am. Chem. Soc.*, **55**, 2613 (1933); **57**, 1251 (1935).

[96] J. Turkevich and P. W. Selwood, *ibid.*, **63**, 1077 (1941).

of the *ortho-para* hydrogen conversion by an organic free radical is further discussed by Harrison and McDowell.[97]

It is well known that the *ortho-para* hydrogen conversion is catalyzed at a measurable, and sometimes fairly high, rate by substances which are considered to be diamagnetic. The rapid conversion by charcoal is one example, and the slow but measurable conversion by supposedly pure lanthana is another. There have been some claims that the susceptibility of lanthana changes with the method of preparation, but the results have been disputed.[98,99] These effects have led to the idea that some diamagnetic solids might possess a kind of "surface paramagnetism." Actually this is less mysterious than might be suspected. Charcoal has been shown (p. 284) by paramagnetic resonance to possess strong absorptions corresponding to unpaired electrons, and Sandler[100] has shown that the *ortho-para* hydrogen conversion on titanium dioxide, which is diamagnetic, is due to some superficial reduction to the paramagnetic sesquioxide. It is probable that all examples of so-called surface paramagnetism may be rationalized by some such explanation as those given.

More difficult to understand is the claim[101] that the velocity of *ortho-para* hydrogen conversion over nickel metal is altered by application of an external magnetic field. The changes are not very great, ranging up to a 10 or 12% increase with fields up to 18,000 oersteds. The effect is said to be measurable in the earth's field.

The possibility that a magnetic field might have an effect on chemical reactivity has received attention for many years. Although some interesting effects had been reported, until very recently none contributed very much to our understanding of either magnetism or chemical kinetics. Earlier work has been reviewed by the writer[1] and will be described here very briefly. There are theoretical reasons for believing that a magnetic field of sufficient intensity might influence the velocity and equilibrium for certain types of reactions. These types are those such as, for instance, the reduction of chromate to chromic ion by a sugar, in which a substantial change of magnetic susceptibility occurs. Many such reactions have been investigated. Positive results are reported by Bhatnagar[102] and, in every case, the change observed is small.

A more promising area for study is the influence of magnetic fields on a micro scale such as may be produced by the introduction of a strongly

[97] L. G. Harrison and C. A. McDowell, *Proc. Roy. Soc. (London)*, **A220**, 77 (1953).
[98] R. B. Haller and P. W. Selwood, *J. Am. Chem. Soc.*, **61**, 85 (1939).
[99] W. Klemm and G. Hartlapp, *Z. anorg. u. Chem.*, **256**, 37 (1948).
[100] Y. L. Sandler, *J. Phys. Chem.*, **58**, 54 (1954).
[101] E. Justi and G. Vieth, *Z. Naturforsch.*, **8a**, 538 (1953).
[102] S. S. Bhatnagar, K. N. Mathur, and P. L. Kapur, *Phil. Mag.*, **8**, 457 (1929).

paramagnetic molecule or ion to a reacting mixture. An example is the catalysis of certain *cis-trans* isomerization reactions by paramagnetic substances or ions in solution.[103] It has been suggested[104] that for certain reactions proceeding by way of an excited triplet state, the velocity would be increased by paramagnetic substances. Successful demonstration of this effect seems to have been made by Gelles and Pitzer[105] for the decarboxylation of phenylmalonic acid in the presence of the highly paramagnetic dysprosium (3+) ion. The effects of nuclear magnetic moments in altering reaction rates may also be significant in explaining certain "isotope" effects in connection with the substitution of carbon isotopes on the rate of decarboxylation of malonic and related acids.[106]

[103] B. Tamamushi and A. Akijama, *Bull. Chem. Soc. Japan*, 12, 382 (1937).
[104] R. H. Harman and H. Eyring, *J. Chem. Phys.*, 10, 557 (1942).
[105] E. Gelles and K. S. Pitzer, *J. Am. Chem. Soc.*, 77, 1974 (1955).
[106] P. E. Yankwich, *Ann. Rev. Nuclear Sci.*, 3, 235 (1953).

AUTHOR INDEX

A

Abe, H., 195
Abe, K., 106
Abletsova, T. A., 258
Abonnenc, L., 72
Abou-El-Azm, A.-E.-M., 184, 185
Abragam, A., 214
Adam, G. D., 313
Adams, S. C., 225, 231 (ref. 150), 236
Adamson, A. W., 225, 226
Adcock, W. A., 45
Adler, S. F., 161, 252, 329, 384, 390
Ady, P., 277
Agallidis, E., 262
Aggarwal, S. L., 95, 100, 102, 108
Agliardi, N., 262
Agner, K., 224
Aharoni, J., 253, 279
Aida, K., 342
Aikawa, H., 303
Akamatsu, H., 122
Akijama, A., 408
Alameda, J. M., 171
Albon, G. d', 293
Albrecht, W. H., 165, 211, 215 (ref. 88), 308, 330, 332
Allard, G., 84
Allard, S., 272
Allen, J. A., 393
Alphen, P. M. van, 364
Al'Thauzen, O. N., 304, 324
Altmann, J., 324
Alyea, H. N., 279
Amiel, J., 169, 172, 173, 341, 384
Amin, H. V., 74, 79
Anantakrishnan, S. V., 98
Anderson, D., 95
Anderson, P. W., 309
Andresen-Kraft, C., 184
Angus, W. R., 25, 72, 73, 85, 94, 95, 98, 107, 283

Anwar-ul-Haq, M., 352
Aravamuthachari, S., 108, 358, 368
Archer, M. S., 330
Argersinger, W. J., Jr., 257
Ariya, S. M., 315
Arnold, J. T., 64
Aron, A., 293
Arreghini, E., 228, 244
Arrott, A., 358
Asai, K., 106
Asmussen, R. W., 196, 207, 215, 232, 236 (ref. 233), 237, 239, 243, 254, 256, 265, 271, 283, 361
Aubel, E. van, 107
Auer, H., 52, 86, 171, 355, 370, 372
Auméras, M., 166
Auwarter, M., 314
Auwers, O. v., 51, 296, 314, 318

B

Bacon, L. O., 324
Baddar, F. G., 79, 97, 99
Bagguley, D. M. S., 396
Baker, C. J. W., 19, 299, 302, 358
Baker, W. O., 284
Bakken, R., 176
Bal, G. S., 344
Bamford, C. H., 279
Banerjee, R. P., 81
Banerjee, S., 32, 33, 111, 117, 118, 120 (refs. 17, 22, 29, 34, 36), 121, 164, 165, 168, 349
Baqi, A., 356
Barkelew, C. H., 226, 236, 237
Barkworth, E. D. P., 225
Barnett, S. J., 39
Baroni, A., 345
Barsh, M. K., 236
Barson, F., 361
Bartlett, B. W., 170, 171, 174
Basolo, F., 234
Basu-Chaudhury, G. P., 187

SUBJECT INDEX

A

Acetylcyanide, 106
Actinides, 176
Active oxides, 378
Additivity law, 107
Adsorption, bromine on graphite, 125
  gases, 279, 397
  ions from solution, 385
  liquids, 404
  water, 101, 404
Alkali metal (see individual elements)
Alkali metal alloys, 371
  amalgams, 368
  hydrocarbon complexes, 264
  ketyls, 264
  polyoxides, 257
  vapors, 138
Alkali nitric oxides, 254
Alloxantin, salts, 271
Alloy structure, 50
Alloys, cobalt, 299
  iron, 296
  nickel, 300
  non-ferromagnetic, 367
Alloys in catalysis, 386
Aluminum, metal, 355
  triethyl, 282
  trimethyl, 282
Amorphous oxides (see hydrous oxides)
Amalgams, 368
  cobalt, 299
  iron, 298
  nickel, 302
Americium, 180
Aminium ion derivatives, 269
Ammonia solutions of metals, 372
Anisotropy, 110
  in aromatic compounds, 113
  in metals, 364
Anthracene, 106, 111
  derivatives, 106

Antiferromagnetic Curie point, 326
Antiferromagnetism, 326
Antimony, metal, 355
  complexes, 239
Argon, 72, 88
Aromatics, anisotropy, 113
Arsenic, 355
  bases, salts, 269
  bromides, 102, 283
  diiodide, 283
Atomic diamagnetism, 69
  paramagnetism, 135
Atomic iodine, 138
Atomic orbital theory of complexes, 197
Average susceptibility, 1

B

Band theory for metals, 354
Barium, 355
Benzaldehyde, 106
Benzene, 88, 91
  adsorbed, 397
  anisotropy, 111
Beryllium, 356
  acetate (basic), 282
  acetylacetonate, 283
Bianthrone, 268, 276
Biphenyl, 116
Biradical, 271
Biradicalette, 275
Biradicaloid, 275
Bismuth, 356
  anisotropy, 364
  compounds, 239
Bohr magneton, 136
Bond-angle distortion, 233
Boron, 356
  hydride, 282

C

Cadmium, 356
  monochloride, 284

427